AURORA

AND

AIRGLOW

Proceedings of the NATO Advanced Study Institute held at the University of Keele, Staffordshire, England, August 15–26, 1966

EDITED BY Billy M. McCormac

Physics Division, IIT Research Institute Chicago, Illinois

REINHOLD PUBLISHING CORPORATION

A subsidiary of Chapman-Reinhold, Inc.

New York   Amsterdam   London

Code 45

PREFACE

This book contains the lectures presented at the NATO Advanced Study Institute, "Aurora and Airglow," which was held at the University of Keele, Staffordshire, England, during the period August 15–26, 1966.

Approximately one-third of the time was devoted to discussion. Essential points brought out in the discussion period after each lecture are summarized at the end of the lecture.

The authors and the publisher have made a special effort to publish an up-to-date status concerning the various aspects of aurora and airglow. Almost all authors turned in their manuscripts prior to the end of the Institute and all prior to September 30, 1966. It was clearly recognized that rapid publication was essential in this ever changing research area.

Special thanks are due to the lecturers for their diligent preparation and excellent presentations. The Session Chairmen were masterful in the stimulating manner in which they directed the discussion periods. Dr. Martin Walt and the Summary Panel worked hard to prepare an excellent summary of the various aspects of aurora and airglow at the end of the Institute.

The University of Keele furnished excellent living and working facilities. Direct financial support was provided the Institute by: North Atlantic Treaty Organization, Air Force Cambridge Research Laboratories, Army Research Office, Defense Atomic Support Agency, Office of Naval Research and the Institute for Telecommunication Sciences and Aeronomy.

BILLY M. MCCORMAC

Chicago, Illinois
April, 1967

CONTENTS

Preface iii
Introduction, *Billy M. McCormac* 1

Session 1 ORIENTATION

History of Aurora and Airglow, *Sydney Chapman* 15
The Worldwide Morphology of the Atomic Oxygen Nightglows,
    F. E. Roach and L. L. Smith 29
Worldwide Auroral Morphology, *T. Neil Davis* 41
The Spectrum and Excitation Mechanisms in Aurora, *A. Omholt* 59
High Latitude Magnetic Disturbances, *J. P. Heppner* 75
Ionospheric Implications of Aurora and Airglow Studies,
    Lance Thomas 93

Session 2 OBSERVATIONS I

Twilight Observations, *M. Gadsden* 109
Dayglow Observations, *J. F. Noxon* 123
Cinematographic Observations of Fast Auroral Variations,
    T. Neil Davis 133
A Statistical Study of Carl Størmer's Height Measurements of
    Aurora Borealis, *Alv Egeland and Anders Omholt* 143
Dynamical Structure of the Atmosphere between 80 and 120 KM,
    J. E. Blamont and J. Barat 159
Coordinated Satellite, Ground-Based and Aircraft-Based Measure-
    ments on Auroras, *R. G. Johnson, R. E. Meyerott, and
    J. E. Evans* 169
Rocket Observations of Low Energy Auroral Electrons,
    David S. Evans 191
Review of Rocket Auroral Measurements, *C. D. Anger* 211
Rocket Measurements of Auroral Parameters, *James C. Ulwick* 225

The Simultaneous Determination of Rocket Trajectories and Rapid
    Auroral Variations, *Keith Burrows*   239
Electron Measurements Near a Weak Aurora, *Keith W. Ogilvie,*
    Nicholas McIlwraith and Don L. Lind   243
Auroral Zone Microbursts, *Kinsey A. Anderson*   249

Session 3   THEORY I

The Auroral Oval and the Internal Structure of the Magnetosphere,
    S.-I. Akasofu   267
The Significance of the Multiple Structure of the Auroral Arc,
    S.-I. Akasofu, S. Chapman, and P. C. Kendall   281
Penetration of Electrons into the Atmosphere, *Martin Walt*   287
Auroral Electric Fields, *Rolf Boström*   293
Interpretation of Twilight Emissions, *M. Gadsden*   305
Interpretation of the Dayglow, *J. F. Noxon*   315

Session 4   ARTIFICIAL AURORA AND AIRGLOW

Conjugate Auroral Measurements from the 1962 U. S. High
    Altitude Nuclear Test Series, *Wallace P. Boquist and John*
    W. Snyder   325
Clarification of Airglow Processes by Nuclear Excitation,
    Irving L. Kofsky   341
Research on Optical Infrared Characteristics of Aurora and
    Airglow (Artificial and natural), *A. T. Stair, Jr., and H. P.*
    Gauvin   365
Use of Artificial Barium Clouds to Study Magnetic and Electric
    Fields in the Atmosphere, *L. Haser*   391

Session 5   OBSERVATIONS II

Airglow Observations Near the Equator, *G. M. Weill*   407
Low Latitude Observations of Airglow, *Walter R. Steiger*   419
Kinetic Temperature Measurements of the 5577Å [OI] Line of
    the Night Airglow, *G. J. Hernandez and J. P. Turtle*   435
Low Latitude Airglow Variations 1962–1965, *Robert D. Sears*   441
High Latitude Night-Sky Emissions, *B. P. Sandford*   443
Polar Cap Aurora, *Knud Lassen*   453
Auroral Observations from West Central Canada, *A. Vallance Jones*   465
Balloon Measurements of Auroral X Rays, *G. Kremser*   477

Session 6 THEORY II

Auroral Particles Accelerated in the Geomagnetic Tail, *T. W. Speiser*   491
The Interaction Between the Solar Wind and the Magnetosphere,
     W. I. Axford   499
F Region Photochemical Nightglow Emissions, *Vern L. Peterson*   511
Radio Aurora, *Günther Lange-Hesse*   519
     Part I: Observations   519
     Part II: Comparison of the Observations with Theoretical Model   519
A Brief Review of Auroral Backscatter Theory, *Walter A. Flood*   563

Session 7 OBSERVATIONS III

Auroral Absorption of Radio Waves, *C. Gordon Little*   575
Ionospheric Observations of Auroral Activity, *G. A. M. King*   589
Very Low Frequency Emission Associated with Aurora and Particle
     Precipitation, *Eigil Ungstrup*   599
VLF Emissions Observed Near and South of the Auroral Zone,
     L. Harang   607
Satellite Observations of Particle Fluxes and Atmospheric Emissions,
     Brian J. O'Brien   623
     Part I: Summary of Relevant Particle Measurements Made from
         Satellites   623
     Part II: Summary of Satellite Observations of Emissions   634
Preliminary Observation of 6300Å Predawn Enhancement at
     Arecibo, *H. C. Carlson, Jr.*   643

Session 8 CONFERENCE SUMMARY

Conference Summary, *Martin Walt*   651
Aurora and Airglow Conclusions, *W. O. Davies and B. M. McCormac*   667

Index   681

INTRODUCTION

Billy M. McCormac

Geophysics Division, IIT Research Center, Chicago, Illinois

Some of the scientific problems facing those who attended this Institute are introduced below. Aurora and airglow are a part of the overall interactions of the solar wind, the earth's magnetosphere, and the earth's atmosphere. It is hoped that this Institute will make a significant contribution toward improving our understanding of these phenomena and will identify those areas wherein there is general agreement, as well as those which deserve additional attention.

As evidenced by the agenda and the diversity of interests of the attendees at this Institute, the study of aurora and airglow is multidisciplinary. There are many definitions of aurora and of airglow; however, I prefer the definition by O'BRIEN, *et al.* (1960) which is, "If excitation results from direct bombardment by energetic (nonthermal) charged particles, it is aurora. Otherwise, it is airglow." It will not be convenient to eliminate the use of the general terms aurora and airglow; however, different users may infer different definitions.

This introduction briefly relates the solar wind, transition region, magnetosphere, and trapping region to aurora and airglow (McCORMAC, 1966). Several points are emphasized. An estimation of the state of knowledge is made.

Solar Wind and Magnetosphere

Solar Wind

The solar wind seems to power most, if not all, the phenomena of interest at this Institute. About 2×10^{20} ergs/sec of solar wind energy is incident on the magnetosphere which is 100 times more than enough to power all known geophysical phenomena above the earth's surface. Figure 1 shows the general relationship of the solar wind, transition region, and the earth's magnetosphere. On the subsolar side, the bow shock forms the boundary between the solar wind and the transition region at about 13 earth radii. The magnetopause forms the boundary between the transition region and the magnetosphere at about 10 earth radii on the subsolar side.

The solar wind varies from time to time. Sometimes all protons seem to be monoenergetic, while at other times there is a large spread in energy. The main body of protons, at times, can only be approximated by a Maxwellian distribution, and there is usually a high energy tail. The average proton energy seems to be correlated with the average magnetic disturbance. The bulk velocity seems to have a base line value of 320–330 km/sec. The energy of the

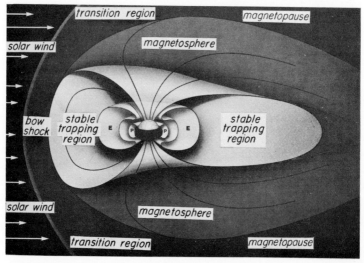

FIGURE 1. Interaction of the solar wind and the earth's magnetosphere and trapped radiation.

protons is usually less than 10 keV with a maximum intensity at about 0.5–1 keV. The flux density is about 10^3 to 10^4 protons/cm^{-2}-sec. Solar wind electrons >350 eV are often observed to have a flux density of about 10^7/cm^2-sec. With a single satellite or probe, temporal and spacial variations in the solar wind cannot be separated. The solar wind is turbulent; however, the type and size of the instabilities have not been resolved.

Transition Region

The solar wind interacts with the earth's magnetic field and produces a bow shock upstream from the magnetopause. The structure of such collisionless shocks is poorly understood. The role of electric fields is yet to be determined. Turbulence in the transition region results from turbulence in the solar wind and turbulence generated by the interaction.

As one passes from interplanetary space into the transition region, the positive ion density increases by a factor of 1.5–2, the spectrum broadens and the average energy decreases. The magnetic field in the transition region is disordered. The particles are more random than in the solar wind. The electrons >350 eV increase from 10^7/cm^{2}sec outside the bow shock to 5×10^8/cm^{2}sec inside the transition region. Proton temperature of 10^5 °K outside increases to 10^6 °K inside the bow shock. Electron temperatures inside the bow shock are 10^6–5×10^6 °K. In passing through the bow shock, rapid fluctuations in the character of the charged particles are observed. The turbulence in the bow shock may be 1–2 earth radii thick, or the bow shock may be shifting by a similar amount, or both.

It is not known if the protons or electrons in the transition region are the same ones as are incident on the subsolar side. The question of stability of the bow shock is important. The energetic particles in the solar wind are highly directional from the sun. In the transition region, there is streaming of particles. All directions are observed, although the maximum is still from the direction of the sun.

Magnetosphere

The magnetopause is the magnetospheric boundary, i.e., the boundary between magnetic field order and disorder. Convection of charged particles into the magnetosphere depends on the stability of the magnetopause. Hydromagnetic waves in the magnetosphere seem to be produced by the interaction collision with the solar wind.

The intensity of electrons >40 keV is greatly increased just inside the magnetopause, whereas the quantity of protons of 0.3–20 keV energy is greatly decreased. The magnetopause seems to be characterized by the disappearance of the streaming protons observed in the transition region. On different orbits, the magnetopause boundary seems to vary by at least an earth radius.

Table I provides a summary of the gross electron and proton characteristics in the different regions.

Table I. Characteristics of Protons and Electrons in Various Regions Compared to the Solar Wind

Region	Protons	Electrons
Solar wind	KeV	$\ll$KeV
Transition	Flux increase	Large flux increase
	T_p increase	T_e increase
	$\bar{E}$ decrease	$\bar{E}$ increase
Magnetosphere	$\ll$KeV	$\gg$KeV

A portion of the magnetosphere has closed field lines and supports trapped charged particles. The criterion for defining trapped particles is arbitrarily selected as "the charged particle which will mirror and drift around the world if it is not perturbed." There are nonthermal electrons and protons throughout the entire stable trapping region.

There are several necessary conditions for trapping. The pressure of the solar wind must be less than the magnetic field pressure, and the kinetic energy of the trapped particles must be less than the magnetic field energy. The ratio of the kinetic energy of trapped particles to the energy in the magnetic field is called β. The β varies from 10^{-5} near the earth to about 10^{-1} at the outer part of the stable belt. The portion of the magnetosphere external to the solid earth has about 8.4×10^{24} ergs of energy compared to 6×10^{22} ergs for all of the energetic trapped particles. Roughly all durably trapped particles in the earth's geomagnetic field lie in a toroidal region bounded by two surfaces of revolution about the magnetic field axis. The inner one is a spherical surface at an altitude of 700 km, and the outer surface is the line of force at about 70° magnetic latitude which extends out to about 10 earth radii on the subsolar side.

The particles in the trapped belts have been poorly measured for electrons below 40 keV and protons below 100 keV. Thus, the particles which seem to be of most interest for auroral studies have been poorly measured. The Van Allen belt is not a sufficient reservoir for auroral electrons.

Although albedo neutron decay may be the source of a significant amount of the protons of energy over 40 MeV, it is an insignificant contributor of lower energy trapped protons and of electrons. The solar wind is the source of essentially all energetic charged particles. However, the mechanism for injection of charged particles is not understood. The tail of the magnetosphere may extend to 100's or 1000's of earth radii. It is not known if the particles in the magnetosphere are convected through the magnetopause on the subsolar side, at the poles, or appear from the open tail. It is also not clear how the charged particles are then injected into the stable trapping region. Once trapped, particles in the outer belt seem to diffuse inward, while being accelerated.

Losses in the lower part of the belt are caused by atmospheric scattering; otherwise, the loss mechanism is not understood, but is related to magnetic activity.

A number of papers will follow which relate solar wind and magnetospheric phenomena to aurora and airglow observations. The influence of the solar wind will be discussed. Magnetic field variations will be surveyed. These fluctuations correlate with many observables. They may participate in the precipitation and acceleration of particles. Charged particle observations in the geomagnetic tail will be related to auroral precipitation.

Coordinate Systems and Particle Motion

Coordinate System

Standard methods are needed for presenting results. Data should be presented in a manner which facilitates its interpretation. Just as spherical coordinates are unsatisfactory for designing homes, geographical coordinates are unsatisfactory for describing phenomena associated with the earth's magnetic field. Some of the many coordinates that are employed are listed in Table II.

Table II. Magnetic Coordinates

B — Scalar magnetic field
L — Magnetic shell parameter
Φ — Magnetic longitude
R — Radial distance from dipole
λ — Magnetic latitude

Much of the charged particle data are presented in B,L or R,λ space. Some aurora and airglow data are still presented in geographical coordinates; however, R,λ and λ,Φ space coordinated systems are commonly employed. There is probably only rare justification for employing geographical coordinates.

A suitable coordinate system in the outer magnetosphere must keep account of the magnetic field lines of force. As more data become available about the tail, especially from multiple satellites employed to resolve temporal and spatial variations, an adequate coordinate system will become imperative. As yet, no suitable system has been suggested.

Earth's Magnetic Field

The four sources for the magnetic field are the: 1) core field, which has a reasonably predictable secular variation of a fraction of a per cent per year in intensity; 2) crustal field, which is important at low altitudes; 3) fields produced by the equatorial and auroral electrojets; and 4) fields from plasma pressures, produced by the solar wind or by the trapped charged particles.

Until the POGO Satellite was launched in October 1965, very few magnetic field measurements existed above 1000 km altitude and very little data exists for much of the earth's surface.

A number of models of the magnetic field in terms of spherical harmonics have been prepared by a least-squares-fit with observations. The commonly used expansion is by Jenson and Cain (48 coefficients). Statistically, nothing can be said about the external field. The error in the magnetic field is now about 0.1–1% at the earth's surface, 10% at a few earth radii, and a factor of 2 at the magnetopause. Significant errors occur at the magnetic field anomalies, especially at the South Atlantic. By 1967, the magnetic field model will be revised with the POGO data.

Charged Particle Motion

A brief description of the motion of charged particles is given to help visualize their precipitation for auroral phenomena. A very detailed discussion is provided by NORTHRUP (1966). The motion of a charged particle in a magnetic field will be a helix about the line of force. The magnetic moment of the charged particle is usually considered to be invariant and is given by

$$M = \frac{\frac{1}{2}mV_{\perp 0}^2}{B_0},\qquad(1)$$

where m is the particle mass, $V_{\perp 0}$ the velocity perpendicular to the magnetic field and B_0 is the field strength at the point of interest. Equation (1) shows that if the particle travels down a field line, B increases and so must $V_\perp$; therefore, the velocity along the field decreases. The value of B where the velocity along the field is zero is given by

$$B = \left(\frac{V^2}{V_{\perp 0}^2}\right)B_0. \tag{2}$$

If the pitch angle (angle between the velocity vector and the line of force) at B_0 is given by α_0 then

$$V_\perp = V \sin \alpha_0. \tag{3}$$

Thus, Equation (2) may be written as

$$B = \frac{B_0}{\sin^2 \alpha_0}. \tag{4}$$

If the point with this value of B is above the atmosphere, the particle will mirror. The mirror point is independent of the particle energy. Generally, particles which mirror below about 100 km altitude will be lost by atmospheric scattering. If the value of B for 100 km altitude on the field line of interest is substituted into Equation (4), each point B_0 on the field line will have a pitch angle, α_0, which defines the loss cone. All particles with pitch angles smaller than the α_0 will be lost if not further perturbed.

Magnetic Shell Parameter, L

McILWAIN (1966) derived L because of its physical significance. It is within one per cent of being a constant along a line of force. Its units are in earth

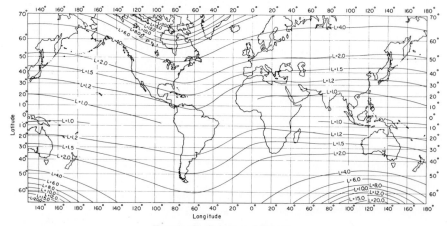

FIGURE 2. Constant L.Traces.

radii. Its value is as accurate as the knowledge of the magnetic field. The space coordinate L is worth consideration for displaying some airglow and auroral phenomena. Figure 2 shows some constant L traces for the earth's surface (DUDZIAK, *et al.*, 1963). The very high values of L may not have physical significance. A trapped charged particle is constrained to remain on a constant L shell and to mirror at a constant B value. Figure 3 shows some constant

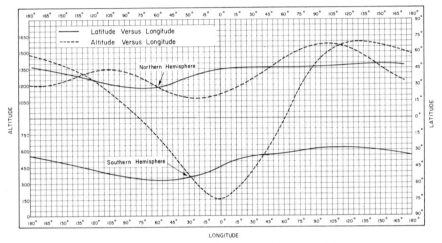

FIGURE 3. Constant B-L traces for $B = 0.28$ Gauss and $L = 2.04$.

B,L traces (DUDZIAK *et al.*, 1963). Thus the latitude and altitude of a constant B and L can be followed around the world in both hemispheres. Particles going below about 100 km altitude will be dumped. These types of plots also provide important information on the location of the conjugate regions.

The B,L Space Coordinate system has been found to be useful whenever B is ordered. To compute B and L, one needs to know the value of B all along the field line. For L less than 4, behavior is good. When the field is distorted, L will not be a constant along the line of force. There do not appear to be suitable coordinates during periods of magnetic fluctuations.

Drift

Several types of drift are possible; however, the most important for trapped energetic particles is caused by the gradient of the magnetic field (POST, 1956). The drift velocity, V_d, is given by

$$V_d = \frac{\rho V_\perp}{2} \frac{\nabla_\perp B}{B}, \tag{5}$$

where ρ is the radius of curvature of the particle. Figure 4 shows that electrons drift east and protons drift west. The drift times are the order of several 10's of minutes.

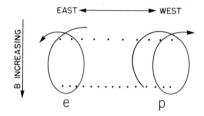

FIGURE 4. Drift of charged particles where the dots represent B coming out of the page.

Trapped Radiation

Trapped Electrons

The low L shell regions provide a sensitive measure of particle precipitation because the flux falls off very rapidly with decreasing L. By measuring the energy spectra, one may study the energy sensitivity of any redistribution process. The longitudinal drift periods for some energy peaks observed in the South Atlantic Anomaly are equal to the period of large scale horizontal magnetic field fluctuations, which were observed on a world wide basis at the same time. Some energy selection process seems to occur during precipitation.

Although the shape of the energy spectrum and the flux of electrons varies with time and location, 40 keV–MeV electrons are observed throughout the stable trapping region.

At the stable trapping boundary there are often very intense spikes for $E > 40$ keV — often a 2 orders of magnitude increase in flux. These are usually soft and occur at night under conditions of relatively high K_p. It is impossible with single satellites to separate the spatial and temporal variations of trapped electrons. A few general characteristics have been deducted. Electrons >280 keV show a 27 day cycle. There is an increase in electron density with an increase in K_p. The flux decays during quiet periods. Electrons of >40 keV show more diurnal variation than >280 keV.

The noon trapped boundary extends to a magnetic latitude of 69° for electrons >280 keV compared to about 67° for electrons >1.2 MeV. The midnight boundaries are 66° and 64°, respectively (WILLIAMS, 1966).

Trapped energetic electrons show a minimum flux intensity at about 44° magnetic latitude. Why the combination of injection and loss produces this so called "slot" is unknown.

Trapped Protons

For trapped protons >40 MeV there are two flux peaks. The first is about $L = 1.5$ and the second is at $L = 2.2$. These may very well result from different sources. The second is only observed near the equator and may not be due to albedo neutron decay. It is believed that most high energy protons (>40 MeV) are injected by albedo neutron decay. However, the proton spectra below 30 MeV cannot be from these neutrons.

At low L values, loss is from atmospheric scattering, whereas the loss mechanism at higher L values is unknown. Below $L = 2$, the protons are very stable. For example, below $L = 2$, the intensity for a very quiet period was the same as for the period of 12 flares of magnitude 2 or 3, 6 magnetic storms, and 4 major solar proton events. Above $L = 2$, there were some decreases from the large magnetic storm in September 1963. MeV protons are not observed at the very high L values.

Implications to Aurora and Airglow

At this Institute, experimental data from satellites, rockets, balloons, and ground stations will be presented on optical, radio, radar, charged particle, and magnetic field observations as related to airglow and aurora. Variables are diurnal and latitudinal, as well as those which are produced by solar rotation and the solar cycle. Each type of measurement imposes some constraints on the overall interpretation.

Aurora

There are many important questions associated with the auroras. The simultaneous particle and auroral emission experiments to be reported here will be very helpful. It seems necessary to try to correlate optical emissions with the charged particle input. The charged particle energies and flux are needed. Where do these keV energy electrons come from? Are the auroral field lines open or closed? The worldwide average energy loss by precipitated charged particles in the whole auroral regions is about 4×10^{17} ergs/sec which is much less than 1% of the solar wind energy. The precipitated flux varies by 10^6 with time and space; however, the solar wind has no such rapid variation. Particle precipitation in the auroral zone is a continuous process. Thus any model connecting the solar wind to the aurora must be inefficient but continuous, and must provide for orders of magnitude more variation in the aurora than in the solar wind.

In spite of many detailed measurements on precipitated particles, the fundamental dynamics are unknown. Apparently, it is even difficult to design a good experiment. It is not known if auroral particles are trapped or not. Measurements of precipitated particles must include backscattering. Sometimes the backscatter of particles in the loss cone can be explained by simple coulomb scattering; however, sometimes the backscattering is much higher. Perhaps E fields become significant on occasion, as will be discussed later. Theoretical studies urgently require E field measurements to reduce the large number of potential possibilities.

Satellites will become much more important for airglow and aurora studies. Satellites can perform simultaneous particle and optical measurements. In addition to the visible and infrared data, satellites are opening up the whole range of uv measurements. Some of these uv results will be reported later. The uv backgrounds seem to be conveniently low. Satellite measurements must be coupled more often with other instrument methods because one satellite cannot resolve spatial and temporal effects in a rapidly changing environment.

Polar cap measurements may help provide a clue as to how particles are injected into the magnetosphere. Do polar cap events start at the magnetic pole or at the trapping boundary, or is the whole polar region covered almost simultaneously? What is the relation of the effects at both poles? The polar cap morphology needs to be connected by suitable measurements to the tail and outer magnetosphere.

Reaction Rates

Studies of the ionization and deionization in the ionosphere often result in 100's of potential reactions without involving numerous, if any, excited states. These reaction rates are, for the most part, poorly known. Laboratory studies have been very unsatisfactory. Highly reproducible results are obtained in laboratory experiments, but one does not seem to know what was really measured. At least above the D region of the ionosphere, the excited states produced are often different than in the laboratory. Rather than going from the laboratory to airglow and aurora, we should interpret the observed airglow and auroral emissions.

Artificial Sources

Artificial sources of energetic charged particles have provided about the only information on trapping efficiencies and lifetimes. Nuclear detonations have yielded fluorescent efficiencies and specific data on certain airglow processes, because the energy source and the quantity of charged particles involved were known. Star Fish was a 1.4 megaton detonation at 400 km altitude over Johnston Island on July 9, 1962, at $L = 1.12$. Approximately 5×10^{26} electrons were emitted. About 2.6 per cent of these electrons were trapped at 10 hours. None of these trapped electrons were detected above an L of 1.5; however, it seems that a magnetohydrodynamic wave from the burst caused an increase in energetic electrons out to an L of 3 or 4.

From time to time, there have been studies on the possibility of artificially injecting electrons, protons, positrons or alpha particles into the magnetosphere. Positrons or alphas would require fewer particles because the natural background is small. There is much resistance to alpha injection until the natural alpha belt is mapped. Positrons are not highly favored because some electromagnetic wave interactions would be different than for electrons.

Chemical releases have been made to study the atmospheric, magnetic, and electric fields, and photochemical emissions. These techniques have not yet been directly applied to auroral zone problems, but there are many possibilities. The study of photochemical emissions by chemical releases does not seem very useful because the chemicals perturb the environment too much.

Electromagnetic Radio Emissions

Several phenomena may result in electromagnetic radio emissions. These are instabilities at the bow shock and magnetopause, instabilities associated with charged particle precipitation in auroras, plasma oscillations, synchrotron radiation, and interactions with the gyrofrequencies of charged particles. Some of the VLF emissions to be reported on later may be related to one or more of these phenomena. The surface has not been scratched for electromagnetic emissions. More effort needs to be given toward presenting VLF emissions in such a manner that they can be considered with other kinds of data.

Radar observations give some indication of the size and character of the ionized region inhomogeneities. Together with absorption measurements, the electron density as a function of time can be estimated. More effort is needed to integrate radar and other data. Radar measurements (ionosonde) have long been coupled to some airglow emission observations.

Airglow

Airglow is becoming more and more exciting. The increase in data during the last five years has been very useful in showing that airglow has an important relationship to other phenomena. Such integrated analyses will greatly increase in the next few years. In addition to showing a significant altitude dependence, airglow varies with latitude, longitude, solar cycle, etc. Magnetic conjugate effects are becoming apparent.

Night Airglow

The two red arcs on either side of the equatorial electrojet require explanation. The magnetic field plays some role. The relation of the F region electron density and the 6300Å luminosity has long been recognized, and now seems to be understood.

Observations of airglow between the equator and the auroral zone show that there are large scale inhomogeneities which seem to correlate with radar backscatter.

Twilight

Twilight measurements show the altitude and efficiency for some resonant scattering species. Interpretation is very preliminary and much more data are required.

Dayglow

Much more data are required. Most of the small amount of data comes from rocket flights, although, in spite of the intense background, surface airglow measurements are now being successfully made.

References

DUDZIAK, W. F., KLEINECKE, D. D., and KOSTIGEN, T. J., 1963, DASA 1372.
MCCORMAC, B. M., 1966, *Radiation Trapped in the Earth's Magnetic Field* (Ed. by B. M. MCCORMAC, D. REIDEL).
MCILWAIN, C. E., 1966, *Radiation Trapped in the Earth's Magnetic Field* (Ed. by B. M. MCCORMAC, D. REIDEL).
NORTHRUP, T. G., 1966, *Radiation Trapped in the Earth's Magnetic Field* (Ed. by B. M. MCCORMAC, D. REIDEL).
O'BRIEN, B. J., ALLUM, F. R., and GOLDWIRE, H. C., 1960, *J. Geophys. Res.* **70**, 161-175.
POST, R. F., 1956, *Rev. of Mod. Phys.* **28**, 338.
WILLIAMS, D., 1966, *Radiation Trapped in the Earth's Magnetic Field* (Ed. by B. M. MCCORMAC, D. REIDEL).

Session

1

ORIENTATION

Dr. Sydney Chapman, Chairman

*National Center for Atmospheric Research
and University of Alaska*

HISTORY OF AURORA AND AIRGLOW

Sydney Chapman

Geophysical Institute, University of Alaska
National Center for Atmospheric Research, Boulder, Colorado

The science of the aurora has a long history; that of the airglow is short. The aurora was discussed by Anaximenes (middle and latter part of the sixth century B.C.), Anaxagoras (born about 500 B.C., settled in Athens about 456 B.C.), and Aristotle (384–322 B.C.) In the Mediterranean region where these men wrote, the aurora is a rare sight, but they could have seen one, or learned from those who had. Pliny the Elder mentions a "blood-colored spectacle" of 349 B.C. as "a terrible portent, a conflagration falling earthward," which could have been an aurora. Other classical writers — Cicero, Seneca, and Livy — also mention auroras. Aristotle,* in his *Meteorologica*, refers to them as chasms (*chasmata*). This may imply that he thought them to be cracks in the dark sky, through which flames beyond could be seen.

Gassendi and Halley

About two millenia after the discussion by Aristotle, the aurora reentered the annals of science in a book of physics, written in Latin by the French mathematician and astronomer Gassendi (1592–1655). In the intervening period many ancient and medieval writers had described auroras in a fanciful or superstitious way. Gassendi* wrote on an outstanding display which he saw in southern France on September 12, 1621 (Fritz reports that Galileo also saw it, at Venice). He gave it the name *aurora borealis* (northern dawn).

Almost another century passed before the next scientific description and discussion of a great aurora, namely that seen in London on March 6, 1715 (old style: owing to a calendar change, dates of the time were often doubly quoted; in our present style, this date was March 16, 1716). The writer was the astronomer, geophysicist, and geometer Halley (1656–1742), and the account was given by request of the then young Royal Society. Halley, who was sixty years old at the time, remarked that this was his first sight of an aurora, which he had wanted to observe for many years. He said that for eighty years after

---

*The asterisk following this and other names given in this article signifies that references are given to editions of their works published posthumously.

1623 the aurora had been infrequent. Long afterwards, this was recognized to have a bearing on the sun and sunspots. These had been independently discovered in Europe in 1610 by Fabricius, Galileo, and Scheiner, though recorded much earlier by the Chinese. The spots were not systematically observed in the following century.

Halley mentioned that the frequent appearance of the aurora is "not far from the times of the two equinoxes." Later KRAFT (1736) showed that among 141 auroras observed at St. Petersburg (now Leningrad), the equinoxes were more favored than the solstices.

Auroral Direction and Perspective

The 1716 aurora, as seen in London, showed a corona. HALLEY (1716) indicated that the convergence of its rays must be an effect of perspective. "According to all likelihood," he said, "they are parallel-sided, or rather tapering the other way." The latter phrase is an acute remark related to a theory he proposed to explain the aurora. Knowing that magnetic force, unlike electric force, can be exerted between a magnet and a piece of iron with solid or liquid interposed, he conceived that there is a continual flow of magnetic particles in both directions, along what we now call the field lines, or lines of magnetic force. He added to his account a diagram of the field lines of a uniformly magnetized sphere, which we know are the same as for a point dipole, a concept then far in the future. He suggested that these particles excite luminescence in the air when it is in some special, sensitive state, which he did not explain. His "tapering the other way" clearly referred to the convergence of the field lines towards the sphere. Halley's diagram was made using steel filings.

Three years later he described another aurora, which he saw both before dawn and after sunset on November 10, 1719. Once again a corona was visible at London, and this time he measured the elevation of the point of convergence; it was 14° south of the zenith, and almost on the meridian. But he did not draw attention to the agreement of this direction with the local direction of the magnetic intensity. The first explicit statement that the auroral rays lie along the geomagnetic field lines is attributed to the Swedish scientist WILCKE (1777), in 1770.

Maier, de Mairan, Euler

In the early eighteenth century the newly founded Russian Academy of Science, then located in St. Petersburg, numbered among its resident members the famous Swiss mathematician Euler. He proposed a theory of the aurora. In 1724, another member, MAIER (1726, 1728), proposed a method of finding the height and location of an auroral arc by observations from one place only. HALLEY (1716) had earlier indicated a method using observations of an aurora from more than one place to "determine, with some degree of exactness, the distance and height thereof, without which we can scarce come to any just conclusion." Maier's method assumed that the lower border of an auroral arc is a small circle on a sphere concentric with the earth.

In 1733 the first treatise wholly devoted to the aurora was published by the French Academy of Sciences. It was written by Jean Jacques d'Ortous de Mairan. He described Maier's method, which required the measurement of the maximum angle of elevation of the arc, and of the azimuths of the points where it ends on the horizon. De Mairan commented on the elegance, advantages, and inconveniences of the method. De Mairan's excellent book, well worth reading today for its clarity and historical interest, ran to a second edition in 1754. Copies of either edition are not difficult to find in libraries, but this has not prevented Maier's method from being forgotten. It has been rediscovered several times — among others, by POTTER (1831, 1833) in England, by FEARNLEY (1859) in Norway, by the American astronomer, NEWTON (1860), and by NORDENSKIÖLD (1882) of Sweden. Treatises on the aurora by the French meteorologist ANGOT (1895) and the Finlander LEMSTRÖM (1886) also mention the method. Angot ascribed it to BRAVAIS (1846), and Lemström to NORDENSKIÖLD (1886). The most recent rediscovery is by REES (1963).

De Mairan criticized the auroral theories of Halley and Euler; his own view was that it is related to the sun's atmosphere — which he thought extended right to the earth — and to the zodiacal light. He ridiculed the idea held by some that the aurora is polar because it is caused by the reflection of sunlight from northern snow and ice; but this explanation is not quite extinct today among the unlearned. He thought that the aurora might be observable round the Antarctic pole, and questioned French explorers, Frézier and Ulloa, who had sailed round Cape Horn. They said they had seen it, but their descriptions do not support their affirmations, and the aurora there is most infrequent.

Graham, Celsius, Hiorter and Franklin

In his second edition, de Mairan mentions the work of GRAHAM (1724). By watching the microscopic changes of compass direction, Graham discovered the transient geomagnetic variations, and distinguished between periods of magnetic quiet and magnetic disturbance. De Mairan also mentioned the discovery by CELSIUS (1701–1744) and HIORTER (1747), in 1741, of the association of magnetic disturbance with the aurora. De Mairan also referred to an auroral theory by Benjamin Franklin, later expounded by Franklin to the French Academy in 1779. Franklin pictured a general atmospheric circulation: hot tropical air rising and travelling at a high level to the polar regions, there to descend with much "auroral" lightning, favored by the insulating property of the snow and ice (Figure 1).

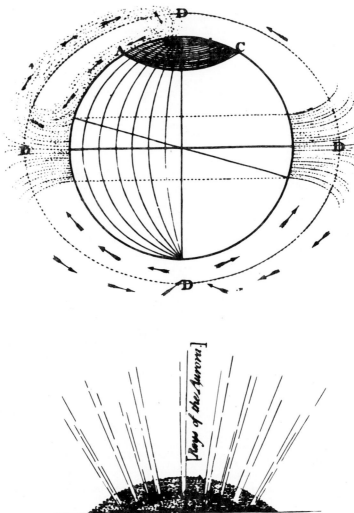

Benjamin Franklin.Philosophical Pieces.London 1779

FIGURE 1. Benjamin Franklin's diagram illustrating his theory of the aurora borealis, expounded in Paris before the French Royal Academy of Sciences in April, 1779. The theory involved "a meridional circulation at high levels, in the proper direction."* At such levels "the low pressure would result in an increased electrical conductivity." Franklin associated the usual polar location of the aurora with the insulating property of the snow and ice often prevalent there. His caption in this diagram reads:

> The Arrows represent the general Currents of the Air.
> A.B.C. the great Cake of Ice and Snow in the Polar Regions.
> D.D.D.D. the Medium Height of the Atmosphere.
> The Representation is made only for one Quarter and one
> Meridian of the Globe: but is to be understood the same
> for all the rest.

*For the quoted phrases see Houghton (1958).

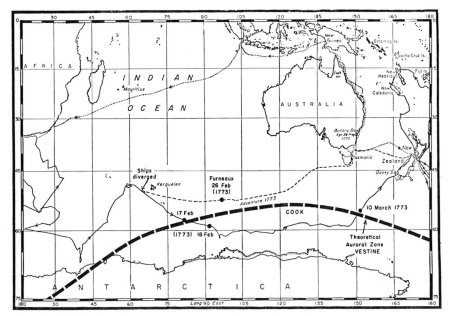

FIGURE 2. The heavy broken line shows the approximate position of the part of the southern auroral zone that crosses the Indian Ocean. During February and March, 1773, in the course of the second voyage (1772–75) of Captain James Cook in his ship *Resolution*, her track for three weeks lay within the zone. His companion ship *Adventure* (under Captain Tobias Furneaux) had lost contact with Cook early in February. Her track lay close to the zone, but outside it. The positions and dates of the first sightings of the aurora australis are shown.

The Aurora Australis

The first record of the southern aurora, whose occurrence was expected by de Mairan, is due to Captain Cook (1728–1779) (Figure 2). He saw it on February 17, 1773, when in latitude 57°6′ S, in the Indian Ocean (Cook's *Journal*, 1961 ed.). He named it the *aurora australis* (southern dawn). Together the aurora borealis and aurora australis (northern and southern auroras) are named the *aurora polaris* or polar aurora. The term *aurora australis*, however, had already been used, less appropriately, to refer to the aurora borealis appearing south of the observer's zenith. Euler was one of the first to do this, in a description of an aurora seen at St. Petersburg on October 22, 1728 (LOVERING, 1868–1871, p. 89). According to this usage, the aurora australis would be most frequent at places not very far to the north of 67° dipole latitude in the Arctic. Halley had sailed to 52° S in the south Atlantic Ocean in 1699 without seeing an aurora.

Cavendish

In 1789 the great amateur-scientist aristocrat CAVENDISH (1790) used three accounts of an aurora seen in England by others on February 23, 1784, to infer its height. The accounts had appeared in the *Philosophical Transactions* of the Royal Society. He obtained lower and upper limits — 52 and 71 miles, or 84 and 114 km — of quite the right order. But so many discrepant height determinations were made by others that the true height remained uncertain until this century (Abbe 1898). De Mairan much overestimated the height, whereas some observers have reported seeing it below the clouds, or silhouetted against distant mountains.

Auroral Catalogs

De Mairan gave a catalog of notable auroras, and many la er writers have followed his example, notably FRITZ (1873), but also, earlier, CELSIUS (1733), the atomic chemist DALTON (1793, 1828, 1834), LOVERING (1868), RUBENSON (1879), GREELY (1881), and TROMHOLT (1902), and, for southern auroras, BOLLER (1898). Despite great care in the search for records, Fritz failed to mention some auroras, and some of those he recorded are doubtful. Still in the eighteenth century, as in the time of Aristotle, auroras were among the many natural phenomena called *meteors;* the word *meteor* only gradually came to have its present meaning, restricted to a shooting star. HALLEY (1716) referred to the meteor then seen as being the only sort of meteor that he had not previously seen in the course of his life. Shooting stars, comets and cirrus clouds have at times been mistakenly reported as auroras.

ARAGO*, BIOT (1820) and HANSTEEN (1819) were among the eminent men of science in the early nineteenth century who interested themselves in the aurora.

Poems on the Aurora

Some scientific works have been written in poetic form, such as the exposition of Democritus' atomic theory by Lucretius. The Russian scientist LOMONOSOV (1747), in 1743, wrote an ode on the northern lights; the two most significant verses in it — the fourth and sixth — are thus translated:

> But, where, O Nature, is thy law?
> From the midnight lands comes up the dawn!
> Is it not the sun setting his throne?
> Is it not the icy seas that are flashing fire?
> Lo, a cold flame has covered us!
> Lo, in the night-time day has come upon the earth.

> What makes a clear ray tremble in the night?
> What strikes a slender flame into the firmament?
> Like lightning without storm clouds,
> Climbs to the heights from earth?
> How can it be that frozen steam
> Should midst winter bring forth fire?

In 1753, however, Lomonosov ascribed the aurora to a movement of the ether. Goethe,* in a poem *An Lida*, referred to the eternal stars shimmering through the moving rays of the northern lights. Nearer to our time, Robert Service wrote a long poem on the aurora. PETRIE (1963) has included many poetic and other literary references to the aurora in his recent book.

The Auroral Zone(s)

The article on the aurora by the German geographer MUNCKE (1833) seems to contain the first mention of the existence and location of a zone of maximum frequency of auroral appearance, which we now call the auroral zone. It was known that the aurora becomes more frequent as one goes northward from temperate latitudes, but Muncke inferred from the accounts of polar explorers that this increase of frequency does not continue to the pole; a maximum frequency occurs along a zone well short of the pole. This fact was independently discovered later by LOOMIS (1860), professor of natural philosophy at Yale, and he gave the first sketch of the zone, showing a band of maximum frequency, bordered on both sides by bands where the frequency, though considerable, is less. FRITZ (1874) extended this work a year after his catalog appeared, by publishing a map of northern *isolines* of frequencies of auroral visibility, which he called *isochasms*, a reference to the term used by Aristotle. His isochasms were later supplemented by VESTINE (1944). Southern isochasms were drawn only during this century (WHITE, 1939; VESTINE and SNYDER, 1945), and are still less well determined than the northern ones.

The Sunspot Cycle

Meanwhile the sunspot cycle was discovered by Schwabe about 1844, and in 1851 its association with magnetic disturbance was discovered. The long known link between magnetic phenomena and the aurora implied a similar auroral-sunspot connection, but the auroral statistics were so incomplete that this could be doubted as late as 1868 (LOVERING, p. 344). This relation is clearly shown, however, by the systematic records of the aurora made throughout three sunspot cycles at the Yerkes observatory (MEINEL et al., 1954).

The Auroral Spectrum

In the latter half of the nineteenth century, the spectrum of the aurora began to be studied. Ångström found a prominent yellow-green line, whose wavelength was not measured with great accuracy until BABCOCK (1923) did so at Mt. Wilson, using a Fabry-Perot interferometer. But the light he used was that of the airglow, not the aurora. As long as the wavelength (5577Å) was not properly known, more than one false identification was possible. As late as 1915, RAMSAY, in his book *The Gases of the Atmosphere* (4th ed.), could report that the auroral spectrum contains numerous lines, "all of which have been shown by Mr. Baly to be identical with strong lines in the spectrum of krypton, but the strongest is one of wavelength 5570."

The true identity of this line was not discovered until 1924, when McLENNAN and SHRUM, at Toronto, showed it to be caused by a transition between the metastable levels ^{1}S and ^{1}D of atomic oxygen. Earlier, in 1913, Vegard had identified important bands in the spectrum as the negative bands of molecular nitrogen. Only in the last two decades have practically all the lines and bands been identified. They are mainly produced by neutral oxygen atoms and nitrogen molecules and positively charged nitrogen (atomic and molecular).

Auroral Heights

Since about 1910 STÖRMER (1955) made his great series of determinations of auroral heights by simultaneous photography (KROGNESS, 1920) from two or more stations distant at least 20 km apart. These clearly established the range of height of auroras seen from Norway. One of his unexpected discoveries was that auroras which lie in the sunlit air — though seen from places in darkness — are unusually high, and may extend up to 1000 km. A few shorter series of such height determinations have been made elsewhere (FULLER, 1935), but there remains a great need to determine the heights and locations of the rare auroras seen in lower, and even tropical, latitudes. In contrast to the interest of Halley, de Mairan, and Cavendish in auroral heights, MUNCKE (1833, p. 166) was convinced that there is little scientific value in knowing the height of the aurora.

Auroral Audibility

Countless observers have stated that they have heard auroral sounds during outstanding displays. DE MAIRAN (2nd ed.) and HAYES (1867) wrote of the silence that reigns during all the auroral phenomena. STÖRMER (1955) himself never heard any auroral sound, but came to believe in its infrequent occurrence, on the evidence of observers he trusted. CHAPMAN (1931) and BEALS (1933) have discussed the evidence. Clear objective observational confirmation or disproof is still to be obtained.

Auroral Theories

From Greek times, almost to this century, a great variety of auroral causes and associations have been proposed: associations with shooting stars, weather, and earthquakes; and as causes, vapors, ether, exhalations, electric discharges. The first detailed approaches toward a rational theory were made (following an incorrect suggestion by PAULSEN, 1894) by two Norwegians, Birkeland and Störmer, the former by laboratory experiments, the latter, mathematically. Their proposed cause was a beam of highly energetic electrons or other charged particles from the sun, all of one sign. They concluded that such a beam could impinge on a uniformly magnetized sphere on the side away from the point of projection. Birkeland found impact zones which he identified with the auroral zones. SCHUSTER (1912) criticized these theories on the ground that the mutual electrostatic repulsion of the charges would disperse the beam to negligible density before it could affect the earth. LINDEMANN (1919), in a justified criticism of a one-sign theory of magnetic storms that I proposed in 1918, indicated that the likely cause is a neutral ionized beam, at present called a beam of plasma. Ferraro and I, around 1930, made some progress on this basis in developing the theory of magnetic storms, and inferred the confinement of the earth's field in a cavity now called the magnetosphere; but we did not infer the auroral consequences of such a beam. Not until 1950 was it definitely proved (MEINEL, 1950) that charged particles descend from outside the atmosphere, and by their impact with the atmospheric particles generate the auroral luminescence. Many details of the atomic and molecular excitation and ionization still remain to be worked out.

Early historical accounts of auroral theory have been given by DE MAIRAN (1733, 1754), FESTER (1781), and BRAVAIS (1846). The last of these works was praised by CARLHEIM-GYLLENSKÖLD (1887) as being perhaps the best account of the aurora available up to his time.

Outstanding Auroras

I conclude this brief historical account of the aurora by mentioning some outstanding past auroras. Probably the greatest of all, of which we have any reliable record, is that of February 4, 1872, which was seen in the tropics at Bombay, as well as in many other parts of India, and in Egypt, and elsewhere (DONATI, 1872; QUETELET, 1872; and CHAPMAN, 1957; CHAPMAN and BARTELS, 1940, p. 328). It was associated with an equally outstanding magnetic storm. Such auroras seen in unusually low latitudes are commonly red. This has led many times throughout the centuries to its interpretation as due to a fire to the north — and fire brigades have actually gone out in search of it. This happened in ancient Rome during the time of Tiberius (as related by Seneca), and even in 1938 in England, when it was thought that Windsor Castle was on fire.

Auroras that have been seen from the tropics include one in 1789 (not mentioned by Fritz) seen in Mexico, one in 1859 (LOOMIS, 1860; QUETELET, 1859; CHAPMAN and BARTELS, 1940), lasting for a few days and coinciding with the first recorded solar flare (seen in total sunlight); one occurring on September 25, 1909, said by ANGENHEISTER (1933) to have been seen at Batavia (now Djakarta), 6° S, and Singapore, 1° N; and one on May 15, 1921, seen from Samoa (ANGENHEISTER and WESTLAND, 1921; CHAPMAN and BARTELS, 1940). Fine colored plates of an aurora seen at Cambridge, England, on October 24, 1847 were published by MORGAN and BARBER (1848).

HEIS (1806–1877) was long the editor (1857–1875) of a weekly journal of astronomical and other data, which is a mine of information on auroral occurrences of the time. Other journals that have occasional auroral reports include *Nature*, the *Journal of the British Astronomical Association*, *Meteorologische Zeitschrift*, *Journal of Geophysical Research*, and *Monthly Weather Review*.

The Airglow

NEWCOMB (1901) attributed the light of the night sky (observable by contrast when an opaque object is held overhead at night) to the flux of radiation from myriads of stars too faint to be seen individually. DUFAY (1933) showed, on the basis of our knowledge of the numbers of faint stars of different magnitudes, that this explanation was inadequate: most of the light must come from the zodiacal light and from the self-luminescence of the atmosphere.

The atmospheric light was studied from 1915 onward at the Lowell Observatory, Flagstaff, Arizona (SLIPHER, 1919, 1933). Slipher found that the prominent auroral line 5577 Å is perennially present in its spectrum. As already mentioned, its wavelength was accurately measured by Babcock, and its source — atomic oxygen — was explained by McLennan and Shrum. Many other radiations were found at Flagstaff, including the two atomic oxygen red lines, 6300 and 6364, prominent also in the aurora. Seasonal, day-to-day, and daily variations of the light were gradually discovered (RAYLEIGH, 1924, 1925, 1928, 1929; McLENNAN et al., 1928). Prominent workers in this field included CABANNES (1935), DUFAY (1933) and BARBIER (1945) in France, the fourth Lord RAYLEIGH (1920–1931) in England, and SOMMER (1929) in Germany (cf. a valuable review by DÉJARDIN (1936)). RAYLEIGH in 1919 and DUFAY in 1929 showed that the degree of polarization of the light is small. Gradually it became clear that the spectrum differs from that of the aurora in that its excitation potential is small.

RAYLEIGH (1931) clearly recognized the distinctions between auroral and night-sky light, and gave the name "non-polar aurora" to the latter, with particular reference to the line 5577. His new term, and the name "light of the night sky," have gradually been superseded by the term *airglow*, proposed by Elvey on the suggestion of O. Struve. Variants of this term are also used: twilight glow (long studied at Flagstaff) and dayglow. The absolute intensity of the light of the line 5577 in the airglow, expressed by the number of photons produced per cm² column per second, was first determined by RAYLEIGH (1930); this has led to the adoption of his name for a unit of sky brightness.

In Déjardin's 1936 review, the theory outlined to account for the airglow emission was one proposed by DAUVILLIER (1932), which invoked a continual flux of highly energetic electrons (10^{10} eV) from the sun. CHAPMAN (1931a) proposed the very different theory, now generally accepted, that the airglow is caused by emission of photons associated with the recombination of ionized and, more particularly, dissociated particles produced by ultraviolet absorption of sunlight during the day. He suggested (1931a) the reaction $O + O + O = O_2 + O^*$ to explain the 5577 emission, and, later (1939), the reaction $NaO + O = Na^* + O_2$ to explain the emission, discovered by BERNARD (1938), of the D-lines of atomic sodium. KAPLAN (1929–1935) and also RAYLEIGH (1922) made many laboratory experiments which threw light on the processes of airglow and auroral emission.

Exceptionally bright night skies are seen occasionally, not produced by moonlight (RAYLEIGH, 1931; POEY, 1860; HOOKER, 1854), or — judging by the absence of great magnetic disturbance — by the aurora.

References

The following list gives only papers mentioned in the text, except that it includes all the papers by the fourth Lord Rayleigh on the aurora and airglow. The list includes but a very small fraction of the extensive pre-1900 literature on the aurora. Nineteenth century papers are listed in the Royal Society Catalogue of Scientific Papers 1800–1900. Papers by writers no longer living may be traced in the lists of their works generally included in their main obituary notices, or in works on the aurora, such as those by CAPRON (1879), FRITZ (1881) or HARANG (1951). Many more recent auroral and airglow references are given by CHAMBERLAIN (1961) and by AKASOFU et al. (1966); for example, they mention many papers by Barbier, Cabannes, Dufay and others, of which only one or two are cited below.

Abbe, C., 1898, *Terr. Mag. and Atmos. Elec.* **3**, 5, 53, 149.
AKASOFU, S. I., CHAPMAN, S., and MEINEL, A. B., 1966, *Handbuch der Physik* **49**, (1), 1-158.
ANGENHEISTER, G., 1933, *Polarlicht, Handbuch d. Naturwiss.* 2 Aufl. **8**; his reference may be based on a report (*Nature* **81**, 524, 1909) which seems to me to be in part doubtful.
ANGENHEISTER, G. and WESTLAND, C. J., 1921, *Terr. Mag. and Atmos. Elec.* **26**, 30, 31, 116.
ANGOT, A., 1895, *Les Aurores Polaires*, Alcan, Paris; 1896 (English trans.) London.
ARAGO, F., 1854/5, *Oeuvres*, 1, Paris, 1854, and *Meteorological Essays*, London, 1855, 315-500.
ARISTOTLE, 1931, *Meteorologica* (English translation of *Works*, Ed. by Ross, Oxford, vol. 3); 341b1-342b24.
BABCOCK, H. D., 1923, *Astrophys. J.* **57**, 209.
BARBER, J. T., 1848, see MORGAN.
BARBIER, D., 1945, *Ann. Géophys.* **1**, 224.
BEALS, C. S., 1933, *Quart. J. Roy. Meteorol. Soc.* **59**, 71.
BERNARD, R., 1938, *Z. Phys.* **110**, 291.
BIOT, J. B., 1820, *J. Savants*, June-Aug., 342.
BOLLER, W., 1898, *Gerlands Beitr.* **3**, 56, 550.
BRAVAIS, A., 1846, *Voyages en Scandinavie, en Laponie, au Spitzberg et au Feröe pendant les années* 1838, 1839, 1840, Bertrand, Paris, 3e div., *Magnétisme terrestre*, Chap. X (Historique des hypothèses faites sur la nature et la cause des aurores boréales), pp. 265-294; 4e div., *Aurores boréales*, pp. 1-566.
CABANNES, J., 1935, *Compt. Rend., Paris*, **200**, 1905.

CAPRON, J. R., 1879, *Aurorae, their characters and spectra*, Spon, London.
CARLHEIM-GYLLENSKÖLD, V., 1886, *Exploration Internationale des régions polaires*, 1882-3, 2, 1, Norstedt, Stockholm.
CAVENDISH, H., 1790, *Phil. Trans. Roy. Soc.* 80, 101.
CELSIUS, A., 1733, *Auroral Catalog*, Nuremberg.
CHAMBERLAIN, J. W., 1961, *Physics of the aurora and airglow*, Academic Press, New York.
CHAPMAN, S., 1931, *Nature* 127, 341.
CHAPMAN, S., 1931a, *Proc. Roy. Soc. A.* 132, 353.
CHAPMAN, S., 1939, *Astrophys. J.* 90, 309.
CHAPMAN, S., 1957, *Bull. Natl. Inst. Sci. India* 9, 180.
CHAPMAN, S., 1966, see AKASOFU.
CHAPMAN, S. and BARTELS, J., 1940, "Geomagnetism," Oxford, Chap. 14.
CHAPMAN, S. and FERRARO, V. C. A., 1930/1, *Nature* 126, 129; *Terr. Magn. & Atmos. Elec.* 36, 77, 171; 37, 147, 421; 38, 79.
COOK, J., 1961, *The journals of Captain James Cook* 2, 95, Cambridge.
DALTON, J., 1793, *Phil. Trans. Roy. Soc.* 53, 144, 2nd ed. 1834.
DALTON, J., 1828, *Phil. Trans. Roy. Soc.* A 118, 291.
DAUVILLIER, 1932, *Rev. Gén de l'élec.* 31, 303, 443, 477.
DÉJARDIN, G., 1936, *Rev. Mod. Phys.* 8, 21.
DONATI, G. B., 1872, *Le Aurore Boreali e la Loro Origine Cosmica*, Florence.
DREYER, J. L. E., 1953, *A history of astronomy from Thales to Kepler*, 2nd ed., Dover, New York.
DUFAY, J., 1929, *J. Phys. rad.* 10, 219.
DUFAY, J., 1933, *Réunions de l'Institut d'optique*, Paris, June 13, p. 6 and many other papers cited by Déjardin.
EULER, L.
FEARNLEY, C. F., 1859, *Forhandlinger Christiania*, 117-149.
FERRARO, V. C. A., 1930/1, see CHAPMAN.
FESTER, A., 1781, *Mathematische og Physische Betoegninger over Nordlyset*, Drontheim.
FRANKLIN, B., 1779, *Political, Miscellaneous and Philosophical Pieces* (Ed. Vaughan), p. 504; Johnson, London.
FRITZ, H., 1873, *Verzeichniss beobachteter Polarlichter*, Gerolds, Wien, Akad., Vienna.
FRITZ, H., 1874, *Petermanns Geog. Mitt.* 20, 347.
FRITZ, H., 1881, *Das Polarlicht*, Brockhaus, Leipzig.
FULLER, V. B., 1935, *Terr. Magn. & Atmos. Elec.* 40, 269.
GASSENDI, P., 1658, *Opera Omnia*, Lugduni (Lyons, France).
GOETHE, W. von, *Lyrische und epische Dichtungen* 1, 226, (1920 edn.).
GRAHAM, G., 1724, *Phil. Trans. Roy. Soc.* 33, 96.
GREELY, A. W., 1881, *Prof. papers, U. S. Signal Service* 3.
HALLEY, E., 1716, *Phil. Trans. Roy Soc.* 29, 406.
HALLEY, E., 1719, *Phil. Trans Roy. Soc.* 30, 1099.
HANSTEEN, C., 1819, *Untersuchungen über den Magnetismus der Erde*, Christiania.
HARANG, L., 1951, "The aurorae," Wiley, New York (English translation of German original, revised).
HAYES, I. I., 1867, *The Open Polar Sea*, London.
HEIS, E., 1857-1875, *Wochenschrift für Astron. etc.*, Halle.
HIORTER, O. P., 1747, *Svensk. Vet. Acad. Handl*, p. 27.
HOOKER, J. D., 1845, *Himalayan Journals* 2, 384, Murray, London.
HOUGHTON, H. G., 1958, *Atmospheric Explorations*. New York and London; p. vii.
IRETON, H. J. C., 1928, see McLENNAN *et al.*
JONES, H. S., 1935, see RAYLEIGH.
KAPLAN, J., 1929-1934, *Phys. Rev.* 33, 154; 42, 807; 45, 671, 675, 898.
KAPLAN, J., 1928-1935, *Nature* 121, 711; 133, 131; 134, 289; 135, 229, 1034.
KRAFFT, G. W., 1736, *Comm. Petersburg Acad.* 9, 340.
KROGNESS, O., 1920, *Geofys. Publ.* 1, 172, Christiania.
LEMSTRÖM, S., 1886, *L'aurore boréale*, Paris.
LINDEMANN, F. A., 1919, *Phil. Mag.* 38, 669.
LIVY, 22/2/11.

LOMONOSOV, M. V., 1747, *Rhetoric*, Moscow; I am indebted to Dr. W. N. Vickery for the translation.
LOOMIS, E., 1860, *Am. J. Sci. & Arts* 30, 89.
LOVERING, J., 1868-1871, *Mem. Am. Acad. Arts & Sci.*, Boston, 10.
MAIER, F. C., 1726, 1728, *Comm. Petersburg Acad.* 1, 351, 365; 4, 128.
MAIRAN, J. J. d'O. DE, 1733, 1754, *Traité physique et historique de l'aurore boréale*, Editions 1, 2, Paris.
MCLENNAN, J. C and SHRUM, G. R., 1924, *Proc Roy. Soc. A.* 106, 138.
MCLENNAN, J. C., MCLEOD, J. H., and IRETON, H. J. C., 1928, *Trans. Roy. Soc. Canada* 22, 397.
MCLEOD, J. H., 1928, see MCLENNAN *et al.*
MEINEL, A. B., 1950, *Phys. Rev.* 80, 1096; *Science* 112, 590.
MEINEL, A. B., NEGAARD, J. B., and CHAMBERLAIN, J. W., 1954, *J. Geophys. Res.* 59, 407.
MEINEL, A. B., 1966, see AKASOFU.
MORGAN, J. H. and BARBER, J. T., 1848, *An Account of the aurora borealis seen near Cambridge, Oct 24, 1847; also of those of Sep. 21, 1846 and March 19, 1847*. With 12 coloured engravings, Cambridge and London.
MUNCKE, A., 1833, *Gehler's Physikalische Wörterbuch*, 2nd ed., 1825-1845, 7, pt. 1, 113.
NEWCOMB, S., 1901, *Astrophys J.* 14, 297.
NEWTON, H. A., 1860, *Am J. Sci. & Arts*, (2) 29, 286.
NORDENSKIÖLD, N. A. E., 1884, *Ann. de chimie et de physique*, (6), 1, 5 (French translation of the original, published in Stockholm, 1882).
PAULSEN, A. F. W., 1894, *K. Danske Vid. Selskab. Forh.*, p. 148; *Ciel et Terre* 16, 197, 227, 259.
PETRIE, W., 1963, *Keoeeit—Story of the Aurora Borealis*, Pergamon, New York.
POEY, A., 1860, *Compt. Rend.*, Paris, 50, 998.
POTTER, R., Jr., 1831, *Edinb. J. Sci.* 5, 23, 209.
POTTER, R., Jr., 1833, *Phil. Mag.* 2, 233; 3, 422.
QUETELET, A., 1861, 1872, *Bull. Acad. Roy. Belges*, 1861, 193; 1872, 312, 375.
QUETELET, E., 1859, *Bull. Acad. Roy. Belges*, pp. 344, 647, 790.
QUETELET, E., 1869-1874, *Bull. Acad. Roy. Belges*, (2) 27; 28, 403; 29, 16, 176; 30, 378; 31, 7; 32, 347; 33; 35, 98; 37, 160.
RAMSAY, W., 1915, *The gases of the atmosphere*, 4th ed., London.
RAYLEIGH, 4th Lord, 1919, *Astrophys. J.* 50, 227.
RAYLEIGH, 4th Lord, 1900, *Nature* 106, 8.
RAYLEIGH, 4th Lord, 1921, *Proc. Roy. Soc. A.* 99, 10.
RAYLEIGH, 4th Lord, 1921a, *Nature* 107, 137, 39; 108, 208, 431.
RAYLEIGH, 4th Lord, 1922, *Proc. Roy. Soc. A.* 100, 366; 101, 114.
RAYLEIGH, 4th Lord, 1922a, *Proc. Roy. Soc. A.* 101, 312.
RAYLEIGH, 4th Lord, 1922b, *Nature* 110, 169.
RAYLEIGH, 4th Lord, 1923, *Proc. Roy. Soc. A.* 103, 45.
RAYLEIGH, 4th Lord, 1924, *Proc. Roy. Soc. A.* 106, 117.
RAYLEIGH, 4th Lord, 1925, *Proc. Roy. Soc. A.* 109, 428.
RAYLEIGH, 4th Lord, 1928, *Proc. Roy. Soc* A. 119, 11.
RAYLEIGH, 4th Lord, 1928a, *Beitr. Geophys.* 19, 292.
RAYLEIGH 4th Lord, 1928b, *Nature* 122, 315, 351.
RAYLEIGH, 4th Lord, 1929, *Proc. Roy. Soc. A.* 124, 395.
RAYLEIGH, 4th Lord, 1930, *Proc Roy. Soc. A.* 129, 458.
RAYLEIGH, 4th Lord, 1931, *Proc. Roy. Soc. A.* 131, 376.
RAYLEIGH, 4th Lord and JONES, H. S., 1935, *Proc. Roy. Soc. A.* 151, 22.
REES, M. H., 1963, *J. Geophys. Res.* 68, 175.
RUBENSON, R., 1879, *Catalogue des aurores boréales observées en Suède depuis le XVI-me siècle jusque a l'année 1877*, Stockholm.
SCHUSTER, A., 1912, *Proc. Phys. Soc*, London, A. 24, 121.
SENECA, *Naturales Quaestiones* 1/15/5.
SHRUM, G. R., 1924, see MCLENNAN.
SLIPHER, V. M., 1919, *Astrophys. J.* 49, 266.
SLIPHER, V. M., 1933, *Mon. Not. Roy. Astron. Soc.* 93, 657.

SOMMER, L. A., 1929, *Z. Physik.* **57,** 582.
STÖRMER, C., 1955, *The Polar Aurora*, Oxford. This book lists the author's multitudinous papers and describes both his mathematical and his observational studies.
TROMHOLT, S., 1902, *Catalog der in Norwegen bis Juni 1878 beobachteten Nordlichter*, Dybwald, Kristiania.
VEGARD, L., 1913, *Phys. Z.* **14,** 680; a list of his very long series of auroral papers is given by Chamberlain.
VESTINE, E. H., 1944, *Terr Magn. & Atmos. Elec.* **49,** 77.
VESTINE, E. H. and SNYDER, E. J., 1945, *Terr. Magn. & Atmos. Elec.* **50,** 105.
WESTLAND, C. J., 1921, see ANGENHEISTER.
WHITE, F. W. G., 1939, *New Zealand J. Sci. Tech.* **20,** 267b.
WILCKE, J. C., 1777, *Svensk. Vet. Acad. Handl*, p. 273.

Discussion

Chapman emphasized that the all-sky camera coverage should be greatly increased and especially extended to lower latitudes during the forthcoming solar maximum.

THE WORLDWIDE MORPHOLOGY
OF THE ATOMIC OXYGEN NIGHTGLOWS

F. E. Roach and L. L. Smith

Institute for Telecommunication Sciences and Aeronomy
Environmental Science Services Administration, Boulder, Colorado

I. Introduction

In this paper we summarize the gross features of the following atomic oxygen emissions: (1) the 100-km 5577Å nightglow between the equator and the auroral zone, (2) the F-region 6300Å–5577Å nightglow with special emphasis on its tropical morphology, and (3) a 6300Å high altitude emission in mid-latitudes (labeled M-arcs in Figure 1) which is associated with auroral activity. Referring to Figure 1, we note the latitude-height relationship of the three

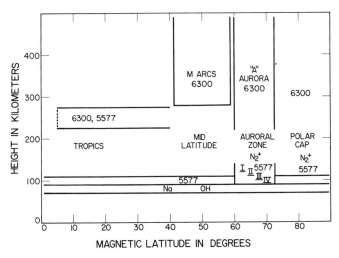

FIGURE 1. Schematic representation of upper atmosphere emissions as a function of height and latitude. The heights of auroras I, II, III, and IV are based on a recent study by HILLIARD and SHEPHERD (1966).

phenomena to each other, to the aurora, to the polar cap, and to the sodium and hydroxyl nightglows.*

The absence of 6300Å in the 100-km region may be attributed to collisional de-excitation of the ^1D state (see Figure 2). On the other hand, the absence of

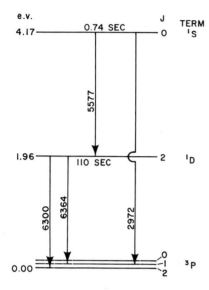

FIGURE 2. The energy level diagram of atomic oxygen for the lowest states.

5577Å in the M-arcs must be due to selectivity in the excitation mechanism. The presence of both 5577Å and 6300Å in the tropical F-region emission suggests that it has a mode of excitation different from either of the other two phenomena.

It is instructive as a survey of many of the upper-atmosphere emissions to arrange them, as in Figure 3, according to radiation "density" and pertinent primary excitation energy. In Figure 3 the auroral process leading to 5577Å is indicated schematically as one of transfer of kinetic energy of particles in the keV domain via ionization of N_2 (and emission of N_2^+, e.g., the 3914Å band). The lower excitations indicated for the progression from bright auroras (IV) through III and II to faint auroras (I) is based on a recent study by HILLIARD and SHEPHERD (1966), who reported that the Doppler broadening of 5577 indicates an *inverse* relationship between temperature and auroral brightness. Interpreting this as due to the ambient temperature of the excited oxygen atoms places the fainter auroras higher (see Figure 1) and therefore, the result of less energetic primary particles.

In Figure 3 the phenomena labelled G, T, and M are under present dis-

*Recent general reviews of the night airglow may be mentioned: BARBIER [1964] discussed, in particular, the status of the subject as affected by the IGY observations; ROACH [1963] gave a similar review; see also ROACH [1964] for a review of the night airglow as a component of the light of the night sky.

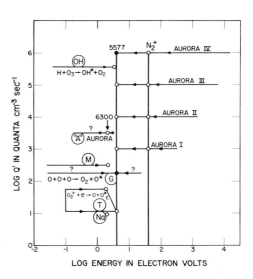

FIGURE 3. Schematic representation of upper atmosphere emissions. Ordinate is emission density; abscissa is the pertinent energy either of the emission or of the excitation mechanism.

cussion. Our purpose is to indicate some of their morphological characteristics and not to review the details of excitation mechanisms. We suggest, however, that a working definition of *airglow* — as distinct from *aurora* — might be processes which proceed from left to right in Figure 3; for example, reactions in which the kinetic energy of the reactants serves to bring them together with photochemical consequences.

II. The Atomic Oxygen 5577Å Emission at 100 kilometers

Studies of 5577Å have been central in observational programs, especially during IGY and IQSY. Even before IGY, systematic observations were in progress at many stations. For a comprehensive review of the observational results to date, the reader is referred to the outstanding paper by MME. J. CHRISTOFFE-GLAUME (1965). Mme. Glaume has reviewed the results of the Haute Provence-Tamanrasset observatories and of the international program. Temporal and spatial variations, solar activity effects, magnetic storm effects, and lunar tidal effects are all examined. In this paper, we call special attention to Glaume's study of the latitude variation of 5577Å (Chapter VI in her paper). Following an earlier suggestion of ROACH (1959), she identified a mid-latitude zone of maximum 5577Å somewhat analogous to, but much less conspicuous than, the maximum in the auroral zone. The general behavior of 5577Å from equator to pole is shown in Figure 4, in which the auroral maximum between 60° and 70° "magnetic" latitude is conspicuous.

The region just equatorward of the auroral zone was the object of Glaume's investigation. The upper part of Figure 5 is plotted from the data in Glaume's Table X. The solid curve gives the seasonal variation with magnetic dip latitude of the 5577Å maximum region in the Europe sector; the dashed curve,

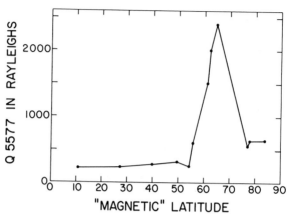

FIGURE 4. Intensity of the median intensity of 5577Å as a function of magnetic latitude.

labelled "all," for some ten stations in Europe — including the Soviet Union — Japan, and America. We have indicated the positions of several observing stations by the symbols FP (Fritz Peak), CP (Cactus Peak), SP (Sacramento Peak), HP (Haute Provence), and KP (Kitt Peak*).

The lower part of Figure 5 illustrates that if geographic latitudes are used, there is a longitude effect. Thus, the seasonal variation of 5577Å in Europe (taken from Figure 46 of Glaume's paper) is similar to that in America (de-

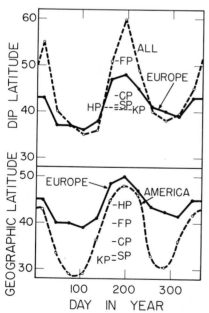

FIGURE 5. The latitudinal position of 5577Å maximum using the method of Glaume. Below: Results for Europe and for America as a function of geographic latitude. Above: Results for Europe and for "all" stations from Table X in GLAUME (1965).

*Results from Kitt Peak were not included in Glaume's analysis.

duced by us by the Glaume method), but the two curves are significantly displaced from each other. It is impossible to apply the Europe curve using geographic latitudes to the observations in America, and vice versa. For example, without exception the American stations observe a maximum of 5577Å to the south over a significant part of the year which is not permitted by the locus of maximum deduced from the European observations. On the other hand, the upper part of Figure 5 in which magnetic dip latitude is used gives a general relationship which is applicable in both the European and American sectors.

The significance of the evidence for geomagnetic control of the mid-latitude 5577Å emission is the implication that such control would seem to require moving charged particles somewhere between cause and effect, although such particles need not be the direct cause by impact of the excitation of the oxygen atoms to the ^1S state, as in the case of the aurora.

We wish to pursue further this matter of geomagnetic control by stressing the semiannual seasonal variation: two maximum (north) positions and two minimum (south) positions in each calendar year. This point is shown in Figure 6, in which we have brought together a number of different north-

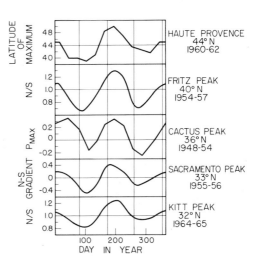

FIGURE 6. Semiannual variation of north to south relative intensities of 5577Å for five observing stations in the northern hemisphere. Several different criteria are used based on the original publications: N/S ratios for Fritz Peak and Kitt Peak; N-S gradient for Sacramento Peak; P (max) for Cactus Peak; and latitude of maximum for Haute Provence. The vertical lines indicate the equinoxes and solstices.

south criteria for five different stations in the northern hemisphere. Without exception, the semiannual nature of the variation is apparent. The relationship of the maxima (farthest north excursions) and the minima (farthest south) to the solstices and the equinoxes is illustrated in Table I. The northern extreme occurs some 22 days after the solstices, and in the southern, 23 days after the equinoxes. That a semiannual variation may be the consequence of an interchange along magnetic field lines of charged particles between hemispheres is an interesting speculation.

Table I. Day in Year

Station	Max I (N)	Min I (S)	Max II (N)	Min II (S)
KP	0	105	195	315
SP	7	90	200	275
CP	42	111	195	286
FP	0	104	183	275
HP	0	102	206	290
Mean	10	102	196	288
Solstice	355		173	
Equinox		81		261
Δ	21	21	23	27

Mean Δ Max (I and II) 22 days
Min (I and II) 23 days

It should be mentioned that the seasonal position of the 5577Å maxima, using Glaume's method, is the positional locus and not necessarily a time variation at a particular location. When the N-S ratio is unity for a given station, the present interpretation indicates that, at this time, the station is at a latitude of maximum brightness. If the migration of this zone of maximum were the only cause of temporal variation at a given location, then there should occur seasonal maxima when $N/S = 1$. That other factors enter into the temporal variation of brightness is apparent from an inspection of Figure 7.

TOHMATSU (1958) and TOHMATSU and NAGATA (1963) have developed a

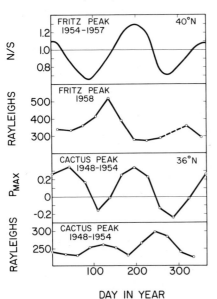

FIGURE 7. Semiannual variations of 5577Å intensity and N–S tendency for two stations: Fritz Peak and Cactus Peak.

model for the explanation of the mid-latitude maximum of 5577Å and its seasonal variation in brightness by invoking meteorological transport of oxygen allotropes by large-scale circulation in the upper atmosphere. The Tohmatsu-Nagata model, as it was developed, would probably not be consistent with a geomagnetic control mechanism. It may be conjectured, however, that meteorological and geomagnetic influences may be combined in producing the observed seasonal-latitude variations.

III. The Atomic Oxygen 6300-5577Å Emission above 200 Kilometers

A recent rocket firing at White Sands (latitude 30.4°) produced evidence for an emitting layer peaking at about 240 km [GULLEDGE et al., 1966]. In this layer, the 6300Å and 5577Å lines were emitted with brightness ratio of about 4:1. The "brightnesses" integrated over the layer were about 40 rayleighs for 6300Å and 14 rayleighs for 5577Å. Previous rocket explorations had delineated the 5577Å layer near 100 km, but had not gone to great enough heights to identify the higher layer.

That there is an airglow layer above 200 km had been inferred by a considerable body of data, especially in the tropics. BARBIER et al. (1961) reported that there are two zones of maximum 6300Å some 15° either side of the geomagnetic equator. Earlier it was shown that tropical 6300Å variations are associated with F-region ionospheric parameters [BARBIER, 1959; DELSEMME and DELSEMME, 1960]. A semiempirical relationship, which is now called the Barbier formula, describes the relationship:

$$Q6300\text{Å(rayleighs)} = A + B(f_0F2)^2 \exp\left(-\frac{h'F2 - 200}{H}\right) \qquad (1)$$

where f_0F2 is the critical frequency of the ionospheric $F2$ layer; $h'F2$ is the virtual height of the layer, A and B are empirical constants, and H is a scale height. The Barbier formula can be derived (PETERSON, 1967) if it is assumed that the principal source of excitation of the oxygen atom is:

$$O_2 + O^+ \rightarrow O_2^+ + O \qquad (2)$$

$$O_2^+ + e \rightarrow O + O^* + 6.96 \text{ eV} \qquad (3)$$

This pair of reactions is capable of exciting atomic oxygen to the ^1S state (4.17 eV) as well as to the ^1D state (1.96 eV) and is, therefore, consistent with the fact that the green line 5577Å ($^1D \leftarrow {}^1S$) and the red line 6300Å ($^3P \leftarrow {}^1D$) are both observed in the tropical enhancements. The fact that the Barbier formula involves F-region ionospheric parameters requires that the emission must occur in the F-region. Triangulation measurements [BARBIER et al., 1961] in Africa also gave heights above 200 km. On the basis of all the data, the existence of a 6300–5577Å nightglow layer centered at about 240 km is well established. Some of the properties of this layer may be enumerated:

(1) The excitation mechanism favors the 6300Å line over the 5577Å by about 4 ± 1 to 1.

(2) The emissions show significant temporal changes, especially at low geomagnetic latitudes (Figure 8).

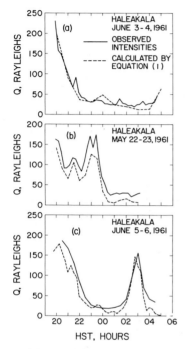

FIGURE 8. Three examples of diurnal variations of intensity of 6300Å over Haleakala. Solid lines are the observations and the dashed lines are based on the predictions of the Barbier formula.

(3) Considerable photometric structure over the earth is often observed. The structure may take the form of arcs which tend to be aligned along geomagnetic parallels [STEIGER et al., 1966], or of patches with dimensions of the order of 100 km [PETERSON et al., 1967].

(4) The optical phenomenon is intimately associated with the so-called equatorial ionospheric anomaly.

(5) The physical explanation of the large-scale temporal and spatial perturbations of both the photometric and the ionospheric phenomena seems to be involved with the guidance of ionization down along magnetic tubes to the F-region. Several papers attempting to account quantitatively for the general ionospheric equatorial anomaly have appeared. A paper by GOLDBERG [1965] gives a bibliography of recent theoretical studies.

(6) No theoretical studies are known which attempt to rationalize the relatively small-scale temporal changes such as in Figures 8b and 8c. The application of the Barbier formula in reverse to deduce ionospheric corrugations from the photometric observations leads to a picture of very steep ionization gradients [PETERSON, 1967].

IV. 6300Å Emission in Mid-Latitudes

As noted in Figure 1, there occurs in mid-latitudes an emission of 6300Å at high altitudes. It is associated with, but is equatorward of, the visual aurora and has an arc-like structure. 6300Å is the predominant emission; 5577Å, if present at all, is extremely weak. Its spectroscopic purity indicates that the excitation cannot be directly, or even indirectly, produced by very energetic "auroral" particles which traverse the very high atmosphere *en route* to the 100 km region. It is thus necessary to invoke a mild excitation mechanism, which can raise the oxygen atom to the ^1D (1.96 eV), but not to the ^1S (4.17 eV) state. Three suggestions have been made: an exothermic photochemical reaction,* an electrical discharge [MEGILL and CARLETON, 1964], and a thermal excitation [COLE, 1965].

The morphological features of the phenomenon have been given [ROACH and ROACH, 1963; extensive bibliography] based on the experience during the IGY period. Here we shall content ourselves with a brief summary of what has been variously called "l'arc auroral stable" [BARBIER, 1960]; "M-arc" [ROACH and ROACH, 1963]; and "SAR arc" [COLE, 1965]:

(1) The arcs have been observed between geomagnetic latitudes 41° and 60° with a median position of 53°. The corresponding McIlwain L values are 1.894, 3.945, and 2.980 [MAROVICH and ROACH, 1963].

(2) They are about 600 km in north-south extent [TOHMATSU and ROACH, 1962].

(3) The spread in height is from about 300–700 km with the photometric center near 400 km [TOHMATSU and ROACH, 1962].

(4) They extend east-west for thousands of kilometers, possibly around the earth.

(5) There is some evidence that they occur simultaneously and conjugately in the northern and southern hemispheres [ROACH *et al.*, 1962].

(6) They are oriented along magnetic, not geographic, parallels. The orientation is better described by the magnetic invariant latitude than by either geomagnetic or dip latitude.

(7) Only rarely have they been intense enough to be visible. The visibility threshold at 6300Å is about 10 kilorayleighs, and a typical integrated intensity is 6 kR.

(8) The intensity is positively correlated with geomagnetic activity [BARBIER, 1958].

*The reactions
$$N_2 + O^+ \rightarrow NO^+ + N \qquad (4)$$

$$NO^+ + e \rightarrow N + O^* + 2.76 \text{ eV} \qquad (5)$$

are energetically capable of raising the oxygen atom to the ^1D state. There are two difficulties: spin is not conserved [DALGARNO and WALKER, 1964] in the second reaction, and the mechanism calls for an inordinately large increase in atmospheric density in order to explain the M-arcs [KING and ROACH, 1961].

(9) Present observational evidence, though spanning less than one complete solar cycle, gives a positive correlation between their occurrence and sunspot activity

(10) The north-south movements are slow but often measurable.

(11) The life of a typical arc is about one day — only rarely has an arc been observed on successive days.

(12) An HF radio wave traversing an arc from a satellite to a ground station has been observed to suffer extensive scintillation [J. R. ROACH, 1963; YEH and SWENSON, 1964]. Scintillation has also been noted for radio frequency beams from radio sources which traverse an M-arc [WARWICK, 1966].

(13) On one occasion, an arc existed directly beneath regions of enhanced outer zone radiation [O'BRIEN et al., 1960].

Acknowledgment   We acknowledge the partial support of NASA Grant R-18 and NSF Grant AG-39 in the preparation of this report.

References

BARBIER, D., 1964, *Airglow in Research in Geophysics*, (Ed. by, Hugh Odishaw), Chapter 16, p. 401 (MIT Press).

BARBIER, D., WEILL, G., and GLAUME, J., 1961, *Ann. Geophys.* 17, 305.

BARBIER, D., 1960, *Ann. Geophys.* 16, 544.

BARBIER, D., 1959, *Ann. Geophys.* 15, 179.

BARBIER, D., 1958, *Ann. Geophys.* 14, 334.

COLE, K. D., 1965, *J. Geophys. Res.* 70, 1689.

DALGARNO, A. and WALKER, J. C. G., 1964, *J. Atmospheric Sci.* 21, 463.

DELSEMME, A. and DELSEMME, D., 1960, *Ann. Geophys.* 16, 507.

GLAUME, J., 1965, *Ann. Geophys.* 21, 1.

GOLDBERG, R. A., 1965, *J. Geophys. Res.* 70, 655.

GULLEDGE, I. S., PACKER, D. M., and TILFORD, S. G., 1966, *Trans. Am. Geophys. Union* 47, 75.

HILLIARD, R. L., and SHEPHERD, G. G., 1966, *Planetary Space Sci.* 14, 383.

KING, G. A. M. and ROACH F. E., 1961, *J. Res. Natl. Bur. Std.* 65d, 129.

MAROVICH, E. and ROACH, F. E., 1963, *J. Geophys. Res* 68, 1885.

MEGILL, L. R., and CARLETON, N. P., 1964, *J. Geophys. Research* 69, 101.

O'BRIEN, B. J., VANALLEN, J. A., ROACH, F. E., and GARTLEIN, C. W., 1960, *J. Geophys. Res.* 65, 2759.

PETERSON, V. L., 1967, This volume.

PETERSON, V. L., VANZANDT, T. E., ROACH, F. E., and STEIGER, W., 1967, (to be published).

ROACH, F. E., 1964, *Space Science Rev.* 3, 512.

ROACH, F. E., 1963, *Adv. in Electron.* 18, 1.

ROACH, F. E., 1959, *Proc. I.R.E.* 47, 267.

ROACH, F. E., BARBIER, D., and DUNCAN R. A., 1962, *Ann. Geophys.* 18, No. 4, 390.

ROACH, F. E. and ROACH, J. R., 1963, *Planetary Space Sci.* 11, 523.

ROACH, J. R., 1963, *J. Res. Natl. Bur. Std.* 67d, 263.

STEIGER, W. R., BROWN, W. E., and ROACH, F. E., 1966, *J. Geophys. Res.* 11, 2846.

TOHMATSU, T., 1958, *Rep. Ionosph. Res. Japan* 12, 253.

TOHMATSU, T. and NAGATA, T., 1963, *Planetary Space Sci.* 10, 103.

TOHMATSU, T. and ROACH, F. E., 1962, *J. Geophys. Res.* 67, 1817.

WARWICK, J. W., 1966, private communication.

YEH, K. C. and SWENSON, J. W. Jr., 1964, *Radio Science* 68d. 881.

Discussion

A question was raised concerning the possible correlation between the airglow intensity and lunar tidal variations. Dr. Roach said that Mme. Glaume did not observe such a correlation.

It was asked if the mid-latitude arcs are related to the great red arcs associated with aurora. Dr. Roach interpreted this as asking if the mid-latitude arc overlies the aurora in the auroral zone, and "slides" down to mid-latitudes. It might be indistinguishable in the auroral zone because there is so much along the line of sight to confuse the issue. He said that this is a tenable hypothesis but has not been established. It was also noted that the time dependence of the mid-latitude arcs is apparently related to that of aurora. The question was raised concerning the existence of radio or radar reflectivity measurements for the M-arc. It was stated that radio emission from a satellite to a ground based receiver shows a dramatic increase of scintillations when the line of sight passes through the arc, which is interpreted as the M-arc being a very unstable configuration. In one case this has been attributed to an increase in the drift velocity of the particles, rather than the size of the irregularities. This may imply electric fields in the region of the arc.

It was stated that in certain laboratory plasma studies one finds noncollision loss processes between fast particles and the relatively stationary background, which could account for the local heating of the ionosphere even though the fast particles are absent when the measurement is made. These are associated with current instabilities. These are two distinct mechanisms. In the first it is assumed that there exists a dc electric field, and in the second, that the incoming particles produce oscillating electric fields, which transfer energy to the ionosphere and thereby provide local heating.

It was suggested that electric fields might provide partial control over the green airglow observed at 45°.

WORLDWIDE AURORAL MORPHOLOGY

T. Neil Davis

Geophysical Institute
University of Alaska, College, Alaska

Abstract   Any aspect of auroral morphology is a function of one temporal and three spatial variables and therefore is difficult to describe adequately on a two-dimensional sheet of paper. Emphasis is given here to examination of the variables and fixed parameters employed in descriptions of auroral morphology.

Auroral morphology includes the study of auroral positions, intensities, form types, form alignments, motions, and spectral characteristics as functions of space and time. The whole topic of worldwide auroral morphology is complicated because of its various aspects and because these aspects are each, in a complex way, dependent upon such variables as geographic and geomagnetic coordinates, local geomagnetic time, and universal time.

Generalized Expressions for the Description of Auroral Morphology

In this and following sections recent morphological information is presented, but the emphasis is upon describing a framework useful for the description of auroral morphology.

Let some aspect of auroral morphology be designated by the symbol A, then in general

$$A = f(\theta, \phi, h, T) \qquad (1)$$

where θ, ϕ, h and T are geographic latitude, geographic longitude, altitude, and time, respectively. Empirically it is found that more symmetry results in expressions of auroral morphology if geomagnetic latitude λ and longitude ψ are employed:

$$A = f(\lambda, \psi, h, T) \qquad (2)$$

It is conceivable, but unlikely, that substitution of the McIlwain L-parameter for geomagnetic latitude could eliminate the need for the longitude variable ψ in expressions describing the intrinsic characteristics of the aurora, then

$$A = f(L, h, T) \qquad (3)$$

41

However, at this stage of our knowledge it is unwise to make the assumption implied by Equation (3). Much of the published descriptive material deals with the areal aspects of auroral morphology, so the height variable h is not used; such descriptions are special cases of a general expression which does not appear to be separable:

$$A = f(\lambda, \psi, T) \neq f(\lambda) \cdot f(\psi) \cdot f(T). \tag{4}$$

The Latitudinal Distribution of Auroras

Examples of latitudinal distributions obtained by DAVIS (1962) and STRINGER and BELON (1966) are shown in Figure 1. It is seen there that the position of maximum is independent of time in the solar cycle, but that the shape of the

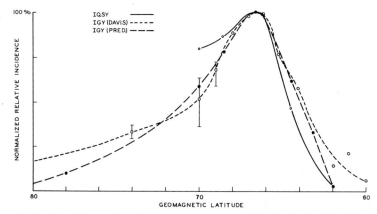

FIGURE 1. Profiles of auroral incidence versus geomagnetic latitude: the IGY (Davis) profile was obtained from Alaskan and Canadian all-sky camera data; the IQSY and IGY (Pred.) profiles were obtained using Alaskan all-sky camera and magnetic data. Note that all profiles peak at the same latitude but that the shape depends upon time within the solar cycle. After STRINGER and BELON, 1966.

distribution is not. In practice a determination of the latitudinal dependence of auroral occurrence is obtained with observations from a fixed station distribution contained within a particular longitude sector; hence ψ is a fixed parameter rather than a variable. The determination is obtained from observations taken over an increment of time ΔT, which may be several days, or a year, or longer. The specific form of this type of distribution is

$$A = f(\underline{\lambda}, \psi = \psi', T = T_0 \text{ to } T_0 + \Delta T), \tag{5}$$

λ being the only unfixed variable. Here, and in all following expressions, the variables are underlined for emphasis.

The Instantaneous Distribution of Auroras

As yet, observational limitations have prevented any determination of the instantaneous worldwide distribution of aurora, although distributions over limited small areas have been obtained; examples appear in Figure 2. An instantaneous distribution can be expressed in the form

$$A = f(\underline{\lambda, \psi}, T = T') \tag{6}$$

with the two spatial variables being unfixed, and the time variable being made into a fixed parameter.

The Auroral Zone

The auroral zone usually is defined as the locus of points at which the occurrence of aurora over the whole observer's sky is greater than for an observer to the north or south. Alternately, the term zone is taken more literally to mean a region of unspecified width within which the occurrence of aurora is near maximum. While the position of maximum overhead occurrence of aurora over a period of a year or so appears to be independent of time within the solar cycle, the variation in shape of the overall distribution is such that the location of the auroral zone probably shifts slightly toward the pole at sunspot minimum, compared to its position at sunspot maximum (see the paper by STRINGER and BELON, 1966). The auroral zone can be represented by a function similar to Equation (6), except that instead of setting $T = T'$, an average is taken over some long interval ΔT:

$$A = f(\underline{\lambda, \psi}, T = T_0 \text{ to } T_0 + \Delta T) \tag{7}$$

Distributions in Latitude and Local Time

Local geographic time t is a function of longitude and universal time, and local geomagnetic time τ is a function of latitude, longitude, and universal time (its dependence upon the changing sun-earth geometry during the year can be considered as being included implicitly in the universal time dependence). Although neither geographic nor geomagnetic local time is an independent variable, it is convenient for the purpose here to express local time in the same manner as the truly independent variables. It is useful to keep in mind that local time, despite its name, is primarily a *spatial* or *geometrical* rather than a *temporal* quantity. A particular phenomenon exhibiting a strong local time dependence does so because of the changing geometry between the observer and the location of the phenomenon rather than because of a true temporal variation in the phenomenon.

Despite the mathematical awkwardness involved with mixing dependent and

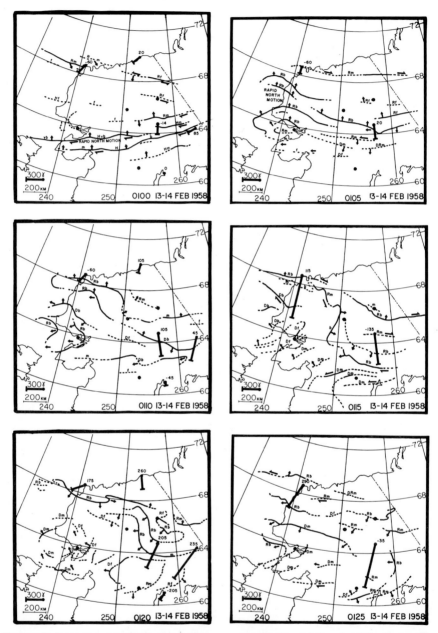

FIGURE 2. Instantaneous distributions of aurora over Alaska at intervals of 5 minutes. The heavy bars represent horizontal magnetic disturbance vectors; the value of the ΔZ component is given at the base of each vector. The first map shows the beginning of an auroral breakup (onset of auroral substorm). After DAVIS and KIMBALL, 1962.

independent variables, the expression contained in Equation (8) is helpful in expressing observational results:

$$A = f(\lambda, \psi, \tau, T). \tag{8}$$

This equation implies dependence upon geomagnetic latitude (or L may be useful), geomagnetic longitude ψ, local geomagnetic time τ, and universal time T, it being recognized that these four variables are not independent. Based upon knowledge gained from empirical results, it is clear that, in general, Equation (8) is nonseparable. Many results from morphological studies have been expressed as distributions in geomagnetic latitude and local geomagnetic time:

$$A = f(\lambda, \psi = \psi', \tau, T = T_0 \text{ to } T_0 + \Delta T) \tag{9}$$

That is, a study of some aspect of auroral morphology has been made using observing stations at particular longitudes ψ' over some universal time interval ΔT (exceeding one day). Equation (9) is the general form of observational results presented as patterns centered on the geomagnetic pole and fixed with respect to the direction of the sun. Examples of these are shown in Figures 3 and 4 and in papers by MALVILLE (1964) and SANFORD (1964).

Equations (5), (6), (7), and (9) all are in a form which describes the *spatially-fixed* aspect of auroral morphology. These equations are special cases of a

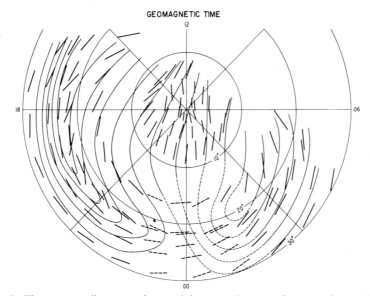

FIGURE 3. The average alignment of auroral forms at the auroral zone and over the polar cap. Short heavy bars represent measured alignments of extended auroral arcs. The near-midnight dashed portion of the smooth pattern deduced from the measurements takes into account the tendency of less-extended forms occurring near midnight to depart radically from the normal east-west alignment. After DAVIS, 1962.

general equation, wherein the number of variables has been reduced by either fixing an instant of universal time or by averaging over some increment of universal time. Even in the case described by Equation (9) (fixed patterns),

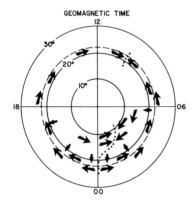

FIGURE 4. Average direction of auroral motions in the speed range below 3 km/sec plotted as a function of geomagnetic colatitude and geomagnetic time. After DAVIS, 1965.

where geomagnetic latitude and local geomagnetic time are unfixed variables, the only apparent temporal variation is caused by the earth's rotation beneath a spatially-fixed pattern.

It is obvious that observational results expressed in the form of Equations (5), (7), and (9) *cannot* yield more than indirect information about temporal variations in the aurora. One can view, for example, two instantaneous distributions (Equation (6)) obtained at times T_1 and T_2 and see that there exist differences other than those simply produced by the earth's rotation between times T_1 and T_2. These differences then must be attributed to true temporal variations.

Temporal (Universal Time) Variation in the Aurora

The term temporal variation is used here to describe any variation not attributable to the rotation of the earth beneath a fixed pattern. Thus, *temporal* variations are distinguished from variations dependent upon local geomagnetic or local geographic time. In order to avoid confusion between apparent local time variations and true variations independent of local time, perhaps it is better to use the term *universal time* variations for the latter. As in the preceding sections, the appropriate independent variable used in the various generalized equations to express time independent of the sun-earth geometry is T. Although this time will be called universal time, it is to be understood that this term does not imply any special characteristic of the Greenwich Meridian; that meridian is simply a convenient zero on the time scale.

It has been known for many years that auroral phenomena are related to events on the sun, and that auroral activity exhibits a long-period variation related to the 11-year solar cycle. These auroral variations are most obvious to observers at low latitude where the aurora occurs only during periods of high solar activity. It is tempting to attribute universal time auroral variations to variations in the characteristics of the solar wind impinging upon the earth's magnetosphere. Yet, it is not at all obvious that this association is correct; in fact, some observations can be taken to suggest that a part of the universal time variation is due to time-varying processes entirely within the magnetosphere or in the region where the magnetosphere interacts with the solar wind.

That significant universal time variations in the aurora do occur can be seen in plots of universal time indices of global distribution of aurora. The functional form of such plots is

$$A = f(\lambda = \lambda', \psi = \psi', \underline{T}), \tag{10}$$

λ and ψ being fixed by the choice of station distribution, and universal time T being left as the only variable.

Universal time variations can be inferred, but not seen directly, from data obtained at a single station. Such data plotted as functions of local time show both local time (geometrical) dependence and universal time (temporal) dependence, but the two dependences cannot be separated easily. This type of plot can be expressed in the form

$$A = f(\underline{\lambda}, \psi = \psi', (\underline{t, T})) \tag{11}$$

or

$$A = f(\lambda = \lambda', \psi = \psi', (\underline{t, T})) \tag{11a}$$

where the term (t, T) is the unfixed variable and is written in this form to emphasize that the plot depends upon both a spatial and a temporal variable. In principle, it should be possible to average a function of this type over a long interval of universal time ΔT to obtain the local time dependence. Then the averaged function is in the form similar to Equation (9):

$$A = f(\lambda = \lambda', \psi = \psi', \underline{t}, T = T_0 \text{ to } T_0 + \Delta T) \tag{12}$$

If this function is subtracted from the function of Equation (11a), the result should show the universal time dependence:

$$A = f(\lambda = \lambda', \psi = \psi', (\underline{t, T})) - f(\lambda = \lambda', \psi = \psi', \underline{t},$$
$$T = T_0 \text{ to } T_0 + \Delta T) = f(\lambda = \lambda', \psi = \psi', \underline{T}) \tag{13}$$

This expression is identical to Equation (10), but the methods of arriving at the two expressions are quite different. To obtain Equation (10), it is assumed that a sufficiently large number of observing locations are employed to remove local time effects, whereas Equation (13) is the result of observations at a single station — or station distribution limited in longitude — averaged over many days to remove local time effects. The two techniques may not yield identical results, and certainly, the latter is useful only for studying rather restricted aspects of morphology: for example, it would be most difficult to apply it meaningfully to the complex results obtained by HEPPNER (1954).

An important temporal characteristic of global morphology is that *auroral activity behaves in a burst-like fashion with individual bursts of activity lasting from several tens of minutes to perhaps 3 hours; the occurrence of the bursts may be random, but the average time between bursts is near 3–4 hours.* This intermittent temporal behavior has been discussed by AKASOFU (1964a, Figure 5) and the similar behavior of the auroral electrojets has been described by DAVIS and SUGIURA (1966). An appreciation of the importance of this short-term temporal variation in the aurora is critical to an understanding of auroral morphology.

So far in this discussion an attempt has been made to avoid consideration of the causes of the aurora. Instead, emphasis has been placed upon the variables on which auroral morphology depends. At this point it is difficult to avoid consideration of causes and effects. On the basis of knowledge accumulated over many years, we know that the aurora depends on the level of solar activity, which has a cyclic component in its variation. Evidently, at least a part of the universal time variation in the aurora can be attributed to variations on the sun and its extension, the solar wind. This being the case, it should be possible to separate the temporal variation within the aurora into components on an empirical basis. Maintaining the general format introduced earlier, let A_1 represent an aspect of auroral morphology dependent upon universal time:

$$A_1 = f(T). \tag{14}$$

An example is the maximum equatorward extent of the aurora at any instant.

It appears that this function can be represented by several multiplicative or additive functions, each having a characteristic behavior;

$$A_1 = f(T) = f_1(T) \cdot f_2(T) \cdot f_3(T) \cdot f_4(T) \cdot f_5(T) \tag{15}$$

or

$$A_1 = f(T) = f_1(T) + f_2(T) + f_3(T) + f_4(T) + f_5(T) \tag{16}$$

where the meaning of these functions of universal time are as given below:

$f_1(T)$ is a slowly varying function which describes the relative level of activity of a solar cycle. This functional dependence is required because it is known that the general level of activity during certain solar cycles is greater than in others. Any periodicity in $f_1(T)$ must exceed 11 years.

$f_2(T)$ is a periodic function with a period of 11 years. It describes the average variation of activity within the solar cycle.

$f_3(T)$ is an irregular function related to short-term solar activity. It contains a periodic component of period near 27 days resulting from the tendency of sunspots to reappear as the sun rotates about its axis.

$f_4(T)$ is a function describing the burst-like temporal dependence in the aurora as noted above. $f_4(T)$ relates directly to the auroral substorm behavior: individual peaks of increased auroral activity with lifetimes near 1 hour occur

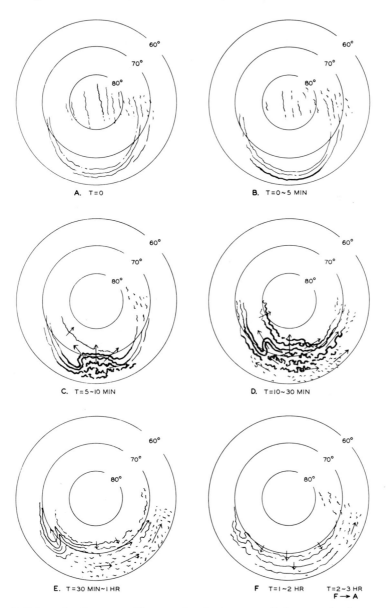

FIGURE 5. Schematic diagram to illustrate the development of the auroral substorm. The center of the concentric circles in each stage is the north geomagnetic pole, and the sun is toward the top of the diagram. After AKASOFU, 1964.

either randomly or quasi-periodically with an average repetition frequency of approximately 6 per day. f_4 (T) actually may be somewhat dependent upon $f_3(T)$ because the intensity and frequency of substorms may depend rather strongly upon the level of short-term solar activity in such a manner that the simple forms of Equations (15) or (16) are inadequate as they stand.

Note that $f_1(T)$, $f_2(T)$ and $f_3(T)$ are functions devised to describe variations directly attributable to activity on the sun. At this stage of our knowledge, it is not obvious that the temporal behavior described by $f_4(T)$ is directly dependent upon the sun or its agent, the solar wind. The behavior described by $f_4(T)$ may be caused by some form of transient but repetitive process within the magnetosphere or near its boundary. A rough analogy is the suspended bucket which remains upright while being filled (perhaps by the solar wind) until the contents reach a certain level, at which time the bucket tips over and spills its contents (energetic particles which reach the atmosphere and produce the aurora). The bucket must be somewhat leaky, because an aurora is always being produced at those times between substorms. Alternately, the irregular behavior described by the function $f_4(T)$ may be produced directly by variations within the solar wind. If this be true, it is more logical to combine f_3 (T) and $f_4(T)$ into a single function. $f_5(T)$ is distinctly different from other terms in Equations (15) and (16) in that it describes an apparent variation due strictly to the regularly changing geometry between the earth's geomagnetic field and the solar wind. As the earth follows its orbit around the sun, the inclination of the earth's spin axis relative to the sun-earth line varies. Presumably, this variation is the source of seasonal variations in the aurora, although another possible cause is the variation in the earth's heliographic latitude during the year (CHAMBERLAIN, 1961). A daily variation in the approach direction of the solar wind relative to the geomagnetic field results from the rotation of the earth about its spin axis. This daily variation may produce a 24-hour variation in auroral phenomena quite apart from the variations expressed in Equations (9), (11), and (12). From a practical viewpoint, it may be difficult to distinguish between those variations and the one possibly caused by the varying aspect angle between the solar wind and the geomagnetic field.

As a consequence of the factors discussed in the preceding paragraph, the function $f_5(T)$ can be expressed as

$$f_5(T) = f'_5(T) \cdot f''_5(T) \tag{17}$$

where $f'_5(T)$ is a periodic function with a period of 1 year, and $f''_5(T)$ also is periodic with a period of 1 day.

The relative importance of the five temporal functions contained in Equations (15) and (16) is somewhat uncertain. Clearly, the function $f_4(T)$ describing the substorm variations and $f_3(T)$ describing variations related to short-term solar activity are very important. $f_2(T)$ probably is less important, and insufficient knowledge is available to indicate the importance of f_1 (T) and $f_5(T)$.

Summary of Variables Upon Which Auroral Morphology Depends

Auroral morphology is a four-dimensional problem which investigators usually try to describe on a two-dimensional piece of paper. Consequently, the accumulated knowledge of auroral morphology is an assembly of bits and pieces whose place and interrelations as parts of the whole can be recognized as long as one is aware of the characteristics and limitations of each piece. Here the attempt has been made to establish a framework designed to enable the classification of empirical results on the basis of their functional form. Once one clearly recognizes which terms in an expression are variables and which are fixed parameters, then the meaning of an expression becomes clear, and different expressions can be compared without confusion.

We recognize that both spatial and temporal variations occur within the aurora but, in general, no single study reported in the literature has been able to adequately describe all aspects of the spatial and temporal variations. The tendency is toward fixing one or more parameters, and then attempting to describe all auroral variations in terms of the remaining variables, usually one or two. For example, DAVIS (1962) made the hypothesis that "the major characteristics of the aurora can be represented by patterns fixed in geomagnetic colatitude and 'approximate' geomagnetic time." In other words, he suggested that the major characteristics of the aurora could be represented by expressions in the form of Equation (9),

$$A = f(\underline{\lambda}, \psi = \psi', \underline{\tau}, T = T_0 \text{ to } T_0 + \Delta T)$$

In contrast to this formulation, AKASOFU (1964) has described auroral morphology in relation to temporal events, namely the auroral substorms. Akasofu's description stresses the dependence upon the universal time *variable*, whereas the "fixed pattern" description as used by Davis and others treats universal time as a *parameter*. Specifically, the "substorm" picture emphasizes dependence upon the $f_4(T)$ term of Equations (15) and (16) rather than upon the general universal time variable, as would be implied by Equation (14). An abbreviated expression of the formulation of the "substorm picture" is

$$A = f_4(T) \tag{18}$$

The desire to express in a self-consistent manner the concepts contained in the preceding paragraph has been the main motivation behind the developments of this chapter. Having attained this objective, at least to a limited extent, it is now easier to discuss meaningfully the adequacy and implications of the various descriptions of auroral morphology.

Discussion of Morphological Observations

A. Spatial Variations. Distribution of Auroras in Longitude and Local time.

Figure 6 represents the distribution of aurora in latitude and local geomagnetic time; the functional form of this representation is that of Equation (9):

$$A = f(\lambda, \psi = \psi', \underset{\sim}{\tau}, T = T_0 \text{ to } T_0 + \Delta T).$$

An important feature illustrated by Figure 6 is the oval shape of the distribution represented: maximum incidence or occurrence appears near latitude 67° on the night side and near 78° on the day side of the earth. This shape has

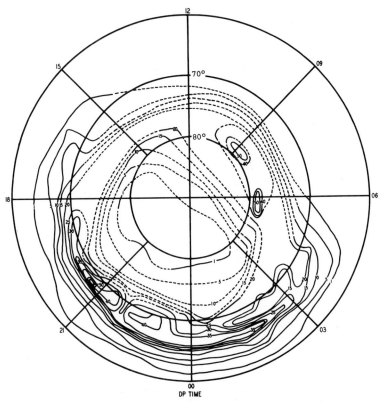

FIGURE 6. Incidence of auroral forms plotted as a function of geomagnetic latitude and time as compiled from all-sky camera data obtained in and north of Alaska during 1964–1965. After STRINGER and BELON, 1966 .

led to the adoption of the term "auroral oval" by FELDSTEIN (1964) and AKASOFU et al. (1965); however, the term also has been used to express the configuration of an instantaneous auroral distribution (Equation (6)):

$$A = f(\lambda, \underset{\sim}{\psi}, T = T').$$

The extent to which instantaneous distributions are truly oval is uncertain because of the lack of widespread observations.

An interesting aspect of several types of observations expressed in the form of Equation (9) is their tendency to exhibit some degree of symmetry about a line extending from the earth toward the direction 20–30° east of the sun. Figure 6 also shows a weak maximum region of incidence near 09 hours and latitude 78°. This peculiar maximum may well be the source of the "inner auroral zone" (WHITHAM, et al., 1960; DAVIS, 1962; NIKOLSKY, 1963; and HULTQUIST, 1964). The distribution in Figure 6 exhibits a bifurcation near latitude 67° and geomagnetic time 01–03 hours. The bifurcation is also evident in the summary description given by FELDSTEIN and SOLOMATINA (1961) using the concept of two oppositely-winding spirals.

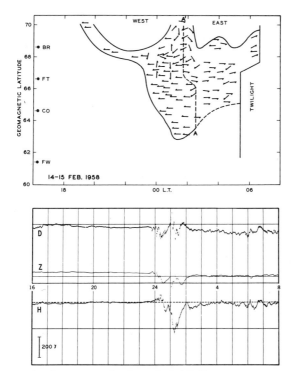

FIGURE 7. Diagram showing a reproduction of the College magnetogram, the extent of auroras over Alaska and their directions of motion. After DAVIS, 1961.

B. Observations Showing Mixed Spatial and Temporal Variations.
Figure 7 expresses results in the form of Equation (11):

$$A = f(\lambda, \psi = \psi', (t, T)).$$

That is, the observations are displayed with latitude and time as variables, but the "temporal" variation is, in reality, partly a spatial variation related to movement of the station (the t dependence) and partly an actual temporal variation (the T dependence). Only by examining several of these diagrams can one obtain some insight as to which of the observed variations are spatial and which are temporal. In making a comparative examination of this type one is, in effect, following the procedure described by Equation (13).

   C. Universal Time Variations. During the past few years Akasofu and co-workers have contributed much to our understanding of auroral morphology by concentrated study of the temporal variations in the aurora. A very abbreviated summary of part of this work is contained in Figure 5. Elaboration of the theme expressed by Figure 5 and reports of related observations made since the construction of Figure 5 are contained in a series of papers: AKASOFU, 1960, 1962, 1964; AKASOFU and KIMBALL, 1964; AKASOFU *et al.*, 1965, 1966.

   These results have been described with reference to a temporal auroral event, the auroral substorm. This temporal dependence is expressed here by Equation (18),

$$A = f_4(T)$$

which is a special case of Equations (15) and (16). A more adequate formulation of the substorm concept is

$$A = f_4(\lambda, \psi, T) \tag{19}$$

where the subscript 4 is applied to stress that the description refers to a specific component of the temporal variation rather than the general universal time variation. It is clear that the $f_4(T)$ dependence is very strong, hence this restriction is quite logical. Figure 5 contains six schematic auroral configurations, one for each of six values of the variable T. Figure 2 also contains six similar configurations except that actual observations are used, the area shown is severely restricted, and the time reference is universal time in the usual sense (local times shown in Figure 2 convert to universal time by adding 10 hours). Because of the time reference used in Figure 2, the auroral descriptions presented there are in the form of Equation (6):

$$A = f(\lambda, \psi, T = T').$$

   Conversion to the form of Equation (19) is obtained by fixing the time of the beginning of the substorm, which in this case is approximately 0100 on February 14, 1958 (local time). Then the diagrams of Figure 2 are in the form of Equation (19); the first diagram is described by the expression

$$A = f_4(\lambda, \psi, T = 0)$$

and the following five diagrams are represented by incrementing T by 5 additional minutes for each subsequent diagram. Note that the actual descriptions shown in Figure 2 agree reasonably well with the appropriate portions of the schematic diagrams of Figure 5.

D. Auroral Motions. The auroral motions under discussion here are those observable with an all-sky camera. These motions are in the speed range 0–3 km/sec; they are of whole auroral forms, portions of forms, irregularities (such as loop structures) in auroral forms, or of streaming (apparent movements of regions of enhanced luminosity across preexisting auroral forms). Davis (1962) described the observed auroral motions near the auroral zone in terms of a fixed pattern (Equation (9)). In this functional form,

$$A = f(\underline{\lambda}, \psi = \psi', \underline{\tau}, T = T_0 \text{ to } T_0 + \Delta T)$$

the longitudinal motions are described as being away from the midnight meridian, and the meridional motions are described as being equatorward near the midnight meridian (see Figure 4).

Using the substorm concept (functional form, $A = f_4(\lambda, \psi, T)$), Akasofu (1964a) described the motions as nonexistent prior to the substorm, then away from the midnight meridian to the east, west, and to the pole during the expansive phase of the substorm ($T = 0$ to $T = 10$–30 minutes), then equatorward and away from the midnight meridian to the east and west during the recovery phase of the substorm. The fixed pattern description used by Davis fails to describe the violent poleward motion accompanying the onset of the auroral breakup (auroral substorm observed at the midnight meridian) because this poleward motion is swamped statistically by the equatorward motion which predominates at all times except during the expansive phase of the substorm. Except for this point, the descriptions of auroral motions as given by Akasofu and Davis would appear to be equivalent; any difference being attributable simply to the functional form in which the two descriptions are couched. However, there are examples of observed westward motion for several hours *before* the onset of a substorm; such examples are counter to the substorm description of motion.

The author concludes that there exists in the ionosphere or magnetosphere a mechanism which determines the direction of auroral motion regardless of the existence or absence of a substorm. This mechanism leads to equatorward motion near local midnight, eastward motion between geomagnetic local hours 00 and approximately 10, and westward motion during the remainder of the local day. This *geometrical* mechanism then is aptly described with a function of the form of Equation (9):

$$A = f(\underline{\lambda}, \psi = \psi', \underline{\tau}, T = T_0 \text{ to } T_0 + \Delta T),$$

yet during the expansive phase of a substorm, violent poleward motions do occur and their *transient* cause evidently overrides the effects of the mechanism mentioned above. In some cases, the normal trend of the longitudinal motions also may be disrupted temporarily during the expansive phase of the substorm, particularly to the west of the midnight meridian (see Figures 19–32 in a report by Davis (1961)).

Thus, in the case of auroral motions it seems that there is an essential difference between the fixed pattern and the substorm "pictures." In this case the fixed pattern representation is more than an average of many instantaneous configurations of motion. Both descriptions contain elements of truth to the extent that they suggest more than a single mechanism for producing auroral motions; if so, one mechanism is transient, and the other is essentially permanent.

E. Auroral Alignments. The alignments of auroral forms inside colatitude 10° are roughly along a line 20–30° east of the sun direction except during some auroral substorms when then the alignment is more nearly east-west (STRINGER, 1966). The region between colatitudes 10 and 20° is transitional, and the region near the auroral zones shows generally east-west alignments except in the vicinity of the midnight meridian when substorms are occurring.

A representation of the average alignments of auroras over the polar regions is shown in Figure 3. Whereas this diagram has merit as a summary of average alignments, it has several unfortunate aspects. Being of the functional form of Equation (8):

$$A = f(\underline{\lambda}, \psi = \psi', \underline{\tau}, T = T_0 \text{ to } T_0 + \Delta T)$$

it cannot account for any temporal variation.

Strictly speaking, the diagram implies that if an aurora occurs at a particular location and local time, the probable alignment will be as shown. However, the diagram creates the impression that a given aurora can extend from the auroral zone into the polar cap with the alignments shown, and that the polar cap and auroral zone (or auroral oval) aurora can be treated as an entity, whereas now it is clear that auroral behavior inside the auroral oval differs from the behavior at the oval in several respects (DAVIS, 1963), (AKASOFU, 1964b). Except during large substorms, when the "auroral zone" auroras expand into the polar cap near the midnight meridian, there appears to be no connection between the cap region and the auroral zone in the sense implied by the configurations drawn on Figure 3. Furthermore, the looping configuration shown near the intersection of the midnight meridian and the auroral zone appears, as AKASOFU (1963 and 1964b) has suggested, to result from the transient, complex looping structures occurring in that region during substorms. Consequently, the functional form of Equation (9) gives an inadequate description of auroral alignments except perhaps during times of magnetic quiet. It is necessary to consider the $f_4(T)$ dependence of auroral alignments in order to give a completely meaningful description of them.

F. Possible Longitudinal Dependencies. An examination of the occurrence rate of auroral forms at the auroral zone suggests that a rather strong longitudinal dependence may exist in auroral and related phenomena. Similarly, the occurrence rate of aurorally-related radio-wave absorption as measured by riometers is found to be twice as great in Alaska as in Norway or Canada (WAITE, 1965). It has been suggested by Waite that the apparent longitudinal discrepancy in absorption may be caused by seasonal or solar cycle effects.

Both the auroral occurrence and the auroral absorption data suggest a strong longitudinal effect. Such an effect could come about in two ways. One possible cause is the diurnal variation in the apparent approach direction of the solar wind relative to the geomagnetic field as described by Equation (17). A second possible cause is the asymmetry of the geomagnetic field. A particle mirroring at an altitude of 200 km over Scandinavia also mirrors at that altitude at the conjugate point. A similar particle at the longitude of Alaska will mirror at 200 km at the conjugate point in the Southern Hemisphere, but will have a pitch angle of approximately 70° at altitude 200 km over Alaska so will mirror at a lower altitude or precipitate into the atmosphere. Thus, there is reason to expect that auroras may occur more frequently and possibly be brighter near geographic longitude 180° than in the conjugate region or to the east and west along the northern auroral zone. The occurrence rate of auroras as a function of position along the northern auroral zone is very suggestive that this difference in mirror altitudes is the cause of the apparent longitudinal dependency.

It must be emphasized that the data examined so far suggest, but do not demonstrate, that a longitudinal dependency does exist. If it does exist, then we must reexamine our knowledge of auroral morphology in light of this dependence. The mechanism suggested here to account for the longitudinal dependence requires that particles moving adiabatically in the geomagnetic field play an important role in the production of auroras.

References

AKASOFU, S.-I., 1960, *J. Atmospheric Terrest. Phys.* **19**, 10-25.
AKASOFU, S.-I., 1962, *J. Atmospheric Terrest. Phys.* **24**, 723-727; and **24**, 785-796.
AKASOFU, S.-I., 1963, *J. Geophys. Res.* **68**, 1667-1673.
AKASOFU, S.-I., 1964a, *Planetary Space Sci.* **12**, 273-282.
AKASOFU, S.-I., 1964b, Ann. Intern. Geophys. Year **20**, 311-364.
AKASOFU, S.-I. and KIMBALL, D. S., 1964, *J. Atmospheric Terrest. Phys.* **26**, 205-211.
AKASOFU, S.-I., KIMBALL, D. S., and MENG, C.-I., 1965a, *J. Atmospheric Terrest. Phys.* **27**, 173-187.
AKASOFU, S.-I., KIMBALL, D. S., and MENG, C.-I., 1965b. *J. Atmospheric Terrest. Phys.* **27**, 189-196.
AKASOFU, S.-I., KIMBALL, D. S., and MENG, C.-I., 1966, *J. Atmospheric Terrest. Phys.* (to be published).
CHAMBERLAIN, J. W., 1961, *Physics of the Aurora and Airglow*, Academic Press, New York, 704 pp.
DAVIS, T. N., 1961, Geoph. Inst. Rept. No. UAG-R117, Geophysical Institute, College, Alaska.
DAVIS, T. N., 1962, *J. Geophys. Res.* **67**, 59-110.
DAVIS, T. N., 1963, *J. Geophys. Res*, **68**, 4447-4453.
DAVIS, T. N., 1965, The Aurora, in *Introduction to Space Science* (Ed. by W. N. Hess), Gordon and Breach, New York, 919 pp.

DAVIS, T. N. and KIMBALL, D. S., 1962, Geoph. Inst. Rept. UAG-R120, Geophysical Institute, College, Alaska.
DAVIS, T. N. and SUGIURA, M., 1966, J. Geophys. Res. 71, 785-801.
FELDSTEIN, Y. I., 1964, Tellus, 16, 252-267.
FELDSTEIN, Y. I. and SOLOMATINA, E. K., 1961, Geomagnetism i Aeronomiya, (U.S. transl.) 1, 475-479.
HEPPNER, J. P., 1954, Thesis, California Institute of Technology, Pasadena.
HULTQVIST, BENGT, 1969, NASA Rept. No. X-611-64-97, Goddard Space Flight Center, Greenbelt, Md.
MALVILLE, J. M., 1964, J. Geophys. Res. 69, 1285-1292.
NIKOLSKY, A. P., 1963, Geomagnetism i Aeronomiya (U. S. transl.) 1, 883-887.
SANDFORD, B. P., 1964, J. Atmospheric Terrest. Phys. 26, 749-769.
STRINGER, W. J., 1966, M. S. THESIS, University of Alaska, College, Alaska.
STRINGER, W. J. and BELON, A. E., 1966, J. Geophys. Res., to be published.
WAITE, C. W., 1965, Can. J. Phys. 43, 2319-2330.
WHITHAM, K., LOOMER E. I., and NIBLET, E. R., 1960, J. Geophys. Res. 65, 3961-3974.

Discussion

Several questions were raised about the auroral zone dependence on geomagnetic longitude. Although the auroral data have scarcely been examined for longitudinal effects, such a dependence should be expected. The loss cone depends very strongly on longitude. Correlation of riometer absorption measurements in the D region and auroral emission from a much higher altitude should be made with caution, as the energy of the electrons producing the two observables are vastly different.

The backscattering characteristics of the particle may also influence a longitudinal effect, since more particles might "mirror" at a given location. It was pointed out that during the period the longitudinal effect was observed, complete observations were not available from Sweden, and this might effect the conclusions. Dr. Davis' opinion is that the available data suggests the possibility of a longitudinal effect, but is not completely convincing. Better longitudinal coverage of auroral activity is needed. Data presentation techniques should be developed to determine the longitudinal effects.

A question was raised concerning the relationship between the auroral zone and polar cap aurora. While there may be some nebulous relation between the two, from all appearances they are two different phenomena. The auroral zone phenomena are positively correlated to magnetic field activity, the polar cap aurora is negatively correlated, i.e., it moves closer to the pole with decreasing magnetic field. Compared to the auroral zone phenomena, the polar cap aurora are more fleeting and weaker.

In response to a question concerning the nature of observed auroral motion, i.e., whether it is real or apparent, it was stated that all observations are apparent and with respect to the observer it is not possible to state whether they are "real" or not.

Dr. King pointed out that ionospheric observations at about 60° latitude made in Canada and Siberia show a very definite longitudinal difference in the amount of absorption and the occurrence of maximum absorption periods. It appears that qualitatively a longitudinal occurrence of aurora would be consistent with other observations, but should not yet be considered as established.

THE SPECTRUM AND EXCITATION MECHANISMS IN AURORA

A. Omholt

The Auroral Observatory, Tromsø, Norway

I. Introduction*

The first spectral studies of the aurora were made by A. J. Ångstrom in 1867 with a simple spectroscope. Photographic studies of the spectrum were initiated by E. S. King in the later years of the nineteenth century. More systematic and extensive spectral studies of the aurora were started by Vegard in 1912 (VEGARD, 1913, 1916a,b). He then organized an expedition to Bosekop in northern Norway with the best available spectrographs and continued his work for nearly fifty years. During the last twenty years, the study of the auroral spectrum has received worldwide interest, and research workers in a great number of countries have devoted much effort to these studies.

The identification of the various spectral lines and bands have advanced along with an advanced knowledge of molecular and atomic spectra from laboratory work, and with the improvement of spectrographic technique (CHAMBERLAIN, 1961; VALLANCE JONES, 1965). For a long time one of the most difficult problems was the identification of the strongest atomic line in the spectrum, the green line at 5577Å. In 1925 it was finally identified by McLENNAN and SHRUM as belonging to the spectrum of atomic oxygen. They succeeded in producing the green line in a laboratory discharge through a mixture of oxygen and helium. It was so difficult to produce and identify in the laboratory because it is radiated from a metastable level with a lifetime of about 0.7 sec. Under laboratory conditions, excited atoms will usually suffer collisions with other atoms and molecules and with the walls of the vessel, and these collisions may deactivate the atoms without radiation.

Spectrographs and Fabry-Perot interferometers with photographic recording of the spectra and fringes were for many years the principal instruments for recording and studying the auroral spectrum. During the last ten to fifteen years, great achievements have been made by employing photoelectric techniques. The application of interference filter photometers, scanning spectrom-

---

*When no particular reference to literature is made, the reader is referred to books by BATES (1960), CHAMBERLAIN (1961a), and to AKASOFU, CHAPMAN, and MEINEL (1966).

eters and Fabry-Perot interferometers with photomultipliers as detectors, and other devices employing photoelectric detection techniques, such as image converters and photoconductive detectors, has made it possible to measure absolute intensities with a much higher accuracy. It has also been possible to study rapid variations in the auroral intensity and relative variations in the auroral spectrum. Whereas the spectrographic technique required exposure times of the order of one hour, photoelectric spectrometers record the spectrum in a few minutes, and filter photometers record the intensities of the stronger emissions in less than one second. In addition to the superiority in sensitivity, the photoelectric technique offers a detection system which is linear, contrary to photographic recording. The main drawback is that a great number of detectors and recorders have to be applied when several spectral features are to be studied simultaneously. Photographic spectrographs are still superior in resolution, and thus are the most useful instruments for spectral identifications. But this subject now receives much less attention than measurements of intensities as a basis for studies of the excitation mechanisms and auroral physics in general.

Observations below the threshold set by the transmission properties of the atmosphere — about 3200Å — and also those above about 9000Å, where detectors become a serious problem, are still fairly scarce. However, balloon, rocket, and satellite techniques, along with improved techniques of detection in infrared, are expected to improve the situation drastically within a decade.

This paper reviews the most important optical characteristics of the aurora and the basic mechanisms which give rise to these characteristics. The limited space available necessitates omission of many details which are interesting, but which are not immediately relevant to the general problem of aurora as discussed at this Study Institute. Thus we cannot discuss in detail all of the possible processes contributing to the excitation of any spectral line or band, but have to limit ourselves to the most significant ones. Following a general description of the major features of the optical spectrum of aurora, we shall discuss the main excitation and ionization mechanisms. Variations in the spectrum are important, and will be discussed at some length. Finally, we shall present a short description of the hydrogen lines in aurora, and discuss temperature measurements from auroral spectra and the most rapid variations in the excitation of aurora.

II. The Spectrum of Aurora: General Description

The auroral spectrum is dominated by molecular bands and atomic lines from nitrogen and oxygen and their ions (BATES, 1960; CHAMBERLAIN, 1961 a, b; VALLANCE JONES, 1955, 1965). So far the spectrum is thoroughly investigated only from the near ultraviolet (above the threshold set by the atmosphere) to the near infrared (below 10–12,000Å, where the threshold is set by the detectors). However, measurements have been made in the ultraviolet by rockets (FASTIE et al., 1961) and in the infrared nearly up to 20,000Å, but with poor resolution (VALLANCE JONES, 1964). The most prominent bands are the First Positive (red-infrared), Second Positive (violet-ultraviolet) and Vegard-Kaplan bands (ultraviolet) of N_2, the First Negative (blue-ultraviolet) and Meinel bands (infrared) of N_2^+, the Atmospheric (infrared) and the Infrared Atmospheric bands of O_2; the First Negative bands (green-red) of O_2 are very weak. A number of atomic lines of O and N appear, most of which are rather faint. The most prominent ones in the visible region are the forbidden oxygen lines $^1D - {}^1S$ and $^3P - {}^1S$ at 5577Å and 6300/64Å. The oxygen multiplets $^5S - {}^5P$ and $^3S - {}^3P$ at 7774Å and 8446Å and the forbidden nitrogen lines at $^2D - {}^2P$ and $^4S - {}^2P$ at 10400 and 3466Å are also reasonably strong.

In addition to these emissions, which all are from the main atmospheric constituents at the heights where aurora occur (the dominant height interval for emission of auroral light is about 90–200 km), some other emissions of great interest occur. In some auroras the hydrogen Balmer lines Hα (6563Å) and Hβ (4861Å) occur (cf. VALLANCE JONES, 1964; GALPERIN, 1963). These are strongly Doppler broadened and shifted, and give evidences for incidence of fast protons in the upper atmosphere. Also, there occasionally seems to occur an enhancement of the sodium doublet 5889/95Å, which is ordinarily observed in the nightglow and twilight (HUNTEN, 1955; DERBLOM, 1964). Some evidence for He-lines in the auroral spectrum has also appeared (SHEFOV, 1963). A series of auroral spectra due to Vegard are shown in Figure 1. For further information, the reader is referred to CHAMBERLAIN (1961a).

III. The Main Excitation and Ionization Mechanisms

On a large scale, the intensity distribution within the auroral spectrum does not change very much. There are, however, some typical variations from one type of aurora to another and some typical variations with height, although the spectral composition usually does not alter sufficiently to change the color impression on the eye, which is that of a grayish-yellow color. In some cases there is a noticeable shift to red; sometimes bright green, red, and violet colors occur. These colors are mostly limited to very high or to rapidly changing auroras, and often are produced by time lag effects in the emission mechanisms. These effects will be separately discussed later.

In ordinary bright auroras displaying a distinct geometry, hydrogen lines are very faint or nonexistent. This seems particularly true in the auroral zone. From the spectral composition and the geometry of the aurora relative to the geomagnetic field lines, it was concluded that aurora is caused by primary electrons with energy of the order of a few keV. This is confirmed by rocket and satellite work (cf. O'BRIEN, 1965; EVANS, 1965).

It is conceivable that most of the excitation is directly caused by the primary particles and by the secondary electrons which they generate. There is a slight

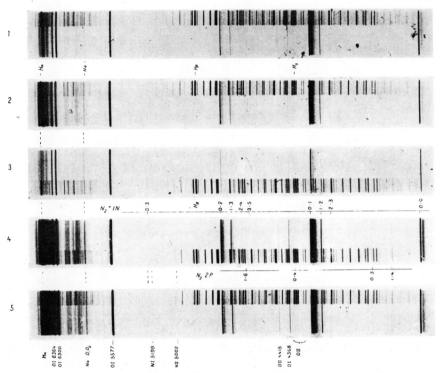

FIGURE 1. Auroral spectra taken by Vegard with a prism spectrograph.

indication that other secondary processes may contribute to a minor part of the excitation (cf. MALVILLE, 1959; EFTESTOL and OMHOLT, 1965; HUNTEN and McELROY, 1966).

Each primary particle entering the atmosphere produces a great number of ions and excited atoms and molecules, expending on the average about 35 eV of its own energy per ion pair produced. However, the actual ionization and excitation is performed to a large extent by the secondary electrons which are produced in the direct encounters between the primary particles and the atmospheric atoms and molecules. Model computations and laboratory data indicate that for each ion pair produced directly by the primary particles, there are about two more ion pairs produced per secondary electron. This means that much of the excitation and ionization is actually performed by electrons with rather low energy. Considerations on the energy spectrum of the secondary electrons also show that one should not expect any great variations in the energy spectrum of the first and higher order secondary electrons, even if the energy of the primary particles varies considerably (OMHOLT, 1959a, b; TAKAYANAGI and YONEZATA, 1961).

The fairly constant ratio between the intensity of the First Negative N_2^+ bands and that of the green oxygen line at 5577Å confirms this view. These two emissions have excitation potentials of about 19 and 4 eV respectively, and the constant ratio between the excitation rates implies that there are very small changes in the energy distribution of the first and higher order secondary electrons. Thus it seems likely, except in extreme cases, that the variations in the auroral spectrum are mostly caused by changes in the atmospheric density and composition.

When the aurora has a height of about 200 km or more, the energy of the primary particles must be only of the order of electron volts. In this case, secondary electrons will not play a dominant role, and the spectrum is influenced strongly by the energy distribution of the primaries. Such a situation will favor the excitation of low-lying energy levels. Thus the extraordinary great enhancement of the red oxygen doublet in rare cases (see p. 64) may perhaps be explained by assuming primary particles with very low energy.

The auroral ionization in the upper atmosphere is strongly linked to the excitation of the optical emissions. The excitation processes of the First Negative and Meinel N_2^+ bands are simultaneous ionization processes, the ionization and excitation being performed on neutral N_2 molecules. From laboratory data it was possible to estimate the ratio between the total rate of ionization and the rate of excitation of the First Negative bands, because the ratio between the cross sections involved is fairly independent of the energy of the active particle (CHAMBERLAIN, 1961a; OMHOLT, 1959a, b; GREEN and BARTH, 1965). Recent work by HAYAKAWA et al. (1965), HARTMAN and HOERLIN (1962), and by LATIMER and McCONKEY (1965) confirm the general view of a constant ratio between the First Negative band intensity and the rate of ionization, but the differences in the quantitative results are as large as 2 (cf. DALGARNO et al., 1965; DAVIDSON, 1966). We adopt here an average value of about 30 ion pairs produced per emitted photon in the 3914 band. Taking into account that about 20% of the air is oxygen, which is also ionized with about the same efficiency, we obtain a production of about 4×10^{10} ion pairs/cm^2 (column) sec in an aurora of brightness coefficient 1.* For auroras of other intensities, the rates of ionization will be proportional to the intensity.

It is beyond the scope of this paper to discuss the partially understood effects of this ionization on the ionosphere. We shall merely point out that the rate of ionization is distributed as the luminosity, whereas the resulting ion density depends on attachment and recombination coefficients, on diffusion as well as on drifts of electrons and ions because of winds and electrical fields.

In some cases, with quiet aurora, it is possible to find a reasonably good correlation between the auroral luminosity in the zenith (i.e., the rate of ionization integrated over the height) and the critical frequency of the associated E layer measured by ionosondes (OMHOLT, 1955, 1959b; KNECHT, 1956; KONENKO, 1965). More often, however, the picture is dominated by strong absorption of radio waves with no regular radio echoes.

---

*The brightness coefficient I, II, III, and IV mean emission rates of respectively 1, 10, 100 kR is the green OI-line 5577Å. 1kR (kilorayleigh) is 10^9 photons/cm^2(column) sec.

IV. Variations in the Spectrum

In this section we shall discuss the most important variations in the intensity distribution of the auroral spectrum. The causes for some of these differences are known, at least qualitatively, whereas others are still obscure.

Perhaps the most striking color variation in auroras is the appearance of strong red colors. Ordinary polar auroras of red color are divided into two groups, A and B. In addition, a type of subvisual, red auroral arcs occur at low latitudes, the M-arcs (cf. CHAMBERLAIN, 1961a; ELVEY, 1965; ROACH and ROACH, 1963). The red auroras of type A usually occur as extensive, weak reddish surfaces or red arcs, the red color being produced by an enhancement of the red, forbidden oxygen doublet at 6300/64Å. A similar enhancement of this red doublet can be seen in very long auroral rays, whose upper part occasionally may have a bright red color. Also in ordinary auroras, the intensity of the red doublet compared to the other spectral components, increases with increasing height, even if the relative intensity of the red doublet is often not sufficient to give a clear color impression on the eye. Whereas the main emissions pass through a maximum and then decrease again, judging from available data the red lines increase slowly or remain constant above the general maximum of the aurora. Because the green oxygen line at 5577Å ($^1D - {}^1S$) is caused by a transition down to the upper state of the red doublet ($^3P - {}^1D$), the latter should be at least as strong as the green line, but in the lower part of the aurora it is weaker. Considering the excitation mechanism, it should, in fact, be at least 10 times stronger than the green line (SEATON, 1954; OMHOLT, 1959a), whereas high latitude auroras seldom show a higher ratio than 5.

The excitation of the forbidden lines and bands observed in auroras involves either a change in multiplicity or that $\Delta L = 2$. Excitation of this kind is most readily performed by electrons with an energy slightly above the threshold energy, through electron exchange (SEATON, 1954). There does not seem to be any difficulty in explaining the great intensity of the forbidden emission. Although the absolute value of the excitation cross section is low, the energy spectrum of the secondary electrons favors the low-lying states. In consequence, the rate of excitation may be formidable, and for the low-lying states such as ^1D of oxygen (2 eV) it is much more elevated than for the higher ones, such as ^1S of oxygen (4 eV).

Therefore, this apparent enhancement of the red doublet is in most cases not real, but rather it is caused by deactivation of these lines at low heights. The red doublet is emitted by oxygen atoms in the metastable ^1D-states, whose lifetime against radiation is calculated to be about 110 sec. Thus if the excited atoms are undisturbed, they remain excited on the average for about 110 sec before they emit their energy. During this time they undergo a great number of collisions with other atoms and molecules in the atmosphere, and the energy may be transferred to other particles without radiation of the red lines. Thus the red doublet is quenched at low altitudes, and this quenching effect decreases in importance with increasing altitude, i.e., decreasing density in the atmosphere.

The deactivation mechanisms for metastable states of importance in aurora recently have been thoroughly discussed by HUNTEN and McELROY (1966). They conclude that the most important deactivation mechanism for the red doublet probably is

$$N_2 + O(^1D) \rightarrow N_2O \rightarrow N_2 + O(^3P),$$

leaving N in a vibrationally excited state. They also point out that from theory and comparison with airglow results, it is likely that the red doublet is even weaker in the lower part of the aurora than inferred from observations. This is not impossible, because height triangulation of the volume emission of aurora is a very difficult subject. Observations of red lines near the bottom of an aurora are very likely to be contaminated by higher auroral glow or other background forms in the same field of view.

Quenching effects also seem to be important in the intensity and height distribution of other forbidden radiations emitted from long-lived excited states, such as the Vegard-Kaplan bands and the forbidden nitrogen lines. There is strong evidence from temperature measurements (BROADFOOT and HUNTEN, 1964) that the emission of the Vegard-Kaplan bands takes place at a height around 200 km or above, which can be explained by collisional deactivation (HUNTEN and McELROY, 1966). For a comprehensive review of excitation and deactivation of forbidden emissions in aurora, the reader is referred to the paper by HUNTEN and McELROY (1966).

The type B aurora is more seldom and short-lived. Its usual characteristic is a strongly colored red lower border. It is generally accepted that this form of aurora has a low height and that the red color is caused by the enhancement of First Positive N_2 bands and a suppression of the green oxygen line (VALLANCE JONES, 1965). The reason for this enhancement is not yet clear, but it is somehow connected to the unusually low height of the emission. The type B aurora is usually short-lived with vivid motions. This makes it difficult to get a comprehensive study of its spectrum and height distribution. The green line comes from a metastable state with a lifetime of about 0.7 second, and therefore, shows a pronounced time lag in rapidly varying aurora (cf. Section VII). This has been used to study its excitation and deactivation, and the latter shortens the effective lifetime. Recent measurements of this time lag indicate strongly that there is a significant collisional deactivation in type B aurora (PAULSON and SHEPHERD, 1965; EVANS and VALLANCE JONES, 1965).

The very high red to green ratio in the M-arcs is difficult to explain. The green line intensity in this case hardly rises above the nightglow background, and the red lines are observed to be 10^3–10^4 times stronger than the green line. Such a spectrum would be produced by the impact of very low energetic electrons as well as by a discharge (MEGILL and CARLETON, 1963), but the primary source of such excitation agents is difficult to explain in both cases.

Theoretical computations (OMHOLT, 1959a, b; TAKAYANAGI and YONEZATA, 1961) as well as observational evidence (cf. CHAMBERLAIN, 1961; OMHOLT, 1959a; O'BRIEN and TAYLOR, 1964) suggest that the ratio between the green oxygen line and the First Negative N_2^+ bands is about the same in all types of aurora, and constant within a factor 2. Recent photometric triangulations by ROMICK and BELON (1964) indicate a peculiar variation of this ratio within an aurora, the 3914 N_2^+ emission having a broader extension in the N-S direction than the green oxygen line. They find that the observations can be explained by assuming the intensity of the green line to be proportional to the square of the intensity of the 3914Å emission. This is not in agreement with the simple picture outlined in Section III. They also speculate that dissociative recombination of O_2^+,

$$O_2^+ + e \rightarrow O(^1S) + O,$$

may contribute to the excitation. This hypothesis has been rejected earlier by other investigators because the time lag between the green line and the N_2^+ bands does not support it (OMHOLT, 1959a). MÅSEIDE (private communication) has found a systematic decrease in the intensity ratio between the N_2^+ bands and the 5577Å line with increasing intensity for two cases of auroral glow. It is difficult to judge the significance of these observations and their general validity before much more work of similar kind has been done.

Other lines and bands in the spectrum also show height effects, but are less pronounced. Measurements of such effects are hampered by the difficulties of separating the aurora from the diffuse background glow which very often occurs, and by the difficulties of guiding any instrument when the aurora moves around. Compared to the green line, the oxygen lines at 7774 and 8446Å and the O_2 atmospheric bands seem to increase slightly with increasing height. The N_2^+ Meinel bands, on the contrary, seem to decrease slightly (OMHOLT, 1957). It is not established whether these variations are typical for all auroras. The excitation of N_2 bands in aurora has recently been discussed by BROADFORT and HUNTEN (1964). They conclude that the spectrum of N_2 can be reasonably explained by electron excitation and by cascading from higher levels. Measurements of the relative behavior of the band systems in question in rapidly varying aurora (EFTESTØL and OMHOLT, 1965) indicate that other mechanisms may contribute to a minor fraction, because the various bands apparently do not vary entirely in phase, but it is premature to draw definite conclusions from the data.

The permitted atomic lines of neutral and ionized oxygen may be caused by direct excitation of oxygen atoms or dissociation of molecular oxygen. Most of the lines are too faint to allow any firm conclusions about this, but some information can be gathered from the intensity ratio between the two multiplets at 7774 ($^5S - {}^5P$) and 8446Å ($^3S - {}^3P$). These arise from the same transition array. Their relative intensity seems to vary a little, but it is of the order of one. Computed cross sections for electron excitation of atomic oxygen indicate that the multiplet at 7774Å should be considerably weaker than the other one, and that both lines should be of orders of magnitude fainter than the green oxygen line at 5577Å (PERCIVAL and SEATON, 1956). This indicates that the excitation mechanism actually may be simultaneous dissociation and excitation of O_2. This seems also to be in agreement with electron bombardment experiments in the laboratory by GRIBBON and STEWART (1956). Some evidence may favor the view that nitrogen lines also are excited through dissociation of molecules. Permitted atomic lines excited through molecular dissociation may show Doppler broadening as a result of the kinetic energy acquired during the dissociation, but this effect has not yet been studied in the auroral spectrum.

VEGARD and KVIFTE (1945) found indications that the sodium doublet 5889/95Å occasionally is enhanced in auroras. This was later confirmed by HUNTEN (1955) and, most conclusively, by DERBLOM (1964). This enhancement seems to be connected to the type B aurora, but no relation between the enhancement of the sodium lines and the height in the atmosphere of the aurora has yet been established. This effect cannot be produced by direct excitation of the sodium atoms present in the atmosphere, because the content of free sodium is very low. HUNTEN (1965) has recently attributed the excitation of sodium in aurora to energy transfer from excited, metastable atoms or molecules, probably vibrationally excited nitrogen molecules with $v = 8$. He finds that this requires a concentration of vibrationally excited nitrogen in auroras of brightness coefficient III of about 3×10^6 cm^{-3}. This concentration can be achieved through excitation by secondary electrons provided the lifetime of the excited molecule is about 1 sec. No other reasonable explanation has yet been advanced.

Auroras in the sunlit part of the atmosphere (sunlit aurora) show a great and noteworthy enhancement of the First Negative N_2^+ bands. These auroras have a grayish-blue color, and it is fairly certain that the enhancement of the First Negative bands is caused by fluorescent scattering (BATES, 1949). At great heights the auroral primary particles produce a very weak aurora below the threshold of visibility as they make their way down to lower levels. They also produce a certain number of N_2^+ ions, and these act as very efficient resonance scatterers of sunlight. This makes the high altitude section of the aurora clearly visible in the sunlit part of the atmosphere, whereas it is usually subvisual in the dark region of the atmosphere. In some cases the primary particles produce an aurora which is visible by itself very low in the atmosphere. Divided auroral rays may then occur. The upper part of the ray becomes visible because of the scattering effect, the middle part is in the dark atmosphere and is subvisual, whereas the lower part is visual because, here, the primary particles give off most of their energy.

V. Hydrogen Lines in Auroras

The Doppler broadened and shifted hydrogen lines in auroras were first detected by Vegard in 1939 (VEGARD, 1939a, b), and later observations (VEGARD and KVIFTE, 1945; GARTLEIN, 1950) demonstrated the large variation of these lines compared to the main auroral spectrum. Since MEINEL (1951) obtained his first spectrogram with sufficient resolution to study the line profile in detail, much work has been done on the interpretation of these lines. A comprehensive review is given by EATHER (1966c). Examples of observed profiles are shown in Fig. 2. The zenith profile is shifted towards shorter wavelengths

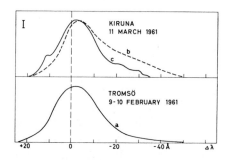

FIGURE 2. Examples of observed hydrogen line profiles (OMHOLT et al., 1963).

because when observing towards the zenith the protons/atoms always have a velocity component towards the observer.

The Balmer lines are excited through

$$H^+ + X \to H' + X^+ \to H + h\nu + X^+$$

and

$$H + X \to H' + X \to H + h\nu + X$$

where X is an atmospheric molecule or atom. The hydrogen atoms are re-ionized by

$$H + X \to H^+ + X + e,$$

and a proton may undergo a number of ionization and neutralization processes before it is brought to rest.

Space does not permit a detailed description of the analysis of hydrogen line profiles here, and therefore, the reader is referred to CHAMBERLAIN (1961a) for a complete discussion. In general, the combined analysis of the profiles observed in the directions of magnetic zenith and horizon yield information on the angular and energy distribution of the incident protons. An intensity distribution on velocity and pitch angle

$$N(v, \theta) = Cv^{-s} \cos^n \theta$$

seems to fit the observed profiles. The value of s is probably about 2.5–2.8; however, there is considerable uncertainty in the evaluation of the constants, in particular of n. Values of n between 0 (isotropy) and 6 have been deduced (cf. CHAMBERLAIN, 1916a; VALLANCE JONES, 1965; ZWICK and SHEPHERD, 1963; JOHANSEN and OMHOLT, 1963), but these depend rather critically on the detailed shape of the profiles. One main problem is that the zenith profile also has a component to the red side of the undisplaced line. It has been discussed as to whether this is a result of light from other directions scattered into the zenith direction or of backscattered protons/atoms in the atmosphere. However, the scattering coefficients are too small to make it probable that scattered light can distort the profiles considerably (EATHER and JACKA, 1966). Recent calculations by EATHER (1966a, b) taking magnetic mirroring effects into account, indicate that the profiles can be explained only if most low energetic protons ($E < 10$ keV or so) have a pitch angle distribution above the atmosphere which is strongly peaked at 70–90°, or if a vertical electric field is applied to the protons in the atmosphere. The latter explanation meets considerable difficulties; the former has been suggested earlier (OMHOLT, 1959c), and such a distribution may be caused by an electric field in the magnetosphere, distorting the angular distribution. (OMHOLT, 1959c; JOHANSEN and OMHOLT, 1963). Mirroring and scattering effects could then probably explain the displacement to the red. Also the tail of the profile is easily contaminated by other emissions. Much more work on this is needed to clarify these problems, but there are also considerable uncertainties in the interpretation resulting from poor laboratory and theoretical data on the excitation processes.

Studies on the morphology of the Hα and Hβ emission yield information on the impact zones of protons (cf. VALLANCE JONES, 1965; OMHOLT et al., 1963; GALPERIN, 1963; OMHOLT, 1963; MONTALBETTI and McEVEN, 1962; YEVLASKIN, 1963; EATHER and SANDFORD, 1966). It appears that the protons impinge in a diffuse, broad band, somewhat equatorwise of the main auroral forms (presumably caused by electrons) in the early part of the night. At midnight and in the latter part of the night the picture is less clear, with protons and electrons being mixed more. Again, additional work is needed to obtain a clearer view.

VI. Temperatures from Auroral Spectra

It is well known that the intensity distribution within and among vibrational-rotational bands of molecules and the Doppler width of atomic lines depend on temperature. To use these effects to derive temperatures in the atmosphere requires that the excited molecule or atom is in thermal equilibrium with the atmosphere and is not affected by the excitation process. It is generally accepted that for electron excitation molecules do not change their rotational energy significantly, and therefore, the rotational distribution of various bands, in particular the First Negative N_2^+ bands, have for a long time been used for temperature measurements of the auroral atmosphere. Also the vibrational structure in the band system is sensitive to the temperature, but the variation in the intensity distribution is usually not very large for temperatures below 1000°K. Forbidden atomic lines are particularly suitable for temperature measurements from Doppler widths, because the metastable atoms make numerous collisions before they radiate their energy. Such measurements are possible by use of interferometric technique, and a review of the present situation is given by HUNTEN (1961), JARETT and HOEY (1965), and AKASOFU *et al.* (1966).

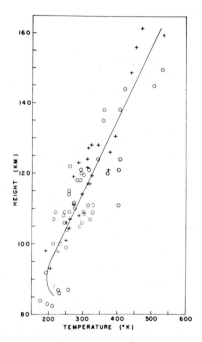

FIGURE 3. Rotational temperatures from auroral spectra, due to BRANDY (1965).

The measurements of auroral temperatures have mainly been made from the rotational structure of the First Negative N_2^+ bands, which are the most simple and reliable to use. These bands, in principle, yield a very reliable temperature, but considerable difficulties arise in relating the measured temperature to the height in the atmosphere. A long series of measurements made by Vegard with spectrographs gives an average temperature of about 250°K, and the scatter in the measured temperatures is only moderate (cf. CHAMBERLAIN, 1961a). This value is in reasonable agreement with the accepted temperature for a height of about 110–120 km, where the aurora is most common. With more advanced techniques, other workers have been able to show that spectra from auroral forms which are supposed to be very high (rays) show greater temperatures (cf. HUNTEN, 1961). The difficulties in the older measurements largely resulted from the very long exposure times which were necessary. This made it very difficult to select light from a particular part of any aurora and relate this to simultaneous height measurements. Photoelectric recording of the spectra has improved the situation, and more recently, rapid spectrometers and photoelectric filter photometers together with parallactic photography have made it possible to measure temperatures as a function of height (JOHANSON and VALLANCE JONES, 1962; HUNTEN *et al.* 1963; BRANDY, 1965). The evidence accumulated so far gives a temperature curve which is in reasonable agreement with rocket and satellite measurements. Auroral spectra suggest a temperature rise from about 200°K at a height of about 100 km to a temperature of about 500°K at 150 km, as shown in Figure 3. Interferometric measurements of the red oxygen line 6300Å yield a temperature of about 1000°K at 250 km.

The measurements made so far are too few to reveal variations in the structure of the atmosphere with the solar cycle, seasons, or night. Systematic temperature measurements from auroras combined with simultaneous height measurements offer a powerful and relatively inexpensive tool for such studies. Recent measurements by BRANDY (1965) indicate that the measured temperature is above the normal just before an auroral break-up event and below the normal afterwards. However, he considered the evidence insufficient to make conclusive statements, except that there seem to be significant differences in the temperature at any given height.

A recent study of HILLIARD and SHEPHERD (1966) on upper atmosphere temperatures from the Doppler width of the 5577Å OI line indicates a systematic relationship between the temperature and intensity of the aurora. They interpret their results as due to systematic changes in the height with auroral brightness, and claim that this systematic change seems to preclude the existence of major dynamical temperature changes in these levels.

VII. Rapid Variations in the Excitation

As is well known, the aurora may change very rapidly, both in shape and intensity. This is either due to movements of the pattern of incidence of the primary particles (for example, moving rays in a form) or to rapid changes in the intensity of the particle stream (for example, pulsating aurora). This has, as was mentioned in Section IV, been utilized to study the excitation and deactivation mechanisms in aurora. A record of pulsating aurora over Tromsø is shown in Figure 4. Comparing the green oxygen line with the N_2^+ band, it is seen that rapid variations are smoothed out and the green line lags behind the N_2^+ band. This is because the lifetime of the excited oxygen atoms is about 0.7 sec, with an exponential decay of the number of excited atoms. This effect has been used to verify the theoretically computed lifetime of the metastable atoms (OMHOLT, 1956; PAULSON and SHEPHERD, 1965; GARSTANG, 1951), and, as mentioned in Section IV, to study deactivation of $O(^1S)$ atoms in type B auroras.

Because a photometer necessarily integrates the light along the line of sight,

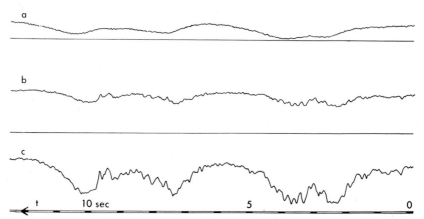

FIGURE 4. Record of pulsating aurora curves (a) OI 5577, (b) N_2^+4278 and (c) without filter are taken simultaneously with three parallel telescopes fitted with filters and photoelectric recording.

similar work on the 6300Å oxygen doublet has proved unsuccessful (OMHOLT, 1960; cf. also HUNTEN and MCELROY, 1966). This is because the observed 6300Å emission and N_2^+ emission originate from very different heights in the atmosphere, thus the excitation of the two emissions may not be in phase. To compute the lifetime from the time lag, accurate knowledge about the relation between the excitation mechanisms is necessary. For the computations on the green line it is assumed that the excitation rates in question are always proportional, which is reasonable from measurements of quiet aurora (cf. Section III). For permitted radiations, the study of the intensity ratio between various emissions in such rapidly changing aurora can be used to determine if the excitation mechanisms are proportional (cf. Section IV). This has not been done to a great extent, and more work is needed.

References

AKASOFU, S.-I., CHAPMAN, S., and MEINEL, A. B., 1966, *Handbuch der Physik* **49**, 1. Springer Verlag.
BATES, D. R., 1949, *Proc. Roy. Soc. (London)* **A196**, 217.
BATES, D. R., 1960, *Physics of the Upper Atmosphere* (Ed. by J. J. Ratcliffe), Academic Press.
BRANDY, J. H., 1965, *Can. J. Phys.* **43**, 1697.
BROADFOOT, A. L. and HUNTEN, D. M., 1964, *Can. J. Phys.* **42**, 1212.
CHAMBERLAIN, J. W., 1961a, *Physics of the Aurora and Airglow*, Academic Press.
CHAMBERLAIN, J. W., 1961b, *Ann. Geophys.* **17**, 201.
DALGARNO, A., LATIMER, I. D., and MCCONKEY, J. W., 1965, *Planetary Space Sci.* **13**, 1008.
DAVIDSON, G., 1966, *Planetary Space Sci.* **14**, 651.
DERBLOM, H., 1964, *J. Atmospheric Terrest. Phys.* **26**, 791.
EATHER, R. H., 1966a, *J. Geophys. Res.* **71**, 4133, 1966b, *J. Geophys. Res.* (to be published); 1966c, (to be published).

EATHER, R. H. and JACKA, F., 1966, *Australian J. Phys.* **19**, 241.
EATHER, R. H. and SANFORD, B. S., 1966, *Australian J. Phys.* **19**, 25.
EFTESTØL, A. and OMHOLT, A., 1965, *Geofys. Publ.* **25**, No. 6.
ELVEY. C. T., 1965, *Auroral Phenomena* (Ed. by M. Walt), Stanford University Press.
EVANS, J. E., 1965, *Auroral Phenomena* (Ed. by M. Walt), Stanford University Press.
EVANS, W. F. and Vallance Jones, A., 1965, *Can. J. Phys.* **42**, 697.
FASTIE, W. G., CROSSWHITE, H. M., and MARKHAM, T. P., 1961, *Ann. Geophys.* **17**, 109.
GALPERIN, Y. I., 1963, *Planetary Space Sci.* **10**, 147.
GARSTANG, R. J., 1951, *Mon. Not. RAS* **111**, 115.
GARTLEIN, C. W., 1950, *Transact. Am. Geophys. Union* **31**, 18.
GREEN, A. E. S. and Barth, C. A., 1965, *J. Geophys. Res.* **69**, 45.
GRIBBON, P. W. F. and STEWART, D. T., 1965, *The Airglow and the Aurora* (Ed. by E. B. ARMSTRONG and A. DALGARNO), Pergamon Press, London.
HARANG, L., 1958, *Geofys. Publ.* **20**, No. 5.
HARTMAN, P. L., and HOERLIN, H., 1962, *Bull. Am. Phys. Soc.* **11**, 69.
HAYAKAWA, S., KUMAZAKI, H., NISKIMURA, H., and OTSUKA, M., 1965, *Rep. Ionosphere and Space Res.*, Japan **19**, 311.
HILLIARD, R. L. and SHEPHERD, G. G., 1966, *Planetary Space Sci.* **14**, 383.
HUNTEN, D. M., 1955, *J. Atmospheric Terrest. Phys.* **7**, 141.
HUNTEN, D. M., 1961, *Ann. Geophys.* **17**, 249.
HUNTEN, D. M., 1965, *J. Atmospheric Terrest. Phys.* **27**, 583.
HUNTEN, D. M. and MCELROY, M. B., 1966, *Quenching of metastable states of atomic and molecular oxygen and nitrogen.* (to be published).
HUNTEN, D. M., RAWSON, E. G., and WALKER, J. K., 1963, *Can. J. Phys.* **41**, 258.
JARETT, A. H. and HOEY, M. J., 1965, *Proc. Roy. Soc.* A**228**, 510.
JOHANSEN, O. E. and OMHOLT, A., 1963, *Planetary Space Sci.* **24**, 203.
JOHANSON, A. E. and VALLANCE JONES, A., 1962, *Can. J. Phys* **40**, 24.
KNECHT, R. W., 1956, *J. Geophys. Res.* **61**, 59.
KONENKO, A. F., 1965, *Geomagnetism i Aeronomiya* **5**, 186.
LATIMER, I. D., and MCCONKEY, J. W., 1965, *Proc. Phys. Soc.* **86**, 463.
MALVILLE, J. M., 1959, *J. Atmospheric Terrest. Phys.* **16**, 59.
MEGILL, L. R., and CARLETON, N. P., 1963, *J. Geophys. Res.* **69**, 101.
MEINEL, A. B., 1951, *Astrophys. J.* **113**, 50.
MCLENNAN, J. C. and SCHRUM, G. M., 1925, *Proc. Roy. Soc. (London)* A**106** 501.
MONTALBETTI, R. and MCEVEN, D. J., 1962, *J. Phys. Soc. Japan* **17** A1, 212.
O'BRIEN, B. J., 1965, *Auroral Phenomena* (Ed. by M. Walt), Stanford University Press.
O'BRIEN, B. J. and TAYLOR, H., 1964, *J. Geophys. Res.* **69**, 45.
OMHOLT, A., 1955, *J. Atmospheric Terrest. Phys.* **7**, 73.
OMHOLT, A., 1956, *The Airglow and the Aurora* (Ed. by E. B. Armstrong and A. Dalgarno), London.
OMHOLT, A., 1957, *J. Atmospheric Terrest. Phys.* **10**, 320.
OMHOLT, A., 1959a, *Geofys. Publ.* **20**, No. 5.
OMHOLT, A., 1959b, *Electromagnetic Wave Propagation,* (Ed. by M. DESIRANT and I. L. MICHELS), Academic Press, New York. 1959c, *Geofys. Publ.* **21**, No. 1.
OMHOLT, A., 1960, *Planetary Space Sci.* **2**, 246.
OMHOLT, A., 1963, *Planetary Space Sci.* **10**, 247.
OMHOLT, A., STOFFREGEN, W., and DERBLOM, H., 1963, *J. Atmospheric Terrest. Phys.* **11**, 1223.
PAULSON, K. V. and SHEPHERD, G. G., 1965, *J. Atmospheric Terrest. Phys.* **27**, 831.
PERCIVAL, I. C. and SEATON, M. J., 1956, *The Airglow and the Aurora* Ed. by E. B. Armstrong and A. Dalgarno, Pergamon Press, London.
ROACH, F. E. and ROACH, J. R., 1963, *Planetary Space Sci.* **11**, 523.
ROMICK, G. J. and BELON, A. E., 1964, Final Report NSF G15725, Geophysical Institute, University of Alaska.
SEATON, M. J., 1954, *J. Atmospheric Terrest. Phys.* **42** 1212.
SHEFOV, N. N., 1963, *J. Planetary Space Sci.* **10**, 73.
TAKAYANAGI, K. and YONEZATA, T., 1961, *Rep. Ionosphere and Space Res.*, Japan **15**, 51.

VALLANCE JONES, A., 1955, *An Atlas of the Auroral Spectrum*. Sci. Rep. No. AR-20. Physics Dep. Univ. Saskatchewan, Saskatoon.

VALLANCE JONES, A., 1964, *Mem. Soc. Roy. Liege, Series 5*, **9,** 289.

VALLANCE JONES, A., 1965, *Auroral Phenomena* (Ed. by M. Walt), Stanford University Press.

VEGARD, L., 1913, *Phys. Z. S.* **14,** 677.

VEGARD, L., 1916a, *Ann. Phys.* **50,** 853.

VEGARD, L., 1916b, *Christiania Vid. Selsk. Skr. Mat.-Nat. kl. 1916, No. 3.*

VEGARD, L., 1939a, *Nature* **144,** 1089.

VEGARD, L., 1939b, *Geofys. Publ.* **12,** No. 14.

VEGARD, L. and KVIFTE, G., 1945, *Geofys. Publ.* **16,** No. 7.

YEVLASKIN, L. S., 1963, *Geomagnetism i Aeronomiya* **3,** 405.

ZWICK, H. H. and SHEPHERD, G. G., 1963, *J. Atmospheric Terrest. Phys.* **25,** 609.

HIGH LATITUDE MAGNETIC DISTURBANCES
(A Brief Review with Initial Results
From Motion Picture Presentation)

J. P. Heppner
NASA-Goddard Space Flight Center
Greenbelt, Maryland

I. Introduction

A comprehensive review of high latitude (i.e., auroral zone and polar cap) magnetic disturbances should treat in sequence the properties of the solar wind and interplanetary fields, their interaction with the earth's magnetic field, the mechanisms for transferring solar wind energy to the outer magnetosphere, the motions of fields, plasmas, and energetic particles within the magnetosphere, the energy coupling between the outer magnetosphere and ionospheric regions, possible influences of wind generated potentials in the ionosphere, and the electromagnetic and hydromagnetic properties of the ionosphere which eventually determine many of the characteristics of the magnetic disturbance seen by a high latitude magnetic observatory. Any attempt at this type of review in a short paper is destined to be too sketchy to be substantive. Some of these topics are discussed in other papers at this symposium.

The discussion here is directed to the geomagnetic time and latitude distribution of magnetic disturbance at auroral and polar cap latitudes. This is an old topic which has assumed new status as a consequence of space measurements in recent years. Among other phenomena of known association with auroral zone magnetic disturbances, we are now aware that sudden changes in the population of low energy trapped particles are closely correlated with bay activity in the auroral zone (McIlwain, 1966; Davis and Williamson, 1966; Konradi, 1966). The importance of the topic is also evident on examination of recent theories (e.g., Axford and Hines, 1961; Dungey, 1961; Piddington, 1963; Taylor and Hones, 1965) in which the basic problem is arriving at an explanation for the high latitude disturbance patterns as an eventual consequence of solar wind interaction with the magnetosphere. To various degrees the problem is usually worked backwards in the sense that conditions in the outer magnetosphere are deduced from an assumed high latitude current distribution, and one then finds a cause for these conditions. There have been only a few attempts at treating this, i.e., the reverse, problem quantitatively (e.g., FEJER, 1963; TAYLOR and HONES, 1965). This lack of quantitative treatment is not surprising, considering that a number of assumptions are required which in turn cast doubt on specific results. Typical steps, not all identified with any one analysis, are: (a) the assumption of a model of the surface magnetic disturbance which in turn usually includes the additional assumption that the disturbance is invariant with time, (b) the assumption that the model disturbance is caused by ionospheric currents whose circuits lie entirely within the ionosphere, (c) the assumption, associated with (b), that magnetic field lines are also lines of electrical equipotential, (d) the assumption of a static model atmosphere for neutral and charged particles at ionospheric heights for calculation of tensor conductivities, and (e) the assumption of a magnetic field model for tracing field lines into the outer magnetosphere.

The missing link in understanding the disturbance phenomena is obviously the lack of measurements of electric fields. However, even when we have these measurements they will have to be referenced in time and location to characteristic stages of magnetic disturbance as recorded by surface observatories. Thus it is important that we have clear conceptual pictures of typical patterns or systems of magnetic disturbance at high latitudes and an equally clear understanding that these patterns are only *quasi-stable*. The most difficult concepts involve recognizing the continuous existence of patterns under highly variable conditions. These concepts, although difficult to convey in words or fixed time illustrations, are relatively easy to grasp through repeated viewing of the motion picture presentation described in Section III.

II. Brief Review of Disturbance Patterns

Birkeland's (1900–1913) descriptions and explanations of "polar elementary storms" coincident with auroral displays represent the first modern attempt to understand high latitude disturbances. Birkeland's "polar elementary storms" are now usually referred to as "magnetic bays" or "auroral electrojet disturbances." The changes in name do not imply any physical difference. Birkeland's concepts were necessarily simple: electrons entered the outer atmosphere from great distances and returned to distant space. Their horizontal paths along a magnetic shell while in the outer atmosphere determined the current flow causing the magnetic disturbance. Thus, he did not close the circuit within the ionosphere. Criticisms are well known, but the basic concept is brought back in different forms as earlier grounds for criticism are found wanting (see, e.g., ALFVÉN, 1966).

Chapman's (CHAPMAN and BARTELS, 1940) harmonic analysis of magnetic storms provided a description of magnetic disturbance in terms of a system of currents forming closed circuits within the ionosphere. Although highly idealized in terms of D_{st} (symmetric about the earth's magnetic axis) and S_D (solar diurnal) parts, this idealization has been a reference system for many subsequent studies. Polar views of Chapman's $D_{st} + S_D$ and S_D systems are shown in Figure 1(A) and 1(B), respectively. In more recent years various symbolisms (e.g., DS, DP, D_p, D_i, etc.) have been used to describe the non-symmetric part of a disturbance largely to escape the restrictive nature of the S_D definition. A review of disturbance classifications has been given by CHAPMAN (1961). As different investigators do not use the same techniques in analysis but may choose to use the same symbols in speaking of the resulting current systems, considerable confusion can, and often does, result from this labelling. An obvious example is the use of the term asymmetrical D_{st}. To avoid semantic confusion here, we will ignore the usual symbolisms.

Chapman's analysis was based on averaging a large number of magnetic storms and most subsequent analyses have been carried out by various techniques of averaging as a function of local time the disturbances occurring on different days. As expected, the sampling of days and hours relative to the number of observatories used and their locations gives variations in the resulting pattern of disturbance. The equivalent ionospheric current systems drawn to represent these patterns are accordingly different in detail. Two well known representations of this type are shown as Figures 1(C) and 1(D) from SILSBEE and VESTINE (1942) and NAGATA (1950), respectively. More recently NAGATA and IIJIMA (1964) have shown that current systems derived by similar averaging procedures at high southern and high northern latitudes are essentially the same, which suggests a conjugate relationship in the average disturbance pattern. This is illustrated in Figures 1(E) and 1(F).

The averaging of a number of disturbances or a number of days has the obvious drawback that temporal variations in the distribution are eliminated. Also, details which persist spatially but do not occur at the identical local time each day or at identical latitudes through a range of disturbance intensities can be lost and thus ignored in subsequent physical interpretation. The smoothing becomes even more extreme when a small number of scattered observatories is used. These points are immediately evident in comparing diagrams such as those in Figure 1 with HARANG'S (1946) analysis of disturbances obtained by rotating in local time a set of stations which were closely spaced along a geomagnetic meridian. Even though Harang used hourly values, the fact that he did not mix widely different levels of disturbance and did use closely spaced stations, brought out the very important detail that there is an overlap in latitude between $+\Delta H$ and $-\Delta H$ disturbances near the local time of transition from positive to negative bays. This is illustrated in Figure 2.

A second category of analysis, designed to show temporal variations in the spatial distribution, has been the construction of disturbance patterns or equivalent current systems for specific hours using hourly mean values (e.g., VESTINE et al., 1947; FUKUSHIMA, 1953; FAIRFIELD, 1963). As this has been

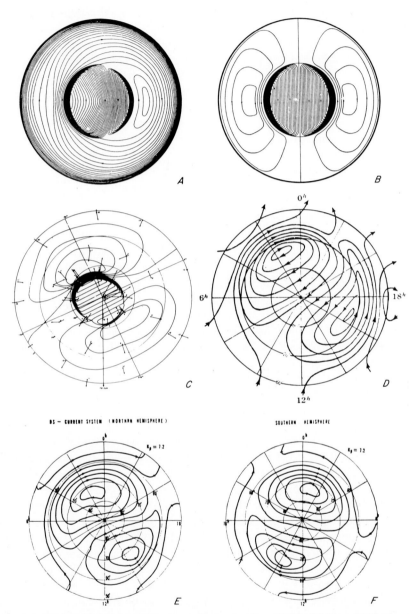

FIGURE 1. High latitude current systems: Chapman (A) and (B), Silsbee and Vestine (C), Nagata (D), Nagata and Iijima (E) and (F) (See text).

done by rather tedious analysis, examples are limited to a small number of hours for particular disturbances. Selection of representative samples is thus a problem, and some detail is lost in the one hour smoothing. There is necessarily an additional loss of detail through smoothing when current systems with ionospheric continuity are constructed from the hourly values.

A third category of analysis involves relating the magnetic disturbance pattern to the behavior of auroras. At electrojet latitudes, it has been well established that the time and space distribution of positive and negative bays correlates, in detail, with: (1) stages of auroral morphology as revealed primarily by sequences of auroral forms (HEPPNER, 1954), and (2) the direction of auroral motion (DAVIS, 1962). Figure 3, Pattern I, illustrates in idealized form the most common coincident behavior of the aurora and magnetic bays. Figure 3, Pattern II illustrates a second type of coincident behavior in which there is a disappearance of activity between the positive and negative bay sectors of the disturbance pattern. The occurrence of Pattern II is generally limited to periods of low activity. DAVIS' figures (this volume or 1963) show the directions of auroral motion associated, respectively, with eastward $(+\Delta H)$ currents and westward $(-\Delta H)$ currents. The lines AB in Figure 3 and AA' in DAVIS' figures (1963) separate the two $(+\Delta H$ and $-\Delta H)$ time and space sectors of the disturbance pattern at electrojet latitudes.

The overlap in latitude between the $+\Delta H$ and $-\Delta H$ sectors that appears between 23^h and 00^h LT in Figure 3 is a typical feature of the disturbance pattern that seldom appears in studies utilizing averages. In fact, this section of the pattern may appear as a time of low disturbance because the $+$ and $-\Delta H$ effects from currents to the south and north, respectively, will mutually cancel each other at an observatory situated in the center noted previously. As the overlap does appear as a major feature in Harang's diagram, Figure 2. This latitudinal overlap illustrated by Figures 2 and 3 and DAVIS' (1963) analysis is a particularly important stage in the disturbance pattern as it represents the condition which exists immediately preceding the event known as "auroral break-up" (i.e., the lowest latitude homogeneous arc breaks into active rayed forms) which is accompanied by a sudden increase in intensity of the westward electrojet and a local time shift of the electrojet pattern. This event is also referred to as negative bay onset, auroral activation, etc.

From the detailed correlation of aurora and magnetic disturbance noted above one would logically assume that statistical patterns of auroral occurrence and magnetic disturbance would also correlate. At electrojet latitudes this expectation is borne out. However, in the central polar cap region (e.g., $>80°$ magnetic latitude) the correlation is apparently negative (DAVIS, 1963; LASSEN, 1963). FELDSTEIN (1966) has compiled statistics on the local time of occurrence of auroras and plotted the distribution on a 24 hour polar scale. The resulting distribution, which he names the "auroral oval," places the region of maximum occurrence for the noon hours near $76°$ magnetic latitude and for midnight hours near $67°$. The term "auroral oval" appears to have the same meaning as an older term "the auroral belt," which has often been used to distinguish between this distribution and the location of the "auroral zone" which defines the latitude of most frequent occurrence without reference to local time. The

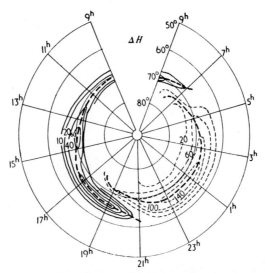

FIGURE 2. Contours of equal disturbance of the horizontal component from HARANG (1946): solid lines for $+\Delta H$, light dashed lines for $-\Delta H$. Time designated is local standard time which is roughly 1–1.5 hours earlier than geomagnetic local time for the meridians studied.

change in latitude with local time of the southern edge of the auroral belt is apparent in Figure 2.

The coincidence of the auroral belt or oval with electrojet magnetic disturbances is well established and need hardly be mentioned further, except for a recent interpretation suggested and questioned by FELDSTEIN (1966), but pursued to great length by Akasofu and co-workers (AKASOFU, CHAPMAN, and MENG, 1965; AKASOFU, KIMBALL, and MENG, 1965, 1966). As summarized by AKASOFU (1965), positive bays in the afternoon sector are not caused by an eastward electrojet current but are instead the result of ionospheric return currents from westward electrojets at higher latitudes. In this interpretation the westward electrojet flows everywhere along the auroral oval, and positive bays at auroral latitudes in the evening are a minor consequence of the westward flow at higher latitudes. Thus, by definition, in this picture there is no direct spatial association between the occurrence of aurora and the eastward current. This view directly conflicts with the observations of many individual studies, some of which involved extensive statistics: e.g., HEPPNER's (1954) study of 95 complete and 50 partial nights at College, Alaska, and BOND's (1960) investigation of 62 nights at Macquarie Island which revealed only two conflicts with the patterns typified by Figure 3, and these were cases when the aurora was rayed during the positive bay. Auroral behavior defies perfect classification, so it is not difficult to find isolated or detailed exceptions in its association with magnetic disturbance. However, observational data on the

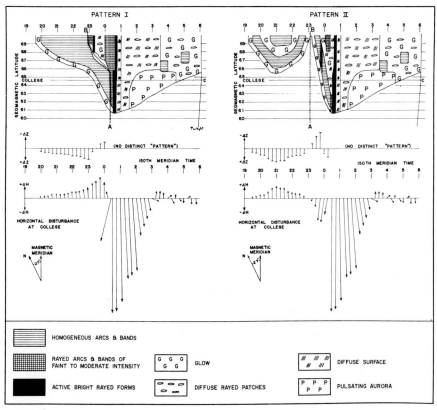

FIGURE 3. Idealized patterns of simultaneous auroral activity and magnetic disturbance from HEPPNER (1954). Time designated is local standard time which is approximately 1.5 hours later than geomagnetic time for region studied.

presence of aurora is overwhelmingly contrary to Akasofu's interpretation. There are other arguments based on auroral morphology which also contradict this interpretation and its implications, but this is a separate topic. It should be noted that the distinction between "electrojet" and "return" current is not purely semantic in that "return" here implies that there is no causative driving potential or auroral particle precipitation associated directly with the eastward current or $+\Delta H$ disturbance. Interpreted broadly, it also means that the total eastward current can never be greater than a small fraction of the integrated westward electrojet current. Or interpreted more along the lines proposed, the total eastward current is not greater than the westward current having similar alignment at slightly higher latitudes. Movies of the disturbance discussed in the following sections make it obvious that there are major flaws in the current system constructed by AKASOFU, CHAPMAN, and MENG (1965).

III. Film Display of Disturbance Patterns

The review in Section II was directed toward the spatial distribution of disturbance patterns. Time variations in the pattern were largely ignored because only very limited information has been available. More recently, magnetograms have been digitized at 2.5 minute intervals under a joint USC & GS - NASA effort. As these data can be handled by computers, analyses of time variations can be performed which previously would not have been feasible from a labor standpoint. Using data in this form for seven auroral zone observatories, Davis and Sugiura (1966) have defined an index for auroral electrojet activity, AE, based on the envelope of superimposed traces of the horizontal component. This envelope clearly illustrates variations in electrojet activity with universal time but is independent of the local time pattern.

For analysis of the local time pattern as a function of universal time the author has used an SC-4020 plotter to display in polar projection the disturbance vector in the horizontal plane simultaneously from 25 high latitude observatories for each 2.5 minutes of universal time for a period of 16 consecutive days in October 1957. The interval October 5–20, 1957 was chosen because: (1) the maximum number of high latitude magnetograms was available for 1957–1958, (2) a wide range of disturbance levels was available between October 5 and 20 without getting into a major storm which would make many records unreadable, and (3) for baseline determination October 5–20 included two 24 hour intervals which were the most quiet days within a four month interval. A 26th observatory, Pt. Barrow, was digitized but not used because the D trace was missing from the magnetograms on the quiet days. K_p indices for the 16 days are shown in Figure 4 to illustrate general activity levels.

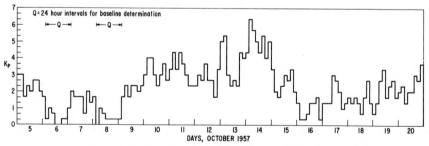

FIGURE 4. K_p indices for period covered in film study.

Restriction of this initial study to 16 days can be best understood by examining the quantity of data involved. For the 16 days there are 9216 independent polar diagrams which mean 230,400 observatory vectors or 691,200 component (i.e., D, H, or Z) scalings. The variation in the vertical component, ΔZ, is not represented in plots made to date. ΔH and ΔD (or ΔX and ΔY) determine the horizontal vector. The individual polar plots are put on 35mm film in time sequence by the SC-4020 plotter. Playback of this film gives a continuous movie of the simultaneous disturbance vectors. Movies in both geographic and geomagnetic coordinate systems have been made by this means. As expected, the vectors are better organized in geomagnetic than in geographic coordinates; i.e., the vector patterns are more stable as a function of geomagnetic local time and latitude than as a function of geographic local time and latitude. Thus, geomagnetic coordinates are used exclusively for detailed study. For movie presentation in which the speed of projection has to be matched to a viewer's ability to follow changes, four frames are inserted between each two independent frames. This is accomplished by linear interpolation at 0.5 minute intervals between consecutive 2.5 minute scalings.

Figures 5–8 contain examples of individual frames. The heavy line passing through the center of each plot is the geomagnetic noon-midnight meridian. The long end of this line points toward the sun, and thus denotes the noon meridian. In the lower right-hand corner of Figure 5 geomagnetic times 0^h, 6^h, 12^h, 18^h and geomagnetic longitudes $0°$, $90°$, $-90°$, $180°$ are illustrated together with numbers identifying the observatories which are listed in Table I. Dotted lines are circles of constant geomagnetic latitude in $10°$ intervals.

Observatories	Geomagnetic Latitude °N
Thule	88.0
Resolute Bay	82.9
Godhavn	79.8
Murchison Bay	75.3
Baker Lake	73.7
Tikhaya Bay	71.1
Julianehaab	70.8
Reykjavik	70.2
Yellowknife	69.0
Churchill	68.7
Cape Chelyuskin	66.3
Kiruna	65.3
College	64.7
Murmansk	64.1
Dixon Island	63.0
Lerwick	62.5
Cape Wellen	61.8
Meanook	61.8
Tixie Bay	60.4
Sitka	60.0
Nurmijarvi	57.9
Agincourt	55.0
Victoria	54.1
Srednikan	53.2
Yakutsk	51.0

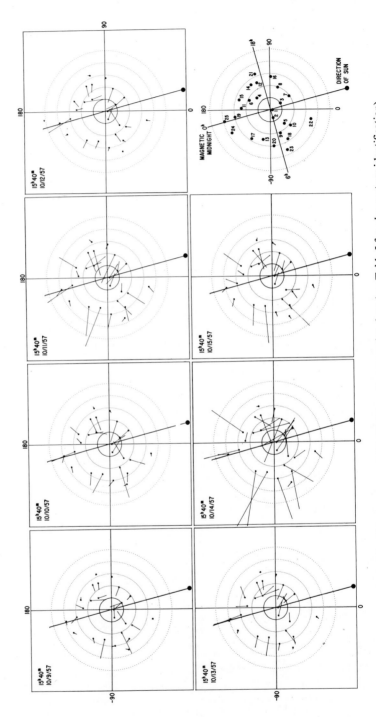

FIGURE 5. Disturbance vectors at 15:40 UT on 7 consecutive days (see Table I for observatory identification).

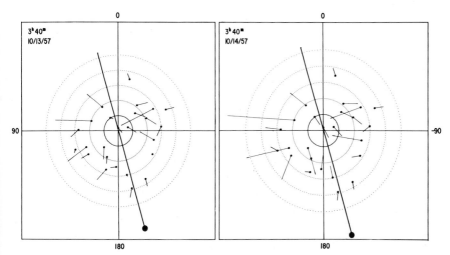

FIGURE 6. Disturbance vectors at 03:40 UT on 2 consecutive days.

In Figures 6–8 the coordinates have been rotated by 90° or 180° such that noon is near the bottom of each figure. The scale of the disturbance vector length is 100 gammas = 10° latitude in all cases.

IV. Discussion Related to Initial Analysis of Disturbance Film

A viewer of the movie described above can form his own general impressions. However, it is only through repeated viewings and careful examination of successive frames that these impressions become at all quantitative. To date, the author has studied primarily the major features. Thus, analyses of many details (e.g., time differences between the appearance of change at different stations, etc.) will have to be given in subsequent reports. Some initial impressions and conclusions are given below:

A. Circuit Closure. The pattern of disturbance vectors at any specific time gives the general impression that systems of closed ionospheric currents could be drawn compatible with the observed disturbances. However, on closer examination the following points are apparent. (1) There is not an adequate number and distribution of observatories to permit such constructions to be accurate. Even qualitative representation may often hinge on being able to place currents where there are not any observatories to confirm or deny the construction. This is particularly true at auroral latitudes where the disturbance is locally concentrated. In polar cap regions the disturbance is often highly uniform, and it is reasonable at these times to assume that the central polar cap disturbance is adequately represented by the available observatories. (2) For specific periods of time, which are not infrequent, there are good reasons for questioning closure in the ionosphere. The most obvious situation of this type occurs when a relatively stable pattern of disturbance is present, and a distinct group of observatories, all showing either $+\Delta H$ or $-\Delta H$, suddenly or gradually undergoes a significant change in the level of disturbance without change in sign, while at the same time, there is no significant change in the disturbance at other observatories. Any attempt to maintain circuit continuity in the ionosphere as a function of time through this sequence is necessarily dependent on adjustments to the current system only in the region of change and those regions which are unobserved. Belief in complete ionospheric closure at these times would appear to be based more on faith than on logic. (3) More generally, from repeated viewings one recognizes that the major sectors of the pattern (i.e., the positive and negative bay auroral disturbances and the polar cap disturbance) are not disturbed proportionally at different times. Thus, although all sectors tend to be either disturbed or quiet for the same periods, the relative and combined intensities of positive and negative bays often vary greatly while the polar cap disturbance level remains relatively stable. Explanation of the various combinations of relative intensity could be sought in terms of closure at lower latitudes which are not represented in the film. This again invokes the unknown in assuming a closed ionospheric system. (4) For the same reasons as (1) above, current systems which do not close completely in the ionosphere could be constructed to be compatible with the observed disturbances.

  B. Biased Distributions. Taking into account item (1) of the preceding subsection, it is apparent that any analysis which is based on the universal time period 20^h to 01^h will de-emphasize, and in many cases, completely miss the presence of $+\Delta H$ positive bay activity at auroral latitudes, and any analysis based on the period 01^h to 04^h is likely to de-emphasize, but not miss, the $-\Delta H$ negative bay activity. This is a direct consequence of the lack of stations below 70° magnetic latitude in the Atlantic region. It is interesting to note that the VESTINE *et al.* (1948) diagrams at two hour intervals illustrating positive bay activity disappearing during progression of a storm show this disappearance at 22^h and 00^h UT. Similarly, SILSBEE and VESTINE's (1942) widely quoted current diagram shown in Figure 1(C) is based on 3 hour averages centered at 21^h, 00^h, and 03^h UT. As this puts maximum weight on the UT period 20^h to 01^h, it is not surprising that the diagram shows a relatively insignificant positive bay sector.

  C. Return Current Question. As noted in Section II, AKASOFU *et al.* (1965, 1966) attribute $+\Delta H$ disturbances at auroral latitudes in the afternoon or evening hours to return currents from the westward electrojet whose circuit is extended from the early morning hours to the afternoon hours at latitudes slightly greater than those of the $+\Delta H$ disturbance. The following observations from the disturbance film are contrary to this return current interpretation. (1) Periods do exist in which the general level of $+\Delta H$, positive bay, activity is greater than the $-\Delta H$, negative bay, activity. (2) It is quite common to observe $+\Delta H$ disturbances over extended areas in the evening hours which are considerably stronger than $-\Delta H$ disturbances over similar areas at adjacent higher latitudes. (3) At lower latitudes, e.g., $\leq 55°$, in the same time sector as the $+\Delta H$ disturbance, the disturbance is most commonly negative. (4) The $+\Delta H$ disturbance in many cases remains relatively stable while there are large excursions in the negative bay, $-\Delta H$, disturbance. Relative to the discussion of biased distributions above, it should also be noted that AKASOFU, CHAPMAN, and MENG (1965) have selected diagrams for 24[h] UT from VESTINE (1948) and for 21[h]15[m] from FUKUSHIMA (1953) as support for their interpretation.

   D. Repetition of Pattern at the Same UT on Successive Days. The film presentation, or examination of magnetograms, makes one conscious of the great variability of high latitude disturbance levels as a function of UT and date. The film also conveys an impression of irregular movements of the pattern with local time. Although such movements take place, as discussed in the following subsection much of this impression is caused by changes in intensity and small shifts in latitude accompanying intensity changes rather than a movement of the configuration in magnetic local time. One test of pattern stability is its repeatability from day to day. Examples of repetitious behavior of bays on successive days have been given in the past for specific observatories (CHREE, 1913; WELLS, 1947; HEPPNER, 1954). The film permits one to examine this type of stability for the complete pattern in detail. Taking the identical UT on successive days is an extreme test which a priori the author thought would show general agreement but not detailed agreement. However, it has become apparent that detailed correspondence between successive days frequently exists. Figure 5 shows the disturbance vectors at 15[h]40[m] UT on 7 successive days in which the 3-hour K_p values for 15[h]–18[h] range from 2[+] to 5[+]. The degree of detailed correspondence in the vector configurations is obvious. To illustrate that the repeatability is not a peculiar property of this UT, an example of two consecutive days is given for 03[h]40[m] UT in Figure 6. It should be noted that although these are selected examples, they are not the findings of a careful selection. A large number of examples of equally detailed repetition could be extracted from the film.

   E. Pattern Movements in Geomagnetic Time. The preceding subsection emphasized the stability of the disturbance vector pattern. However, we know quite well from previous studies that the pattern is not completely fixed in geomagnetic time or in any other known time scale even when we take into account possible false impressions caused by latitude shifts. Space will not permit a general discussion here, but some generalization on movements of the $+$ to $-\Delta H$ discontinuity in magnetic local time as seen in movie form is important. The first generalization is that this discontinuity persists most of the time within a sector of several hours near 22[h] magnetic local time. It is thus convenient to visualize a pattern fixed in magnetic local time (i.e., relative to the sun) and examine deviations from the fixed position. When this is done it is rather surprising to find that for the majority of time the transition

from + to −Δ*H* disturbance progresses rather smoothly, moving successively
from one observatory to the next as the earth rotates relative to the fixed
position. This is essentially just a restatement of the stable condition subject to
the observatory distribution which does not permit distinction between a
smooth transition and irregular, small time jump transitions over hour angles
less than the east-west separation of successive observatories. This apparent
smooth transition is usually interrupted several times a day by discrete jumps
in which the discontinuity shifts suddenly (e.g., within 10 to 20 minutes) to an
earlier geomagnetic local time. However, it is clear that these sudden jumps
are in most cases confined to time sectors of less than 3 hours; that is, they do
not extend far enough back in local time to wipe out the positive bay sector.
Figure 7 between 8:40 and 09:00 UT illustrates a small jump for the case of a

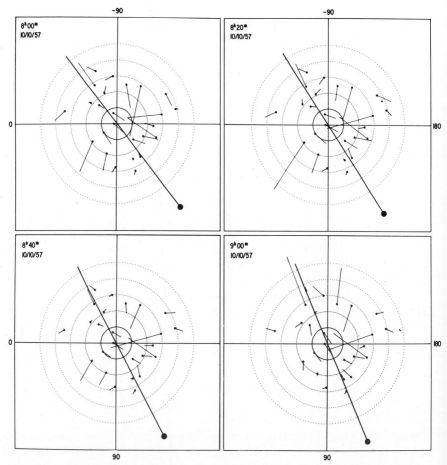

FIGURE 7. Disturbance vectors at 20 min. intervals 08:00 to 09:00, October 10, 1957.

weak disturbance. Following such sudden shifts to earlier local time, the discontinuity in geomagnetic local time gradually returns to roughly the same time zone where it was located prior to the shift. This is an interesting feature in that the return to the previous location appears to progress approximately at the earth's rate of rotation. If correct, this implies that one cannot visualize the pattern entirely in terms of position relative to the sun (i.e., local time) but must also allow for the possibility that the pattern to some degree rotates with the earth and becomes interrupted when it rotates into the time zone of the $+$ to $-\Delta H$ discontinuity.

The sudden shifts discussed above are aceompanied by increases in negative bay intensity and are undoubtedly associated with auroral break-ups. A more complete discussion of the time morphology of these events and other features is beyond the scope of this presentation.

F. Additional Comments.

(1) Although intensity vs. location in pattern has been largely ignored in the above discussion, one feature that appears consistently which has apparently not been noted previously should be mentioned. This is the persistence of the positive bay $(+\Delta H)$ disturbance for sometime after a negative bay has largely decayed following an active period. Figure 8 is a typical example. Figure 7 also gives some indication of this behavior, although in this case there is also a local time shift in the region of maximum negative bay activity.

(2) Examination of Figures 5–8 illustrates the nearly identical behavior of the polar cap disturbance at Thule and Resolute Bay. This is a general condition which appears to become invalid only during quiet times or periods of weak disturbance. The disturbance at Godhavn often duplicates that of Thule and Resolute Bay. These features have been noted previously by FAIRFIELD (1963). An additional feature of this stable polar cap behavior is that the perpendicular to the Thule and Resolute Bay disturbance vector consistently intersects the nighttime electrojet region either at the $+\Delta H$ to $-\Delta H$ local time discontinuity or to the positive bay $(+\Delta H)$ side of this discontinuity within several hours of the local time at the discontinuity.

(3) Considerable insight into disturbance and auroral mechanisms might be obtained if one could determine the local time and latitude where a disturbance begins at high latitudes. It has frequently been implied that a disturbance begins with the sudden onset of a negative bay. This is a misleading concept. Both the film discussed above and auroral studies (e.g., HEPPNER, 1954) show that the sudden onset or rapid growth of a negative bay is a feature which occurs within a previously existing disturbance pattern. One must thus look at the transition from very quiet periods to disturbed periods if a point of origin is to be found. The initial study of the film has not revealed a point of origin; in fact, the impression is obtained that there is usually a slow growth, not particularly confined to either the polar cap or a given sector. This point and others will be treated in greater detail following more detailed studies incorporating the film technique.

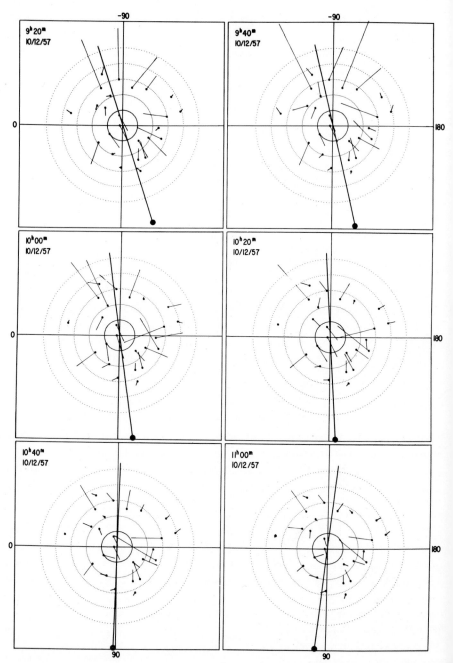

FIGURE 8. Disturbance vectors at 20 min. intervals 09:20 to 11:00, October 12, 1957.

Acknowledgment   Computer and plotter programming of the film display was performed by Mr. Herbert Gillis. For this work and his general assistance in the data preparation I am highly appreciative.

References

AKASOFU, S.-I., 1965, Univ. of Iowa, Report 65–37 (to be published).
AKASOFU, S.-I., CHAPMAN, S., and MENG, C. I., 1965, *J. Atmospheric Terrest. Phys.* **27,** 1275.
AKASOFU, S.-I., KIMBALL, D. S., and MENG, C. I., 1965, *J. Atmospheric Terrest. Phys.* **27,** 173.
AKASOFU, S.-I., KIMBALL, D. S., and MENG, C. I., 1966, *J. Atmospheric Terrest. Phys.* (to be published).
ALFVEN, H., 1966, ESRO Colloquium, Stockholm, November 1965 (to be published *Sp. Sci. Rev*).
AXFORD, W. I. and HINES, C. O., 1961, *Can. J. Phys.* **39,** 1433.
BOND, F. R., 1960, *Australian J. Phys.* **13,** 477.
CHAPMAN, S. and BARTELS, J., 1940, *Geomagnetism*, Oxford Univ. Press.
CHAPMAN, S., 1961, *Studia Geophys. Geod.* **5,** 30.
CHREE, C., 1913, *Quart. J. Roy. Meteorol. Soc.*, London, **39,** 231.
DAVIS, L. R. and WILLIAMSON, J. M., 1966, *Radiation Trapped in the Earth's Magnetic Field*, (Ed. B. M. MCCORMAC)., D. Reidel Publishing Co.
DAVIS, T. N., 1962, *J. Geophys. Res.* **67,** 59.
DAVIS, T. N., 1963, *J. Geophys. Res.* **68,** 4447.
DAVIS, T. N. and SUGIURA, M., 1966, *J. Geophys. Res.* **71,** 785.
DUNGEY, J. W., 1961, *Phys. Rev. Letters.* **6,** 47.
FAIRFIELD, D. H., 1963, *J. Geophys. Res.* **68,** 3589.
FEJER, J. A., 1963, *J. Geophys. Res.* **68,** 2147.
FELDSTEIN, Y. I., 1966, *Planetary Space Sci.* **14,** 121.
FUKUSHIMA, N., 1953, *J. Faculty Sci.*, Univ. of Tokyo, **8,** 293.
HARANG, L., 1946, *Geofys. Publ.* **16,** No. 12; *Terr. Mag.* **51,** 353.
HARANG, L., 1951, *The Aurorae*, John Wiley & Sons, Inc., New York.
HEPPNER, J. P., 1958, Thesis, Calif. Inst. of Tech., 1954, Defence Research Board, Canada, Report No. DR135.
KONRADI, A., 1966, Goddard Space Flight Center, Document X-611-66-332, July.
LASSEN, K., 1963, *Publ. Dan. Meteorol. Inst.*, No. 16, Charlottenhund.
MCILWAIN, C. E., 1966, Presentation and Abstract, AGU Annual Meeting, April.
NAGATA, T., 1950, *J. Geophys. Res.* **55,** 127.
NAGATA, T. and IIJIMA, T., 1964, *J. Geomag. and Geoel.* **16,** 210.
PIDDINGTON, J. H., 1963, *Planetary Space Sci.* **11,** 451.
SILSBEE, H. C. and VESTINE, E. H., 1942, *Terr. Mag.* **47,** 195.
STAGG, J. M. and PATON, J., 1939, *Nature* **143,** 941.
TAYLOR, H. E. and HONES, E. W., 1965, *J. Geophys. Res.* **70,** 3605.
VESTINE, E. H., LANGE, I., LAPORTE, L., and SCOTT, W. E., 1947, Carnegie Inst. of Washington, Report 580.
WELLS, H. W., 1947, *Terr. Mag.* **52,** 315.

Discussion

It was noted that at times it appeared as though there are magnetic field disturbances originating in the auroral zone near midnight, and at other times they appear to start in other regions. Heppner replied that this has not been thoroughly examined, and is one facet of the problem that will require a detailed investigation. It is not yet obvious where the disturbances begin. One also gets the general impression that the level of activity increases everywhere. However, it is clear that disturbances do not start with a large negative bay; there is always a pattern developed or being developed before the sharp onset of the negative bay occurs. Much additional study is required before the understanding of this phenomenon will be improved.

Akasofu pointed out that the vertical components of the magnetic field fluctuations were not accounted for, and that they do not necessarily change in the same manner as the horizontal components. A pictorial presentation of a three-dimensional figure in two dimensions does present some difficulty, but Heppner thinks very little is lost in this presentation.

Akasofu pointed out that the major disagreement with Heppner concerns the eastward ionospheric current which flows in the afternoon sector of the auroral zone. Heppner seems to support a current system with a pair of jet currents: an eastward jet in the afternoon sector of the auroral zone and a westward jet in the morning sector. The eastward current produces a positive change $(+\Delta H)$ in the horizontal component, and in the westward current, a negative change $(-\Delta H)$. On the other hand, Akasofu proposes that a westward polar jet flows along the oval band and that the eastward current in the afternoon sector is the return current from the westward jet current.

Akasofu stated that the observed correlation of positive bays with summer time can be explained by assuming that the ionospheric conductivity in the afternoon sector of the auroral zone is mainly controlled by the solar radiation and not by energetic particle precipitation. Heppner states that positive bays occur in winter time as well as summertime and that this point is meaningless.

Akasofu also suggested that the magnetic field disturbance picture is incomplete because of the small number of observatories at latitudes corresponding to the auroral oval (70-75°). Heppner listed about six stations in this region, and noted that the closer one gets to the pole, fewer stations are needed to cover the area. The observations for sites close together tend to follow each other closely, although they do not appear to be "locked in" as those in the polar cap region. However, Akasofu noted that magnetic records from the IGY north-south chain of stations in Alaska show that an intense westward current exists when a positive change is observed in the auroral zone in the afternoon sector. Also, if observation from the two highest latitude observatories, Barrow and Barter Island, was absent, an entirely different conclusion might be possible. Heppner used the data only from College and Sitka in the Alaskan sector. As the night progressed, the region of negative bay expanded toward the equator. As the morning progressed, the negative bays became less intense in the auroral zone stations, with the opposite being true at Barrow and Barter Islands. This cannot be explained by the conventional current system but by the supposition that the earth rotates under the westward polar electrojet of changing intensities along the auroral oval. The model by Akasofu can combine the results of the two types of study of polar magnetic storms, namely, the SD analysis and the spiral analysis, into a single picture. Heppner noted that the distribution of stations in the Scandinavia-Western USSR sector was even more ideal for study of this point than the distribution in Alaska.

Akasofu could not understand Heppner's current system, wherein the westward current extends into the polar cap, rather than being terminated suddenly in the midnight sector. Heppner suggests an intense return current from the westward polar jet to both the polar cap and the middle low latitude belt. However, it is rather difficult to understand the lack of the return current from the extended westward jet toward lower latitudes. It seems much more reasonable to Akasofu to infer the existence of such a return current and unreasonable to claim that the entire eastward current in the afternoon sector is driven independently from the westward electrojet without giving any specific reason for the lack of the lower latitude return current from the extended jet. It is also difficult to understand why the westward current is terminated essentially in the late evening sector, since a high conductive region of the ionosphere extends along the auroral oval toward the day sector.

IONOSPHERIC IMPLICATIONS OF
AURORA AND AIRGLOW STUDIES

Lance Thomas

S.R.C. Radio and Space Research Station,
Ditton Park, Slough, Bucks.

I. Introduction

During the past decade there has been considerable progress in the experimental methods of studying the upper atmosphere and of recording radiations from the sun. These have led to corresponding advances in our knowledge of the ionized regions — the ionosphere. It can be claimed that the essential features of the formation of the ionosphere are understood (c.f. YONEZAWA, 1966). There are, however, a number of problems concerned with the absolute rates of certain chemical reactions, the presence of minor neutral constituents, the importance of ionization produced by corpuscular radiation, and the effects of thermal nonequilibrium between electrons, ions, and neutral gas in the F region. Furthermore, the ionospheric layers show marked seasonal anomalies which seem to indicate marked changes in atmospheric composition. The effects of magnetic disturbances are poorly understood (RATCLIFFE and WEEKES, 1960). The purpose of the present article is to draw attention to some pertinent results derived from aurora and airglow studies (c.f. reviews by CHAMBERLAIN, 1961; KRASSOVSKY, 1964; KRASSOVSKY and SHEFOV, 1965) and to indicate their bearing on these ionospheric problems.

The principal auroral and airglow features associated with the F, E, and D regions of the ionosphere will be discussed in Sections 2, 3 and 4 respectively, and an attempt will be made to indicate how our knowledge of these features and their interpretation contribute to our understanding of the aeronomy and ionization processes of the appropriate ionospheric region. For convenience, the auroral and airglow features associated with a given region will be considered together, but this does not imply that there is no physical distinction between them. Finally, in Section 5 the information derived from aurora and airglow studies will be used to consider the energy input into the ionosphere and the possible importance of a source of ionization at nighttime in middle latitudes.

2. F Region

λ6300 emission of O

Early observations of the λ6300 ($^3P_2 - {}^1D_2$) emission of O showed that the intensity variations were similar to the electron density changes in the F2 layer, and subsequent observations by BARBIER (1959) have demonstrated that the emission originates at F region heights. Rocket observations, as reported by TOUSEY (1956), indicate that little emission occurs from heights below 160 km, but SEATON (1958) has shown that this is to be expected on the basis of collisional deactivation of the O(^1D) state.

BARBIER (1957) found that the red line intensity was related to the parameters of the F region in a manner consistent with the proposal by BATES (1946) that the O(^1D) state could be excited during the dissociative recombination of molecular ions. More recent studies have confirmed this result for several of the red line features distinguished by BARBIER (1961) at middle and low latitudes. Dissociative recombination forms part of a two stage electron loss process in the F region beginning with reactions between O$^+$ ions and either O_2 or N_2 gases:

$$O^+ + O_2 \rightarrow O_2^+ + O \qquad (1a)$$

$$O_2^+ + e \rightarrow O^* + O^{**} + 6.9 \text{ eV} \qquad (1b)$$

$$O^+ + N_2 \rightarrow NO^+ + N \qquad (2a)$$

$$NO^+ + e \rightarrow N^* + O^* + 2.7 \text{ eV} \qquad (2b)$$

the asterisks indicating that the atoms might be left in excited states. In the F2 region, reactions (a) are slower than the corresponding reactions (b) and therefore govern the rate of loss of ionization.

The energy yield of (1b) is sufficient to provide both O(^1D) and O(^1S) terms whereas that of (2b) can provide either O(^1D) and N(^4S) or O(^3P) and N(^2D). Thus, in principle, both (1b) and (2b) can give rise to red line emission and it has been customary to take into account both reactions. It is to be noted, however, that DALGARNO and WALKER (1964) have pointed out that production of O(^1D) and N(^4S) in the dissociative recombination of NO$^+$(X$^1\Sigma^+$) is unlikely because spin is not conserved.

A generalized theory of the excitation of the O(^1D) state in dissociative recombinations (1b), (2b) has been formulated recently by PETERSON et al. (1966) who took account of cascading from O(^1S) to O(^1D) states and collisional deactivation of O(^1D); they included reactions (2b) on the assumption that O(^1D) can be formed by deactivation of N(^2D) in collision with O(^3P). From an application of this theory to ionospheric measurements and λ6300 data at Hawaii (21°N, 156°W), PETERSON and STEIGER (1966) have demonstrated that only a small proportion of the recombinations (10% at 300 km) is effective in producing a photon of 6300Å. Moreover, while a part of the λ6300 emission varies in accordance with the variations in height, shape, and electron density of the F region, a background emission persists which is fairly constant during a given night but might vary considerably from one night to another. A less detailed analysis by BARBIER (1964) gave similar results. Peterson and Steiger point out that the background component is partially explained by contamination by OH bands and other extraneous light. It is possible, however, that it represents a small energy source as invoked to explain the observation at slightly higher latitudes that the electron temperature at nighttime in the F region exceeds that of the neutral gas (WILLMORE, 1964; BRACE et al., 1965).

PETERSON et al. (1966) assumed in their analysis that movements of molecular ions could be ignored. However, radio observations often show very large, rapid changes in the height of maximum ionization, and cases have been found of the whole layer being moved downward near the equator (VAN ZANDT, private communication, 1965). As might be expected on the basis of the recombination mechanism, BARBIER et al. (1962) found that the height changes and λ6300 intensities at Hawaii were negatively correlated. YOSHIZAKI (1965) has found that movements of ionization cannot be ignored in comparisons of F region and λ6300 data near the magnetic equator. It is now clear that the "tropical arcs," i.e., the two zones of maximum intensity of λ6300 located at 15° magnetic latitude North and South (BARBIER and GLAUME, 1962), are related to the well-known equatorial anomaly in the F region in which the latitude variation of critical frequencies shows a minimum near the magnetic equator and maxima in the vicinity of the tropical arcs. Recent theoretical studies by BRAMLEY and PEART (1965) and HANSON and MOFFETT (1965) have shown that the ionospheric anomaly probably arises from the vertical movement of ionization from above the magnetic equator and its subsequent diffusion down the geomagnetic lines of force to lower altitudes North and South of the equator. Detailed comparisons of ionospheric and airglow data near the equator must take account of the effect of such vertical movements on the molecular ion concentrations.

While dissociative recombination certainly contributes to all red line features in the airglow and aurora, other mechanisms must sometimes be of comparable or greater importance. Attempts to explain mid-latitude red arcs (c.f. ROACH and ROACH, 1964) on the basis of dissociative recombination alone (e.g. KING and ROACH, 1961) require rate coefficients and molecular densities which imply a much faster decay rate for the arc than is observed (REES, 1961), and also prohibitively large electron loss rates in the F regions. Similarly, DALGARNO and WALKER (1964) have suggested that the dayglow intensity predicted by BRANDT (1958) on the basis of dissociative recombination and photodissociation of O_2 in the Schumann-Runge continuum cannot be reconciled with recent observations by NOXON (1963) and ZIPF and FASTIE (1963). As another process involving sunlight, DALGARNO and WALKER (1964) propose that excitation by photoelectrons might be important, and DALGARNO

(1964) and COLE (1965a) believe that such electrons arriving from the sunlit conjugate area (c.f. CARLSON, 1966) could account for the predawn enhancement of the red line (BARBIER, 1959). DALGARNO and WALKER (1964) also point out that the great variability of the dayglow red line intensity observed by NOXON (1964a) could be due to excitation by thermal electrons; this mechanism also forms the basis for current ideas on the generation of mid-latitude red arcs.

It might be expected that the changes in electron temperature invoked to explain the variations of λ6300 emission in the dayglow would be associated with inverse changes in the peak electron density of the F region due to effects on the ambipolar diffusion rate (EVANS, 1965; THOMAS, 1966). Furthermore, the changes in the rate of the ion-atom interchange reaction (2a) with electron temperature arising out of vibrational excitation of N_2 (SCHMELTEKOPF et al., 1966; THOMAS and NORTON, 1966) might be expected to enhance these electron density changes. In fact, Noxon found no evidence that the λ6300 emission and electron density changes were correlated, but it seems likely that other factors are also involved because marked changes in atmospheric temperature have been revealed by the Doppler broadening of the red line in the dayglow (JARRETT and HOEY, 1964).

No direct measurements of electron temperature have been taken in mid-latitude red arcs, but the increased scintillation effects imposed on radio signals transmitted through such arcs (ROACH, 1963) might be some evidence of enhanced temperatures. Furthermore, the character of the oblique radio echo reported to be associated with arcs (KING and ROACH, 1961 and private communication, 1965) might also be related to the presence of hot electrons. It appears that the reduction in the peak electron density of the F2 region associated with these arcs is not confined to the location of the arc but can occur over a range of latitudes about the arc. In fact, it seems that the arc represents a particular situation within a broad latitude range in which the F region is disturbed. The significance of this result awaits more information on the F region effects, but it could indicate a different dependence on electron temperature of the excitation of $O(^1D)$ and of the electron loss process which is related, at least in part, to the degree of vibrational excitation of N_2.

The mechanisms proposed for heating electrons in mid-latitude red arcs (DALGARNO, 1964; MEGILL and CARLETON, 1964; COLE, 1965b) should themselves imply interesting effects in the F region. Dalgarno suggests that the heat is provided by a flux of electrons of energy about 400 eV which requires an input of about 0.5 ergs cm^{-2} sec^{-1} for a red line intensity of 10kR; such a flux would contribute a substantial electron production, and give rise to a noticeable enhancement of the First Negative band system of N_2^+, but no such enhancement has been observed (ROACH and ROACH, 1963). MEGILL and CARLETON (1964) have considered that an electric field of magnitude about 1mV/cm is responsible for increasing the electron temperature. Such an electric field would give rise to very large movements of the F region at night as are often observed during disturbed conditions. However, COLE (1965b) has put forward arguments against such an electric field mechanism and proposes as an alternative that heat is conducted from the magnetosphere after this has been energized by compression during a magnetic storm. This compression is also believed to cause an increase in F region electron content over an arc but no such increase has been reported. As Cole points out, the enhancement of the red line should be observable at all local times but observations by NOXON (1964a) at Cambridge, Massachusetts, during 1962–63 showed no evidence for a relationship between the red line enhancement in daytime and magnetic activity. However, very few red arcs were observed over North America during this period, and, furthermore, the latitude to be expected for the arc in daytime is not clear.

First Negative system of N_2^+

Another important feature of emissions from F region heights is the First Negative band system of N_2^+ observed in high auroral rays and in twilight airglow (HUNTEN, 1963). These emissions are related to the N_2 content of the upper atmosphere and to the distribution of N_2^+ ions. The rotational structure of the bands in sunlit rays demonstrates that the emission results from fluorescence rather than from simultaneous ionization and excitation by corpuscular radiation (KRASSOVSKY, 1964). The observations of sunlit rays have revealed N_2^+ concentrations in excess of 10^5 cm^{-3} at several hundred km altitude and it has been suggested that such densities require an enhancement of N_2 concentrations at great heights during disturbed conditions. A similar suggestion was made by KING and ROACH (1961) in their explanation of mid-latitude red arcs, and by SEATON (1956) and KING (1962) to account for the depletion of F region ionization observed at middle and high latitudes during magnetic disturbances. Some confirmation of such changes has been obtained from a satellite-borne mass spectrometer experiment (REBER and NICOLET, 1965).

Attempts have been made to relate the intensities of the First Negative band system of N_2^+ at twilight with those expected from photoionization and resonance scattering (CHAMBERLAIN and SAGAN, 1960; SWIDER, 1965a). More recently, BROADFOOT and HUNTEN (private communication, 1965) have postulated a continuous source of ionization which could be photoelectrons produced locally or at the sunlit conjugate area. Such photoelectrons would require an energy of about 19 eV. This mechanism will account for the similar intensities of the 0-0 band at λ3914 observed in morning and evening periods (SWINGS and NICOLET, 1949) and, thereby, removes the need for invoking a nighttime source of ionization. The enhancement of the twilight λ3914 emission during magnetic disturbances noted by DUFAY and DUFAY (1947) could again result from changes in atmospheric composition, as proposed for the sunlit rays.

3. E Region

LYTLE and HUNTEN (1962) have noted that auroras located below 130 km do not exhibit fluorescence of λ3914; therefore, the scattering N_2^+ ions seem to be concentrated above this height. A similar conclusion can be drawn from the high rotational temperatures of the N_2^+ bands observed in twilight by DUFAY (1953). These observations and the results derived from the daytime rocket flight of ZIPF and FASTIE (1964) have indicated a rapid loss of N_2^+ ions at E region heights. It is expected that this loss process involves charge-exchange and atom-ion interchange reactions with O, O_2, and N, and from a recent analysis by FERGUSON et al. (1965), it appears that the reaction

$$N_2^+ + O \rightarrow NO^+ + N$$

is the most rapid loss process, imposing a lifetime of about 0.25 sec for the N_2^+ ions.

Observations of the First Negative system of N_2^+ in auroras can be interpreted directly in terms of the N_2^+ production rate integrated along the line of sight (OMHOLT, 1959). From the observed correlation between the intensity of the 0-1 band at λ4278 and the maximum electron density in the E layer found from ionospheric records, OMHOLT (1960) has derived an effective recombination coefficient of 10^{-6} cm^{-3} sec^{-1}. This is somewhat larger than the values derived from E region studies carried out at lower latitudes (c.f. SWIDER, 1965b) and those expected from laboratory measurements on the major ions present (BIONDI, 1964; GUNTON and SHAW, 1965).

Another important emission originating at E region heights in aurora, and at both E and F heights in airglow, is the λ5577 ($^1D-^1S$) of O. It is believed that the $O(^1S)$ in auroras originates from excitation by secondary electrons (SEATON, 1954), whereas the airglow emission at F region heights is produced by dissociative recombination of O_2^+, and at E region heights by 3-body association of O (CHAPMAN, 1931).

$$O + O + O \rightarrow O_2 + O(^1S).$$

In view of the correlation found between E layer electron densities and the First Negative band system of N_2^+, it is not surprising that a similar correlation has been found for auroral λ5577 emission (OGUTI, 1960). Little study has been made of the correlation of λ5577 airglow emission and the E layer, but McCAULLEY and HOUGH (1959) did report an association with a layer detected by low frequency soundings in the height range of 90–110 km.

An intriguing feature of the middle latitude ionosphere is the frequent occurrence of an intermittent layer in the height range 100 to 110 km — the sporadic E layer (SMITH, 1957). In recent years a theory has been produced to explain this layer by a redistribution of E layer ionization under the action of a wind shear operating in the presence of the geomagnetic field (c.f. BOWHILL, 1966 and papers therein). It has been found, however, that this theory cannot account for sufficient ionization to maintain the layer if the recombination coefficients of the major ionic constituents are of the order of 10^{-7} cm^{-3} sec^{-1}. Attention has recently been drawn to the possible importance of the slowly recombining meteoric ions in the E region, as observed by ISTOMIN (1963), because it has been shown that the electron density in the layer is determined by the ion with the smallest recombination rate. The observation of the resonance lines of Ca ions in twilight spectra by VALLANCE JONES (1958) and DUFAY (1958) is clearly relevant to these ideas. It would seem that a study to correlate this and perhaps other emissions with the occurrence of sporadic E layers would be profitable.

4. D Region

The entry of high energy particles into the high latitude ionosphere is considered to be responsible for two distinct D region disturbances as revealed by the anomalous attenuation imposed on radio waves — the PCA and auroral absorption events (REID and COLLINS, 1959). During a PCA event, 5-300 MeV protons arriving in the interval between the solar flare and the SC of the subsequent magnetic storm produce ionization mainly below 70 km and give rise to auroral type emissions (c.f. BAILEY, 1964). SANDFORD (1963) has found that the First Negative 0-0 band of N_2^+ at $\lambda 3914$ is the most intense emission, having a maximum brightness at a height of 65 km, but $H\beta$ and $\lambda 5577$ of O were also observed. From the 4 kR intensity of $\lambda 3914$ emission observed during the November 12, 1960 event, an integrated N_2^+ production rate of about 6×10^{10} cm^{-2} sec^{-1} is deduced using the results of DALGARNO et al. (1965). On the assumption that this production is distributed over an altitude range of about 50 km, one finds an average production rate of about 10^4 electrons cm^{-3} sec^{-1}, which is reasonably consistent with that required to explain the radio observation (c.f. REID, 1961). The second type of event is associated with certain auroras (HEPPNER et al., 1952) and is considered to be caused by ionization in the upper part of the D region. CHAPMAN and LITTLE (1957) have suggested that bremsstrahlung radiation could cause a part of this ionization, and in this case one might expect a relatively poor correlation between individual auroral features and the auroral absorption.

It is, perhaps, at middle latitudes that studies of emissions might make the greatest contribution to our understanding of the D region. According to the model proposed by NICOLET and AIKIN (1960), the ionization in the 70–85 km height range during quiet conditions is produced by the photoionization of NO by solar Lyman-α radiation. The concentration of this minor constituent is, therefore, of major importance. A recent observation by BARTH (1964) of the fluorescence of NO molecules in the ultraviolet dayglow indicated a column density of about 10^{14} cm^{-2} which corresponds to a density in the D region two or three orders larger than that adopted by Nicolet and Aikin. It is worth noting that such a large content is consistent with that deduced by KRASSOVSKY and SHEFOV (1965) and NICOLET (1965) from the green airglow continuum believed to be produced in the reaction (KRASSOVSKY, 1951):

$$NO + O \rightarrow NO_2 + h\nu.$$

The concentration of NO in the D region and the resulting implications concerning the electron loss process are currently the subject of some controversy (c.f. AIKIN et al., 1964; DONAHUE, 1966), and further information provided by airglow studies would be invaluable.

The concentration of NO in the D region is considered to be determined by the reactions (c.f. NICOLET, 1965)

$$N + O_2 \rightarrow NO + O, \tag{3}$$

$$NO + N \rightarrow N_2 + O. \tag{4}$$

Laboratory measurements have shown that the rate coefficient of (3) is very temperature dependent and it would, therefore, be useful to inquire whether the D region electron density is correlated with atmospheric temperatures in the 70–100 km height range. Such temperature measurements could be provided by observations of the Doppler broadening of the λ 5577 line or by the rotational structure of the OH bands (HUNTEN, 1961). In such a correlation study, care must be taken to eliminate temperature changes resulting from changes in altitude of the emitting region.

The information that might be obtained on dynamical processes in the atmosphere from airglow studies could be of major importance in understanding the behavior of the D region of the ionosphere. Several types of ionospheric measurements have demonstrated the probable role of meteorological influences; HF radio waves experience anomalously large attenuation on groups of days in winter (APPLETON and PIGGOTT, 1954), and the day-to-day changes in this attenuation are correlated with changes in stratospheric temperature (BOSSOLASCO and ELENA, 1963; SHAPLEY and BEYNON, 1965); D region electron densities show far more irregularity in winter than summer (BELROSE et al., 1966); phase heights of 16 kc/sec signals show anomalous effects (BELROSE, 1958) and the amplitude of LF signals are anomalously large in winter STRAKER, 1955); the electron collision frequency shows changes within a month (AIKIN et al., 1964) and with season (PIGGOTT and THRANE, 1966). It is evident from the above discussion of the formation of NO that changes in NO concentration arising out of changes in temperature observed at D region heights (NORDBERG, et al., 1965) could contribute to these ionospheric effects. However, the circulation and mixing of the atmosphere in the 70–100 km height range indicated by rapid changes in the intensities of certain airglow emissions and their seasonal-latitude variations are perhaps more important.

The OH bands which represent one of the most powerful airglow emissions are attributed to the formation of excited hydroxyl radicals from collisions of

H atoms with O_3 (BATES and NICOLET, 1950) or vibrationally excited O_2 (KRASSOVSKY, 1956);

$$O_3 + H \rightarrow (OH)^* + O_2$$

$$(O_2)^* + H \rightarrow (OH)^* + O$$

$$(OH)^* \rightarrow OH + h\nu.$$

There is some uncertainty about whether the O_3 or $(O_2)^*$ concentrations near 90 km are sufficient to account for the observed intensities (KRASSOVSKY and SHEFOV, 1965 HUNT, 1966), and it seems that the increased intensities observed in winter (WALLACE, 1962) imply some atmospheric circulation and perhaps vertical movements. Moreover, it has been suggested by NAKAMURA (1961) that the intensity changes observed in a single night could result from changes in O_3 and H concentrations resulting from vertical movements. HURUHATA (1965) has found that the daily variation in OH intensity is related to the features on 10 mb weather maps. Dynamical processes have also been invoked to explain the anomalous seasonal variations of 1.58μ twilight emissions arising from the 0-1 band of the transition ($^1\Delta_g{}^3\Sigma_g-$) of O_2 (NOXON and VALLANCE JONES, 1962) the anomalous seasonal variation (HUNTEN, 1956) and irregular variation (BULLOCK and HUNTEN, 1961) of free Na as revealed by the twilight emission of the $\lambda5890$, $\lambda5896$ doublet; and the seasonal-latitude variations of the $\lambda5577$ emission of O (ROACH, 1955; HURUHATA and NAKAMURA, 1958). With regard to the latter emission it has been shown by TOHMATSU and NAGATA (1963) and HESSTVEDT (1966) that the inclusion of the effects of vertical movements of about 1 cm sec^{-1} and of horizontal movements of about 10 m sec^{-1} could seriously modify the intensities expected on the basis of photochemistry and 3-body association of atomic oxygen (CHAPMAN, 1931). A circulation of O together with subsidence has been proposed by KELLOGG (1961) as a source of heating the polar mesosphere in winter. Such heating could itself influence D region chemical processes. REID (1966) has, in addition, postulated that the O transported downward into the D region by subsidence and eddy diffusion could be involved in a series of dissociative detachment processes with the negative ions O^-, O_2^-, O_3^-, thereby liberating sufficient electrons to explain the relatively large radio wave absorption observed at nighttime during PCA events, and certain other high latitude radio observations. It seems evident that the information on dynamical processes in the atmosphere derived from either airglow or D region studies will be of mutual benefit to both disciplines.

5. Energy Input Into the Ionosphere

Observations of twilight emissions can provide an estimate of the energy input into the ionosphere in the form of hard ultraviolet solar radiation and will therefore supplement more direct measurements using rockets. The twilight enhancement of $\lambda 10830$ of He first observed by SHEFOV (1961) has been attributed to fluorescence of metastable He in the 2^3S state. SHEFOV (1962) has suggested that at heights below 1000 km this metastable will be excited by electrons with energy of about 25 eV which are produced during photoionization by solar radiations of wavelengths less than 304Å. Observations of this emission can therefore yield information on the intensity of hard solar UV radiation, and corresponding information could be obtained from studies of the $\lambda 6300$ emission of O and of the First Negative band system of N_2^+ at twilight (c.f. pp. 96-97).

Measurements of atmospheric temperatures can be derived from observations of the Doppler broadening of certain atomic lines and from the rotational or vibrational structure of molecular bands (HUNTEN, 1961). Such measurements deduced from auroral and airglow features have shown marked heating effects near the auroral zones, and these have been attributed to the entry of corpuscular radiation and perhaps hydromagnetic waves. In principle, these temperature measurements can be used to estimate the energy input into the atmosphere (MULYARCHIK and SCHEGLOV, 1963; DALGARNO, 1964), but difficulties arise in their interpretation. More direct information can be obtained from observations of auroral intensity or from direct measurements of particle fluxes. Thus, for an IBC III aurora the total intensity of the First Negative system of N_2^+ is reported as 165 kR (CHAMBERLAIN, 1961). This alone corresponds to an energy input of several hundred ergs $cm^{-2}sec^{-1}$, and corresponding amounts are present in the infrared and far ultraviolet wavelength ranges. Such energy inputs have been confirmed in direct measurements of electron flux in auroras (McILWAIN, 1960).

Little direct information is available on corpuscular fluxes in the polar areas in the absence of auroras or at middle and low latitudes, but the presence or absence of these fluxes can be inferred from the intensities of the First Negative band system of N_2^+. Such fluxes at middle latitudes have been invoked to explain the persistence of the nighttime F region (ANTONAVA and IVANOV-KHOLODNY, 1961), and to explain the observation that the electron temperature at nighttime in the F region exceeds that of the neutral gas (WILLMORE, 1964; BRACE et al., 1965). The pertinent nightglow data have been summarized and interpreted by DALGARNO (1964). When account is taken of recent revisions in cross-section data (DALGARNO et al., 1965), it is found that energy fluxes of up to 0.5 ergs $cm^{-2}sec^{-1}$ are possible at subauroral latitudes. Such energy fluxes could represent an important source of ionization. At lower latitudes, it seems that the energy flux is probably less than 10^{-2} ergs $cm^{-2}sec^{-1}$, and a similar upper limit is indicated by a rocket observation at Wallops Island (O'BRIEN et al., 1965).

The ground-based observations of emissions give no indication of the level in the atmosphere at which the energy is deposited, and it is not clear whether this energy would contribute to F region ionization. In fact, the rocket flight described by O'BRIEN *et al.* (1965) showed that most of the 5R emission of $\lambda 3914$ observed above 85 km probably originated between 100–150 km, and the corresponding energy would, therefore, contribute to the nighttime E region. On the assumption that this emission is emitted uniformly over this height range, it is estimated that the emission implies an electron production of about 14 electrons $cm^{-3}sec^{-1}$. Such a rate would be consistent with electron densities of about $10^3 cm^{-3}$ observed at middle latitudes during nighttime (SMITH, 1962), and the dissociative recombination rate of $10^{-7} cm^{-3} sec^{-1}$ expected from laboratory measurements and studies of the daytime E region.

The presence of Lyman-α radiation in the nightglow (KUPPERIAN *et al.*, 1959) provides another possible ionization source for the nighttime E region. SWIDER (1965b) has shown that the intensity of 2–6 kR (KUPPERIAN *et al.*, 1959; DONAHUE and FASTIE, 1964) will maintain an electron density of about $10^3 cm^{-3}$ provided the NO density is near $10^7 cm^{-3}$.

Early ground-based observations of the rotational temperatures of OH bands seemed to indicate an increase of temperature with latitude north of about 50°N (c. f. WALLACE, 1962). This result together with the large temperature fluctuations sometimes indicated by these bands and $\lambda 5577$ line widths, could have been interpreted as large energy inputs at D region heights. However, it now seems doubtful whether such a latitude variation exists (c.f. NOXON, 1964b). The observed temperature fluctuations are believed to have arisen from changes in heights of the emitting layers (c.f. KRASSOVSKY and SHEFOV, 1965).

6. Conclusions and Proposals for Further Study

Perhaps the most obvious advances are to be expected in detailed studies of the relation between $\lambda 6300$ of O and changes of the F2 region. For instance, red line features in which dissociative recombination represents the dominant excitation mechanism for $O(^1D)$ should provide further information on electron loss processes and movements of ionization. More detailed F region data within and adjacent to mid-latitude red arcs could contribute to our understanding of ionospheric disturbances and of the arcs themselves and, perhaps, of the more general question of the nature of the associated magnetic storm. The rapid latitude coverage provided by satellites would be ideally suited to this study.

Further insight into the cause of F region disturbances would be obtained if more evidence concerning changes in atmospheric composition were available. The information provided on N_2 densities by observations of the First Negative band system of N_2^+ in sunlit auroral rays and in twilight airglow could serve as a useful supplement to more direct satellite observations.

It is becoming increasingly clear that rocket observations of certain nightglow features can help understand the production sources which seem to be necessary to maintain the nighttime E layer at middle latitudes. Corresponding observations of auroral emissions can usefully supplement the information derived from direct measurements of ionizing electron and proton streams. Moreover, simultaneous rocket observations of the height variation of the First Negative band system of N_2^+ and of the electron density in an aurora could provide reliable estimates of the effective recombination coefficient.

Information provided by auroral or airglow studies on minor constituents present in the D region could be of major importance to the understanding of this region. While D region studies have to date concentrated on the importance of NO it seems that other constituents could also be directly involved in the behavior of the region. Moreover, the information on dynamical processes that can be derived from observations of the emissions from such constituents could help in understanding the meteorological character of this region.

Acknowledgment   This paper is published by permission of the Director of the Radio and Space Research Station of the Science Research Council.

References

AIKIN, A. C., KANE, J. A. and TROIM, J., 1964, *J., Geophys. Res.* **69,** 4621.
ANTONOVA, L. A. and IVANOV-KHOLODNY, G. S., 1961, *Space Research* 2, (Ed. H. C. van de Hulst, C de Jager, and A. F. MOORE), North Holland Publishing Co., Amsterdam, 981.
APPLETON, E. V. and PIGGOTT, W. R., 1954, *J. Atmospheric Terrest. Phys.* 5, 141.
BAILEY, D. K., 1964, *Planetary Space Sci.* 12, 495.
BARBIER, D., 1957, *Compt. Rend.* **244,** 2077.
BARBIER, D., 1959, *Ann. Géophys.* **15,** 179.
BARBIER, D., 1961, *Ann. Géophys.* **17,** 3.
BARBIER, D., 1964, *Ann. Géophys.* **20,** 22.
BARBIER, D. and GLAUME, J., 1962, *Planetary Space Sci.* **9,** 133.
BARBIER, D., ROACH, F. E., and STEIGER, W. R., 1962, *J. Nat. Bur. Std.* **66D,** 145.
BARTH, C. A., 1964, *J. Geophys. Res.* **69,** 3301.
BATES, D. R., 1946, *Monthly Notices Roy. Astron. Soc.* **106,** 509.
BATES, D. R. and NICOLET, M., 1950, *J. Geophys. Res.* **55,** 301.
BELROSE, J. S., 1956, Ph.D. Thesis, Cambridge University.
BELROSE, J. S., BOURNE, I. A., and HEWITT, L. W., 1966, *Electron Density Profiles in Ionosphere and Exosphere*, (Ed. by J. Frihagen), North-Holland Publishing Co., Amsterdam, 48.
BIONDI, M. A., 1964, *Ann. Géophys.* **20,** 34.
BOSSOLASCO, M. and ELENA, A., 1963, *Compt. Rend.* **256,** 4491.
BOWHILL, S. A., 1966, *Radio Science* 1, 129.
BRACE, L. H., SPENCER, N. W., and DALGARNO, A., 1965, *Planetary Space Sci.* 13, 647.
BRAMLEY, E. N., and PEART, M., 1965, *J. Atmospheric Terrest. Phys.* 27, 1201.
BRANDT, J. C., 1958, *Astrophys. J.* **128,** 718.
BULLOCK, W. R., and HUNTEN, D. M., 1961, *Can. J. Phys.* **39,** 976.
CARLSON, H. C., 1966, *J. Geophys. Res.* **71,** 195.
CHAMBERLAIN, J. W., 1961, *Physics of the Aurora and Airglow*, Academic Press, New York.
CHAMBERLAIN, J. W. and SAGAN, C., 1960, *Planetary Space Sci.* 2, 157.
CHAPMAN, S., 1931, *Proc. Roy. Soc.* A132, 853.
CHAPMAN, S. and LITTLE, C. G., 1957, *J. Atmospheric Terrest. Phys.* 10, 20.
COLE, K. D., 1965a, *Ann. Géophys.* **21,** 156.
COLE, K. D., 1965b, *J. Geophys. Res.* **70,** 1689.
DALGARNO, A., 1964, *Ann. Géophys.* **20,** 65.
DALGARNO, A., LATIMER, I. L., and McCONKEY, J. W., 1965, *Planetary Space Sci.* 13, 1008.

DALGARNO, A. and WALKER, J. C. G., 1964, *J. Atmos. Sci.*, **21**, 463.
DONAHUE, T. M., 1966, *J. Geophys. Res.* **71**, 2237.
DONAHUE, T. M. and FASTIE, W. G., 1964, *Space Research* **4**, (Ed. by P. MULLER) North-Holland Publishing Co., Amsterdam, 304.
DUFAY, M., 1953, *Ann. Phys.* **8**, 813.
DUFAY, M., 1958, *Ann. Géophys.* **14**, 391.
DUFAY, J. and DUFAY, M., 1947, *Compt. Rend.* **224**, 1834.
EVANS, J. V., 1965, *J. Geophys. Res.* **70**, 1175.
FERGUSON, E. E., FEHSENFELD, F. C., GOLDAN, P. D., and SCHMELTEKOPF, A. L., *J. Geophys. Res.* **70**, 4323.
GUNTON, R. C. and SHAW, T. M., 1965, *Phys. Rev.* **140**, A748.
HANSON, W. B. and MOFFETT, R. J., 1965, *Nature* **206**, 705.
HEPPNER, J. P., BYRNE, E. C., and BELON, A. E., 1952, *J. Geophys. Res.* **57**, 121.
HESSTVEDT, E., 1966, Paper read at WMO-COSPAR Symposium, Vienna, May.
HUNT, B. G., 1966, *J. Geophys. Res.* **71**, 1385.
HUNTEN, D. M., 1956, *The Airglow and the Aurora*, (Ed. E. B. ARMSTRONG and A. DALGARNO), Pergamon Press Ltd., London, 183.
HUNTEN, D. M., 1961, *Ann. Géophys.* **17**, 249.
HUNTEN, D. M , 1963, *Planetary Space. Sci.* **10**, 37.
HURUHATA, M., 1965, *J. Geophys. Res.* **70**, 4927.
HURUHATA, M. and NAKAMURA, J., 1958, *Ann. Géophys.* **14**, 175.
ISTOMIN, V. G., 1963, *Space Research* **3**, (Ed. by W. PRIESTER), North-Holland Publishing Co., Amsterdam, 756.
JARRETT, A. H. and HOEY, M. J., 1964, *Planetary Space Sci.* **12**, 1139.
KELLOGG, W. W., 1961, *J. Meteorol.* **18**, 373.
KING, G. A. M., 1962, *Planetary Space Sci.* **9**, 95.
KING, G. A. M. and ROACH, F. E., 1961, *J. Nat. Bur. Std.* **65D**, 129.
KRASSOVSKY, V. I., 1951, *Doklady AN SSSR*, **78**, 669.
KRASSOVSKY, V. I., 1956, *The Airglow and the Aurora*, (Ed. by E. B. ARMSTRONG and A. DALGARNO), Pergamon Press, London, 193.
KRASSOVSKY, V. I., 1964, *Space Sci. Revs.* **3**, 232.
KRASSOVSKY, V. I. and SHEFOV, N. N., 1965, *Space Sci. Revs.* **4**, 176.
KUPPERIAN, J. E., BYRAM, E. T., and FRIEDMAN, H., 1959, *Planetary Space. Sci.* **1**, 3.
LYTLE, E. A. and HUNTEN, D. M., 1962, *Can. J. Phys.* **40**, 1370.
MCCAULLEY, I. W. and HOUGH, W. S., 1959, *J. Geophys. Res.* **64**, 2307.
MCILWAIN, C. E., 1960, *J. Geophys. Res.* **65**, 2727.
MEGILL, L. R. and CARLETON, N. P., 1964, *J. Geophys. Res.* **69**, 101.
MULYARCHIK, T. M. and SHCHEGLOV, 1963, *Planetary Space Sci.* **10**, 215.
NAKAMURA, M., 1961, *Rept. Ionosph. Space Res. Japan* **15**, 346.
NICOLET, M., 1965, *J. Geophys. Res.* **70**, 691.
NICOLET, M. and AIKIN, A. C., 1960, *J. Geophys. Res.* **65**, 1469.
NORDBERG, W., KATCHEN, L., THEON, J., and SMITH, W. S., 1965, *J. Atmos. Sci* **22**, 611.
NOXON, J. F., 1963, *J. Atmospheric Terrest. Phys.* **25**, 637.
NOXON, J. F., 1964a, *J. Geophys. Res.* **69**, 3245.
NOXON, J. F., 1964b, *J. Geophys. Res.* **69**, 4087.
NOXON, J. F. and VALLANCE JONES, A., 1962, *Nature* **196**, 157.
O'BRIEN, B. J., ALLUM, F. R., and GOLDWIRE, H. C., 1965, *J. Geophys. Res.*, **70**, 161.
OGUTI, T., 1960, *Rept. Ionosph. Space Res., Japan* **14**, 291.
OMHOLT, A., 1959, *Geophys. Publikasjoner* **20**, 1.
OMHOLT, A., 1960, *Electromagnetic Wave Propagation,* (Ed. by M. DESIRANT and J. L. MICHIELS) Academic Press, London, 75.
PETERSON, V. L. and STEIGER, W. R., 1966, *J. Geophys. Res.* **71**, 2267.
PETERSON, V. L., VAN ZANDT, T. E., and NORTON, R. B., 1966, *J. Geophys. Res.* **71**, 2255.
PIGGOTT, W. R. and THRANE, E. 1966, *J. Atmospheric Terrest. Phys.* **28**, 721.
RATCLIFFE, J. A. and WEEKES, K., 1960, *Physics of the Upper Atmosphere*, (Ed. J. A. RATCLIFFE), Academic Press, London, Chapt. IX, 378.
REBER, C. A. and NICOLET, M., 1965, *Planetary Space Sci.* **13**, 617.
REES, M. H., 1961, *Planetary Space Sci.* **8**, 198.

REID, G. C., 1961, *J. Geophys. Res.* **66**, 4071.
REID, G. C., 1966, *Electron Density Profiles in Ionosphere and Exosphere*, (Ed. J. Frihagen), North-Holland Publishing Co., Amsterdam, 17.
REID, G. C., and COLLINS, C., 1959, *J. Atmospheric Terrest. Phys.*, **14**, 63.
ROACH, F. E., 1955, *Ann. Géophys.* **11**, 214.
ROACH, F. E. and ROACH, J. R., 1963, *Planetary Space Sci.* **11**, 523.
ROACH, J. R., 1963, *J. Res. Nat. Bur. Std.* **67D**, 263.
SANDFORD, B. P., 1963, *Planetary Space Sci.* **10**, 195.
SCHMELTEKOPF, A. L., FEHSENFELD, F. C., GILMAN, G. I., and FERGUSON, E. E., 1966, *Planetary Space Sci.*, in press.
SEATON, M. J., 1954, *J. Atmospheric Terrest. Phys.* **4**, 295.
SEATON, M. J., 1956, *J. Atmospheric Terrest. Phys.* **8**, 122.
SEATON, M. J., 1958, *Astrophys. J.* **127**, 67.
SHAPLEY, A. H. and BEYNON, W. J. G., 1965, *Nature* **206**, 1242.
SHEFOV, N. N., 1961, *Astr. Circ. Acad. Sci. USSR.* **222**, 11.
SHEFOV, N. N., 1962, *Ann. Géophys.* **18**, 125.
SMITH, E. K., 1957, *Nat. Bur. Std. Circular 582* (Washington: National Bureau of Standards).
SMITH, L. G., 1962, *Geophys. Corp. Amer. Tech. Rept. 62-1-N*, Bedford, Mass.
STRAKER, T. W., 1955, *Proc. I.E.E. Monograph No. 114.*
SWIDER, W., 1965a, *Planetary Space Sci.* **13**, 529.
SWIDER, W., 1965b, *J. Geophys. Res.* **70**, 4859.
SWINGS, P. and NICOLET, M., 1949, *Astrophys. J.* **109**, 327.
THOMAS, L., 1966, *J. Géophys, Res.* **71**, 1357.
THOMAS, L. and NORTON, R. B., 1966, *J. Geophys. Res.* **71**, 227.
TOHMATSU, T. and NAGATA, T., 1963, *Planetary Space Sci.* **10**, 103.
TOUSEY, R., *Ann. Géophys.* **14**, 186.
VALLANCE JONES, A., 1958, *Ann. Géophys.* **14**, 179.
WALLACE, L., 1962, *J. Atmos. Sci.* **19**, 1.
WILLMORE, A. P., 1964, *Proc. Roy. Soc.* **A231**, 526.
YONEZAWA, T., 1966, *Space Science Revs.* **5**, 3.
YOSHIZAKI, W., 1965, *Rept. Ionosph. Space Res. Japan* **19**, 299.
ZIPF, E. C. and FASTIE, W. G., 1963, *J. Geophys. Res.* **68**, 6208.
ZIPF, E. C. and FASTIE, W. G., 1964, *J. Geophys. Res.* **69**, 2357.

Discussion

The enhanced concentration of ions in sunlit auroras was discussed. It was concluded that it is important to determine if they were produced locally or if they arose from lower altitude heating.

Dr. Blamont raised a question concerning the possibility that the observations of the OI 6300Å red line are influenced by contamination from OH emission. In his measurements of the vertical distribution of oxygen emission, he found layers of OI emission at 90km and 240km, and asserted that at least the 90km layer was contaminated with OH emission; Blamont believes this is a large effect that is usually not considered. Steiger and Peterson agreed that OH could influence their observations, and that it had not been accounted for. Dr. Roach pointed out that the resolution used on Blamont's experiment ($\sim$30Å band pass) was lower than that of the ground based measurements, but the question of OH contamination was left unresolved.

It was also brought out that more direct observations should be made of the electron distribution, with an effort to observe the concentration of nonthermal electrons. The observations of the OI 6300Å line, the He emission, and the N_2^+ emission all yield indirect information about the electron distribution. More direct evidence might consist of electron temperature measurements; these should include directional measurements during nonsunlit periods, to evaluate conjugate effects.

Session

2

OBSERVATIONS I

Dr. A. Vallance Jones
University of Saskatchewan

TWILIGHT OBSERVATIONS

M. Gadsden

Institute for Telecommunication Sciences and Aeronomy
Environmental Science Services Administration
Boulder, Colorado

Introduction

At twilight, the upper atmosphere is available for study under transitional conditions. The photochemical and ionospheric regions of the atmosphere are ending a natural period of prolonged sunlight or darkness: in general, therefore, they are changing at twilight. The progress of the changes can be used to study either the daytime or nighttime condition of the atmosphere by treating the changes as perturbations of a quasi-steady state.

In this review, we shall consider mainly the observational data that have been obtained, leaving the interpretation and theory of atmospheric aerosols, helium, and metallic atoms to the accompanying paper "Interpretation of Twilight Observations." The technique of the twilight observations will be discussed, with comments on the complications in interpretation.

The inherent analytical advantage of twilight rests on the effective probing of the upper atmosphere, with altitude as an independent parameter. When the sun is below the observer's horizon, only part of the atmosphere over the observer above a particular height is directly illuminated. The simplest picture for twilight analysis is shown in Figure 1. The observer, looking out along a slant view, sees only those parts of the atmosphere illuminated above a height h. Allowance for the finite solar angular diameter and Rayleigh scattering leads to an irradiance along the line of sight somewhat as sketched in Figure 1. A more sophisticated analysis involves the consideration, if not inclusion, of several complications of this simple picture. Figure 2 represents contributions by:

A. Refraction

In the optical regions of the spectrum, refraction of radiation amounts to a little over 0.5° when the radiation grazes the surface of the Earth. The grazing ray will be bent approximately 1.1° in the double passage through the atmosphere. This effect is of considerable importance in height determination but leads also to a decrease in the solar irradiance since originally parallel radiation emerging from the atmosphere becomes divergent.

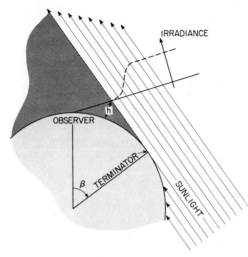

FIGURE 1. The simplest interpretation of twilight observations — a singly scattering Rayleigh atmosphere.

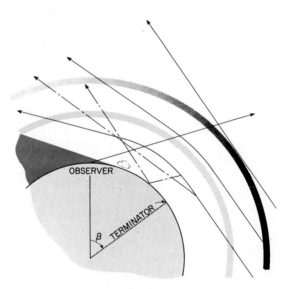

FIGURE 2. Schematic indications of the interfering processes that can occur during twilight.

B. Multiple Rayleigh Scattering

The optical depth of the atmosphere from Rayleigh scattering alone varies from 0.02 (near infrared)–0.5 (near ultraviolet) for vertical incidence. In observing the sky in broad spectral regions, multiple scattering is important; however, a reasonable rule for observations in the visible is that when the sun is less than about 6° below the horizon, the radiance of the twilight sky can be considered as arising from a single scattering (DIVARI, 1962). For depressions of the sun more than 10°, the entire sky radiance is produced by multiple scattering.

C. Clouds

The phenomenon of crepuscular rays after twilight demonstrates that under some conditions clouds in the neighborhood of the terminator can modify the distribution of solar radiation incident on the upper atmosphere. In the visible region, negligible amounts of radiation are transmitted through the atmosphere at grazing heights of less than 3 km, and normally the effects of clouds can be ignored. In considering observations in the infrared, the possibility of modification by cumulus clouds at the terminator should be considered.

D. Absorption by Ozone

HULBURT (1953) and GADSDEN (1957a) have shown that absorption in the weak Chappuis bands of ozone, peaking in the yellow region of the spectrum, controls the color of the twilight sky. In fact, if it were not for the Chappuis absorption, the sky would turn white shortly after sunset. Although the absorption coefficient of these bands is small (VASSY, 1941; INN and TANAKA, 1953; HEARN, 1961), the oblique path through the ozone layer can be many hundreds of kilometers, an equivalent path of many centimeters of ozone.

E. Earth's Albedo

Scattering of radiation from the surface of the earth can be appreciable (up to about 10% in likely situations) and has been considered in the case of sodium resonance radiation (CHAMBERLAIN, 1956; DONAHUE and STULL, 1959).

F. Self-Absorption of Resonance Radiation

The solar radiation on its way to the observer's line of sight will generally traverse the resonant scattering region along an oblique path. Self-absorption can then become important. Calculations by CHAMBERLAIN, HUNTEN, and MACK (1958) and DONAHUE and STULL, *loc. cit.*, for the case of sodium resonance radiation show that this becomes important for vertical optical depths greater than approximately 0.04. Thus, in the case of emission from sodium (for which the vertical optical depth is several times this figure), self-absorption must be included in the analysis.

G. Doppler Shift of Fraunhofer Lines

DONAHUE and STULL, *loc. cit.*, have considered the effect on the emission from sodium of movement of the position of the solar absorption lines with respect to the terrestrial line. The Doppler shift is caused by the relative motion of the sun and the earth arising from the earth's rotation and orbital motion. The scattering atoms see an absorption line whose effective position, and therefore depth, varies in a systematic manner with time of day, latitude on the earth, and season of the year. Donahue and Stull find that the maximum effect is of the order of 10%, but the effects, it must be remembered, are systematic.

H. Time Dependence of Atmospheric Constitution

An insidious complication in the interpretation of twilight observations arises from possible physical changes in the atmosphere occurring during the period over which the twilight observations are made. There seems to be no way, a priori, of distinguishing rapid changes in the height distribution of a constituent from the height distribution itself derived from twilight observations. Recent rocket observations of the sodium dayglow shortly after sunrise (HUNTEN and WALLACE, 1966) show that the height distribution of atomic sodium had changed significantly in about two hours. (Twilight observations of the sodium emission typically last approximately twenty minutes.)

Another complication results from the existence of strong zonal winds in the mesosphere. The terminator moves west across the earth's atmosphere at a speed of approximately 470 cos λ meters sec^{-1}, where λ is the latitude, while zonal winds as strong as 100 meters sec^{-1} are known to occur in the 90–100 km region (cf. ELFORD, 1959; MANRING, BEDINGER, and KNAFLICH, 1961; and WITT, 1962). Thus the atmosphere can see a terminator moving at a speed that may differ by 20% or more from that expected for a static atmosphere.

Scattered Light Observations

Twilight observations made in broad spectral regions, or "white" light, will be considered first. These observations are relevant to the scattering properties of the atmosphere, and interest is attached particularly to the occurrence of aerosol, or large particle, scattering in the high atmosphere. Such scattering is exemplified by the spectacular occurrences of noctilucent clouds, mainly at high latitudes during the summer. Recent work by HEMENWAY, SOBERMAN, and WITT (1964) suggests that the clouds are produced by appreciable quantities (8×10^6 cm^{-2} in the height range 75–98 km) of submicron dust particles in the 80–90 km region of extraterrestrial origin. Presumably these particles arise from meteoric bombardment, and are present at all latitudes, although it may be that meteorological conditions in the high atmosphere (WEBB, 1965) are necessary for the dust to occur in thin, dense strata and become obvious as noctilucent clouds. From the results of a second rocket flight, made in the absence of noctilucent clouds, HEMENWAY *et al.* (1964) conclude that the total dust between 75–98 km is at least 10^3 greater than normal in the presence of noctilucent cloud.

The "purple light" seen in the west after sunset has been extensively studied by a number of workers since late in the nineteenth century. There is general agreement that this is caused by forward scatter from aerosol particles. The most recent study is by VOLZ and GOODY (1962) who conclude that the aerosol concentration in the stratosphere is of the order of $10^{-3} cm^{-3}$. Assuming a constant mixing ratio, they note that the concentration in the 80–85 km region at mid-latitudes would be of the order of $10^{-5} cm^{-3}$, which is much lower than that derived by LUDLAM (1957) from the luminance of noctilucent clouds. The assumption of a constant mixing ratio, however, may be a poor one, and possibly the best estimate of the aerosol concentration is that given by HEMENWAY et al. (1964). It should be noted that MIKIROV (1963) has measured the optical thickness of the atmosphere at heights in the 80–100 km region by determining the radiance of the daytime sky observed from rockets. He finds an aerosol layer about 20 km thick, peaking at 92 km in "northern U.S.S.R. latitudes," and 85 km in middle latitudes. The optical thickness of the layer is found to be approximately 1.5×10^{-5} (cf. Ludlam's value of 2×10^{-6} for noctilucent clouds), with the scale height of the top of the layer being generally similar to that of the atmosphere. (This should be compared with the indication found by HEMENWAY et al. (1964) that the scale height of the aerosol under noctilucent cloud conditions is perhaps three times smaller than this.) If we assume that the particle size in the aerosol is mainly in the 0.05μ region and that the particles are metallic, Mikirov's scattering coefficients suggest an aerosol concentration peaking at about $0.06 cm^{-3}$ and a column density of $6 \times 10^4 cm^{-2}$, compared with the HEMENWAY et al. (1964) noctilucent cloud density of $8 \times 10^6 cm^{-2}$.

It is interesting to note that Mikirov's measurements are in agreement with the observations of occasional discontinuities in the decrease of radiance of the twilight zenith sky. These have been observed by GRANDMONTAGNE (1941), GAUZIT and GRANDMONTAGNE (1942), VAUCOULEURS (1951) and BIGG (1956); one such discontinuity can be seen in a curve published by HULBURT (1948), and similar discontinuities were found in colorimetric observations by GADSDEN (1957b). The failure of KARANDIKAR (1955) to observe these discontinuities possibly results from his choice of wavelength regions, and the relatively low overall sensitivity of his equipment when allowance is made for the angular diameter of the sun. Typically, the luminance discontinuities appear as a departure of perhaps 5–20% from a smooth exponential decay when the sun is about 6° below the horizon.

The irradiance of the sun, in the visible region, is approximately 4–5×10^{13} quanta $cm^{-2}Å^{-1} sec^{-1}$. Mikirov's scattering layers will have a radiance, therefore, of about 5×10^7 quanta $cm^{-2}Å^{-1}sec^{-1}sr^{-1}$. In twilight at a solar depression of about 6°, the radiance will be reduced to approximately one half this because of ozone absorption. The twilight sky at this time has a radiance of approximately 3×10^8 quanta $cm^{-2}Å^{-1}sec^{-1}sr^{-1}$. From Mikirov's measurements, therefore, one would expect the twilight radiance curve to show a departure from a smooth curve amounting to about 20%. If, in comparison with the Hemenway *et al.* measurements, one takes Mikirov's measurements to be representative of unusually large amounts of dust, the agreement with the "discontinuity" observations becomes quite good.

Recently, the existence of a scattering layer in the 80 km region has been shown by the optical radar (pulsed laser backscatter) observations of FIOCCO and SMULLIN (1963) and FIOCCO and GRAMS (1966). At present, the technique can demonstrate only that the layer exists; the returned signals are barely above the statistical noise level. DEIRMENDJIAN (1965) has pointed out some of the difficulties of interpretation of these observations.

Emission-Line Observations

Considerable efforts have been put into observations of atomic and molecular emission lines during twilight. Therefore, the following only attempts to summarize what has been done and refers to the latest reports and reviews. The interpretation of the helium and metallic atom observations will be dealt with in some detail in the accompanying paper.

A. Emission from the Alkali and Alkaline-Earth Metals

Observations of resonantly scattered sunlight have established that the alkali metals, sodium, potassium, and lithium, are present in atomic form in the 85–100 km region. Of these, the first to be recognized was the presence in twilight spectra of strong emission of the resonance lines of sodium. Polarization and interferometric measurements, together with determination of the relative intensities in the doublet and the apparent screening height of the atmosphere, soon established that the excitation process was one of resonant scattering of sunlight. The early observations have been admirably reviewed by CHAMBERLAIN (1961), and more recent measurements are reviewed by VALLANCE JONES (1963) and HUNTEN (1964). Since then, further observations of the twilight sodium emission have been published by BLAMONT and DONAHUE (1964), CRESSWELL (1964), GADSDEN (1964), GUILINO and PAETZOLD (1965), HUNTEN *et al.* (1964), NGUYEN (1964), and SULLIVAN and HUNTEN (1964).

Observations of the other alkali metals, lithium and potassium, are reviewed by VALLANCE JONES (1963). More recent observations are reported by NGUYEN (1964), STOFFREGEN, DERBLOM, and ANGER (1963), SULLIVAN and HUNTEN (1964), and TINSLEY (1964), including also observations from Saskatoon (GAULT and RUNDLE, 1966) and Alaska (DEEHR *et al.*, 1966) of a lithium cloud released from a rocket over Fort Churchill. Observations of what is probably lithium released in high altitude nuclear explosions are reported by GADSDEN (1962); GAULT and HUNTEN (1963), SHEPHERD and BENS (1963), STOFFREGEN *et al.* (1963), and SULLIVAN and HUNTEN (1962). LYTLE and HUNTEN (1959), using a scanning spectrometer, searched unsuccessfully for the resonance emission from potassium. The emission lines are very weak and were not detected until SULLIVAN and HUNTEN (1964) used an improved form of a birefringent photometer.

Emission from ionized calcium has been observed intermittently at Saskatoon since 1956 (VALLANCE JONES, 1956, 1958) and has been observed also by DUFAY (1958). The most recent observations to be reported, and the first from the southern hemisphere, are those of WEILL (1966). It is interesting to note that the resonance line of atomic calcium at 4227Å has not yet been observed.

The twilight observations of the resonance lines have been usually presented in terms of the total abundance of the free atoms in an atmospheric column. HUNTEN (1962) has tabulated the solar irradiance versus height profiles for the resonance lines, so that the observed intensity versus solar depression angle can be analysed to give the apparent height profile of the atomic concentration. The observed intensity is the integral convolution of the irradiance with concentration. HUNTEN (1960) recommends the solution of this convolution by the method of BRACEWELL and ROBERTS (1954) and BRACEWELL (1955).

Briefly, the established results show that, first, the abundance of the alkali metals indicates great fluctuations from twilight to twilight. Second, there is an increase in abundance during local winter, amounting to about a two to three times increase over the abundance observed in summer. (Figure 3

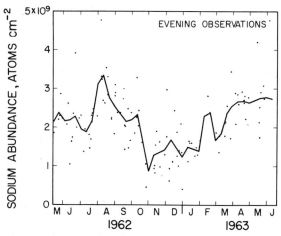

FIGURE 3. The seasonal variation in sodium abundance observed from Lauder, New Zealand. The solid line connects twenty-day running means; the great day-to-day variation is well illustrated.

shows a typical set of observations.) Third, in mid-latitudes, the sodium concentration peaks in the region 85–95 km (BULLOCK and HUNTEN, 1961; BLAMONT and DONAHUE, 1964), the scale height on the upper side being approximately equal to that of the atmosphere generally. (At low latitudes, there is some evidence (HUNTEN and WALLACE, 1966) that the top-side scale height is appreciably smaller on occasion.) The morning and evening abundances of sodium exhibit no large systematic difference; BLAMONT and DONAHUE (1964) show a statistical tendency for the morning intensity to be 10–20% above the evening intensity. (A trend of this magnitude is hidden in the day-to-day variations in abundance, and can be derived only after a prolonged series of observations.) It should be noted that the conclusions on morning and evening abundances derived by Blamont and Donahue need modification in the light of a recent reassessment of the dayglow measurements (GADSDEN, BLAMONT, and DONAHUE, 1966). The morning/evening ratio appears to be a little higher than the figure derived earlier.

Observations of the lithium and potassium emissions show that potassium has a behavior very similar to that of sodium The lithium observations show a layer some 10 km lower than the sodium layer, as predicted by GADSDEN (1964) from the higher specific ionization rate of lithium. The prominent characteristic of lithium is the presence of a low abundance with short-lived, manyfold enhancements which are local in character. The first of these was observed in 1958 in Antarctica by GADSDEN and SALMON (1958) and DELANNOY (1960). This enhancement occurred shortly after the explosion of a thermonuclear bomb in the ionosphere over Johnston Island in the Pacific. Since then, many similar enhancements have been observed (see GADSDEN, 1964, for a review of these). There can be little doubt that the natural lithium content of the atmosphere has been significantly perturbed by many such explosions. In recent years, there have been numerous rocket releases of lithium (see GAULT and RUNDLE (1966), DEEHR, ROMICK, and BELON (1966) for observations of rocket-seeded contamination), and probably one can regretfully conclude that determinations of the lithium abundance, with a view to deciding the origin of the alkali metals in the atmosphere, are now impossible.

The observations of ionized calcium emission (see above) are of interest in that apparently Ca^+ is most abundant in summer, and there is an undetectable amount of atomic calcium in the atmosphere. It would be of great interest to get an estimate of the Ca/Ca^+ abundance ratio. NARCISI and BAILEY (1965), using a rocket-borne mass spectrometer, find a concentration of Ca^+ equal to a little under 200 cm^{-3} at 95 km, the total column abundance being approximately 4×10^7 cm^{-2}. JONES (1956, 1958) finds that the abundance derived from twilight observations is very variable, but that the abundance can be as high as 10^8 cm^{-2}. Narcisi and Bailey found a high concentration of magnesium ions (peak 6×10^3 cm^{-3}). The resonance lines of Mg^+ and Mg are at 2795Å and 2852Å, respectively, and are in the region where ozone has strong absorption in the Hartley continuum. An instrument flown to a height of 50 km in order to get above most of the atmospheric ozone should be able to see the resonance lines of Mg^+ quite easily, even in daytime, and thus check the mass spectrometer measurements.

B. Emissions from Atomic Oxygen

The forbidden red line at 6300Å shows a considerable enhancement in twilight, both evening and morning, together with an extension of the enhancement into the period of full night (see Figure 4, from MEGILL, 1960). CHAMBERLAIN (1961) has reviewed the observations and interpretations. Resonant scattering of the 6300Å line can be ruled out as a major contribution. Excitation of atomic oxygen to the ¹D level by dissociation of molecular oxygen by sunlight in the Schumann-Runge region seems equally incapable of providing a sufficient radiance.

The long-lived post-twilight decay seems almost certainly related to F-region recombination by a dissociative recombination process such as

$$O_2^+ + e \rightarrow O(^1D) + O(^3P, {}^1D, {}^1S).$$

The $O(^1D)$ atoms radiate the 6300, 6364Å doublet and $O(^1S)$ can give the 5577Å (green) line, followed by the 6300, 6364Å doublet. Another recombination process is

$$NO^+ + e \rightarrow O(^1D) + N(^4S)$$

although this is unlikely because spin is not conserved.

It will be seen from Figure 4 that there is an appreciable pretwilight en-

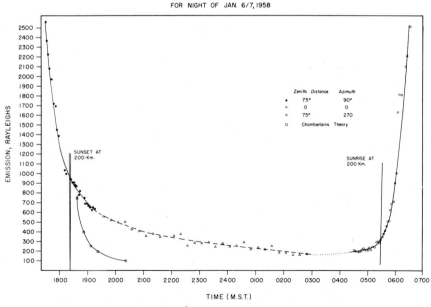

FIGURE 4. A typical history of the 6300Å atomic oxygen emission throughout an entire night, from MEGILL (1960). The curve labeled "Chamberlain's Theory" refers to some early calculations by Chamberlain of the dissociative recombination of oxygen.

hancement. COLE (1965) has suggested that this is due to photoelectrons back-scattered from the magnetically conjugate twilight region. The necessary energy flux seems quite possible. The hypothesis can be tested by its predictions of seasonal and latitude changes, and also by the predicted change with longitude caused by the varying inclination of the magnetic meridians relative to the geographic meridians.

Resonance fluorescence of the 5577Å atomic oxygen line from incident 2972Å solar radiation is to be expected, but it is very weak, of the order of 10^6 quanta cm^{-2} sec^{-1} sr^{-1}. Furthermore, radiation at 2972Å is strongly absorbed by ozone so that the screening height of the atmosphere is approximately 50 km. With the peak concentration of atomic oxygen occurring near 100 km, the effective sunset for 5577Å fluorescence occurs very early in twilight. Thus it is doubtful whether the small late twilight enhancement observed by MEGILL (1960) can be attributed to this process. It more likely is related to one of the dissociative recombination processes invoked for the 6300Å twilight enhancement:

$$O_2^+ + e \rightarrow O(^3P, {}^1D) + O(^1S),$$

followed by radiation of the 5577Å line from the $O(^1S)$. The production of $O(^1S)$ relative to $O(^1D)$ in the dissociative recombination of oxygen is being studied by PETERSON et al. (1966a, 1966b).

SHKLOVSKY (1957) has suggested that atomic oxygen should show fluorescence arising from absorption of the solar Lyman-β emission. There is an accidental resonance between the Lyman-β line and the $^3P_2$-^3D transition in oxygen, leading to resonant population of the upper level. Cascading radiation then follows, leading to radiation at 11299, 11287, and 8446Å. The expected radiance of the 8446Å was calculated by Shklovsky to be low, approximately 10^7 quanta cm^{-2} sec^{-1} sr^{-1} at low solar activity. BRANDT (1959) has shown that the twilight intensity will be much lower than this (approximately 1%) because of the severe attenuation of Lyman-β under oblique incidence of sunlight, and the consequent high screening level. SHEFOV (1962) reports twilight observations at the high-latitude station of Zvenigorod; the observed radiance is in the vicinity of 10^6 quanta cm^{-2} sec^{-1} sr^{-1}. While Shefov took pains to eliminate the effect of auroral electron precipitation from his measurements, it would seem to be desirable to repeat the observations at a low-latitude station.

C. Molecular Nitrogen Ions

The first emission features to be observed as enhanced in twilight, independently of auroral activity, were the First Negative bands of N_2^+. CHAMBERLAIN (1961) reviewed the earlier observations. Recent studies include those of MAARTENSE and HUNTEN (1963) and a very detailed observational and theoretical study to be published shortly by BROADFOOT and HUNTEN (1966). In their study, it is shown that at low latitudes there is little seasonal variation of N_2^+ concentration in the morning twilight, but that the evening observations show a pronounced winter maximum. Broadfoot and Hunten suggest that this results from increased N_2^+ concentration produced by back-scattered photoelectrons from the atmosphere magnetically conjugate to the atmosphere observed from Kitt Peak. The authors also find that the N_2^+ bands exhibit a high rotational temperature, which they suggest is due to a proportion of the ions being produced by charge exchange from O^+ in the metastable ^2D level.

D. Molecular Oxygen

Twilight enhancements occur, as might be expected, in the Atmospheric and Infrared Atmospheric bands of oxygen, indicating appreciable excitation of oxygen to the $a^1\Delta_g$ and $b^1\Sigma_g^+$ levels. The 1.58μ band of the infrared system has been found to show a strong seasonal dependence, being almost unobservable from ground level in the summer and rising to an intensity of about 5×10^{10} quanta cm^{-2} sec^{-1} sr^{-1} in winter. The most recent results are those of GATTINGER and JONES (1966) from which they confirm their earlier conclusion that the process is not resonant scattering of sunlight but production of $^1\Delta_g$ oxygen by the Hartley dissociation of ozone:

$$O_3 + h\nu(\lambda < 2950\text{Å}) \rightarrow O(^1D) + O_2(^1\Delta_g).$$

Airborne (NOXON, 1966) and balloon-borne (EVANS, LLEWELLYN, and VALLANCE JONES, 1966) observations of the (O-O) band of the infrared atmosphere system will be published in the very near future.

E. Helium

Resonant scattering of sunlight from helium in the 2^3S (metastable) level has been observed in the twilight sky at 10830Å, both in the presence and absence of aurora (SHEFOV, 1963a, b; SHCHEGLOV, 1962). The observed intensity is about 8×10^7 quanta cm^{-2} sec^{-1} sr^{-1}. BRANDT, BROADFOOT, and McELROY (1965) have reported the observation of another line, at 3889Å, scattered by the 2^3S helium. The predicted intensity is $1/160$ that of the 10830Å line; the intensity was found to be approximately five times less than this. The discrepancy may or may not be significant as the measurements of the 10830Å radiance have yet to reach a high precision.

F. Continuum Emission

YARIN (1962) reports the appearance of emission in the region 5800–6100Å during the middle stages of twilight, the intensity of which decreases with an increasing solar depression angle. He suggests that this is due to fluorescence from NO_2. However, it seems more likely that he observed the structure in the peak of the Chappuis absorption band of ozone and not an emission at all.

SHEFOV (1959) reports a general "filling-in" of the Fraunhofer lines in the 3900–4700Å region, which he ascribes to a continuum emission. GRAINGER and RING (1962) report a similar effect in the H Fraunhofer line of Ca^+ observed in the spectrum of moonlight and scattered daylight. For the twilight observations, a spectral intensity in the neighborhood of 10^7 quanta cm^{-2} sec^{-1} sr^{-1} Å^{-1} is required. As yet, there are no confirming observations of this continuum, and it is difficult to envisage a process capable of yielding such a radiance.

G. Other Emissions

CHAMBERLAIN (1961) discusses the twilight enhancement of the hydroxyl bands in the red and infrared and of the forbidden doublet of atomic nitrogen at 5199Å. There appear to be no recent observations of these features, with the possible exception of the observations through broad-band filters by WOLSTENCROFT, BRANDT, and ROSE (1966). These authors found an enhancement, low in the western sky, lasting for about thirty minutes after astronomical twilight. The filters being used were centered at 7100Å and 9550Å, with widths of 300Å and 400Å, respectively. The likely emission features in the band passes of the filters are the (8-3) and (8-4) hydroxyl bands, but the authors note that the enhancement differs in character from that observed by BERTHIER (1956). The diurnal variation of the hydroxyl emission possibly shows a quite complicated form (HUNT, 1966), and more data on the twilight variations are called for. Some balloon-borne observations are to be published shortly (LYTLE, 1966).

References

BERTHIER, P., 1956, *Ann. Geophys.* **12**, 113.
BIGG, E. K., 1956, *Nature* **177**, 77.
BLAMONT, J. E. and DONAHUE, T. M., 1964, *J. Geophys. Res.* **69**, 4093.
BRACEWELL, R. N., 1955, *J. Opt. Soc. Am.* **45**, 873.
BRACEWELL, R. N, and ROBERTS, J. A., 1954, *Austral. J. Phys.* **7**, 615.
BRANDT, J. C., 1959, *Astrophys. J.* **130**, 228.
BRANDT, J. C., BROADFOOT, A. L., and McELROY, M. B., 1965, *Astrophys. J.* **141**, 1584.
BROADFOOT, A. L. and HUNTEN, D. M., 1966, *Planetary Space Sci.* **14**, 1303.
BULLOCK, W. R. and HUNTEN, D. M., 1961, *Can. J. Phys.* **39**, 976.
CHAMBERLAIN, J. W., 1956, *J. Atmospheric Terrest. Phys.* **9**, 73.
CHAMBERLAIN, J. W., 1961, *Physics of the Aurora and Airglow*, Academic Press, New York.
CHAMBERLAIN, J. W., HUNTEN, D. M., and MACK, J. E., 1958, *J. Atmospheric Terrest. Phys.* **12**, 153.
COLE, K. D., 1965, *Ann. Geophys.* **21**, 156.
CRESSWELL, G. R., 1964, *Austral. J. Phys.* **17**, 257.
DEEHR, C. S., ROMICK, G. J., and BELON, A. E., 1966, *J. Atmosph. Sci.* **23**, 362.
DEIRMENDJIAN, D., 1965, *J. Geophys. Res.* **70**, 743.
DELANNOY, J., 1960, *Ann. Geophys.* **16**, 236.
DIVARI, N. B., 1962, *Geomagnetism and Aeronomics* **2**, 600.
DONAHUE, T. M. and STULL, V. R., 1959, *Ann. Geophys.* **15**, 481.
DUFAY, M., 1958, *Ann. Geophys.* **14**, 391.
ELFORD, W. G., 1959, *Planetary Space Sci.* **1**, 94.
EVANS, W. F. J., LLEWELLYN, E. J., and JONES, A. V., 1966, *Nature* (to be published).
FIOCCO, G. and GRAMS, G., 1966, *Tellus* **18**, 34.
FIOCCO, G. and SMULLIN, L. D., 1963, *Nature* **199**, 1275.
GADSDEN, M., 1957a, *J. Atmospheric Terrest. Phys.* **10**, 176.
GADSDEN, M., 1957b, *Ph. D. Thesis*, London University, London.
GADSDEN, M., 1962, *Ann. Geophys.* **18**, 392.
GADSDEN, M., 1964, *Ann. Geophys.* **20**, 261.

GADSEN, M., BLAMONT, J.-E., and DONAHUE, T. M., 1966, *J. Geophys. Res.* **71**, 5047.
GADSDEN, M. and SALMON, K., 1958, *Nature* **182**, 1598.
GATTINGER, R. L. and VALLANCE JONES, A., 1966, *Planetary Space Sci.* **14**, 1.
GAULT, W. A. and HUNTEN, D. M., 1963, *Nature* **198**, 469.
GAULT, W. A. and RUNDLE, H. N., 1966, *Can. J. Phys.* **44**, 1099.
GAUZIT, J. and GRANDMONTAGNE, R., 1942, *Pub. Obs. Lyon* **3**, No. 10.
GRAINGER, J. F. and RING, J., 1962, *Nature* **193**, 762.
GRANDMONTAGNE, R., 1941, *Cahiers Phys.* **3**, 39.
GUILINO, G. and PAETZOLD, H. K., 1965, *J. Atmospheric Terrest. Phys.* **27**, 451.
HEARN, A. G., 1961, *Proc. Phys. Soc.* **78**, 932.
HEMENWAY, C. L., SOBERMAN R. K., and WITT, G., 1964, *Tellus* **16**, 84.
HULBURT, E. O., 1948, *The Emission Spectra of the Night Sky and Aurorae*, Physical Society, London.
HULBURT, E. O., 1953, *J. Opt. Soc.* **43**, 113.
HUNT, B. G., 1966, *J. Geophys. Res.* **71**, 1385.
HUNTEN, D. M., 1960, *J. Atmospheric Terrest. Phys.* **17**, 295.
HUNTEN, D. M., 1962, *J. Atmospheric Terrest. Phys.* **24**, 333.
HUNTEN, D. M., 1964, *Science* **145**, 26.
HUNTEN, D. M., JONES, A. V., ELLYETT, C. D., and McLAUCHLAN, E., 1964, *J. Atmospheric Terrest. Phys.* **26**, 67.
HUNTEN, D. M. and WALLACE, L., 1966, *J. Geophys. Res.* (to be published). /
INN, E. C. Y. and TANAKA, Y., 1953, *J. Opt. Soc. Am.* **43**, 870.
KARANDIKAR, R. V., 1955, *J. Opt. Soc. Am.* **45**, 389.
LUDLAM, F. H., 1957, *Tellus* **9**, 341.
LYTLE, E. A., 1966, *Appl. Opt.* (to be published).
MAARTENSE, I. and HUNTEN, D. M., 1963, *Can. J. Phys.* **41**, 1729.
MANRING, E., BEDINGER, J., and KNAFLICH, H., 1961, *Space Res.* **2**, 1107.
MEGILL, L. R., 1960, *J. Atmospheric Terrest. Phys.* **17**, 276.
MIKIROV, A. Ye., 1963, *Planetary Space Sci.* **11**, 417.
NGUYEN-HUU-DOAN: 1964, *Ann. Geophys.* **20**, 1.
NOXON, J. F., 1966, *Nature* (to be published).
PETERSON, V. L. and STEIGER, W. R., 1966, *J. Geophys. Res.* **71**, 2267.
PETERSON, V. L., VAN ZANDT, T. E., and NORTON, R. B., 1966, *J. Geophys. Res.* **71**, 2255.
SHCHEGLOV, P. V., 1962, *Aurorae and Airglow,** No. 9, 59.
SHEFOV, N. N., 1959, *Aurorae and Airglow,** No. 1, 25.
SHEFOV, N. N., 1962, *Aurorae and Airglow,** No. 9, 55.
SHEFOV, N. N., 1963a, *Aurorae and Airglow,** No. 10, 56.
SHEFOV, N. N., 1963b, *Planetary Space Sci.* **10**, 73.
SHEPHERD, G. G. and BENS, A. R., 1963, *Nature* **198**, 470.
SHKLOVSKY, I. S., 1957, *Astron. Zh.* **34**, 127.
STOFFREGEN, W. DERBLOM, H., and ANGER, B., 1963, *Nature* **197**, 783.
SULLIVAN, H. M. and HUNTEN, D. M., 1962, *Nature* **193**, 1064.
SULLIVAN, H. M. and HUNTEN, D. M., 1964, *Can. J. Phys.* **42**, 937.
TINSLEY, B. A., 1964, *Can. J. Phys.* **42**, 779.
VALLANCE JONES, A., 1956, *Nature* **178**, 276.
VALLANCE JONES, A., 1958, *Ann. Geophys.* **14**, 179.
VALLANCE JONES, A., 1963, *Planetary Space Sci.* **10**, 117.
VASSY, A., 1941, *Ann. Phys.* **16**, 145.
VAUCOULEURS, G., 1951, *Comptes Rend.* **232**, 342.
VOLZ, F. E. and GOODY, R. M., 1962, *J. Atmospheric Sci.* **19**, 385.
WEBB, W. L., 1965, *J. Geophys. Res.* **70**, 4463.
WEILL, G., 1966, *Ann. Geophys.* **22**, 266.
WITT, G., 1962, *Tellus* **14**, 1.
WOLSTENCROFT, R. D., BRANDT, J. C., and ROSE, L. J., 1966, *Planetary Space Sci.* **14**, 445.
YARIN, V. I., 1962, *Aurorae and Airglow,** No. 9, 61.

Aurorae and Airglow — Section 4 of the IGY Program. Monographs published by the Academy of Sciences of the U.S.S.R., Moscow.

Discussion

There was a discussion about the calcium observations, primarily concerned with the reasons for the appearance of Ca^+ and not the neutral Ca atom resonance lines. Dr. Weill mentioned that on a large number of plates examined for evidence of these resonance lines, Ca^+ did not appear whereas Ca neutral did. On cometary spectra for which Ca^+ is observed, the neutral Ca line is in evidence, but has intensities no greater than one-tenth that of the Ca^+. It was mentioned that some observations have been made in which the Ca appears sporadically, which suggests that meteors rather than a Ca layer might be the source.

There was a question raised concerning the statement that the predawn enhancement of the OI 6300Å line is due to transport to the conjugate region. If so, it was suggested that there should exist certain seasonal and longitudinal variations of the predawn enhancement. There are a number of fairly simple geometrical tests that could be conducted, and it was noted that some unpublished observations conducted in Devon tend to confirm this effect. It was also pointed out that there is a small predawn enhancement that can be explained by the photochemistry.

DAYGLOW OBSERVATIONS

J. F. Noxon

Blue Hill Observatory, Harvard University, Cambridge, Massachusetts

In discussing dayglow observations we restrict ourselves to only a small portion of the optical emission arising in the atmosphere during the daytime. Thus we do not consider the vast amount of measurement carried out on the coherent scattering of sunlight by aerosols and air molecules nor the "gray body" thermal emission of the atmosphere at longer wavelengths. For our purpose these dominant components of the "dayglow" form an unwanted background; until recently this background has prevented observation of the energetically insignificant portion of the dayglow with which we shall be concerned.

The portion which does concern us consists almost entirely of atomic and molecular emissions which originate in the atmosphere lying above 20 km. We expect these dayglow emissions to reflect in some measure the response of the atmosphere to the concurrent input of solar energy; we anticipate that attempts to understand the origin of this emission must inevitably affect our comprehension of the state of the sunlit atmosphere. In reviewing the dayglow observations we shall first consider the techniques used to overcome the background problem and then summarize the observations presently at hand.

I. Observational Techniques

A. Ground Based Instruments

Although detection of daytime emission by means of balloon or rocket borne instrumentation might seem to be the most promising line of attack, the first observations were in fact carried out using ground based instrumentation. To be successful any ground based technique must be capable of detecting an emission line of a few kilorayleighs against a sky background amounting to several thousand kR/A; to make matters worse, the background is not a smooth continuum but is strewn with Fraunhofer lines. The general requirements thus involve some combination of high resolution scanning with a means of subtracting the residual background component; even when the resolution is sufficient to reveal the Doppler broadening of a dayglow line, the background signal is usually an order of magnitude greater.

Thus a direct attack might be to scan the sky spectrum at perhaps 0.02Å resolution and then subtract a normalized solar spectrum in order to remove the Fraunhofer structure. In effect this was what BLAMONT and DONAHUE (1961) did in order to obtain the first measurements of the sodium D lines in the dayglow. In their instrument the high resolution spectrometer was a cell containing sodium vapor; the wavelength scattered from the cell could be varied by means of the Zeeman splitting produced with an external magnetic field. The measurements require careful interpretation because of a complex interaction between the hyperfine components of the sodium in the cell, the dayglow emission line, and the partially polarized sky background (GADSDEN, BLAMONT, and DONAHUE, 1966). The technique is a powerful one, but it is limited to those few dayglow lines, such as sodium, which can be resonantly scattered by a vapor cell.

BENS, COGGER, and SHEPHERD (1965) achieved the required wavelength discrimination by placing high and low resolution Fabry-Perot interferometers in series; they were able to detect the OI 6300Å line in the dayglow by comparing a sky spectrum with a solar spectrum. Yet a positive identification of the line emission came only after a painstaking series of trials; their paper reveals the many pitfalls which may occur, and it is a model of careful critical analysis applied to a difficult observation. Their work, and the subsequent study by COGGER and SHEPHERD (1965), have cast some doubt on the technique used by JARRETT and HOEY (1963) in which the sky was photographed through a Fabry-Perot etalon. Although Jarrett and Hoey obtained a fringe system which they identified as due to 6300Å dayglow emission, it now appears that full account may not have been taken of the fringe structure which must result from a superposition of Fraunhofer absorption lines.

In order to avoid problems arising from Fraunhofer lines in the sky background, NOXON and GOODY (1962) distinguished the dayglow line from the background by virtue of a difference in polarization between the two. At 90° from the sun, the molecular scattering component gives a strong polarization to the sky background; over a few Ångstroms the degree of polarization is nearly constant and is also expected to be independent of the presence or absence of Fraunhofer lines. In contrast to this, dayglow emission lines should have a negligible polarization; the polarization should be zero when the excitation is photochemical in origin and small, in most cases, when excitation involves resonance fluorescence. Over a small range in wavelength, one thus expects to find a nearly constant value of polarization except for a decrease at the position of the dayglow line. The technique is insensitive both to the presence of Fraunhofer lines and to intensity fluctuation in the sky background. In practice, the spectral scanning polarimeter has been successfully employed for investigation of both the 5577Å and 6300Å lines of oxygen in daytime airglow and aurora as well as the sodium dayglow (NOXON, 1963, 1964; NOXON and JOHANSON, 1967). The instrument is ultimately limited both by random noise and real fluctuations in polarization associated with Fraunhofer lines, but it has been possible to record dayglow emission lines as weak as 1kR. A gain in sensitivity could be obtained by improving the resolution and light gathering power of the Fabry-Perot interferometer used for spectral scanning.

It is well to remember that any scheme which seeks to cancel out the sky background cannot avoid the random shot noise arising from the large DC background, assuming the detector to be a photomultiplier. Although time averaging can suppress this noise, it nevertheless sets a limit on the effectiveness of any instrument, however idealized. Despite the limitations which exist, ground based observation does permit dayglow emission to be studied as a function of time. The great disadvantages, apart from being subject to poor sky conditions, are of course the limited spectral range available and the absence of any information on how the emission intensity is distributed with altitude.

B. High Altitude Observation of the Dayglow

A number of measurements have now been made on the dayglow with the aid of instruments carried aloft by aircraft, balloons, and rockets; all information on ultraviolet and infrared features has come from such observations. Although the sky background may be of negligible importance at high altitude, care has to be taken to prevent scattered sunlight from entering the spectrometer or filter photometer; a number of otherwise successful high altitude observations have been compromised or ruined by inadequate precautions against such contamination. Apart from this the observations are straightforward in principle, but the problem of accurate absolute calibration still exists, particularly in the ultraviolet. The advantages and disadvantages of high altitude measurements are fairly obvious; the disadvantage is primarily the limited time available for observation. It seems likely that for some time to come progress in dayglow observation will involve an appropriate combination of both ground based and high altitude study.

II. Dayglow Observations

We shall describe the principal emission features in order of wavelength. For convenience we include much of the information available in Table I which lists the wavelength, range of intensity observed, the altitude when known, and appropriate references to published work. When a range of intensity is given, it spans the reported values.

A. Ultraviolet Dayglow Emission

This must all be observed from a high altitude; the preponderance of the information available has come from the rocket investigations by Fastie, Barth, and their collaborators. The emissions so far reported inclnde Lyman α, the OI triplet at 1302Å, [OI] (1355Å), the NO γ bands, and the N_2 Second Positive

Table I. Dayglow Observations

Emission	Wavelength	Altitude	Zenith Intensity	Reference
Lyman α	1216Å	>100 km	5–12 kR	FASTIE, CROSSWHITE, and HEATH (1964)
OI ^{3}P-^{3}S	1304Å	>100 km	2–6 kR	FASTIE, CROSSWHITE, and HEATH (1964)
[OI] ^{3}P-^{5}S	1355Å	100–300 km	0.4 kR	FASTIE, CROSSWHITE, and HEATH (1964)
NO γ	2000–3000Å	80–140 km	1 kR	BARTH (1966)
N$_2$ 2PG	3000–4000Å	obs > 170 km	0.4 kR	BARTH and PEARCE (1965)
N$_2^+$ 1 Neg	3914A	130–300 km	2–7 kR	ZIPF and FASTIE (1963) ZIPF (1966) WALLACE and NIDEY (1964) WALLACE and McELROY (1966) NAGATA et al. (1965)
[NI]^{4}S-^{2}D	5200Å	>100 km	0.1 kR	WALLACE and NIDEY (1964) WALLACE and McELROY (1966)
[OI]^{1}D-^{1}S	5577Å	80–250 km	0.4–3 kR	WALLACE and NIDEY (1964) WALLACE and McELROY (1966) SILVERMAN et al. (1965)
Na D	5893Å	85–95 km	2–40 kR	BLAMONT and DONAHUE (1961, 1964) GADSDEN et al. (1966) HUNTEN and WALLACE (1966) DONAHUE (1966) NOXON and JOHANSON (1967)
[OI]^{3}P-^{1}D	6300Å	>125 km possibly to >300 km	3–60 kR	NOXON and GOODY (1962) ZIPF and FASTIE (1963) NOXON (1964) WALLACE and McELROY (1966) NAGATA et al. (1965) BENS et al. (1965) JARRETT and HOEY (1963)
[O$_2$]$^1\Delta$g-$^3\Sigma_g^-$	1.27μ	not measured, probably 40–80 km	$\sim$30 mR	NOXON and VALLANCE JONES (1962) NOXON (1967) EVANS et al. (1967)
OH	2.8–4.0μ	not measured, probably 50–90 km	$\sim$5 mR	LYTLE and HAMPSON (1964)

bands. Both Lyman α and the 1302Å triplet involve permitted resonance transitions; the density of H and O atoms above 100 km is great enough to make the atmosphere optically thick at the line centers so that multiple scattering is important. Thus the distribution of primary emission with altitude cannot be obtained directly from the change of zenith intensity with height. These two features, as well as the forbidden 1355Å line, appear only above 100 km where absorption by O_2 is no longer strong; Lyman α remains intense up to great heights, whereas the oxygen lines have a maximum zenith intensity in the 100–200 km region (FASTIE, CROSSWHITE, and HEATH, 1964).

The NO bands, on the other hand, are emitted strongly in the region between 80–140 km with less than 10% coming from above 135 km (BARTH, 1966); the zenith intensity at 80 km is 1 kR and is considerably greater than had been anticipated.

BARTH and PEARCE (1965) have observed the Second Positive bands of N_2 and report the zenith intensity at 165 km to be 0.4 kR for the 0,0 band.

B. Visible Dayglow Emission

The emissions reported include the N_2^+ First Negative bands, [OI](5577Å and 6300Å), [NI](5200Å), and the sodium D lines. Of these, only 6300Å and the D lines have been systematically studied for any length of time, using ground based instrumentation.

N_2^+ *First Negative Bands.* The rocket measurements of the 3914Å 0,0 band are in fair agreement in showing a sharp rise in the emission rate per unit volume between 150–200 km (Figure 1). Only NAGATA *et al.* (1965) report measurements above 220 km; their observations suggest a maximum emission rate near this altitude. The emission rate is obtained by differentiating the observed zenith intensity with respect to altitude, and the result is not sensitive to

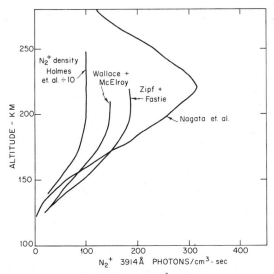

FIGURE 1. Observed emission profiles of N_2^+ 3914Å in the dayglow. A direct measurement of N_2^+ ion density is also shown multiplied by 0.1 to give the corresponding dayglow brightness from resonance fluorescence.

the presence of any false but constant background signal. When the original zenith intensities are plotted together there is a more obvious disagreement; the Wallace measurements indicate that half the emission lies below 200 km, whereas the others show only 15% to lie below this altitude. The Zipf-Fastie intensities have later been reduced by about 4.5 kR (ZIPF, 1966) and so now agree well with Wallace. The Japanese measurements remain anomalous in suggesting that the majority of the emission lies above 300 km.

[NI] (*5200*Å). Both of Wallace's flights measured the forbidden nitrogen line, but the intensity was not sufficient to permit differentiation of the zenith intensity curve.

[OI] (*5577*Å). The observations by WALLACE and MCELROY (1966) clearly show two maxima in the green line emission rate as a function of altitude; over half the total emission comes from above the intervening minimum at 130 km. The lower peak corresponds well with the location of the green line emission in the night airglow, although it is somewhat more intense in the day. These measurements, as well as those reported earlier by WALLACE and NIDEY (1964), are shown in Figure 2. The only other rocket measurement

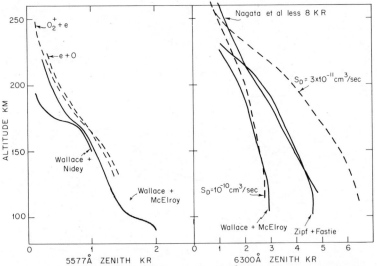

FIGURE 2. *Left:* Observed zenith intensity of OI 5577Å as a function of altitude together with emission predicted for two reactions. *Right:* Observed OI 6300 zenith intensity as a function of altitude together with two theoretical curves calculated by WALLACE and MCELROY (1966).

of the line is that by SILVERMAN *et al.* (1964) who report much smaller zenith intensities at low altitude. Ground based observation (NOXON, 1963) gave an upper limit similar to the intensity observed above 80 km by Wallace.

Na (*5890–5896*Å). BLAMONT and DONAHUE (1961, 1964) found that the sodium dayglow appeared to be several times brighter than had previously been expected on the basis of theory and observation at twilight. Although a revision has altered their results somewhat (GADSDEN *et al*., 1966), the essential conclusion remains unchanged and is in good agreement with other recent ground based observations (NOXON and JOHANSON, 1967). The dayglow intensity remains between 10 to 40 kR without apparent systematic seasonal change, although there may be a considerable variation from day to day and even within a single day. Rocket measurements by HUNTEN and WALLACE (1966) and MEIER *et al*. (see DONAHUE, 1966) show that the dayglow comes from a narrow layer near 90 km, just as in twilight.

[OI] (*6300*Å). This is the only other dayglow emission besides sodium that has been systematically studied over an extended period from the ground (NOXON, 1964). When it was first observed in 1962, the intensity varied between 20–30 kR with occasional excursions as high as 60 kR. In later years the average intensity became less and at times was found to be below 2–3 kR. Three measurements have been made using rocket borne photometers (ZIPF and FASTIE, 1963; NAGATA *et al*., 1965; WALLACE and MCELROY, 1966). There is agreement to within a factor of 2 or 3 on the emission rate per unit volume below 230 km with a broad maximum being evident near 200 km. The Japanese measurements extend up to 320 km and indicate, rather surprisingly, that two thirds of the red line emission observed came from even greater heights (Figure 2). Because of the possible effects of scattered light in a filter photometer system, it may be desirable to have a separate confirmation of such a high altitude component from a relatively high resolution scanning spectrometer.

In 1962 and sometimes in 1963 the ground based observations showed the red line to be not only rather intense but also quite variable in its brightness. Day-to-day fluctuations of a factor of two were not uncommon, and there were a few occasions during which the intensity underwent large fluctuations for a period of several hours. No clear correlation could be found between the 6300 intensity and magnetic disturbance, electron density in the F region, or indeed, anything except perhaps a spread in range of ionosonde echoes from the F_1 layer.

The years during which the rocket measurements were made appear to have been a period of low red line intensity; the ground based observations also usually show intensities of only 5–10 kR. In early 1966, there have been several days on which the intensity has once again reached over 25 kR, although it is still usually less than 10 kR.

C. Infrared Dayglow Emission

O_2 Infrared Atmospheric Bands. An intense dayglow emission of the 0,0 band of the $O_2(^1\Delta g\text{-}^3\Sigma_g^-)$ system has been reported by NOXON and VALLANCE JONES (1962); the observation was made from an aircraft in order to overcome both the problem of sky background and the reabsorption of the

emission by oxygen in the lower atmosphere. The zenith intensity was reported to be 10 megarayleighs but this should be raised to 25 mR due to an underestimate of the residual attenuation by O_2 above the aircraft. The band has been observed from a balloon by EVANS *et al.* (1967) and by LYTLE (private communication); an unidentified emission at 1.25μ, reported by GOPSHTEIN and KUSHPIL (1965), is undoubtedly the 0,0 band. Although fragmentary, the evidence accumulated so far does not indicate any significant variation of the midday intensity with either season or latitude (NOXON, 1967). The most interesting aspect of this emission, apart from its great intensity, has to do with its twilight behavior; it is much brighter in the evening and in the winter.

OH *Bands.* A balloon observation of the $\Delta v = 1$ sequence of the OH vibration-rotation bands between $2.8–4.0\mu$ has been reported by LYTLE and HAMPSON (1964). The intensity at midday appears to be comparable with that in the night airglow. Later measurements by LYTLE (private communication) have revealed a sudden and dramatic drop in the OH intensity at dawn, followed by a slow recovery lasting for several hours. It is not yet known whether any similar transitory effects occur at dusk.

D. Other Dayglow Emission

Because of its great intensity we mention finally what appears to be a dayglow continuum due neither to coherent scattering by air molecules or aerosol nor to thermal emission from the atmosphere. Ground based spectra of the daytime sky reveal that Fraunhofer lines are more shallow there than in the spectrum of direct sunlight, and that the sky polarization is somewhat less at the center of Fraunhofer lines than at the adjacent continuum (see NOXON and GOODY, 1965). The effects do not appear to be instrumental in origin but require instead the presence of a quasi-continuum, of low polarization and free of Fraunhofer lines, whose intensity in the visible is a few per cent of the overall sky brightness. The total intensity is thus at least 10^7 kR. It has been suggested that the origin may lie in fluorescence by aerosols but there is as yet no satisfying explanation.

Acknowledgment This work has been partly supported by the Atmospheric Sciences Section, National Science Foundation, NSF grant G-24903 to Harvard University.

References

BARTH, C. A., 1966, *Ann. Geophys.* 22, 198.
BARTH, C. A. and PEARCE, J. B., 1965, *Space Res. 6.*
BENS, A. R., COGGER, L. L., and SHEPHERD, G. G., 1965, *Planetary Space Sci.* 13, 551.
BLAMONT, J. E. and DONAHUE, T. M., 1961, *J. Geophys. Res.* 66, 1407.
BLAMONT, J. E. and DONAHUE, T. M., 1964, *J. Geophys. Res.* 69, 4093.
COGGER, L. L. and SHEPHERD, G. G., 1965, *Planetary Space Sci.* 13, 1163.
DONAHUE, T. M., 1966, paper given at COSPAR.
EVANS, W. J. F., VALLANCE JONES, A., and LLEWELLYN, E. J., 1967, *Nature* 213, 352.

FASTIE, W. G., CROSSWHITE, H. M., and HEATH, D. F., 1964, *J. Geophys. Res.* **69**, 4129.
GADSDEN, M., BLAMONT, J. E., and DONAHUE, T. M., 1966, *J. Geophys. Res.* **71**, 5047.
GOPSHTEIN, N. M. and V. I. KUSHPIL, *Planet. Space Sci* **13**, 457, 1965.
HUNTEN, D. M. and WALLACE, L., 1967, *J. Geophys. Res.* **72**, 69.
JARRETT, A. H. and HOEY, M. E., 1963, *Planetary Space Sci.* **11**, 1251.
LYTLE, E. A. and HAMPSON, J., 1964, *Nature* **202**, 76.
NAGATA, T., TOMATSU, T., and OGAWA, T., 1965, *Planetary Space Sci.* **13**, 1273.
NOXON, J. F., 1963, *J. Atmospheric Terrest. Phys.* **25**, 637.
NOXON, J. F., 1964, *J. Geophys. Res.* **69**, 3245.
NOXON, J. F., 1967, *Nature* **213**, 350.
NOXON, J. F. and GOODY, R. M., 1962, *J. Atmospheric Sci.* **10**, 342.
NOXON, J. F. and VALLANCE JONES, A., 1962, *Nature* **196**, 157.
NOXON, J. F. and GOODY, R. M., 1965, *Atm. and Oceanic Physics* **1** 275.
NOXON, J. F. and JOHANSON, A. E., 1967 (to be published).
SILVERMAN, S. M., LLOYD, J. W. F., COCHRUN, B. L., and NARDONE, L. J., 1964, *Nature* **304**, 461.
WALLACE, L and NIDEY, R., 1964, *J. Geophys. Res.* **69**, 471.
WALLACE, L. and MCELROY, M. B., 1966, *Planetary Space Sci.* **14**, 677.
ZIPF, E. C., 1966, *J. Geomag. and Geoelec.*
ZIPF, E. C. and FASTIE, W. G., 1963, *J. Geophys. Res.* **68**, 6208.
ZIPF, E. C. and FASTIE, W. G., 1964, *J. Geophys. Res.* **69**, 2357.

Discussion

It was asked if the terrestrial aerosols contribute to the polarization of the radiation received by the detector, as they do in zodiacal light. It was agreed that this is so, but that one would expect the Fraunhofer structure to remain the same. The scattering will affect the polarization, but it will not change appreciably as one scans across the Fraunhofer lines.

There were a number of questions raised concerning the effect of the Fraunhofer spectrum on the dayglow measurements. The presence of Fraunhofer lines seriously affects ground based techniques which only measure the sky intensity of a function of wavelength. With the scanning polarimeter technique the effects are greatly reduced; real changes in sky polarization do seem to be present at Fraunhofer lines, however, and these limit the effectiveness of this instrument in detecting dayglow emission. These polarization effects are not yet well understood.

It was pointed out that nothing is presently known concerning the early evening behavior of OH. There are no balloon or upper atmosphere measurements, and it is not possible to obtain useful information from the ground.

CINEMATOGRAPHIC OBSERVATIONS
OF
FAST AURORAL VARIATIONS

T. Neil Davis

Geophysical Institute, University of Alaska
College, Alaska

Abstract The relatively high quantum efficiency of the photocathodes now used in photo-electric devices is an essential feature which makes these devices attractive for use in auroral observations. In addition to possessing high sensitivity by virtue of the photocathode, certain types of photoelectric devices allow an image to be accumulated over some increment of time and then be read in the form of an electrical signal which can be processed directly or used to produce a two-dimensional image. One of these devices, the image orthicon television tube, has been found to be quite useful for obtaining auroral photographs and auroral and airglow spectra of very short exposure. Application of image orthicon techniques to the observation of the pulsating auroras has resulted in improved knowledge of the characteristics of this phenomenon.

In recent years advances in the development of image storage devices and image intensifiers have made these photoelectric image devices useful in auroral research. With the improved photoelectric image devices now available, it is possible to obtain real-time cinematographic photographs of the aurora and to obtain auroral spectra with exposures of 1 sec or less. This ability facilitates the quantitative study of those auroral variations too fast to be recorded by direct photography.

The versatility and commercial availability of image orthicon television systems provide the primary reasons for the application of these instruments to auroral studies. This application has come about only within the last few years and is still in its infancy. The first real-time photographic recordings of an aurora with an image orthicon system were obtained by SPAULDING and ANDERSON (1963) at Schenectady, New York in 1960. Carl W. Gartlein assembled an image orthicon system and used it as a detector for a spectrograph. The first extensive collection of real-time cinemaphotographs of auroras was obtained by DAVIS and HICKS (1964) at Fort Churchill, Manitoba in 1963. Additional auroral data were obtained at College in 1964 and 1965 (CRESSWELL and DAVIS,

1966). As yet the scientific results from the image orthicon data are rather meager. Cresswell and Davis found the observations to be particularly useful in the study of pulsating auroras because both temporal and spatial variations of the pulsating forms could be examined in more detail than allowed by other observational techniques.

An auroral observing system now used at College, Alaska is built around two image orthicon subsystems and is capable of obtaining auroral photographs and spectra simultaneously. Direct view photographs are obtained with one image orthicon system by employing interchangeable lenses providing angular fields of view of 16, 30, and 165°. The second image orthicon is used as a detector for a low-dispersion spectrograph mounted so as to view the same portion of the sky as the direct view television camera. A narrow-field photometer similarly mounted provides data for intensity calibrations of both systems; the photometer records the intensity of N_2^+ near 4278Å. Figure 1 contains an example of the data display format.

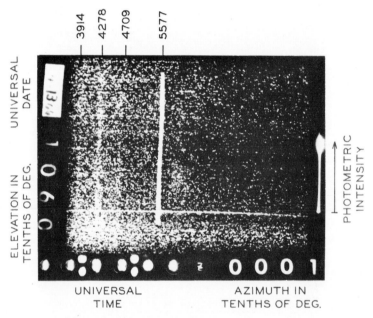

FIGURE 1. The format of the data display showing one frame of "real-time" spectra recorded at the rate of 24 frames per sec and with effective exposure times of 1/60 sec.

Light coming from the sky to the spectrograph is focused onto the spectrograph slit by an f/2.5, 150 mm focal length lens. The slit is located at the focus of an f/2 parabolic mirror which returns parallel light to a slanted flat mirror. The reflected parallel light then passes through a plane transmission grating and into the lens of the slave television camera. Because the sky is focused onto the spectrograph slit, a given position on a recorded spectral line corresponds to a particular angular position in the sky. The present arrangement provides a field of view approximately $\frac{1}{4}$ by 7°; thus with the aid of the direct view photographs, it is possible to determine precisely the angular location of the spectral source. A graphic example of the capability of the overall system is contained in Figure 2: there the spectrum of a single auroral ray is shown together with a photograph of it. Note the decrease in luminosity of the ray upwards from its

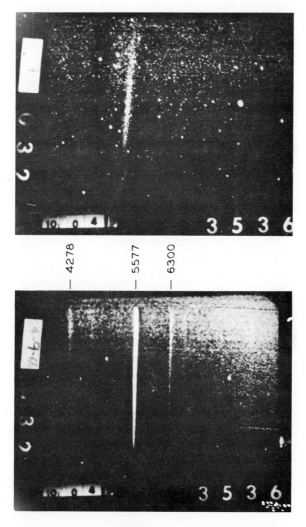

FIGURE 2. Photograph (top) and spectrogram of a single auroral ray. The photograph shows a field of view approximately 20 by 30°; the exposure is 1/60 sec. Except near the top of the picture where noise is evident, the white spots are star images; the brighter stars have the larger images. An exposure (time integration) of 4 sec was used for obtaining the spectrogram. The ray was drifting to the left across the field of view of the spectrograph during this interval. The spectral lines are inverted top for bottom; hence, the light from the lower part of the ray appears at the top of the lower photograph.

base (from top to bottom in the lower photograph), as shown by the wedgelike shape of the spectral lines. The vertical distribution of the OI 6300Å line relative to that of the OI 5577Å line in this spectrum is curious; usually, the 6300Å emission is more extended in altitude than that of 5577Å. Figure 3 contains a similar example of the spectrum observed at the bottom edge of an active auroral arc containing small-scale ray structure. The high sensitivity of the

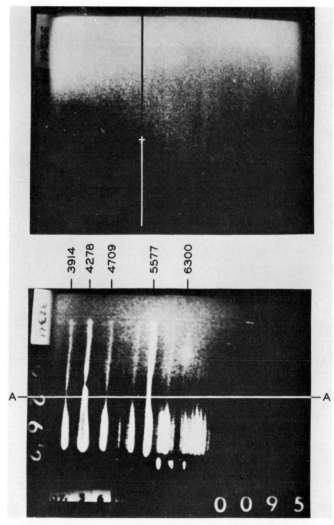

FIGURE 3. The spectrum observed at the lower border of an active auroral arc. The position of the spectrograph field of view is shown by the black and white vertical line drawn on the direct view photograph (~10° field of view). The point A on this line corresponds to the positions A-A indicated on the spectrogram. The spectral lines above the line A-A result from auroral luminosity beyond and below the arc shown (due to inversion of the slit image).

image orthicon spectrograph is illustrated best by the spectrogram presented in Figure 1. This spectrogram was obtained by using a framing rate of 30 frames per sec with an effective exposure of $\frac{1}{60}$ sec. This "real-time" spectrogram clearly exhibits the OI 5577 line and barely shows several N_2^+ First Negative bands. When the recorded film strip is viewed in cinema fashion, several other spectral lines or bands are evident.

At the low light levels common to aurora and airglow work, the main limitation to resolution is due to the characteristics of the image orthicon tube rather than the scanning pattern employed to extract information from the tube; the resolution decreases with decreasing photocathode illumination. The various factors entering into the available resolution are discussed more fully elsewhere (DAVIS, 1966). It is sufficient here to note that the image orthicons now in use provide a gain in sensitivity of 500–1000 times that of film but at the expense of lower resolution. The resolution of the data recorded with these systems under field conditions is about 300 television lines per frame. Thus, 16 mm film (effective area 7.2 × 9.6 mm) with photographic resolution of 30 line pairs per mm is just adequate to record the data.

The temporal resolution in the recorded data is related to the framing rates of the television camera and the photographic recording camera. In normal operation 30 television frames (60 television fields, either interlaced or noninterlaced scanning patterns) are presented on the television monitor each second. So far practical considerations dictate the use of conventional cinema cameras for data recording. These operate at 24 frames per sec with an exposure of $\frac{1}{60}$ sec so as to record every other field of each TV frame, except for 6 frames per sec. Due to the mismatch in framing rates 6 and 12-cycle flicker occurs with interlaced TV scanning patterns and 12-cycle flicker results when noninterlaced patterns are employed.

The image orthicon with a magnesium oxide target can be operated over the range of 6 × 10^{-7}–10^{-3} footcandle illumination on the photocathode; however, the dynamic range at any one setting of amplifier gain, beam current, and target voltage is limited to about 200 in spectroscopic applications (SPAULDING and ANDERSON, 1963) and to 20–60 when used to record extended images (ANDERSON, 1965). The dynamic range is limited by the weak scanning beam current required for low light level detection; then the beam current becomes insufficient to discharge the target in those areas corresponding to scene highlights. Methods are available to increase the dynamic range, and present plans are to include such a modification in one system operated at College.

The transfer characteristics of the image orthicon depend critically upon the settings of gain, target voltage, and beam current; all of these settings are continuously variable. Once the settings are made and a system is operated for several hours at a constant ambient temperature and on well-regulated power supplies, the transfer characteristic will usually remain constant. However, due to the low dynamic range of the system, it is often desirable to alter the control settings; consequently, a continuous calibration of the entire system is necessary. In addition to the limitations inherent in the image orthicon systems, we find that various problems in the circuitry often limit the quality of data obtained. Such problems tend to be more serious when operating under field conditions.

The study of auroral morphology is not unlike the parable describing the examination of an elephant by a number of blind men. Each observational technique gives a bias determined by the limitations of that particular method. For example, if a description of auroral morphology were to be developed only on the basis of real-time cinema photographs, it would be quite different from the morphology based upon visual observation and direct narrow-field and all-sky photographs. There would be much overlapping of details, but the morphology derived from the television observations would tend to emphasize the small-scale and high-speed aspects of auroral phenomena because these aspects are so obvious in the data. As yet, few morphological descriptions have been derived from the television data, primarily due to a dearth of analysis. The complexities involved are a factor and have led us to concentrate first on one phase of the auroral display, namely the pulsating aurora.

Pulsating auroras are characterized by their quasi-periodic intensity variations, their eastward drift, and their low intensity. Pulsating auroras appear to be restricted to the equatorward boundary of the normal display and tend to occur during and after the recovery phase of negative bays in H observed at stations lying near or equatorward of the peak of the auroral zone. The regularity of the luminosity variations of the pulsating aurora clearly distinguishes it from auroral types which also may vary rapidly in luminosity but almost never in a periodic or quasi-periodic way. On occasion, a narrow-field photometer will record quasi-periodic variations when viewing rayed auroral forms; however, the television observations show that these apparent variations are due strictly to horizontal movements of rays within the auroral structure.

The internal structure of pulsating forms also is distinctive in that this structure is quite homogeneous, whereas auroras typical of other parts of the display usually show internal structure. This statement pertains to "homogeneous" as well as "rayed" forms in the context of the terminology used by the visual observer. The television observations have been used by CRESSWELL and DAVIS (1966) to distinguish several types of pulsating forms on the basis of their shapes observed viewing up along a magnetic field line occupied by the pulsating form. The application of the television system to the study of pulsating aurora has shown that the observed characteristics of this phenomenon depend strongly upon the viewing aspect angle relative to the local magnetic field and the angular field of view. Particularly useful is the ability to determine which of the apparent variations result from motions or changes in shape rather than from actual temporal changes in luminosity.

From visual and photographic observations, it is well known that auroral forms undergo large-scale motions and changes from one type to another. Now, with the application of television techniques to auroral observation, it is becoming more evident that an important aspect of the aurora is its temporal and spatial variation. Even those auroral forms which the visual observer

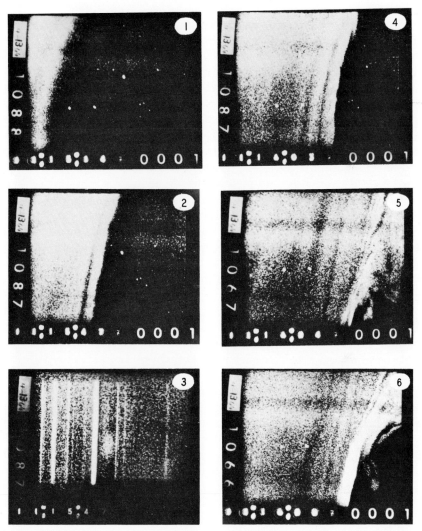

FIGURE 4. Photographs (10° field of view) of a "homogeneous" auroral band with north-south alignment slowly moving eastward across the field of view of the television system. In the third frame is presented the spectrum arising from the leading (right-hand) edge of the auroral structure. Except for Frames 2 and 3, which are 1/24 sec apart in time, these photographs show the structure at intervals of 15–33 sec. The horizontal dark streak near the top of each photograph is the result of temporary electronic difficulty in the television system.

describes as "stable" or "quiet" are observed with the television to possess an internal structure which apparently is never static. The television observations appear to justify the statement that, within the time scales observable (1/24 sec and longer), the aurora is continuously changing. An example of the type of variation which occurs is one frequently observed when viewing a homogeneous auroral arc (HA) in the magnetic zenith. To the visual observer, the arc appears to be homogeneous, hence, its name. However, narrow field of view television observations often reveal that such an arc is composed of parallel, thin (100–300m) arclike structures which appear to be streaming horizontally parallel to the orientation of the overall structure. An example is shown in Figure 4. Minor irregularities in the shape of the arclike elements develop and decay, sometimes in a fraction of 1 sec. Quite often the development is in the form of drifting sinusoidal wavelike patterns which usually last less than 1 sec and then quickly decay. Occasionally the folding progresses until interconnected "spots" appear; these, if viewed from the side, would be called filaments or rays. At other times the folding grows, and the entire arc may become distorted and "active." It is not yet clear whether all auroral rays develop in the manner described above; quite likely they do not.

In addition to the study of the detailed structure and change in shape or form type, an examination is being made of the various types of motion evidenced by auroras. The motions range in speed from barely perceptible to more than 100 km per sec. These apparent motions include drift of entire forms, movements of internal structures, and streaming (the apparent movement of regions of enhanced luminosity across preexisting structural elements in the aurora).

The use of a spectrograph incorporating a lens to focus the sky onto its slit allows the location of a spectral source to be identified. With this instrument the variation in spectral characteristics with the type of auroral form and within a single auroral form is being examined. Another problem being investigated is the distribution of hydrogen emissions and the spatial relationship between these emissions and those due to electron precipitation.

During the course of the next year it is planned to utilize several image orthicon systems for triangulation studies to make accurate height determinations of various auroral form types. These instruments will also be used for the detection and location of artificial auroral rays or spots; an attempt to produce such artificial auroras will be made by the National Aeronautics and Space Administration employing rocket-borne electron accelerators.

References

ANDERSON, J. E., 1965, Application of electro-optics to auroral studies—Phase II, Final Rept., Project No. 7661, General Electric Company, Schenectady, New York.
CRESSWELL, G. R. and DAVIS, T. N., 1966, *J. Geophys. Res.* **71** (to be published).
DAVIS, T. N., 1966, *Space Science Reviews*, V, 4 (to be published).
DAVIS, T. N. and HICKS, G. T., 1964, *J. Geophys. Res.* **69**, 1931-32.

SPAULDING, J. F. and ANDERSON, J. E., 1963, Application of electro-optics to auroral studies, Final Rept., Project No. 8653, General Electric Company, Schenectady, New York.

Discussion

Cresswell pointed out that he had observed fast auroral waves at Alaska with photometers. With a frequency of about 1 cps they moved equatorward at least 150 km with a velocity of 50–300 km sec. The light intensity of 5577Å is about 1 kR. The waves are observed to originate from a stable form arc. They persist for times up to 3 hours between 0100–0500 local time. No auroral absorption was associated with these wave motions.

A question was raised as to whether the measurements of aurora widths were made on stable arcs or rapidly moving arcs. Dr. Davis stated that they tried not to select either the stable or moving arcs, but felt that there is a tendency to make observations of fast moving forms. He emphasized the point that with the resolution provided by the image orthicon system, they actually see almost no "stable" arcs, i.e., they are all moving. Also, arcs that occur homogeneous to the TV system are very rare and short-lived (∼a few seconds). As to whether measurements made at different wavelengths yield different auroral widths, the answer is that such measurements have not yet been made, but are presently planned.

A STATISTICAL STUDY OF CARL STØRMER'S HEIGHT MEASUREMENTS OF AURORA BOREALIS

Alv Egeland

The Norwegian Institute of Cosmic Physics
Oslo, Norway
and

Anders Omholt

The Auroral Observatory,
Tromsø, Norway

Abstract   From Størmer's extensive height measurements of auroras in the years between 1911 and 1943, the heights of more than 12,000 accurately measured auroral points are available for statistical studies. Some of the most important conclusions which may be drawn from this material are summarized in this paper.

The distributions of the measured auroral points as functions of geomagnetic latitudes show that visually pulsating auroral forms and the high auroral arcs around 200 km are observed particularly at subauroral latitudes, whereas single rays seem to be more dominant at higher latitudes.

Some variations of auroral height with geomagnetic latitude, particularly for draperies, are found. There is also a general tendency for lower auroras at low latitudes than at high latitudes.

A comprehensive study of the height distribution for various auroral forms as a function of geomagnetic latitudes shows that all auroral forms, except for rays, show a pronounced peak in the height distribution around 100–110 km. There is little or no variation with latitude in the height of this peak. Rays are evenly distributed on heights from about 100 km and upwards. There is a small but significant decrease in the average lower border of aurora after local geomagnetic midnight.

Seasonal effects in the height of auroras seem to occur. Both sunlit and ordinary aurora show a somewhat greater average height in the autumn than in the spring. For sunlit aurora there is also a markedly greater probability of occurrence during the spring than during the autumn.

As expected, there is a good correlation between occurrence of aurora and sunspot number, except for homogeneous arcs, which show no such correlation. There is a tendency for higher aurora during the years of high solar activity, whereas for homogeneous arcs the opposite seems to be the case. Also, sunlit aurora is most often observed during the solar maximum years, and their average altitudes are somewhat higher during these years.

I. Introduction

In a biography of Fredrik Carl Mülertz Størmer, CHAPMAN (1961) writes that Størmer's photographic auroral studies have earned for him an undying name in the history of auroral science. From a net of twenty well equipped observing stations in southern and middle Norway (between 59–64°N, geomagnetic latitude) Carl Størmer carried out the most extensive collection and analysis of auroral photographs for height and position measurements ever made. From a great number of parallactic photographs (more than 40,000), he derived the heights, location forms, etc. of the aurora. Størmer has given the main results of this major work in his book, *The Polar Aurora*, published in 1955.

Størmer's height measurements and his discovery and studies of sunlit aurora form the main basis of our knowledge in this field. In this book, STØR-MER (1955 cf. p. 89) wrote that the statistical study of his extensive visual auroral material was far from completion, but he intended to continue this work. For most of his diagrams and statistics Størmer used only a small part of his large collection of data. During the last years of his life he worked hard to complete the statistical analysis of his total observations. It was a great loss for the auroral science when Størmer died before his statistical analyses were finished. Unfortunately, we do not know his exact program for this work, but before his death, he had marked out the most accurate material for the period 1911–44, which amounted to more than 12,000 auroral points derived from more than 7,200 sets of pictures.

As it was strongly felt that a similar collection of height measurements is not likely to be carried out again and that a considerable amount of new statistical information on visual auroras could be available from this material, a statistical study was undertaken. The work presented in this paper, based on the valuable material left by Størmer, is considered a supplement to the results given in Størmer's book. It does not exhaust all possible uses of this material, and a number of detailed studies can still be carried out. However, this paper presents some major results, and demonstrates the possibilities for future work. A more detailed description, of this material is given by EGELAND and OMHOLT (1966).

II. General Remarks Concerning the Analysis and Presentation of Størmer's Data

For all 12,232 auroral points, the following information has been punched on IBM cards: year, month, time, geomagnetic colatitude of the aurora foot-point, form, height, where in the auroral form the height has been measured (bottom, top, and/or average), if the aurora was in sunlit position (sunlit aurora), observing stations involved, and the angles μ, ϵ and ρ (cf. STØRMER, 1955, Chapter V).

The classification of auroral forms used throughout this paper is in accordance with the recommendations of 1930 of the International Union of Geophysics (cf. STØRMER, 1955 and *The Photographical Atlas of Auroral Forms*, 1930). A list of the auroral forms studied is given below, together with the number of measured points used in this work:

HA:	Homogeneous arcs	1234 points
HB:	Homogeneous bands	142 points
RA:	Arcs with ray structure	584 points
RB:	Bands with ray structure	2269 points
R:	Rays	5740 points
D:	Draperies	857 points
DS:	Cloudlike auroras or diffuse luminous surfaces	592 points
PA:	Pulsating arcs	390 points
PS:	Pulsating surfaces	424 points

By means of a computer, we have carried out the following analyses:

1. Relative frequency of occurrence and height of auroral forms as function of geomagnetic colatitude.
2. The height distribution of various auroral forms for different geomagnetic latitudes.
3. The height of the lower border of aurora as a function of local time.
4. Seasonal variation of occurrence and average heights for the measured auroral points.
5. Yearly variation of occurrence and average heights for various auroral forms. In this study comparison with the sunspot numbers has been made.

Some of the material obtained from this analysis will be presented in Sections III–VII.

III. Geomagnetic Distribution of the Observed Auroral Points and Their Heights

A. Introduction

In order to study the occurrence and height of aurora as a function of geomagnetic latitude, the total number of measured auroral points and their average heights have been computed for each of the following geomagnetic colatitude (θ) regions: $\theta < 20°$, $20 \leq \theta < 22$, $22° \leq \theta < 24°$, $24 \leq \theta < 26°$, $26 \leq \theta < 28°$, $28 \leq \theta < 30°$, and $\theta \geq 30°$. (The geographical location of these regions over Scandinavia is shown in Figure 68 in Størmer's book.) This study also includes a detailed account of the various forms listed in Section II with the exception of homogeneous bands (HB) for which the number of observations were too few to yield significant results.

B. Geomagnetic Distribution of All the Observed Auroral Points

In Figure 1 the distribution of all the measured points is shown as a function of geomagnetic colatitude. It appears from this figure that more than 50% of all points were observed in the colatitude region $24° < \theta < 28°$ and that the number of observations decreases rapidly both south and north of this region. It must be emphasized that this distribution does not reflect the frequency of visual aurora for geomagnetic colatitudes below 26°. Because there is a concentration of observing stations at colatitudes above 26° (south of 64° N geomag-

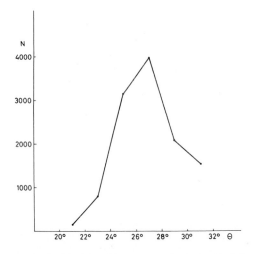

FIGURE 1. Number of observed auroral points (N) as function of geomagnetic colatitude (θ).

netic latitude), this part of the curve is probably reliable. From $\theta = 26°-$ $\theta = 30°$ the frequency of auroral occurrence decreases by more than 60%.

The number of observations of the various auroral forms listed in Section II relative to the total number of observed auroral points at various geomagnetic colatitudes are shown in Figures 2(A) and 2(B). Even if the distributions of absolute numbers of observations are strongly influenced by the distributions of observing sites, this is probably not the case for the relative occurrences given in Figure 2, because it is rather unlikely that the observer's selection of auroral forms depends significantly on his position. Therefore it is felt that significant information may be drawn from these curves, which we shall refer to as relative distribution curves. It should be stressed, however, that the data have not been collected for this particular purpose. Thus, it may be somewhat subject to selection in other criteria. For example, it is not clear whether the homogeneous arcs really contribute less than 10% of all observed forms, counted at random times. This low per cent could reflect the fact that the heights of these are more difficult to measure accurately because they are more diffuse.

The most striking feature of Figure 2 is the relatively high frequency of pulsating arcs and also of draperies at low magnetic latitudes. This is also partly the case with pulsating surfaces. However, the pulsating forms measured by Stormer were necessarily those in which pulsations were visual. From more recent measurements it appears that pulsations are much more frequent than previously believed, but that the pulsations very often are too weak to be noticed through visual observations (cf. IYENGAR and SHEPHERD, 1961; JOHANSEN and OMHOLT, 1966).

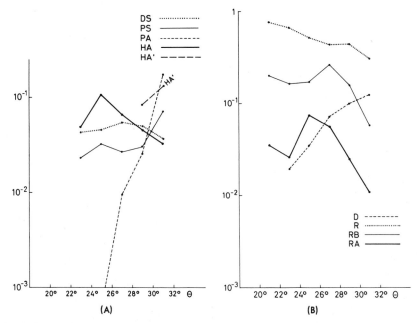

FIGURES 2(A) and 2(B). Relative distribution curves for the different auroral forms showing the ratio between the number of measured points for a given auroral form and the total number of measured auroral points, as a function for the given interval of geomagnetic colatitude θ. The curves for HA and HA' are for homogeneous arcs below and above 150 km, respectively.

The homogeneous arcs at heights below 150 km show a relative distribution curve which is somewhat similar to those of most other forms. Homogeneous arcs at heights above 150 km seem to be a phenomenon distinctly different from other arcs. This is evident from Figure 6, Section IV. The high arcs occur exclusively at low latitudes, for θ > 28°, where they are measured in much greater numbers than the low ones.

C. Variation of the Average Height with Geomagnetic Colatitude

STØRMER (1955) discussed the geomagnetic distribution of the average height for three different auroral forms. In this study, however, he used only a small fraction of all his observations. Using all the 12,232 points measured, the variation of average height with geomagnetic colatitude was derived. The result, which is presented in Figure 3, shows strongly that the height of all observed points, averaged over the given colatitude intervals, decreases systematically with increasing colatitude from 20°–30°.

It should be stressed that the points measured are structures which can be recognized on simultaneous photographs from at least two stations, and that the measurements include points from the higher as well as the lower part of the aurora. Even so, we feel that the observed variation reflects a significant

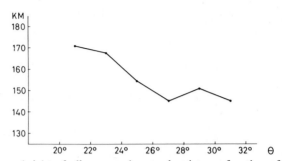

FIGURE 3. Average height of all measured auroral points as function of geomagnetic co-latitude θ.

variation in the energy distribution of the auroral primary particles, particularly in the low-energy end of the spectrum.

In Figures 4(A) and 4(B) the distribution, similarly derived, is shown for the various auroral forms. Sunlit auroras are included, but this significantly affects only the height distribution of auroral rays (R). The auroral forms, D, RB, and RA (cf. Figure 4(A)) show height variations with latitude which are similar to that for the average of all forms, even if the actual heights are very different. The height for rays shows a decrease at small values of θ, which is probably significant. From Figure 4(B) it appears that DS, PS, and PA, as well as the ordinary HA, show little or no significant height variation with latitude. The high arcs, HA', have an average height of 204 km.

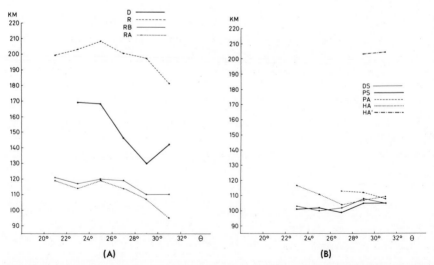

FIGURES 4(A) and 4(B). Average height of measured points in the different auroral forms, as a function of geomagnetic colatitude θ. (A): D, R, RB, and RA. (B): DS, PS, PA, and HA.

In general, the results given here are consistent with those given by Størmer. The selection of the material and the number of points included in the statistics necessarily makes the detailed shape of the curves somewhat different.

IV. The Height Distribution of the Measured Points as a Function of Geomagnetic Colatitude

A. Introduction

In the preceding section the average height of all measured points as function of geomagnetic colatitude was presented. In this section a more detailed account of the distribution of heights will be presented. STØRMER (1955) gave the distribution of the height of all auroral points measured from 1911–44 for heights between 70–1100 km. Also for some particular forms, he has plotted on a diagram the measured points at their appropriate heights, thus giving a typographic density impression of the height distribution. In this section a more complete analysis is presented for the height interval 65–300 km. The curves in Figures 5–10 display the number of measured auroral points per 5 km height interval and per 2° latitude interval. We believe that the actual height distribution as a function of geomagnetic latitude may be of special interest for detailed comparison with auroral theories. It again should be stressed that the points used lie partly at the bottom of the forms and partly at a higher level.

B. The Height Distribution of All Measured Points

Figure 5 shows the height distributions of the measured auroral points, regardless of auroral form, for the various geomagnetic latitude ranges. The most characteristic features of these curves may be summarized as follows:

a. For all geomagnetic colatitude intervals between 30°–22°, a very pronounced maximum of auroral occurrence is observed between 90–120 km.
b. The peak height of maximum frequency is found between 100–110 km for all latitude intervals. It does not seem to vary with latitude, although there is a slight tendency for the peak to increase with increasing latitude.
c. The half-width of the height distribution curves seems to vary with latitude, increasing with increasing θ above 24°. This, together with the curve given in Figure 1, may indicate that the average energy as well as the energy spread of the primary particles is larger at high values of θ than closer to the auroral zone.

C. The Height Distribution of Various Auroral Forms

In Figures 6–10 are shown the height distributions for the auroral forms HA, RA, D, DS, and PS, respectively, within the various latitude ranges. Here we shall give only some brief comments to the figures in the order they appear.

Figure 6. Homogeneous Arcs (HA): STØRMER (1955) discussed in some detail the height distribution of auroral arcs, but no detailed information con-

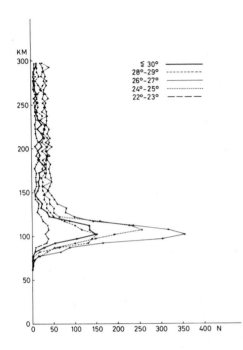

FIGURE 5. Height distribution of all measured auroral points for various intervals of geomagnetic colatitude θ. N is the number of measured points per 5 km height interval and 2° colatitude interval.

cerning the latitude variation of heights was derived. He remarks that "very high narrow arcs generally appear isolated near the zenith in Oslo." This is easily verified by these curves, which show that high arcs ($h \geq 150$ km) appear exclusively for $\theta > 28°$, and here they even seem to be the dominating form. It is striking that very few homogeneous arcs were observed at heights around 150 km.

This minimum in the curves at 150 km strongly suggests that two distinctly different types of arcs occur, the high ones and the low ones. For the low arcs there is a shift in the peak towards lower heights with increasing θ. Thus it seems justified to extend Størmer's conclusion regarding homogeneous arcs at low geomagnetic latitude ($\theta > 28°$) and state that these are either observed at markedly greater altitudes or at lower altitudes than the average for higher geomagnetic latitudes ($\theta > 28°$).

Figure 7, Rayed Arcs (RA): Rayed arcs also exhibit a marked decrease in the distribution peak with increasing θ, but contrary to the curve for all forms in Figure 6, the half-width of the distribution curve seems to decrease with increasing θ.

Figure 8, Draperies (D): For these there seems to occur a shift in the peak of the distribution curves which is opposite to that for homogeneous arcs and rayed arcs, e.g., there is an increase in the height of the peak with increasing θ.

Figure 9, Diffuse and Cloudlike Aurora (DS): Auroras between 150–200 km are very rare, and the peaks in the distribution curves as well as the average

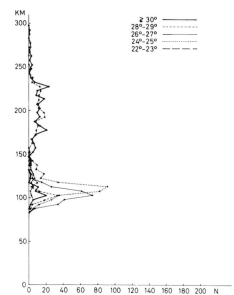

FIGURE 6. Height distributions for homogeneous arcs (HA).

height are low (cf. Figure 4(B)). There is no pronounced shift in the peak with θ. However, this analysis does not include auroras above 300 km, and it turns out from the data available that this kind of aurora actually does occur at great heights.

Figure 10, Pulsating Surfaces **(PS):** These are also particularly low-lying

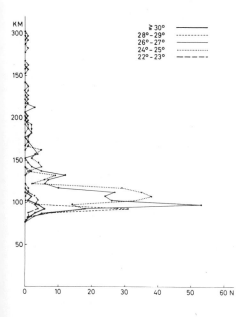

FIGURE 7. Height distributions for rayed arcs (RA).

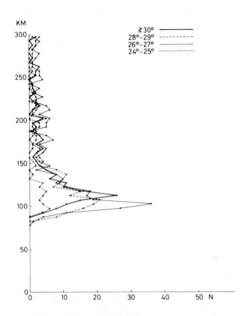

FIGURE 8. Height distribution for draperies (D).

forms, with their average height close to 100 km (cf. Figure 4(B)). However, they seem to be distributed over a broader height interval than pulsating arcs. STØRMER (1955) has given a closer description of some of these auroras, having

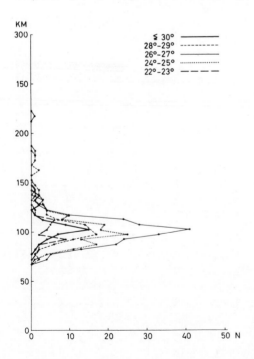

FIGURE 9. Height distribution for diffuse surfaces (DS).

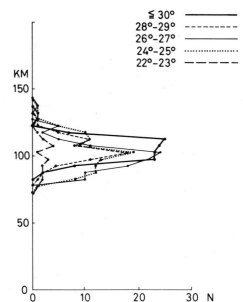

FIGURE 10. Height distribution for pulsating surfaces (PS).

diffuse contours and often resembling clouds. He used, however, only a fraction of his observations (up to the year 1922) in his own statistical analysis.

Concerning diagrams of the height distributions for rayed bands (RB), rays (R), and pulsating arcs (PA) for various latitude ranges, the reader is referred to the paper by EGELAND and OMHOLT (1966). Here it should be pointed out that:

1. Rayed bands show distribution curves which are very similar to those for all forms given in Figure 5.
2. As expected, rays show no pronounced height maxima.
3. Pulsating arcs are, as pulsating surfaces, very rare above 150 km. The peak height of PA decreases with increasing colatitude.

V. The Height of the Lower Border as Function of Local Time

For this study we have used only the auroral points that Størmer stated refer to the lower border or the base of the aurora. In Figures 11(A) and 11(B) the average values of these heights, for each whole hour are given for all forms for which more than about a hundred measurements were available. These are the homogeneous arcs (HA), homogeneous bands (HB), rayed arcs (RA), and rayed bands (RB). As seen from Figure 11(A), there is no large variation in the height of the lower border of HB, RA, and RB. To increase the significance, we have also plotted the mean curve for these three forms. This shows a fairly constant height around 105 km until local midnight, followed by a slight drop, to well below 100 km. The corresponding change in the necessary energy of the primary electrons is significant; it amounts to at least a factor of 2. For the homogeneous arcs (HA) below 150 km, no drastic changes occur with time (cf. Figure 11(B)). It appears that these are scarce in the early morning hours. The high arcs are observed exclusively before midnight, but there is no significant change in their heights with time.

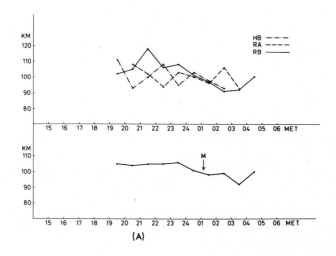

(A)

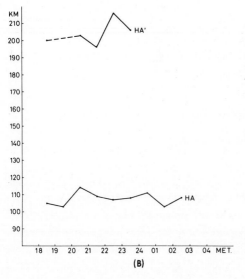

(B)

FIGURES 11(A) and 11(B). Average height of measured lower limit for some auroral forms. Curve M is the average curve for homogeneous bands (HB), rayed arcs (RA), and rayed bands (RB), the curves of which are also drawn separately. The curves for HA' are for homogeneous arcs below and above 150 km.

VI. Seasonal Variations in the Frequency and Heights of Aurora

In order to limit this paper, only a brief summary of the results obtained from the study of seasonal variations is given. For more details, refer to the paper by EGELAND and OMHOLT (1966). Also this investigation is based on more than twenty full years of observations. It should be emphasized that the material was not originally intended for studies of auroral occurrence.

From auroral observations in the dark atmosphere it was found that:

1. The seasonal variation in the occurrence was in general agreement with other observations (cf. CHAMBERLAIN, 1961).
2. Concerning the seasonal variation in auroral heights there was a significant tendency for the auroral point to lie at greater heights in the autumn months than during the rest of the year. This may be due to systematic changes in the primary particle spectrum, but one may also speculate that it reflects seasonal changes in the atmospheric structure.

The corresponding results for sunlit aurora are:

1. For sunlit aurora there was a markedly greater probability of occurrence during the spring than during the autumn.
2. The height difference between spring and autumn is about the same for auroras in the dark (approximately 50 km), whereas the heights, themselves, are about 200 km greater. In this connection it should be mentioned that 92% of all measured sunlit auroras are rays, which thus constitute the principal form of sunlit aurora.

VII. Occurrence and Average Height of the Measured Auroral Points between 1917 and 1942 Averaged Over a Sunspot Cycle

A. Introduction

As observed a long time ago (cf. STØRMER, 1955), the occurrence of visual aurora has an 11 year periodicity similar to the sunspot numbers. However, no detailed investigation has been made to determine whether individual auroral forms and their heights show the same periodicity. It should also be pointed out that there is a systematic tendency for the maximum occurrence of aurora to follow the sunspot peak by a year or two.

Although more than 12,000 auroral points have been measured during the 26 year period, there is not enough data to give a significant picture of the year-to-year variation of the auroral activity during the whole period. For this reason, all data have been used to draw average sunspot cycle curves. By this method some of the irregularities in this data collection (i. e., yearly variations in hours of observations, number of observing stations, and meteorological conditions, etc.) have been somewhat corrected.

B. Variation in Occurrence and Average Height of Aurora
in Shadow During the Sunspot Cycle

As the sunlit aurora will be discussed separately in Section VII.C., all the curves and figures given in this section refer to aurora in shadow.

The occurrence of all measured points averaged over one 11 year sunspot cycle is shown in Figure 12, Curve A, while Curve B shows the relative sunspot

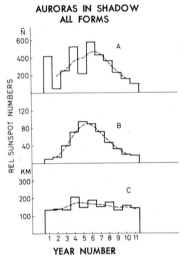

FIGURE 12. The average occurrence of aurora (A), sunspot number (B), and average auroral heights (C) averaged over the solar cycle. Sunlit auroras are excluded. The smoothed curves give the value of $Y_s = \frac{1}{4} Y_{-1} + \frac{1}{2} Y_0 + \frac{1}{4} Y_{+1}$.

numbers averaged over the same period. By comparing these two curves, a high correlation between auroral occurrence and the solar activity is found. Furthermore, the auroral activity reaches its maximum one year after the sunspot maximum. (The peak in the first year of the cycle is due to the extremely high observing-activity during the second polar year, 1932–33. This peak is also found in the yearly variation of particular auroral forms, as shown in Figures 13 and 14).

The average auroral heights for the same 11 year period are drawn in Figure 12, Curve C. As this curve shows, the yearly average altitudes vary from more than 200 km down to 120 km. The significance of the apparent variation with the sunspot cycle is uncertain, but it appears as though the average altitudes are somewhat higher during years of high solar activity.

In Figures 13(A), 13(B), and 13(C), the three different auroral forms HA, RB, and R have been plotted in the same way. While the occurrences of RB and R are rather closely correlated with the 11 year sunspot cycle, this is not the case for RA. (As the statistical material is relatively small, some irregularities are also seen for R and RB). Homogeneous arcs, on the other hand, show no correlation with the sunspot activity. In fact, HA's are probably observed more often during years of low solar activity.

It may be pointed out that the unusual high arcs discussed in Sections IV and V were observed during relatively strong local magnetic disturbances. The average 11 year height curves, which are also seen in Figure 13, show some variations, but these are not correlated with the solar activity. (As

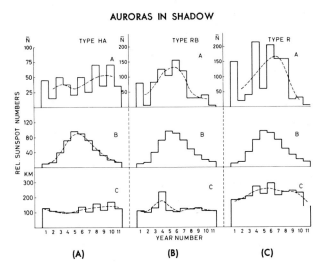

FIGURES 13(A), 13(B), and 13(C). The occurrences (N), sunspot number, and average heights (km) for homogeneous arcs (HA), rayed bands (RB), and rays (R), respectively, averaged over the solar cycle.

pointed out earlier, these peaks are probably due to observations and selection of points.) For homogeneous arcs the average heights seem to be somewhat lower during solar maximum than during years of low solar activity, but it is not certain if this change in height is significant. As already shown in Figure 4(A), the average heights of rays are more than 100 km greater than, for example, those of HA and RB.

C. Variation in Occurrence and Average Height of Sunlit Aurora During an 11 Year Sunspot Cycle

The average 11 year sunspot cycle curve for the 3,064 measured sunlit auroral points is shown in Figure 14, Curve A, while Curve B shows the variation in sunspot number. By comparing these two curves, it is found that sunlit aurora occurs mostly during years of high solar activity. The correlation coefficient is not too high, but this may be due to relatively small statistical material and irregularities in observations. (The peak during the first year of the cycle is due to the extremely high observing activity during the second polar year.) The average 11 year height curve of sunlit aurora is shown in Figure 14,

Curve C. Also for sunlit aurora no correlation between the height variations and the solar activity is found. It should be pointed out that the average height of all 3,064 points is 330 km. This means that the average height of sunlit aurora is approximately 200 km higher than for aurora in shadow.

AURORAS IN SUNLIGHT
ALL FORMS

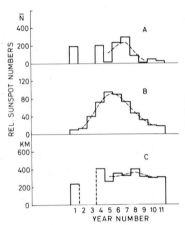

FIGURE 14. The occurrence, sunspot number and average height for sunlit aurora, averaged over the solar cycle.

Acknowledgment   The authors wish to express their thanks to Mr. H. S. Fotland and Mr. A. Gulbrandsen for carrying out the computations and numerical work.

This work was supported by grants from the Norwegian Research Council for Science and the Humanities.

References

CHAMBERLAIN, J. W., 1961, *Physics of the Aurora and Airglow*, Academic Press.
CHAPMAN, S., 1958, *Biographical Memories of Fellows of the Royal Society* **4**, 257.
EGELAND, A. and OMHOLT, A., 1966, *Geofys. Publikasjoner*, Vol. XXVI, No. 6. The Norwegian Academy of Science.
IYENGAR, R. S. and SHEPHERD, G. G., 1961, *Can. J. Phys.* **39**, 1911.
JOHANSEN, O. E. and OMHOLT, A.,1966, *Planetary Space Sci.* å, Vol. 14, 207.
STØRMER, C., 1930, *Photographic Atlas of Auroral Forms*, Brøggers Boktrykkeri, Oslo.
STØRMER, C., 1955, *The Polar Aurora*, Oxford University Press.

Discussion

There were a number of questions raised concerning the subjectivity that must be associated with a study of this nature. It was asked how the average height was determined, and if the median rather than average was ever used. The average height was consistently defined as the height of the lower border averaged over a one hour interval. There was some concern that since all the observations were made by one man that this might bias the information if, for example, no observations were made in certain periods (e.g., vacation, sick, holidays), and it was also questioned whether the need to select a definite height might bias the results by the omission of aurora with less well defined borders. It was agreed that these factors might bias the results, but there is no way to account for them.

DYNAMICAL STRUCTURE OF THE ATMOSPHERE
BETWEEN 80 AND 120 KM

J. E. Blamont and J. Barat

Service d'Aéronomie du C.N.R.S.,
91 - Verrières-Le-Buisson, France

Structure of a Sodium Cloud

Sodium atoms above 90 km of altitude recombine slowly with the atmosphere. When free, they are excited by solar light and reemit light by optical resonance at the doublet $\lambda = 5890$–96Å. A cloud is created from a rocket by a continuous ejection of vapor from 80 km to apogee (around 200 km) and down and is subjected to three types of motions (BLAMONT, 1959): (a) diffusion of sodium in the medium on a horizontal plane. The diffusion speed varies inversely with the density. Therefore, it increases exponentially with altitude; (b) horizontal winds with velocity up to 200 m/sec, a randomly distributed direction and horizontal scale superior to 100 km; and (c) turbulence in the lower part of the cloud (below 105 km), which gives it the appearance of a cumulus cloud and stops abruptly above this altitude. The subject of this paper is to present a few data obtained with sodium clouds relative to this last factor, turbulence.

Dynamic Parameters Measured with a Sodium Cloud

Diffusion. From the width of the cloud measured as a function of time, the diffusion coefficient can be directly deduced without further hypotheses. It is found that above 105 km the diffusion can be explained by a purely molecular process, with coefficients computed from the kinetic theory (provided collision cross sections are known). Below the altitude of 105 km, experimental evidence shows that this motion is not purely molecular, but obeys the laws of eddy diffusion. Immediately after ejection the motion of sodium atoms is described as a Brownian motion. The radius of the cloud r is described as a function of time by an equation of the type $r^2 \alpha t$.

After sodium atoms have traveled a distance of the order of the microscale of the turbulence, the diffusion equation depends on the spectrum of eddies. Should the turbulent field be isotropic, the radius would be given by an equation of the type $r^2 \alpha t^3$. Should the field be anisotropic, subjected to a wind gradient, the diffusion equation would be $r^2\alpha t^2$. From the study of diffusion a study of the spectrum of the field can be undertaken.

Hodographs. From the changes in the overall shape of the cloud as a function of time, the horizontal wind vector at each altitude can be deduced. It usually has the same value for the descending and ascending part of the ejection, since the horizontal dimension of a system of winds is of the order of hundreds of kilometers. The motions are represented in a diagram where direction and magitude of the wind vector are plotted for each altitude.

It has been shown that the wind vector rotates in the anticyclonic direction when the altitude increases from 90–150 km, and that superimposed on this basic movement are various and random wind structures, essentially below 110 km.

Structure Functions. These functions, easier to handle than correlation functions when the average value of a parameter has a slow variation (stationary first increment), can be obtained directly for the field of velocity of the atmosphere from the study of the velocities measured with a sodium cloud (BLAMONT and DE JAGER, 1961; BLAMONT, 1963). The knowledge of these functions is essentially similar to the knowledge of the spectrum. The values of the microscale of turbulence, of the large scale, and of the rate of turbulent energy dissipation can be obtained from these functions.

The Concept of Turbopause

Mass spectrometers mounted on rockets have shown by a measurement of the ratio of concentration of argon to nitrogen as a function of altitude that if the atmosphere is completely mixed up to 100 km of altitude, above 120 km, on the contrary, the constituents are separated by gravity and their concentration is governed by diffusion equilibrium. There exists between 100 and 120 km a transition from complete mixing to diffusion (MEADOWS and TOWNSEND, 1960).

BLAMONT (1959), however, has discovered a striking difference between the lowest part of a sodium cloud (below 102 km) and the highest part (above 102 km). Observed with a 20 cm focal length camera, the lowest part is constituted by a series of puffs, as if it were mixed by eddies of a few hundred meters of dimension. The highest part has a smooth, laminar shape, as if there were no eddies. The two parts are separated by a sudden transition. At times it has been seen that after a few minutes the lowest part of the laminar region would become turbulent. Relating these two facts, BLAMONT and BAGUETTE (1961) have suggested that the sharp transition observed in the sodium cloud corresponds to the change from mixing to diffusion. The atmosphere would be turbulent below a certain altitude (around 102 km) and not turbulent above this altitude. This boundary has been called turbopause.

Evidence for a Complex Dynamical Structure of the 80-110 km Region

When pictures are taken of a sodium cloud with a larger focal length (60 cm) and immediately after ejection (during the first 30 sec), it is found that the simple structure of the field of motion (turbulent and laminar regions separated by a turbopause) is only a very crude prime approximation. This configuration can be replaced by the following:

(a) Below a certain level of around 85 km, where the vertical temperature gradient is negative, the atmosphere is always turbulent.

(b) Above a certain level of about 110 km, where the vertical temperature gradient is positive, the atmosphere is in diffusion equilibrium (the field is laminar).

(c) Between these two limits, in the zone between 85 and 110 km where the vertical gradient is zero or positive, the atmosphere has the vertical structure of a sandwich with alternate regions. At a given altitude, the field is turbulent; above or below, at other altitudes, the field is laminar. The vertical span of each region is of the order of a few kilometers. The complete zone between 85 and 110 km can be filled with a turbulent field or with a laminar field, because the vertical location of each region changes with time. The horizontal dimensions of this structure are much larger (at least one order of magnitude) than the vertical dimensions. This situation is a typical example of a free turbulent flow, where turbulent and irrotational regions coexist, separated by a sharp dividing boundary.

Figure 1 shows a schematic illustration of the proposed picture. The evidence for this picture comes from the observations of a series of sodium clouds

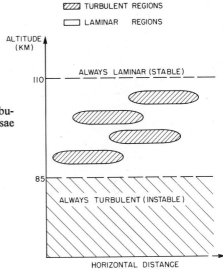

FIGURE 1. Separation into laminar and turbulent regions as a function of altitude (abcissae and ordinates *not* on same scale).

where a careful analysis of their shape below 110 km has been performed. In all these clouds the sandwich structure has been found. The following examples are chosen from a variety of others:

(a) On November 5, 1964 a sodium cloud was ejected from Hammaguir, Algeria, during evening twilight. The cloud shows the following structure:

(1) From 111 to 104.25 km, the cloud is turbulent. A complete study of all the dynamical characteristics, including a direct measurement of the turbulent energy, has been performed on this part.

(2) From 104.25 to 102 km, the cloud is laminar.

(3) From 102 to 97 km, the cloud is again turbulent.

(4) From 97 to 96 km, the cloud is laminar.

(5) Below 96 km, the cloud is turbulent.

Figure 2 shows the descending part of the cloud 8 seconds after the rocket has crossed the field of view at the altitude of 104.25 km. The helicoidal motion

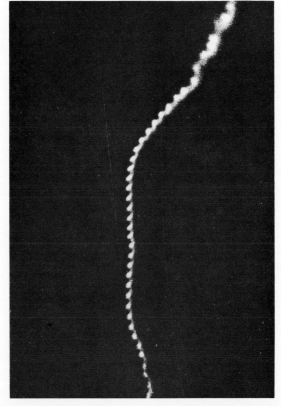

FIGURE 2. Descending portion of sodium cloud for a November 5, 1964 launch at Hammaguir, Algeria.

of the rocket has created this particular shape of the cloud, visible for a few seconds only. This shape makes it easy to determine the velocity of the expanding sodium cloud at every altitude. On the top of the picture it can be seen that the cloud above a certain altitude (here at 104.25 km) has been distorted from a straight line into a fuzzy pseudosinusoidal shape. When the velocities are deduced from such pictures, it is found (Figure 3) that below 104.25 km, the

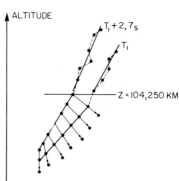

FIGURE 3. Velocities for path shown in Figure 2. Below 104.25 km the relative motion of the points vary regularly, but above this altitude the motion of the points is highly irregular.

relative motion of each point varies regularly, but above this altitude the motion of the points becomes highly irregular. This indicates the presence of turbulent pulsations in the wind velocity. The measurement of the diffusion coefficient above and below the transition confirms these data. We then have a typical sandwich situation.

(b) On September 18, 1965 a sodium cloud was ejected at Surinam (Dutch Guiana) during the evening. In the ascending part, the cloud is weakly turbulent between 95 and 90 km and is laminar outside these limits. In the descending part, the cloud is laminar at all altitudes. Thus it must be concluded that turbulence, if weak, can differ in different regions situated at the same altitude. Here we are very near the equator and find a situation where the turbulent structure is appearing just marginally.

(c) On January 16, 1966 a sodium cloud was ejected from Hammaguir, Algeria, during the evening. The cloud is laminar below 96 km and is turbulent from 96–102 km.

This phenomenon of a sandwich structure is difficult to observe because the turbulence can be mistaken for a variety of other phenomena, such as irregular wind motions varying quickly with altitude and vertical convective motions of certain parts of the cloud appearing as columns of sodium arising from the body of the cloud.

Origin of the Sandwich Structure

The best experimental evidence available for a discussion of the relation of the turbulent to the laminar region is the hodograph of the Hammaguir,

November 4, 1964 cloud (Figure 4). On the top of the usual anticyclonic rotation is superimposed a nearly sinusoidal wave. This wave is visible only between 90 and 110 km and is situated in the NE-SW plane. It is easy to separate the wave

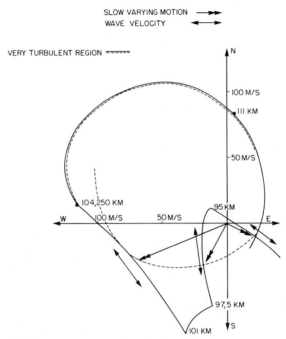

FIGURE 4. Hodograph as a function of altitude from Hammaguir, November 4, 1964.

motion from the slow varying (anticyclonic rotation) component since, when on the hodograph, the velocity gradient as a function of altitude is maximum (that is, at the nodes of the wave motion), the wave component is zero and the residual velocity is due to the slow varying component. This component can then be interpolated. Figure 5 shows the projection of the wave on the NE-SW plane and the projection of the slow varying component. It now becomes obvious that the wave component is not pure. We consider this appearance as due to two facts: 1) the primary motion is a pure sinus wave (dotted line) and 2) when the amplitude of this wave increases above a certain limit (which we relate to a critical Reynolds number), the wave is modified by the onset of a turbulence which is generated from the kinetic energy of the wave and disturbs the shape of the wave. The turbulent part of the field can now be obtained by subtracting the real curve from the dotted curve. Structure functions of the three components of the velocity field (slow varying, wave, and turbulent) can now be obtained since the components have been separated. The result is shown in Figure 6.

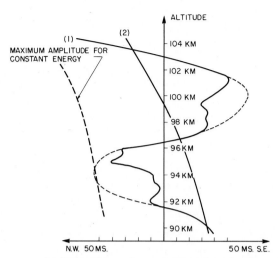

FIGURE 5. Components of velocity due to the wave (1) and to the slow varying motion (2) as projected into the NE-SW plane for Hammaguir, November 4, 1964.

From this figure the following conclusions can be obtained:

(a) The wave has a half wavelength of 6–7 km.

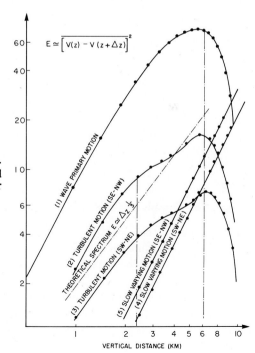

FIGURE 6. Structure function of the velocity field for the different separated fields of motion between 91–104 km for Hammaguir, November 5, 1964.

$$E \simeq \overline{\left[V(z) - V(z+\Delta z) \right]}^2$$

(b) The slope of the structure function for the wave and for the turbulent motion is the same for distances less than 2.5 km. Its value is 4/3.

(c) The wave is the only source of energy which could generate the turbulence.

(d) The difference between the spectrum of the wave and the spectrum of the turbulent field generated by this wave, for distances greater than 2.5 km, may be attributed to damping in a stable atmosphere.

(e) On the contrary, the spectrum of the slow varying motion does not have the same shape (different shape, no maximum) and has not enough energy to generate the turbulent motion.

We can now propose an explanation of the "sandwich" structure. There exist in the atmosphere at all times waves (or organized motions) with a half wavelength of 6–7 km and with amplitude and direction variable with space and time. Since their phase velocity is not horizontal, the maxima of amplitudes will not always be located at the same altitude but will change with time. It is tempting to identify these waves with the gravity waves predicted by Hines which have essentially the properties of these waves which we observe experimentally.

In the region where the amplitude of the wave is larger than a certain limit,

(a) The region is turbulent, with an eddy diffusion coefficient (mixing).

(b) The wave is completely distorted and loses energy by turbulent friction.

In the region where the amplitude is inferior to a certain limit,

(a) The region is laminar, with a molecular diffusion coefficient (diffusion equilibrium).

(b) The wave is not disturbed and loses practically no energy by dissipation.

This sandwich system cannot exist above about 110 km because the wave, essentially generated at low altitudes and propagating upwards, has lost all of its energy in the turbulent regions and cannot generate turbulence in a viscous zone. Neither can it exist below 85 km because there the atmosphere is unstable and no laminar flow will appear.

Onset of Turbulence in the Turbopause: the Critical Reynolds Number

Following BLAMONT and DE JAGER (1961), BARAT (1966) has introduced a critical Reynolds number which is essentially the experimental value of the ratio Re_{cr} for which the laminar motion becomes turbulent:

$$Re_{cr} = \frac{vL}{\nu} \tag{1}$$

ν is the kinematic viscosity, v and L are defined from the following considerations.

Let a horizontal laminar flow in a vertical plane (z,x) with a distribution $v(z)$ of the fluid velocity. The structure function of the velocities $(v(z_1) - v(z_1 + \Delta z))^2$ when z_1 is the altitude of an extremum of velocities, has a maximum for a value of Δz corresponding to the following extremum of $v(z)$. Between these two extrema the fluid has an average motion, with $\dfrac{dv}{dz}$ keeping the same sign. In Equation (1), if the field is laminar, L will be defined as the distance between the two successive extrema. If it is turbulent, L will be the distance between one extremum and the place where the turbulence starts. v will be the difference of the corresponding velocities.

It can be said that each stratum of fluid flows as if it is contained in a pipe between extrema of velocities. Barat has measured Re_{cr} at a well defined transition and found a value of around 600. When the motion of the wave creates shears whose Re_{cr} is higher than 600 the turbulent layer will appear. Using this critical number, defined somewhat arbitrarily, it is possible to predict whether the field will become turbulent or not when the kinematic properties of the wave have been measured.

References

BARAT, J., 1966, Thesis, Paris (to be published).

BLAMONT, J., 1959, *C-R. Acad. Sci. Paris* **249**, 1248.

BLAMONT, J., 1963, *Planetary Space Sci.* **10**, 89.

BLAMONT, J. and BAGUETTE, J. M., 1961, *Ann. Geophys.* **17**, 319.

BLAMONT, J. and DE JAGER, C., 1961, *Ann. Geophys.* **17**, 134.

MEADOWS, E. and TOWNSEND, J., 1960, *Space Research* **1**, North-Holland Publishing Co. 175.

COORDINATED SATELLITE, GROUND-BASED AND AIRCRAFT-BASED MEASUREMENTS ON AURORAS

R. G. Johnson, R. E. Meyerott, and J. E. Evans

Lockheed Palo Alto Research Laboratory
Lockheed Missiles & Space Company
Palo Alto, California

I. Introduction

The simultaneous observation of several different effects produced during an auroral event is a technique which has been used effectively for many years by ground-based observatories to increase our understanding of auroras. In recent years this technique has been extended to include satellite measurements which are made simultaneously with ground- and aircraft-based auroral observations [EVANS and BELON, 1963; JELLY *et al.*, 1964; HARGREAVES and SHARP, 1965; HOOK and OWREN, 1962; MAEHLUM and O'BRIEN, 1963].

Satellite and rocket measurements have shown that energetic electrons and protons are precipitating into the atmosphere [MCILWAIN, 1960; DAVIS *et al.*, 1960; O'BRIEN, 1964; SHARP *et al.* 1965a; and EVANS *et al.*, 1966a] with sufficient energy flux to produce many of the observed auroral phenomena such as the luminosity, cosmic noise absorption, etc. However, the quantitative relations between the spatial distributions and energy fluxes of the incident particles and the resulting energy and spatial distributions of the luminosity and ionization are still largely unknown. For example, even the relatively simple measurement of the amount of 3914-Å radiation from molecular nitrogen which is produced per erg of electron energy incident on the upper atmosphere has not been made with any precision and the value is still uncertain to at least a factor of 2 [HULTQVIST, 1964]. The electron and ion removal processes and the associated rate coefficients which connect the production rates and equilibrium densities are not known reliably. Therefore, at present it is not feasible to start with the luminosity observed from an aurora and deduce the detailed energy, angular, and spatial distributions of the energetic electrons and protons which produced the luminosity.

Conversely, it is generally not possible from satellite measurements alone to separate the spatial and temporal variations in the particle fluxes which produce the auroral luminosity. A satellite measurement is representative of the particle flux over only a very narrow strip across the aurora and is obtained in a very short time (about 1 sec for an average quiet arc). Such a measurement will not adequately identify the type of auroral form on which the measurement was made; from the particle data alone, it is not possible to tell whether the particle flux was contributing to a quiet arc, a rayed arc, or a narrow patch of luminosity. At present, ground- or aircraft-based optical observations on the same form are essential if the particle flux characteristics are to be associated with a particular type of auroral form. The future use of image orthicon television tubes on satellites may sufficiently identify the type of forms under certain conditions [DAVIS, 1965; 1967].

A determination of the quantitative relationships between the luminosity distributions of several prominent emissions in auroral forms and the characteristics of the precipitating particle fluxes should not only lead to a better understanding of the auroral excitation processes but should also make the large body of ground-based auroral data more useful in the study of the morphology of the precipitating particle fluxes. It is equally important to seek particle flux characteristics which can be associated with a particular type of auroral form in order to extend the usefulness of the satellite data on particle fluxes.

Prior to November, 1965, the most complete set of ground- and aircraft-based radio and optical measurements which were coordinated with satellite measurements on precipitating particle fluxes was obtained in February, 1962 [EVANS and BELON, 1963; MEYEROTT and EVANS, 1964]. Ground-based optical and radio measurements provided vertical luminosity profiles and electron content measurements on a relatively quiet homogeneous arc at the time of an overpass of the satellite which measured precipitating particle fluxes. The feasibility of operating an aircraft in the satellite orbital plane with the necessary timing and locational accuracies for a coordinated experiment was also established. The particle flux data were acquired from only two detectors due to failure of the primary satellite telemetry, and thus were inadequate for a detailed energy comparison with the ground- and aircraft-based data. A good correlation between the location of the precipitating particle fluxes and the observed luminosity was obtained, and electron content measurements were acquired using the dispersive Doppler technique with signals from a phase coherent 20- and 40-Mc/sec radio beacon on the satellite. From scintillations of the radio signals, field-aligned irregularities in the E-region ionization were observed and were correlated with the location of the precipitating particle fluxes [HOOK and OWREN, 1962].

A large number of coordinated experiments have also been performed by using rocket and ground-based observations and by using particle flux data from satellites and ground-based riometer data. These types of experiments are discussed elsewhere in this book.

This paper will be limited principally to a discussion of satellite-, ground-, and aircraft-based techniques and measurements which provide nearly simultaneous information on the auroral particle fluxes (input) and the effects (output) produced by the particles as they interact with the atmosphere. This will include simultaneous measurements on the satellite of several parameters associated with the auroras. The primary objective of these measurements is to provide quantitative data on both the ion production rates (using the particle flux data) as a function of altitude and on the resulting auroral luminosity and equilibrium electron densities. Such quantitative data are needed to improve our understanding of the energy balance between the particle fluxes and their effects and to establish well-defined conditions which must be met by proposed electron and ion reaction processes. To acquire the coordinated and quantitative data, more stringent requirements are imposed on the measurements than those generally associated with isolated observations to acquire data on a statistical basis. These requirements and some of the associated experimental problems will be reviewed. Coordinated data acquired from a satellite flight in November, 1965, will be presented.

II. Experimental Approach and Techniques

The concept for the coordinated satellite-, ground-, and aircraft-based measurements on auroras is shown schematically in Figure 1. This is a sec-

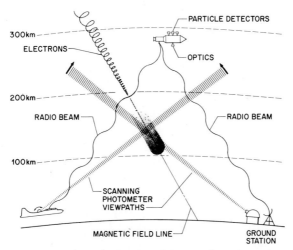

FIGURE 1. A schematic diagram of the coordinated experiment.

tional view in the plane of a polar-orbiting satellite and illustrates a desirable configuration of an isolated aurora and the ground- and aircraft-based instrumentation.

Particle detectors aboard the satellite measure the characteristics of the precipitating electrons and protons as the satellite moves across the aurora. The energy distribution measurements emphasize the region below 25 keV since particles in this range are generally the dominant contributor to the night-side auroral luminosity [SHARP et al., 1965b]. The angular distributions of the particle fluxes are also made to provide the data necessary to compute the total precipitated energy.

The luminosity from the aurora is measured at several different wavelengths with $1° \times 4°$ scanning photometers aboard the aircraft and with comparable angular resolution on the ground. These photometers scan from horizon to horizon to give vertical luminosity profiles and absolute intensities for the prominent auroral emissions such as 3914Å (N_2^+), 4278Å (N_2^+), 4861Å (H_β), 5577Å (OI), 6300Å (OI), and 6704Å (N_2). Particular emphasis is given the 3914Å or 4278Å measurements because these emissions are most easily related to the local ion-production rates due to the energetic auroral particles.

The electron density in the aurora is determined from the radio signals transmitted from the satellite to the ground- or aircraft-based receivers. The radio beam is swept through the auroral ionization by the satellite motion. A phase-coherent multi-frequency beacon which operates at 20, 40, and 120 Mc/sec is used, and measurements of the phase changes between different signals give the total electron content along the transmitted path.

In addition to the foregoing measurements, the coordinated experiment imposes two additional requirements on the luminosity observations. The homogeneity and the time history of the auroral luminosity must be determined. Since the particle flux measurements pertain to only a thin strip (comparable to the radii of gyrations of the particles) across the aurora, the homogeneity measurements are required to establish the validity of comparing the data with the vertical luminosity and radio measurements which include regions that are typically a few kilometers out of the satellite orbital plane. The time-history measurements on the spatial distribution of the luminosity are needed to determine whether the coordinated measurements were obtained under essentially equilibrium conditions. Since the lifetimes of the electrons produced in an aurora are expected to range from seconds to minutes depending on the altitude and local electron densities, it must be established whether the auroral conditions have been essentially constant for several minutes before the satellite transit.

An array of automatic 35-mm small-angle cameras on the aircraft can provide detailed information on both the inhomogeneities and the motion of the luminous regions. Photographs of a 25° strip of sky in the satellite orbital plane are obtained with exposure times as short as one second. The 60-lines/mm resolution, which is possible with commercially available film, corresponds to a spatial resolution of 100 m at 150 km. The scanning photometers also provide information on the motion of the aurora. Horizon-to-horizon scans are made in about 1 sec, and sensitivities in the range from 10^{-2}–10^3 kR are normally used.

The instrumented aircraft, although less convenient and more difficult to operate than a ground station, has several desirable features in obtaining the optical and radio data for the coordinated experiment. With accurate satellite orbital data, the aircraft can be flown into the satellite orbital plane once (or more with jet-engine aircraft) each night. With this geometry, data can be acquired for radio transmission and optical scanning paths which pass through the same regions of space that are ionized by the particle fluxes being measured on the satellite. Ground-stations are normally not in the satellite orbital plane, and the optical and radio data are thus acquired in regions well removed from the region ionized by the particle fluxes being measured. The usefulness of correlating the data is then a function of the specific geometry and the homogeneity of the aurora. The aircraft can also get above most of the cloud covers which often distort or obscure the ground-based optical measurements.

The location of the aircraft in the satellite orbital plane can be achieved with standard Doppler navigation equipment. Latitudinal accuracies of ± 2 km and heading accuracies of $\pm 2°$ are adequate for the scanning photometers. The amount and direction of aircraft motion can also be monitored from star patterns on the small-field camera photographs. Additional details on the aircraft instrumentation and operation have been reported [EVANS, 1967].

The relatively high velocity of 8 km/sec for a low-altitude satellite establishes the time scale for most of the coordinated particle, optical, and radio measurements. For a quiet auroral arc having a width of 9 km [KIM and VOLKMAN, 1963], the particle flux measurements on the satellite must be made in approximately 1 sec. This is comparable to the time needed to obtain the vertical luminosity profile with the scanning photometers. The radio beam would scan vertically over an aurora located at a zenith angle of 45° from the aircraft or ground station in about one-half minute.

To meet the requirement that many instruments on the satellite be sampled very rapidly, a 64-channel electronic commutator has been used to provide 64 samples per second on each channel. This provided at least eight readings of each instrument across a 1-km aurora. Higher resolution was obtained for selected instruments by placing each output on several channels of the commutator. Data have been taken only 1.6 msec or 13 m apart [SHARP et al., 1965b], but the actual spatial resolution for the data was limited to about 40 m by the response time of the instrument.

Two notable advances have recently occurred in the satellite instrumentation techniques for measurements on auroral particle fluxes. These advances are based on the development of the gallium phosphide light-emitting diode and the channel multiplier. The gallium phosphide diode is a small semiconductor device which produces light when an electrical current is passed through it. The intensity of the light can be varied over several decades by varying the current. These units have been used for in-flight calibration of satellite-borne photomultiplier tubes which were used with particle flux and optical sensors [REAGAN et al., 1966]. In-flight calibrations are nearly essential to obtain the accuracies needed for coordinated particle and optical measurements on auroras. The previous use of filament lights and movable radioactive sources often introduced additional instrumental problems.

The spectral measurement of auroral electrons with energies less than 40 keV and protons with energies less than 100 keV has, until recently, been a major instrumentation problem. As a result of the pioneering work on channel multiplier detectors for low-energy particle detection by D. S. EVANS [1965], it is now possible to measure almost routinely both electrons and protons at these low energies. Some care must still be exercised to avoid pulse-amplitude degradations in the channel multipliers for pulse rates above about 10^5/sec. This provides some limitations to the useful dynamic range for short duration events. The channel multipliers are also very sensitive to ultraviolet radiation [HUNTER, 1962], and although this feature can be a problem when measuring particle fluxes, it may make the channel multiplier an important sensor for future ultraviolet spectrometers and photometers. These detectors are now commercially available and have been successfully flown for auroral proton and electron measurements on rockets and satellites [EVANS, 1965; WESTERLUND et al., 1965; SHARP et al., 1966; SHOOK et al., 1966].

A satellite instrument package designed to make the particle flux measure-

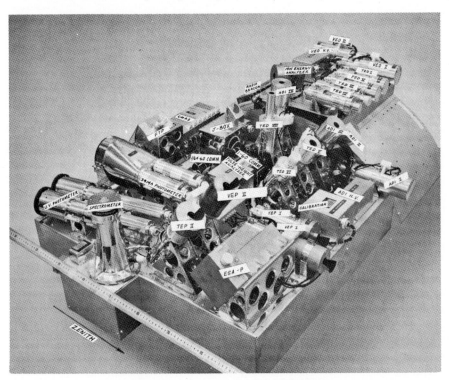

FIGURE 2. 1965-I satellite instrument package.

Table I. Particle and Optical Detectors on 1965-I Satellite Instrument Package

Instrument		Threshold (keV)	Direction from Zenith (deg)	Aperture Angle (deg)
Electron detectors				
Variable energy detector	VED 1	0.015–10	0	±20
	2	0.015–10	180	±20
Angular distribution instrument	ADI 1	1	0	±15
	2	1	35	±10
	3	1	55	±10
	4	1	85	±10
Total energy detector	TED 1	2	0	±30
	2	9	0	±30
	3	25	0	±30
	4	60	0	±30
	5	9	55	±20
	6	25	55	±20
	7	25	85	±10
Channel multiplier magnetic	CMAE 1	1 (a)	55	±5
analyzer	2	2 (a)	55	±5
($\Delta E/E = 15\%$)	3	5 (a)	55	±5
	4	12 (a)	55	±5
	5	28 (a)	55	±5
	6	70 (a)	55	±5
	7	Background	55	±5
High energy spectrometer	SPEC	100	90	±80
Proton detectors				
Variable energy detector	VEP 1	0.2–10	0	±20
	2	0.2–10	55	±20
Total energy detector	TEP 1	57	0	±30
	2	57	55	±20
Fixed threshold detector	FTP 1	21	55	±12
	2	38	55	±12
	3	56	55	±12
	4	1000	55	±12
Electrostatic analyzer	ESAP	1–15	55	24° × 10°
Optical detectors				
3914Å photometer	PHOT 1	0.6 (b)	169	1° × 4°
($\Delta\lambda = 40$ Å)	2	0.3 (b)	191	1° × 4°
Ultraviolet photometer				
1250–1800Å	UV 1	0.3 (b)	169	1° × 4°
1300–1800Å	2	4.0 (b)	169	1° × 4°

(a) Central Energy (keV)
(b) Threshold Sensitivity ($\sim$kR)

ments discussed previously for a coordinated experiment is shown in Figure 2. The instruments and their general characteristics are given in Table I. All scintillation-type phototube detectors, except the high-energy spectrometer, were operated in the constant current, variable-high-voltage mode. Energy thresholds were determined either with aluminum foils or with planar electrostatic grids followed by post-acceleration voltages [REAGAN et al., 1964]. These detectors were calibrated in flight at four intensity levels using the gallium phosphide light-emitting diodes. Weak radioactive sources set the output levels at the low ends of the dynamic ranges to serve as backup gain monitors. The rate meters for the channel multiplier outputs were calibrated in flight at four levels using an on-board pulse generator. The channel multiplier counting efficiencies were monitored using weak radioactive sources to set the output levels at the low end of the dynamic range of each rate meter. Additional details on the particle detectors are available elsewhere [REGAN *et al.*, 1966; SHEA *et al.*, 1966].

The 3914Å photometers, the ultraviolet photometers, and the ion-energy analyzer were included to supplement the ground- and aircraft-based data on the effects produced by the precipitating particle fluxes. Narrow field-of-view instruments at 3914Å and ultraviolet radiation measurements in the 1250–1800Å range previously had not been obtained from a satellite. The ion-energy analyzer measured the positive ion density and temperature at the satellite altitude.

The instrument package shown in Figure 2 was successfully flown by the Lockheed Palo Alto Research Laboratory in November, 1965, aboard an earth-center-oriented polar-orbiting satellite at altitudes near 200 km. Of the 34 detectors, all except the proton electrostatic analyzer performed satisfactorily and provided data.

III. November, 1965, Coordinated Measurements

Coordinated satellite-, ground-, and aircraft-based measurements were conducted on November 9, 10, and 11, 1965 (U.T.). Well equipped ground stations for optical measurements were operated at College, Fort Yukon, and Bar I by the Geophysical Institute of the University of Alaska. The College and Fort Yukon stations also operated 40- and 120-Mc/sec radio receivers to obtain signal strength and differential Doppler measurements. The Stanford Research Institute operated a 139- and 398-Mc/sec radar station at Homer, Alaska, to study radar reflections in the auroral zone at the time of the satellite overpass. A B-17 aircraft, owned and operated by Aero Service Corporation, was instrumented by the Lockheed Palo Alto Research Laboratory for optical measurements and for radio signal strength and phase measurements. Other ground-based observatories in Canada, Norway, Sweden, and the United States also participated on an informal basis.

Coordinated observations were made on three consecutive nights in the Alaskan region with all the stations operating. A near-full moon and some cloud-cover limited the optical observations, but luminosity measurements were acquired on the first night by the aircraft and the College station on an aurora north of Fort Yukon. Precipitating electron and proton fluxes were observed during the satellite overpass, and radar returns were observed at the Homer station. During the times of the satellite overpasses on the second and third nights, no auroras were observed optically and no auroral echoes were obtained with the radar. Precipitating protons of low intensity (about 0.02 erg/cm²-sec above 10 keV) were observed by the satellite during the second and third nights. Precipitating electron fluxes were found to be less than 10^{-2} erg/cm²-sec. The indices of auroral activity indicate that the three-day period was a very quiet one. The 24-hour K_p sums were 8_0, 1- (the lowest value in 1965), and 6_0 for the three days, respectively.

The locations of the satellite orbital plane, the ground stations, and the aircraft are shown for the three consecutive nights on the map in Figure 3.

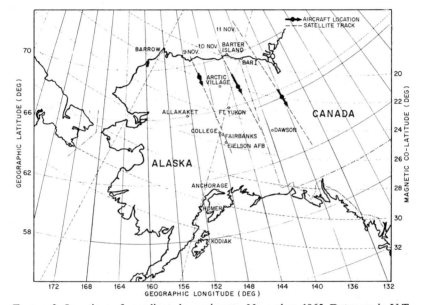

FIGURE 3. Locations of coordinated experiments, November, 1965. Dates are in U.T.

The geometry of the observations and some of the data acquired on the first night are shown in Figure 4 with the stations and observations projected along magnetic latitudes into the satellite orbital plane.

At the time of the satellite overpass on the first night, a weak aurora was observed from College at a zenith angle of about 65° on the magnetic meridian north of Fort Yukon with a narrow band interference filter 5577-Å photometer and a 5577-Å birefringent photometer. The luminosity was observed to be relatively stable in location and intensity at the time of the satellite overpass. Optical data were also acquired with the photometers on the aircraft, but very high moonlight backgrounds were present in the region of greatest interest which was south of the aircraft and thus in the general direction of the moon. The luminosity scan from the 5577-Å birefringent photometer is shown in Figure 4 as a function of the scan angle from College.

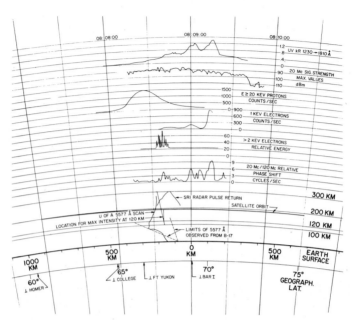

FIGURE 4. Coordinated observations on November 9 (U. T.), 1965.

The regions of precipitating electron and proton fluxes as observed from the satellite are also shown in Figure 4. The peak intensity of the protons is seen to be well separated from and equatorward of the electron fluxes. The precipitating electrons are observed in two separated regions. In the region south of the aircraft location, the electron spectrum is relatively hard, and electrons were observed with scintillation detectors with thresholds at 0.2, 1, 2, 10, and 25 keV. Low energy electrons were observed north of the aircraft only with the more sensitive channel multiplier detectors at 1.0 ± 0.15 and 2.0 ± 0.3 keV. Preliminary values for the peak proton and electron intensities south of the aircraft are about 0.2 and 0.3 erg/cm²-sec. The intensities of the electron fluxes north of the aircraft were less than about 0.01 erg/cm²-sec-sr for electron energies greater than 1 keV.

The intensity of the auroral luminosity was not great enough to be seen above the moonlight background with the 3914-Å photometer aboard the satellite. However, data were obtained with the ultraviolet photometers, since the uv photometers were not sensitive to scattered moonlight. These data are shown by the top curve in Figure 4. Relatively little uv is seen in the region of the hard electron flux compared to that observed in the region of the soft electron flux. The relationship between the observed uv and the energy distributions of the precipitating electrons is still being investigated.

Good quality radio data were acquired from the 20-, 40-, and 120-Mc/sec beacon on the satellite. Signal strength and phase measurements were acquired on the aircraft and at College and Fort Yukon. Relatively large phase shifts were observed during the satellite overpass, and these data will be used to determine the electron content along the signal path. The 20-Mc/sec signal strength variations and the relative phase shifts of the 20- and 120-Mc/sec signals as measured on the aircraft are shown in Figure 4. Scintillations observed in the radio signal strengths will be used to investigate the irregularities in the ionization.

A preliminary analysis of the radar data by the Stanford Research Institute group revealed that relatively strong auroral echoes were observed at Homer at the time of the satellite overpass on the first night of the experiment. The location of the reflecting region and intensity of the signals were relatively constant for several minutes before and after the satellite overpass. The direction of the radar beam was such that the echoes were obtained from a region about 50 km east of the satellite orbital plane. The echo signal strength from this region, projected along the magnetic latitudes into the satellite orbital plane, is shown in Figure 4. It is seen that the radar-returns, which indicate inhomogeneities in the ionization, are coming from the general region of the precipitating electrons. No measurable returns were observed on the second or third nights. These measurements represent the first radar measurements on auroras coordinated with satellite measurements on the precipitating particle fluxes. A review of radar measurements on auroras has recently been given by LEADABRAND [1965].

IV. November, 1965, Satellite Measurements

In addition to the coordinated satellite, ground-based, and aircraft-based measurements, many cases of simultaneous data on the particle fluxes, ion density, and 3914-Å and ultraviolet radiations were acquired from the satellite. The data were acquired by means of an on-board tape recorder, and nearly continuous coverage was obtained in the auroral regions during a $2\frac{1}{2}$ day period. These measurements provide the first satellite data on the ultraviolet radiation from auroras [EVANS et al., 1966], on the proton energy distributions below 50 keV [SHARP et al., 1966], and on the detailed electron energy, angular, and spatial distributions below 40 keV [SHOOK et al., 1966; JOHNSON et al., 1966]. These data will establish a much broader basis for the planning and design of future coordinated experiments and, hopefully, will contribute to our present understanding of auroral phenomena. Most of the data and results are in a preliminary form.

An example of the data acquired from several different detectors is shown in Figure 5. This case is one of the more intense precipitation events and was obtained with the tape recorder in the northern auroral zone on the night side. Electron fluxes at zenith angles of 0° and 55° are indicated by the bottom two curves. They reached peak intensities of about 2.5 and 10 ergs/cm²-sec-sr, respectively. Relatively broad regions of electron precipitation are observed quite frequently on the night side and are similar in extent to those observed previously [SHARP *et al.*, 1965b]. The 3914-Å photometer, TOT-II, which was pointing approximately down the magnetic field, gave peaks in the same location as the particle fluxes. The ultraviolet photometers, UV-I and UV-II, and the other 3914-Å photometer, TOT-I, are looking down at 22° to the magnetic field direction. The peaks in the luminosities are about 3 sec later

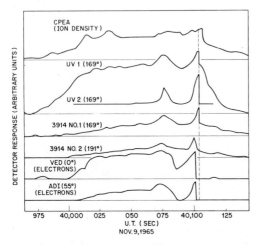

FIGURE 5. Simultaneous ion density, optical, and particle flux data over a wide auroral region.

than the particle fluxes. Thus, these vertical scans of the luminosities show that the peak intensities are about 75 km below the satellite. The top curve in Figure 5 shows the ion density variation at the satellite altitude (190 km). It was found to increase by about a factor of ten in the region of the particle flux precipitation.

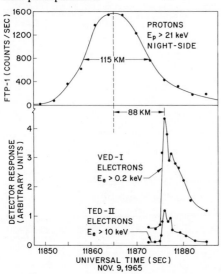

FIGURE 6. A narrow region of electron precipitation separated from proton precipitation.

Although widespread regions of electron precipitation are typical of the night-side auroral zone data, electrons are also observed precipitating into narrow regions with essentially no electron precipitation elsewhere in the zone. An example of this is seen in Figure 6 for the night-side northern auroral zone. Precipitating protons were also observed on the pass, and the position of the peak intensity was well separated from and equatorward of the peak intensity of the electrons. This separation is typical of the night-side data which were acquired at local times near 2230 hours [SHARP *et al.*, 1966]. Similar spatial separations were observed in the ground-based optical data at local times before midnight [JONES, 1965].

A measurement of the angular distribution of the electron fluxes is essential for determining the total precipitating energy and the altitude distribution of the energy deposition in the atmosphere. To obtain angular distribution data, four identical scintillation detectors with electrostatic thresholds at 1 keV were used to make electron measurements at zenith angles of 0°, 35°, 55°, and 85°. The angular distributions were occasionally found to be quite variable over short distances. Such variations are easily seen from a comparison of the detector output voltages, as shown in Figure 7. The relative variation,

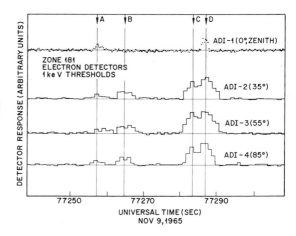

FIGURE 7. Measurements of the angular distribution of auroral electrons (E $\geq$ 1.0 keV).

particularly of ADI-I, is most noticeable at positions A, B, C, and D. The angular distributions at these positions are shown in Figure 8. The corresponding pitch angles are 11°, 34°, 54°, and 84°. A preliminary analysis of the angular distributions for 30 night-side cases showed the flux to be frequently anisotropic with a greater flux at the higher pitch angles. In none of the cases thus far analyzed has the 0° flux exceeded that at 55°.

It is important to know whether particle fluxes moving upward are consistent with the backscattering of downward flux or whether another acceleration mechanism is required. In recent rocket experiments, electron and proton fluxes at energies above 40 keV have been reported moving up the magnetic field lines with intensities greater than would be expected from coulomb scattering of the downward moving flux from the atmosphere [McDIARMID et al., 1961; MOZER and BRUSTON, 1966; CUMMINGS et al., 1966]. O'BRIEN

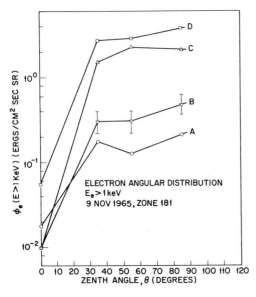

FIGURE 8. Angular distributions of auroral electrons at times indicated in Figure 7.

[1964] reports from Injun III satellite measurements that the "backscattered" electron flux above 40 keV is about 10% of the precipitated flux. Two identical scintillation detectors of the post-acceleration type [REAGAN et al., 1964] with electrostatic thresholds at 0.015 keV were flown to investigate the ratio of the upward to downward moving electron flux. Each had viewing angles of 20 ± degrees, and one (VED I) pointed at the zenith and the other (VED II) at the nadir. Thus far, eleven cases have been found with enough response in VED II to determine the ratio of the responses in the two detectors. The values for the response of VED II/VED I for these cases were typically less than 10%. No values greater than 25% were obtained.

The energy distributions of the precipitating electrons were found to be highly variable in the night-side zones [SHOOK et al., 1966a]. Spectral measurements were obtained with the channel multiplier detectors with 15% energy resolution, and examples are shown in Figure 9. These data are from the same region of electron precipitation as shown in Figure 5. Wide variations in the spectra are seen. Although peaks in the spectra are observed, these do not seem to be typical of the data thus far examined. It is typical for the dominant electron flux to be less than 14 keV. The electron energy distributions in the two rather distinct regions of precipitation observed on the day side are quite different [JOHNSON et al., 1966; O'BRIEN, 1967]. The dominant electron energies were less than 5 keV in the high latitude zone, whereas a significant fraction of the electron energy was generally found above 25 keV in the lower latitude zone. The proton energy input to the atmosphere in the auroral zones, although widespread, is often 10–20% of the total energy input of electrons [Evans

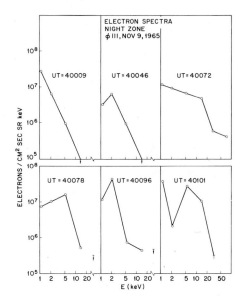

FIGURE 9. Energy spectra of precipitating auroral electrons obtained from channel multiplier magnetic analyzers.

et al., 1966a] and cannot be ignored in a coordinated experiment. Proton data were acquired for proton energies above 10 keV with scintillation-type detectors and above 21 keV with channel multiplier detectors. (Measurements at lower energies were to be obtained with a spherical-segment electrostatic analyzer which failed to operate.) Precipitating protons were observed on most night-side passes in the auroral zones, and generally, the peak intensities were found equatorward of the electron peaks. The night-side proton peaks were located near 68° magnetic latitude, but the day-side peaks were observed in two rather distinct regions near 70° and 80° magnetic latitude [Sharp *et al.*, 1966]. The proton energy distributions at the peaks, when fitted with an exponential form, had characteristic energies generally in the range of 10–20 keV [Sharp *et al.*, 1966]. Examples of some energy distributions on the night-side are shown in Figure 10. The night-side proton precipitation was typically widespread and had relatively little structure.

Ion density and temperature measurements at the satellite altitude were also acquired simultaneously with the particle flux data. The ion measurements were made with a planar grid ion trap [Sharp, 1966b] with in-flight analysis to provide the ion density and temperature information in a form that could be stored on the tape recorder. An example of the correlation of the ion densities

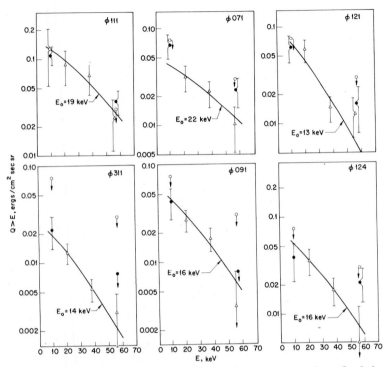

FIGURE 10. Energy spectra of precipitating auroral protons obtained from fixed threshold proton detectors.

and the precipitating electron fluxes is seen in Figure 11. The relatively large increase in the ion density in the region of the electron fluxes is typical of the present nighttime data. Figure 12 shows a case in the southern hemisphere at an altitude of 290 km where ion temperatures are peaking at about 2500°K in the auroral zone in the same general regions as precipitating electrons. Similar temperatures have been reported in auroras from ground-based optical observations [Jones, 1965]. For coordinated experiments in which the electron content is determined from the ground- or aircraft-based radio measurements, a knowledge of the ion density at the satellite altitude is also valuable in relating the contribution to the electron content from the ionization outside the auroral form to the ionization in the form.

Two 3914Å photometers and two uv photometers were flown to assess the fluorescence efficiency in the 100–200-km region for the 3914Å N_2 bands, the LBH bands, and the 1304 OI line. Satellite photometers with small fields of view (1° corresponds to 1.75 km at 100 km below the satellite) are more appropriate than large field photometers for making direct comparisons with particle energy deposit because uniformity over the field of view must be assumed for the luminosity. The uv detectors proved to be very sensitive

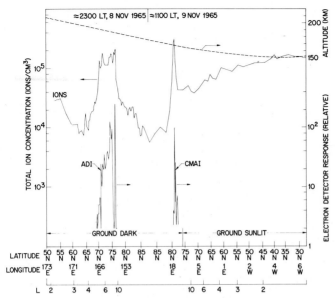

FIGURE 11. A comparison of the ion density and the precipitating electron flux.

detectors of auroral activity, giving readings for uv on essentially all nighttime auroral zone crossings in which the instruments were operating and on 50% of the day-zone crossings for the quiet 3 day period. It is especially interesting that there was more than 0.3 kR of uv radiation across the polar cap area for an appreciable fraction of the cases studied.

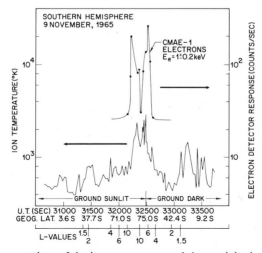

FIGURE 12. A comparison of the ion temperature and the precipitating electron flux.

A detailed interpretation of the uv data which allows separation of LBH emissions from the 1304Å OI triplet will not be possible in most cases. However, in one case which has been analyzed, the geometry and timing of the observations made it possible to ascertain that most of the radiation in the 1230–1810Å band came from an altitude of about 125 km. This makes it quite certain that LBH emissions are being observed without serious contamination by 1304Å radiations. In this case the OI emissions at 1304Å could not have reached the satellite (at 200 km) unless they had been generated above 140 km. Estimates of the effects of atmospheric scattering and absorption on these uv radiations can be seen in Figure 13. Emission heights from

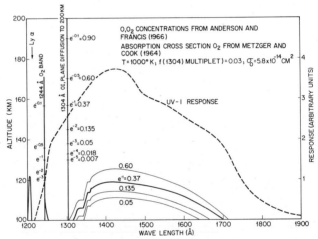

FIGURE 13. Attenuation of uv radiations traveling from different emission heights to a detector at 200 km and the response of the UV-I photometer.

which emissions at different wavelengths will suffer the attenuations in leaving the atmosphere are marked on the curves. The absorption was considered to be due to molecular oxygen alone, and the absorption coefficients used are those given by METZGER and COOK (1964). A model atmosphere given by ANDERSON and FRANCIS (1966) for solar minimum and 21:00 hr local time was used. The effect of resonance scattering of the 1304Å triplet was combined with the molecular oxygen absorption in a plane diffusion calculation for emission at selected heights and plane diffusion to the satellite detector at 200 km.

From a preliminary analysis of the data shown in Figure 5, it appears that the ratio of the intensity for uv in the 1230–1810Å band to the 3914Å radiation is near 0.3 (where the intensities are expressed in kilorayleighs) for the region where the 1304Å radiation is an unimportant factor. A few uv/3914Å ratios for regions near the peak intensity regions are shown in Figure 14. These preliminary ratios vary from about 0.3–1.5. Because of the variable background produced by reflected moonlight from the earth's surface within the 3914Å filter band pass, only cases where the 3914Å intensity was more than 5 kR above background were accepted. That there are so few cases is a consequence

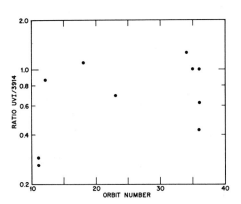

FIGURE 14. Ratio of uv emissions (1230–1810Å) to 3914Å emission near intensity peaks.

of the full moonlight and the quiet period. For a few of the more intense cases it will be possible to calculate effective fluorescence efficiencies for 3914Å and uv, but detailed particle energy and angular distributions and directional sensitivities of the photometers will have to be incorporated to obtain more accurate values. Preliminary values for the 3914Å fluorescence efficiency are in the range from 1–5 kR of 3914 per erg/cm²-sec of particle energy. Theoretical estimates of the fluorescent efficiency for the production of the 1304Å triplet by energetic electrons incident on atomic oxygen are in the range of 10–30%. Values in this range are consistent with the high uv/3914Å ratios obtained in some cases, but the limited number of intense cases in the present data and the large corrections for atmospheric attenuation make the quantitative determination of the OI fluorescent efficiency difficult.

V. Conclusions

Coordinated satellite and ground- or aircraft-based observations on auroras and the simultaneous measurements from a satellite of several parameters associated with auroras can provide quantitative information on the effects produced by energetic particles interacting with the atmosphere. The experimental techniques are now rather well developed, and some valuable coordinated data have been acquired. However, these data are not adequate to meet most of the needs for quantitative data discussed in Section I, and additional experiments should be undertaken. In view of the apparent greater stability and homogeneity of the proton and "mantle" auroras in comparison to other auroras, greater efforts should also be made to utilize them for coordinated studies, particularly, when quasi-equilibrium conditions are required.

Acknowledgments The authors wish to thank their colleagues at the University of Alaska, the Stanford Research Institute, and the Lockheed Palo Alto Research Laboratory who participated in the coordinated experiments and made their data available for this paper prior to publication elsewhere. This research has been supported by the Defense Atomic Support Agency and the Advanced Research Projects Agency through the Office of Naval Research Contract NOnr 3398(00) and by the Lockheed Independent Research Program.

References

ANDERSON, A. D. and FRANCIS, W. E., 1966, *J. Atmos. Scien.* **23**, 110.

DAVIS, L. R., BERG, O. E., and MEREDITH, L. H., 1960, *Space Research* **1**, North-Holland Publishing Co., 271.

DAVIS, T. N., 1965, *Auroral Phenomena*, Stanford University Press, Chapter 1.

DAVIS, T. N., 1967, This volume.

CUMMINGS, W. D., LaQUEY, R. E., O'BRIEN, B. H., and WALT, M., 1966, *J. Geophys. Res.* **71**, 1399.

EVANS, D. S., 1965a, *Rev. Sci. Instr.* **36**, 375.

EVANS, D. S., 1965b, *Trans. Am. Geophys. U.* **46**, 60.

EVANS, J. E. and BELON, A. E., 1963, *Trans. Am. Geophys. U.* **44**, 1073.

EVANS, J. E., JOKI, E. G., JOHNSON, R. G., and SHARP, R. D., 1966a, *Space Research* **6**, North-Holland Publishing Co.

EVANS, J. E., Joki, E. G., and Starr, W. L., 1966b, *Trans. Am. Geophys. U.* **47**, 64.

Evans, J. E., 1967, "Proc. Douglas Symposium on Recent Advances in Cosmic Ray Research, Western Periodical Co., 261.

HARGREAVES, J. K. and SHARP, R. D., 1965, *Planetary Space Sci.* **13**, 1171.

HOOK, J. L. and OWREN, L., 1962, *J. Geophys. Res.* **13**, 5353.

HULTQVIST, B., 1964, *Aurora*, NASA Report X-611, 64–97.

HUNTER, W. R., 1962, *Space Research* **3**, North-Holland Publishing Co., 1187.

JELLY, D. H., McDIARMID, I. B., and BURROWS, J. R., 1964, *Can. J. Phys.* **42**, 2411.

Johnson, R. G., Sharp, R. D., Shea, M. F., and Shook, G. B., 1966, *Trans. Am. Geophys. U.* **47**, 64.

JONES, A. V., 1965, *Auroral Phenomena* (Ed. by M. Walt), Stanford University Press, 33.

KIM, J. S. and VOLKMAN, R. A., 1963, *J. Geophys. Res.* **68**, 3187.

LEADABRAND, R. L., 1965, *Auroral Phenomena* (Ed. by M. WALT), Stanford University Press, 99.

MAEHLUM, B. and O'BRIEN, B. J., 1963, *J. Geophys. Res.* **68**, 997.

McDIARMID, I. B., ROSE, D. C., and BUDZINSKI, E., 1961, *Can. J. Phys.* **39**, 1888.

McILWAIN, C. E., 1960, *J. Geophys. Res.* **65**, 2727.

METZGER, P. H. and COOK, G. R., 1964, *J. Quant. Spectr, Radiative Transfer* **4**, 107.

MEYEROTT, R. E. and EVANS, J. E., 1964, *Amer. Inst. of Aero. and Astro. J.* **2**, 1169.

MOZER, F. S. and BRUSTON, P., 1966, *J. Geophys. Res.* **71**, 2201.

O'BRIEN, B. J., 1964, *J. Geophys. Res.* **69**, 13.

O'BRIEN, B. J., 1967, this volume.

REAGAN, J. B., CARR, D. L., McDANIEL, J. D., and SANDERS, T. C., 1966, *IEEE Trans. on Nucl. Sci.*, **NS-14**, No. 1.

REAGAN, J. B., CARR, D. L., McDANIEL, J. D., and SMITH, L. F., 1964, *IEEE Trans.*, **NS-11**, 441.

SHARP, G. W., 1966a, *J. Geophys. Res.* **71**, 1345.

SHARP, G. W., 1966b, *Trans. Am. Geophys. U.* **47**, 54.

SHARP, R. D., EVANS, J. E., JOHNSON, R. G., and REAGAN, J. B., 1965a, *Space Research* **5**, North-Holland Publishing Co., 282.

SHARP, R. D., REAGAN, J. B., SALISBURY, S. R., and SMITH, L. F., 1965b, *J. Geophys. Res.* **70**, 2119.

SHARP, R. D., SHEA, M. F., SHOOK, G. B., and JOHNSON, R. G., 1966, *Trans. Am. Geophys. U.* **47**, 63.

SHEA, M. F., SHOOK, G. B., REAGAN, J. B., SMITH, L. F., and SANDERS, T. C., 1966, *IEEE Trans. on Nucl. Sci.*, **NS-14**, No. 1.

SHOOK, G. B., SHARP, R. D., SHEA, M. F., JOHNSON, R. G., and REAGAN, J. B., 1966, *Trans. Am. Geophys. U.* **47**, 64.

WESTERLUND, L., O'BRIEN, B. J., and LAQUEY, R. E., 1965, *Trans. Am. Geophys. U.* **46**, 528.

ROCKET OBSERVATIONS OF
LOW ENERGY AURORAL ELECTRONS

David S. Evans

Auroral & Trapped Radiation Section
NASA/Goddard Space Flight Center
Greenbelt, Maryland

Introduction and Review of Rocket Observations
of Primary Auroral Particles

A close connection has long been observed between the occurrence of solar activity and a subsequent auroral display. This has led to the suggestion that the sun is the basic source of energy for the generation of the aurora. Recent measurements of the flow of solar plasma outward from the sun, when integrated over the frontal area of the earth's magnetosphere, have directly shown that the solar wind does indeed carry an energy flux sufficient to drive the aurora ($\sim 10^{20}$ ergs/sec against an estimated 10^{17}–10^{18} ergs/sec dissipated in the aurora) (O'BRIEN, 1964).

Assuming that the solar wind does provide the energy necessary to drive the aurora, one encounters the problem that the energies of the particles comprising this flow are far below those energies required to excite the auroral glow. Furthermore, if a closed field model of the magnetosphere is assumed, these particles are excluded from auroral lines of force. Thus mechanisms for the transfer of energy — if not the solar particles themselves — across the magnetospheric boundary must be invoked.

On the other hand, in an open model of the magnetosphere, those magnetic lines of force which extend backward in the tail and terminate in the interplanetary field may allow direct access of the low energy solar wind particles (and the energy they possess) onto the auroral lines of force. It only would remain to accelerate these particles to the energies needed to drive the aurora and precipitate them into the auroral zone atmosphere. In either case it is the entire process by which the auroral particles are energized and precipitated which has become the central problem in the field.

Quite apart from the questions of particle energizing and energy balance are the constraints placed upon auroral theories by the behavior of the visual aurora itself. The appearance of thin stable forms, the development of a display during a night, the abrupt change in the character of the aurora at the time of auroral breakup, and the very rapid but often systematic motions and luminosity fluctuations seen in active aurora are a few of the many diverse properties for which a comprehensive auroral theory should account, if a single mechanism is, in fact, at work.

Many of these observations have themselves suggested theoretical models. For example, the occurrence of very thin arcs may be taken to indicate a mechanism involving acceleration or particle loss along neutral lines, while the observation of rapid motions in auroral forms and variations in brightness could point toward instabilities in the outer magnetosphere as responsible for the particle influx (CHAMBERLAIN, 1966).

Similarly, knowledge about the properties of the auroral particles being precipitated will aid the development of auroral theory both by providing quantitative observations with which theoretical predictions may be compared and by exposing possible characteristics in the particle influx which could immediately be linked to specific acceleration mechanisms. Among the parameters to be studied in an effort to better describe the properties of this unknown acceleration process are the energy spectrum and particle intensities over the entire range of interest (less than 1 keV to more than 100 keV), any periodic or random time variations in these quantities, and spatial properties — location and extent — of the precipitation.

Three methods, each with its own advantages, have been used to investigate the primary auroral particle flux: satellite, sounding rocket, and balloon. The long life of a satellite makes it an ideal tool for determining such averaged properties of the auroral particle bombardment as its latitude limits, any diurnal variation in the position or intensity of the influx, average flux values, etc. (O'BRIEN, 1964; FRITZ and GURNETT, 1965). However, the high velocity of a satellite makes it less useful for the study of rapid time variations or any fine spatial structure in these particle fluxes. Also, coordinated satellite-ground observations to describe in great detail a single auroral event have proven difficult to make, but are of extreme importance (EVANS, 1965).

Balloon-borne scintillation counters are used to investigate the precipitation of electrons of energies greater than $\sim$30 keV by detecting the bremsstrahlung x rays generated in the atmosphere by these particles. Although the very important lower energy electrons remain inaccessible to these detectors, the stationary nature of a balloon platform allows spatial-temporal effects in the precipitation to be separated and the rapid time variations in the energetic electron influx to be investigated very effectively (ANDERSON, 1964).

Sounding rockets provide an opportunity to study directly the entire energy spectrum of both auroral electrons and protons. In addition, the use of extensive ground observations to supplement and aid in the interpretation of the data obtained by the rocket instrumentation is facilitated by the fact that exact time and conditions at the time of firing are chosen by the scientist. Although spatial-temporal ambiguities enter into the interpretation of time fluctuations measured by the rocket instruments, the rocket's slower velocity compared to a satellite's allows solution of this problem in special cases.

The initial use of the rocket in auroral zone studies was by VAN ALLEN (1957), who found an influx of electrons of energies greater than 50 keV into the atmosphere to be associated with auroral zone latitudes. No correlation could be made, however, between these particle measurements and visual aurora because of the summer season.

The first such measurements of the primary particle spectrum associated with the visual aurora were made during IGY by DAVIS et al. (1960) of the Naval Research Laboratory and MCILWAIN (1960). The prime detectors used by both groups were similar, being scintillation detectors where the total energy deposited in the scintillator by the incident particles was measured. Particle energy discrimination by means of a swept magnetic spectrometer was used by MCILWAIN. The results of both series of flights generally confirmed what had been inferred previously from ground observations:

1. The major portion of the energy influx associated with the visual auroral form was carried by electrons rather than protons; the modest proton fluxes that were detected were found to be uniform over large areas and not dependent upon being near an aurora.

2. Most of the electron influx was made up of particles having energies less than 10 keV.

Specifically, Davis' group observed a net energy influx of ~ 2 ergs/cm^2/sec/sr associated with a faint auroral form. The differential energy spectrum of these electrons was determined through atmospheric absorption observations to be roughly of the form E^{-2} over the energy range 8–30 keV.

McIlwain observed on one flight a very steep electron energy spectra of the form $e^{-E/5 keV}$ for energies greater than 3 keV. The second of McIlwain's flights, which penetrated a bright arc, encountered energy influxes as large as 2000 ergs/cm^2/sec. Analysis of the energy spectra data produced the striking result that this precipitation was composed in the main of electrons of energy ~ 6 keV. This observation strongly suggests that an electrostatic mechanism was responsible for the particle energization and has often been cited in support of auroral theories invoking such an acceleration.

MCDIARMID et al. (1961) have launched a series of rockets during times of auroral absorption (as opposed to visual aurora) to study the primary electron influx under these conditions. In one instance, electron fluxes of 10^5/cm^2/sec/sr (energy greater than 30 keV) were encountered having an energy spectra deduced from atmospheric absorption of the form $e^{-E/22\ keV}$. It is seen that this precipitation is much richer in the higher energy particles. Balloon data have shown that auroral zone x rays (hence energetic electron bombardment) are often associated with auroral absorption and, therefore, the requirement for absorption at launch clearly biases McDiarmid's flights toward hard electron fluxes (BROWN, 1966; BARCUS, 1965).

Investigations of the particle influx associated with visual aurora have been continued by CUMMINGS et al. (1966) and EVANS (1965). Rocket flights to investigate particles linked with other auroral zone effects such as the disturbed ionospheric or x-ray production have been continued by McDIARMID and BUDZINSKI (1964) and LAMPTON and ANDERSON (1966). In general, the results from rockets passing through aurora have substantiated earlier ones in that electrons of lower energies (i.e., ∼10 keV) are the primary energy sources for the auroral glow, but often admixtures of more energetic electrons are encountered which may indicate that two particle sources — each with a characteristic energy — should be considered.

The particle intensities measured during these flights have proven to be highly variable in space and time (as well might have been expected from visual observations of auroral forms), changes of decades in flux over a fraction of a second or a few tens of meters distance being often seen. The energy spectra observed during these flights have likewise been variable with no characteristic shape apparent as yet. The range in electron energy and fluxes involved may be gauged by setting McIlwain's observation of intense fluxes of electrons near 6 keV energy with very few above 10 keV at one extreme and the satellite observation of fluxes of auroral electrons of energy greater than 40 keV which approached $10^9/cm^2/sec/sr$ (60 ergs/cm^2/sec/sr) at the other (McDIARMID and BURROWS, 1965).

McDIARMID et al. (1961) reported a case of a flux of 40 keV electrons directed upward from the atmosphere which was much too large to be accounted for by the backscattering of the observed downward flux. The existence of a vertical electric field between the rocket and the top of the atmosphere was suggested as accounting for this.

MOZER and BRUSTON (1966) made a similar observation of the anomalous reflection near the top of the atmosphere of auroral protons in the energy range above 140 keV. This also was explained by postulating a low altitude acceleration of the proton influx which prevented them from reaching the atmosphere and being lost.

Recently CUMMINGS et al. (1966) have detailed an instance of the ratio of the downward to upward fluxes of 40 keV electrons (as measured at supplementary pitch angles) approaching 1 as compared to the 0.1–0.2 predicted by atmospheric scattering. A number of explanations for this were examined, among them:

1. A pitch angle distribution in the downward flux which peaked strongly at a value not viewed by the detectors thus leading to a gross underestimate of the downward flux.

2. A strong spatial distribution in the precipitation which would result in detecting large fluxes of backscattered electrons from a nearby, intense downflux not sampled by the detectors.

3. A modification of the normal B_{mirror} condition imposed upon the incident electrons by strong, local ionospheric current systems.

Although this observation could not be accounted for in its entirety, it is clear that these anomalous reflections of auroral particles just above the atmosphere are due to processes occurring close to the atmosphere and thus presumably not connected with the fundamental energizing of these particles.

Investigations concerning time variations in the incident auroral particles have been conducted primarily with balloon instrumentation and the results are appropriate to the more energetic electrons. Examples of periodicities in the particle precipitation have been observed over the period range from ≈ 1000 to ≈ 1 sec (ANDERSON, 1964). Photometric observations of the aurora indicate that the short period limit may be extended to at least 0.1 sec (JOHANSEN and OMHOLT, 1966).

Explanations for the appearance of periodicities in the particle precipitation seem to fall into two categories. The first would be to ascribe the fluctuations to a mechanism which modulates the precipitation of previously or independently energized auroral particles. BARCUS and CHRISTENSEN (1965) propose a model to account for a very pure 75 sec periodicity in bremsstrahlung x rays detected at balloon altitude which makes use of hydromagnetic waves in the outer magnetosphere to modulate the ambient field and thus the size of the loss cone for particles accelerated in that region.

Very short period fluctuations in the particle precipitation, on the other hand, may be a reflection of fundamental frequencies or rise time in a dynamic particle acceleration mechanism, for example, a plasma instability.

The high time resolution study of sudden changes in auroral particle fluxes detected at the atmosphere can, in principle, provide information about the distance between the point of observation and the point of particle release or energizing through measurement of the velocity dispersion of the particles. One such observation of possible velocity dispersion leading to a source distance of several earth radii has been reported by ANDERSON and MILTON (1964).

Only the most rapid of these time variations lend themselves to study by rocket instrumentation because of the difficulty in separating spatial motion from pure temporal effects. In spite of this, the ability of the rocket-borne detector to study the full range of particle energies with a greater sensitivity than possible with balloon instrumentation, together with the possible use of ground-based, high-speed observations of the aurora to aid in separating time and motion, has led a number of groups (LAMPTON and ANDERSON, 1966; LEQUEY et al., 1965; EVANS, 1965) to specific rocket-borne studies of transients in the auroral particle influx.

Rocket measurements of the primary auroral particles are continuing with increasing emphasis upon the study of the lower energies with the greatest possible time resolution. Much greater effort is also being put into providing extensive ground-based observations (TV camera photography, especially) during these flights so as to better interpret the often very ambiguous rocket data (WESTERLUND *et al.*, 1965).

The following details some recent results of two rocket flights launched into aurora upon which observations were made of electron energy spectra which suggest electrostatic acceleration of particles, and still another observation of the anomalous reflection of particles from a point above the atmosphere.

Instrumentation Details

The instrumentation in these rocket payloads was directed almost exclusively toward the detection of primary auroral electrons over the energy band extending from 1 keV to more than 300 keV. Special emphasis was put on achieving rapid time response on the part of the detector and counting systems so as to better study rapid variations in the energy spectrum or flux of the incident electrons.

Electrons having energies in the range below 30 keV were examined using channel electron multipliers in a magnetic spectrometer configuration. The detectors are identical to those previously used for auroral studies (EVANS, 1965) except that the energy resolution was sharpened to about 70% of the analyzer center energy E_0 and improved shielding and baffling were introduced to better suppress the contribution of multiply scattered electrons to the detector count rate.

Six such detectors were included in the payload with center energies E_0 nominally at 1 keV, 2 keV, 4 keV, 8 keV, 16 keV, and 32 keV. A seventh background detector was used to demonstrate that no significant portion of the count rates of the six exposed detectors was due to penetrating radiation.

Electrons having energies greater than 60 keV were detected using a plastic scintillator–phototube detector. An electron integral energy spectrum was obobtained by feeding the phototube pulses to a three channel threshold discriminator. The thresholds were nominally set to pulses corresponding to energy losses in the scintillator of 60 keV, 120 keV, and 250 keV. An aluminum layer over the plastic scintillator suppressed the effect of auroral light on the detector response. The possibility that a large number of low energy electrons incident onto the scintillator could result through pulse pileup in a spurious 60 keV count rate was reduced by using very fast pulse circuitry. No instance was encountered of a low energy particle flux sufficiently large to cause such a pileup effect.

The count rates from each of these individual electron detectors were fed through logarithmic count rate circuits the outputs of which were telemetered continuously to the ground. In this manner more than three decades of dynamic range in count rate could be handled while preserving better than 30 ms response time to variations in flux. The count rates as decoded on the ground are accurate to about 10%.

A ZnS powder scintillator detector identical to that described by DAVIS *et al.*

(1960) was included in the payload to provide a measure of the integrated energy influx (above a 4 keV threshold set by an aluminum layer over the scintillator used to suppress light). This instrument was primarily intended to act as an independent check on the performance of the particle counters.

A photomultiplier tube coupled to an optical interference filter having a broad transmission band centered about 3914Å was flown to provide a rough measure of the auroral brightness and to indicate whether the responses of any of the particle detectors were due in part to auroral light emissions.

All of the detectors were mounted such that their fields of view were co-aligned at an angle of 45° to the rocket spin axis. This permitted intercomparisons between detectors without confusing phase lags because of the rolling motion of the rocket.

The rocket spin rate and aspect were provided by a flux gate magnetometer. Table I summarizes these detectors and their characteristics.

Table I. Rocket Payloads

Detector	Energy Band	Flux Dynamic Range
Channel multiplier	1 keV	$5 \times 10^6 - 5 \times 10^9$ electrons/cm²/sec/ster/keV
	2 keV	$2.5 \times 10^6 - 7.5 \times 10^9$ "
	4 keV	$10^6 - 10^9$ "
	8 keV	$5 \times 10^5 - 5 \times 10^8$ "
	16 keV	$2.5 \times 10^5 - 2.5 \times 10^8$ "
	32 keV	$10^5 - 10^8$ "
Plastic scintillator	> 60 keV	$10^4 - 10^7$ electrons/cm²/sec/ster (E > 60 keV)
	> 120 keV	$10^4 - 10^6$ "
	> 250 keV	$10^4 - 10^6$ "
ZnS total energy det.	E > 4 keV	$0.1 - 300$ ergs/cm²/sec/ster
3914Å photometer		Threshold $\sim$ 500 Rayleigh

Results of Measurements of the Primary Electron Influx Associated with the Aurora

The first of the two flights discussed here — identified as 14.188 — was launched from Fort Churchill, Manitoba, at 2351 local time on February 9, 1966 into a rather structured and active auroral form covering an extensive portion of the sky. By 127 secs after launch the brightness of the display had decreased somewhat, and all-sky photographs show that the form had become considerably more homogeneous. The rocket was above this broad homogeneous form during the entire flight.

The magnetic activity during the display was modest, the maximum excursion in the X component being 240γ observed at the time of launching. This field component recovered toward its quiet value at the rate of 15γ/min throughout the flight.

Both the rocket performance and the operation of the various particle detectors were normal except for the total energy scintillator. Detector operation was checked by noting that all particle detectors displayed both a roll modulation equal to the 2.4 rps rocket spin rate and in phase with the output of the aspect magnetometer (indicating that the response was due to a stimulus which was controlled by the geomagnetic field) and by the decrease in count rates as the rocket reentered the atmosphere due to the absorption of the incident particles. The total energy scintillator appeared to respond properly early in the flight in regard to both the typical roll modulation and an observed increase in energy flux as the rocket exited from the atmosphere. However, after approximately +200 sec of flight the output of this detector decayed toward the phototube dark current, and during reentry no evidence of a decrease in energy influx due to atmospheric absorption was observed. This is in spite of the channel multiplier detectors showing such an absorption curve (Figure 3,) and the all-sky photograph clearly displaying a homogeneous glow at the point of reentry. No firm explanation has been found for this apparent loss of sensitivity, but the thermal shock caused by heat conducted from the payload outer skin may have played a role.

The motion of the rocket was such that during a full precession period the detectors scanned pitch angles ranging from $\approx 0°$ to $\approx 100°$.

A possible problem with respect to the channel multiplier low energy electron detectors — especially pertinent to the first flight — is the chance that electrons could gain access to the detector by scattering through an air vent intended to hasten the evacuation of air from the detector housing during ascent. If such were the case, these electrons would give rise to a spurious background rate, and thus, questionable data.

The access to this port lies along a line $\approx 130°$ from the normal electron entrance and is largely obscured by portions of the rocket payload. This fact — that electrons entering this port must be incident along an axis so different from the intended look angle of the collimator — allows an estimate to be made of the magnitude of this effect by examining the spin modulation shown by all detectors. It was determined that up to +200 sec, the behavior of the magnetic electron spectrometers during a roll closely duplicated the roll modulation of the total energy detector. In particular, that portion of the roll which viewed the particle loss cone was virtually identical on both types of detectors.

Such a result indicates that the channel multiplier response is due primarily to electrons incident along the same axis as those particles causing the response in the total energy detector. Further consideration along these lines would place the upper limit on the contribution to the net electron multiplier count rates by such unwanted electrons at about 30%. This has no significant effect upon the important details of the electron spectrum results presented below.

The area of this vent was reduced by over an order of magnitude for those detectors flown on the second and third flights in this series (14.189 and 14.190) which presumably would reduce the effect of electrons entering this vent still further.

It is unfortunate that the apparent loss of sensitivity of the total energy detector on 14.188 (and the clear failure of this detector on the second flight, 14.189) prevents a detailed comparison to be made of the absolute responses of the array of detectors so as to further examine the exact effect, if any, of the electron scattering in this air vent. It is relevant to add, however, that preliminary results from the third flight in this series (14.190, not reported here), when all detectors operated satisfactorily, show excellent agreement with the observed response of the total energy detector and that response predicted by integration of the responses of the individual channel multiplier detectors.

Figure 1 shows the 1 sec average count rate of the 4 keV electron detector

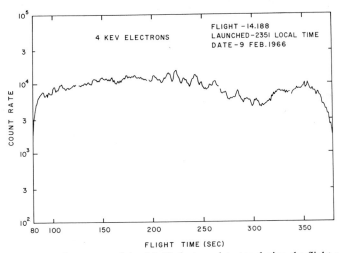

FIGURE 1. 1 sec averaged response of the 4 keV electron detector during the flight of 14.188.

during the flight. (This average suppresses the roll modulation exhibited by the detector and, thus, the details of the pitch angle distribution.) The lack of significant time structure in the count rate history of this detector was typical of the behavior of all detectors during the flight and bears out the homogeneous nature of the auroral form.

The rocket, during the portion of the flight above the atmosphere, moved horizontally about 50 km approximately along the magnetic meridian — a distance which would map along the field lines into many hundred km in the equatorial plane. The lack of any spatial structure in the electron bombardment over this distance would seem to speak against the view that the precipitation should take place along neutral lines or sheets where much structure is expected, particularly in the north-south plane.

Although valuable information on the energy spectrum of the primary auroral electrons encountered on this flight is obtained by means of the array of detectors aboard the rocket, ambiguities in the generation of such a spectrum are present, and a discussion of the problem would be worthwhile.

Because the detectors used are not of infinitely high energy resolution — indeed, the width of the energy window accepted by the magnetic spectrometers is quite broad — it is, in principle, impossible to recover the exact details of the energy spectrum of incident electrons. This arises from the fact that the net count rate of an individual detector is dependent not only upon the particle intensities but also upon the shape of the energy spectrum being measured. It is this need for assuming a spectral shape prior to generating the energy spectrum from the data which results in a lack of uniqueness on the part of the results. However, if the spectrum to be measured is smooth over the width of the detector energy window, the assumption of nearly any shape (for example, exponential) in the analysis will yield an energy spectrum which would both reproduce the responses observed on the detectors and would probably be a reasonable reproduction of the energy distribution of the particles being measured.

On the other hand, if the actual energy spectrum is discontinuous — for example, monoenergetic or exhibiting abrupt changes of intensity over an energy increment which is small compared to the resolution of the detectors — an analysis assuming smoothness, in spite of yielding a spectrum accounting for the observed count rates, will lead to a very distorted view of the actual spectrum. This distortion often takes the form of an unreasonable amplification of the magnitude of the discontinuity present in the actual spectrum. In such cases it seems best to take an empirical approach rather than an analytical one in dealing with the electron energy spectrum.

The spectra inferred from the data obtained on 14.188 appear to be of this discontinuous nature and thus the emphasis is placed upon describing the salient features of the spectrum rather than attempting an accurate reproduction. The differential particle intensities were generated from the observed count rates, taking into account the detector efficiencies, the shape of the analyzer energy window, and by using a weighting factor found to be applicable over a fairly wide range of spectral slopes. The resultant intensities ordinarily would be regarded as zero order approximations but, as pointed out above, further refinement is not felt to be appropriate.

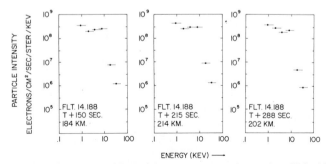

FIGURE 2. Sample electron differential energy spectra observed on flight 14.188.

Figure 2 displays three such electron differential energy spectra obtained at times when the rocket spin axis was aligned roughly with the magnetic field thus eliminating distortion due to any peculiarities in the pitch angle distribution. The flux of electrons of energy greater than 60 keV remained less than 10^4/cm²/sec/sr throughout the flight, and these data have not been incorporated in Figure 2.

The most notable features of the spectra are the relatively flat characteristics below 10 keV and the very rapid falloff in intensity above 10 keV. Comparison between the count rates of the 16 keV and 8 keV detectors suggest that the energy at which the intensity decline begins cannot be much higher than 12–13 keV. Whereas the point of initial decline can be lower than 12 keV, if it were significantly lower in energy, the intensity at 8 keV would need to be increased in order to achieve the observed count rate. A peaking in the differential particle flux would then result in the energy range near 8 keV. The data cannot preclude such an intensity peak, but the constant intensity observed from 1–8 keV might suggest that such a peak is not present.

Data obtained during the reentry of the rocket into the atmosphere (Figure 3) show that these electron fluxes are reduced by more than a factor of 20

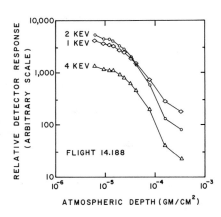

FIGURE 3. The relative responses of the low energy electron detectors during reentry of 14.188 as plotted against atmospheric depth.

at an atmospheric depth of 1.5×10^{-4} gms/cm², confirming that few electrons of energy greater than 10 keV could have been present in the primary beam.

Existence of a well defined maximum energy in the electron influx would be consistent with an electrostatic acceleration having energized the electrons in the case where a maximum potential difference was available for the acceleration. Models based upon statistical processes such as instabilities or Fermi accelerations would generate electron energy spectra having a high energy tail which is definitely not observed on this flight.

The second of the two flights discussed here (14.189) was launched into a moderately active breakup phase aurora at 2356 local time on February 18,

1966. The rocket performance was normal and all detectors operated properly, except the total energy detector which failed during first stage burning.

The auroral display at the time of launch was composed of a folded band in the zenith into which the rocket penetrated, together with a widespread diffuse aurora background of modest intensity. The brightness of the zenith form reached a maximum of more than 15 kR at 135 sec after launch and promptly faded to a nominal 2–5 kR level as measured by a ground-based photometer.

The magnetometer at Churchill displayed a 200γ negative bay in the X component of the field at the beginning of the display and remained remarkably close to this depressed level throughout the flight.

Corresponding in time to the peak auroral luminosity was a 1.2 dB peak in the absorption of 30 Mc/sec radio noise by the ionosphere as observed with the launch site riometer. This absorption decayed roughly as the zenith form faded.

The attitude of the rocket during the flight was such that the spin axis was aligned roughly perpendicular to the geomagnetic field. Thus the array of detectors scanned electron pitch angles ranging from 45° to 135° as the rocket spun with a 22 sec period.

Figure 4 displays the count rate responses of the 4 keV and 60 keV electron

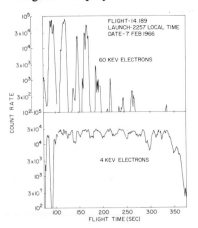

FIGURE 4. 1 sec averaged responses of the 4 keV and 60 keV electron detectors during the flight of 14.189.

detectors during the flight. It is seen that the low and high energy electrons behave in a strikingly different fashion. The 4 keV electron influx maintains a rather constant level throughout the flight and only a modest variation in count rate as the detector viewed pitch angles from 45° to 135°. This history was also typical of both the 1 keV and 2 keV detectors.

In contrast to this the higher energy electrons exhibit both a decreasing electron influx as the flight progresses and a much larger ratio of electrons detected at a pitch angle of 45° to those detected at 135° than the case at lower energies. Moreover, rapid time variations (a factor of 10 within a few seconds at $T + 145$ sec) in the electron flux above 60 keV are evident, al-though superimposed upon the 22 sec period roll modulation.

It is the decrease in the influx of the more energetic electrons which best follows the observed decrease in the intensity of the zenith auroral form. This suggests that while the diffuse background aurora was caused by a low energy influx, the structure was generated by a spatially restricted beam of electrons much richer in particles of energy greater than 10 keV.

The energy spectrum inferred from the available detector count rates on 14.189 is discontinuous in much the same fashion as was observed on 14.188. Consequently, only the first approximations of the electron differential in-tensities are used to obtain the spectral details, and no further refinement is attempted.

Figure 5 displays two such spectra, one obtained early in the flight when

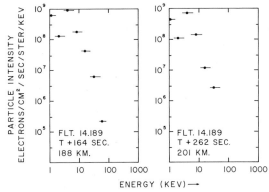

FIGURE 5. Sample electron differential energy spectra observed on flight 14.189 at a pitch angle of 45°.

the intense influx of higher energy electrons was observed, the second later in the flight when the flux of 60 keV electrons had become negligible. These spectra represent 1 sec averages taken when the detector array was viewing particle pitch angles of near 45°.

The most striking aspect of these spectra is the apparent peak in the electron intensity in the energy range 4–8 keV. Indeed one possible spectrum which would be consistent with the observed count rates is composed of the super-position of a spectrum which is smooth between the 2 keV and 16 keV points in Figure 4 and a near monoenergetic flux of electrons of energy between 4 keV and 8 keV. A comparison of the relative responses of the 4 keV and 8 keV detectors together with a knowledge of the analyzer energy pass band would suggest the energy of such a beam would be ≈ 5.5 keV with a total flux of $\approx 3 \times 10^9$ electrons/cm²/sec/sr involved. Such a beam alone would account for one-half of the estimated total energy influx into the atmosphere.

The significance of observing a near monoenergetic beam of auroral electrons cannot be underestimated as it would point very explicitly toward an electrostatic acceleration mechanism. For this reason the data from the three detectors (2 keV, 4 keV, and 8 keV) which together set off the peak in the energy distribution were examined for an indication of malfunction in flight, while calibration and assembly records were consulted for any prior history of abnormality.

The presence of roll modulation in the count rate to prove that the response is dependent upon magnetic aspect, and the characteristic decrease in count rates during reentry because of atmospheric absorption are two reliable qualitative checks upon the operation of these low energy particle detectors. All three detectors in question exhibit the proper behavior in these respects. In addition, the following specific causes of abnormal operation were eliminated on the basis of flight data or discounted on the basis of preflight calibration and checkout data.

a. The miscalibration or shift in the calibration of a logarithmic count rate circuit.

b. The interference from either power supply ripple or from the telemetry transmitter.

c. Corona pulsing from exposed high voltage.

d. An abnormally low gain channel multiplier used in the 2 keV detector which would not produce pulses of sufficient amplitude to trigger the threshold discriminator.

e. The misalignment of the particle detector with respect to the collimators and magnet.

f. Significant contribution to the count rates by auroral ultraviolet light.

g. The contribution to the count rates by electrons scattering through the air vent as described earlier.

Although the failure of the total energy detector prevents the magnitude of this process from being estimated directly, the experience on flight 14.188 using a completely open vent together with the excellent agreement observed between measurements made by these detectors and a total energy detector on a subsequent flight (14.190) suggest that these spurious counts cannot contribute more than about 10% to the total count rate.

The possibility remains that a partial obstruction in the collimator could result in an abnormally low count in the 2 keV detector relative to the incident flux (as inspection of Figure 5 shows, a factor of 4 increase in the 2 keV count rate would largely remove the peaking of the differential energy spectrum). X-ray photographs of this detector assembly taken after calibration do not show an obstruction or other abnormality, and it is highly unlikely that any foreign matter could have been introduced during final checkout. It may be of interest to note that if the 2 keV detector were arbitrarily ignored, the spectrum would appear much as that encountered on 14.188, except that the energy at which the decline in the electron intensity sets in is somewhat lower than that seen on 14.188.

It was concluded on the basis of the above considerations that there is no reason for discarding any detector as producing invalid data and that the differential energy spectrum of these low energy electrons did in fact possess a peak near 6 keV.

As was pointed out above, this sort of energy spectrum was inferred by McIlwain from data obtained on one of his rocket firings during I.G.Y.

It is significant that this peak in the spectrum was a persistent feature during this flight — the position of the peak shifting perhaps a few hundred volts lower in energy late in the flight. This stability is achieved even though the more energetic electrons observed by the plastic scintillator undergo a large variation. This may be indicative that the generation of these 60 keV electrons proceeds more or less independently of the production of the lower energy particles.

It was mentioned above that the lower energy electrons viewed by the 1 keV, 2 keV, and 4 keV detectors were further distinguished by the large ratio of electron flux detected at 135° pitch angles to that detected at 45°. Figure 5 displays the energy spectrum observed when the detector array was viewing particles having 135° pitch angle at a time one-half of a roll after the first of the two spectra in Figure 4 was observed. It is seen that the 1 keV, 2 keV, and 4 keV fluxes have decreased by less than a factor of 2, while the high energy fluxes display more nearly a factor of 10 reduction.

The origin of an anomalously high count rate in these detectors when viewing downwards cannot be due to electrical interference of any sort causing spurious counts. The possibility of auroral ultraviolet light exciting the channel multipliers was examined. The detectors do not view auroral light directly at the 45° pitch angle orientation, but a comparison between the photometer and the particle detector data when the array is oriented downwards reveals that some degree of response of the channel multipliers to the ultraviolet was present. This amounted to about 200 counts/sec and represented a significant contribution to the responses of the 16 keV and 30 keV detectors. It has been corrected for the spectrum obtained when viewing downwards. However, this introduces only an approximate 10–15% correction to the 2 keV count rate and considerably less to the 4 keV or 1 keV responses and thus cannot account entirely for the detection of the large upflux.

The uniformly low count rate of the background channel multiplier detector in the payload eliminates response to x rays or energetic particles as an explanation for this observation.

The possibility that scattering electrons could produce the 30% spurious contribution to the count rate necessary to attain the nominal 10:1 ratio between downward directed and upward directed electron fluxes at 1, 2, and 4 keV is remote.

Thus it is concluded that this observation of an abnormally large outflux is valid. It may be noted that this conclusion is not affected by the factors such as collimator obstructions which entered into the discussion of the validity of the spectrum.

Inspection of the spectrum observed when the detectors view the outflux at a pitch angle of 135° reveals the same peaking of the particle intensity near 6 keV energy, indicating that the reflection of these electrons from some point above the atmosphere was nearly elastic. However, the fact that the flux of electrons detected by the 8 keV detector displayed a 10:1 ratio between influx and outflux (cf. Figures 4 and 5) shows that some energy loss on the part of the electrons was present. The very sharp low energy cutoff of the magnetic spectrometers would require only a 0.5 to 1 keV energy loss on the part of the incident electrons to completely remove the monoenergetic portion of the beam from the response band of the 8 keV detector.

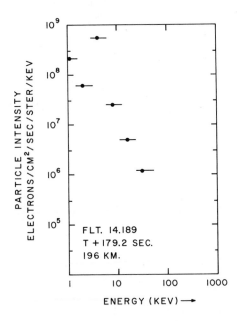

FIGURE 6. An electron differential energy spectrum observed on flight 14.189 when the detector viewed a pitch angle of 135°.

Data obtained during the reentry of the rocket into the atmosphere (Figure 7) reveal that the response of the lower energy detectors begins to decline at an atmospheric depth of about 10 μgm/cm^2 (130 km altitude) and that the reflection (or absorption) is essentially complete by 30 μgms/cm^2 ($\approx$117 km altitude). Comparison of Figure 6 with the corresponding absorption curve obtained on 14.188 (Figure 3) points up the rapidity with which the electrons are removed from the beam during the reentry of 14.189.

No model has been formulated to explain this observation but if a field aligned electric field were invoked to account for the reflection, a field strength on the order of 10^{-3}V/cm would be required roughly over the altitude interval 120 to 130 km. This field is very nearly that proposed by McDIARMID *et al.* (1961) to account for a similar observation of electrons reflected from above

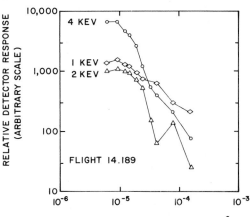

FIGURE 7. The relative responses of the low energy electron detectors during reentry of 14.189 plotted against atmospheric depth (cf. Figure 3).

ATMOSPHERIC DEPTH (GM/CM²)

the atmosphere. The effects of such a field upon the ionosphere should, however, be spectacular.

To move somewhat further into the realm of speculation, the question of how the position of the peak in the spectrum maintains its stability arises. If the electrons being measured are trapped on closed field lines, those electrons reflected from below the rocket will presumably spiral back on the field line to the southern hemisphere where they will either be 1) lost into the atmosphere, 2) reflected subject to the normal B_{mirror} condition, or 3) reflected by an even more efficient mechanism similar to that apparently operative in the northern hemisphere. VESTINE (1960) shows that for a magnetic line of force passing near Churchill, the B_{mirror} condition will be met at a higher altitude in the southern than the northern hemisphere. This may suggest that reflection of electrons should be at least as efficient in the south as it is observed to be in the north. Thus, in order to maintain the spectral shape, electrons must receive at some point in their trajectory between the two hemispheres an additional amount of energy roughly equal to that loss observed in the atmosphere. This balance appeared too fortuitous to be true.

An alternative explanation would be that the line of force down which the electron influx was directed was open, not closed. The particle influx was then entirely composed of freshly precipitated electrons, while those electrons reflected from the atmosphere were entirely lost from the beam.

Summary and Conclusions

The most significant result of the auroral electron measurements performed on the two flights described above is the observation on two separate occasions of differential energy spectra which are suggestive of electrostatic acceleration mechanisms having been responsible for the energizing of the auroral electrons. While the prominent peak at ≈ 5.5 keV in the energy spectrum encountered on 14.189 is the most dramatic indication of this, the sharp high energy cutoffs evident in the spectrum observed during 14.188 are no less associated with electrostatic processes, the absence of a tail of high energy electrons being the distinguishing feature.

It is further seen that the process responsible for the electron influx exhibited great stability in time, as shown by the constancy of the energy spectrum during the flights, particularly the position of the spectral peak observed on 14.189, and the homogeneous nature of the influx over 50 km distance. These points additionally serve to eliminate the more dynamic mechanisms, for example, plasma instabilities, as being the source of the electron energizing and precipitation.

As a general rule, the flight data indicated that while the influx of electrons < 10 keV remained quiescent, the flux of electrons > 40 keV underwent large variations, believed to be time variations rather than spatial. A similar conclusion about the relative behavior of low and high energy auroral electrons was reached by SHARP et al. (1965) on the basis of satellite observations. It is very tempting to describe this as being due to a static precipitation of low energy electrons together with a differing, more dynamic process which generates the energetic electrons. The energy and particle reservoir needed for the generation of the higher energy electrons may be, in fact, the low energy (< 10 keV) electron population.

Certainly the theoretical explanations for the full range of auroral behavior would become simpler if two basic acceleration and precipitation mechanisms rather than a single mechanism could be operating semi-independently of one another.

The observation of an apparent reflection of the incident electrons from above the atmosphere represents still another instance of such an effect to add to that data of MOZER and BRUSTON (1966), MCDIARMID et al. (1966) and CUMMINGS et al. (1961). While the full explanation of these reflections is yet to be proposed, it is likely that acceptable models will involve details of the electric and magnetic field structure in the lower ionosphere.

References

ANDERSON, K. A., 1964b, *Univ. Calif. Publ.* UCB 64/4.
ANDERSON, K. A. and MILTON, D. W., 1964, *J. Geophys. Res.* **69**, 4457.
BARCUS, J. R., 1965, *J. Geophys. Res.* **70**, 2135.
BARCUS, J. R. and CHRISTENSEN, A., 1965, *J. Geophys. Res.* **70**, 5455.
BROWN, R. R., 1966, Cosmic Ray Group, Dept. of Physics, Univ. of Calif.
CHAMBERLAIN, J. W., 1965, *Auroral Phenomena* (Ed. by M. Walt).
CUMMINGS, W. D., LAQUEY, R. E., O'BRIEN, B. J., and WALT, M., 1966, *J. Geophys. Res.*, **71**, 1399.

DAVIS, L. R., BERG, O. E., and MEREDITH, L. H., 1960, *Space Res.*, North Holland Publ. Co., 721.
EVANS, D. S., 1965, Goddard Ener. Part. Series, NASA.
EVANS, J. E., 1965, *Auroral Phenomena* (Ed. by M. Walt).
FRITZ, T. A. and GURNETT, D. A., 1965, *J. Geophys. Res.* 70, 2485.
JOHANSEN, O. E. and OMHOLT, A., 1966, *Planetary and Space Sci.* 14, 207.
LAMPTON, M. and ANDERSON, K. A., 1966, Paper delivered at 1966 annual meeting of the AGU, Washington, D. C.
LeQUEY, R. E., O'BRIEN, B. J., and WESTERLUND, 1965, Paper delivered at the Fifth Western National Meeting of the AGU, Dallas, Texas.
McDIARMID, I. B. and BUDZINSKI, E. E., 1964, *Can. J. Phys.* 42, 2048.
McDIARMID, I. B. and BURROWS, J. R., 1965, *J. Geophys. Res.* 70, 3031.
McDIARMID, I. B., ROSE, D. C., and BUDZINSKI, E. E., 1961, *Can. J. Phys.* 39, 1888.
McILWAIN, C. E., 1960, *J. Geophys. Res.* 65, 2727.
MOZER, F. S. and BRUSTON, P., 1966., *J Geophys. Res.* 71, 2201.
O'BRIEN, B. J., 1964, *J. Geophys. Res.* 69, 13–43.
SHARP, R. D., REGAN, J. B., SALISBURY, S. R., and SMITH, L F., 1965, *J. Geophys. Res.* 70, 2119.
VAN ALLEN, J. A., 1957, *Proc. Nat. Acad. Sci.* 43, 57.
VESTINE, E. H., 1960, *Rev. Mod. Phys.* 32, 1020.
WESTERLUND, O'BRIEN, B. J., and LeQUEY, R. E., 1965, Paper delivered at the Fifth Western National Meeting of the AGU, Dallas, Texas.

REVIEW OF ROCKET AURORAL MEASUREMENTS

C. D. Anger

Department of Physics
The University of Calgary, Alberta, Canada

Introduction

The quantities which are both relevant to auroral physics and amenable to measurement by rocket instruments include electron densities, ionization rates, particle energy fluxes, energy spectra, and pitch angle distributions, fields, currents, optical emissions, and atmospheric composition. Measurements of these parameters are important — even if some of them prove to be secondary to what actually "causes" the aurora, since all have pronounced effects on the phenomena which together constitute the auroral disturbance.

An attempt is made below to review some of the more important recent results in various of the categories discussed above. Some results from an experiment involving a new technique for examining auroral precipitation in a wide region around a rocket will also be presented. Electric field, magnetic field, and electrical current measurements, which are as difficult as they are important, will not be discussed.

Ionization and Luminosity

The electron density in the ionosphere is a quantity which governs electrical conductivities and the propagation and absorption of radio waves. Furthermore, it plays a vital role in many ionospheric reactions. Several techniques have been developed for measuring electron densities, and they seem to be achieving a high degree of reliability. The rocket measurement has the advantage of directness and is capable of providing a continuous height profile of electron densities.

An example of such a measurement, obtained with a Langmuir probe, is shown in Figure 1. The rocket passed through an auroral form on its descent as indicated by a ground-level 5577Å photometer. A spectacular rise in measured electron density was observed. Norwegian workers have carried out a number of flights in which densities during auroral events were measured by a radio technique (JESPERSEN et al. discussed by MAEHLUM, 1966). Their results suggest a considerable decrease in the relative amount of ionization below 80 km at night as compared to day, and this is attributed to electron attachment to neutral molecules (BROWN, 1966). Detachment becomes important during the day, producing the day-night difference.

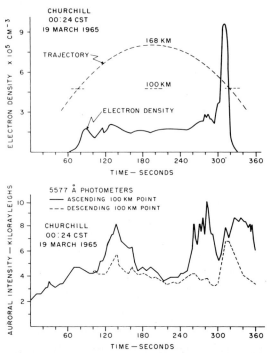

FIGURE 1. Electron density and auroral luminosity during a rocket flight (courtesy A. G. McNamara). The auroral luminosity curves were obtained from two ground-level photometers which were pointed at the ascending and descending 100 km points respectively.

Electron density measurements are most valuable when they can be compared directly with the rate of ionization as a function of height. It is then possible to say something about the important reactions which govern electron recombination and attachment, and hopefully to establish rate coefficients. McDIARMID and BUDZINSKY (1964) compared values for q, the ionization rate per unit volume, and N, the electron density, as a function of height for the (nighttime) ascent of one rocket during which the flux of particles appeared to remain fairly constant with time. The results are shown in Figure 2. The upper part of the diagram shows q and N, plotted as functions of height while the lower part shows the ratio q/N^2. This ratio would be expected to remain constant in regions where simple recombination of electrons and positive ions (dissociative recombination) is the dominant process, in which case the value of this "effective recombination coefficient" would give the actual value for the recombination coefficient. The dotted line gives the minimum nighttime values which would be expected for the ratio if electron attachment to neutral molecules and collisional detachment become dominant processes at the lower altitudes (CRAIN, 1961). The observed ratio is relatively constant above 85 km, but clearly takes on much larger values and changes at a much more

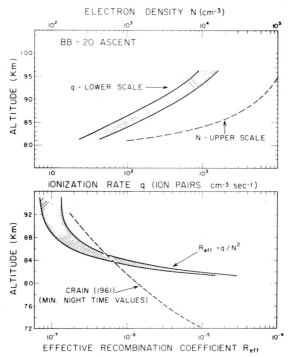

FIGURE 2. Ionization rate (q) and electron density (N) as a function of altitude (courtesy I. B. McDiarmid). The ratio q/N^2 departs drastically from values consistent with a significant collisional detachment rate at the lower altitudes.

rapid rate at the lower altitudes than that allowed by the above mentioned processes.

It is interesting to note that values obtained for q and N below 85 km are consistent with a relatively simple three-body attachment process (i.e., attachment rate proportional to the square of the pressure), together with no detachment. An attachment rate of 0.1 sec^{-1} at 83 km is implied. Additional measurements of this type are needed.

Rocket measurements can also provide data on the relationship between particle flux and auroral luminosity. Nevertheless, current estimates are still based on laboratory measurements. In practice, it has proven very difficult to carry out a rocket measurement due to uncertainties in measuring the flux of low energy particles and due to the highly transient character of auroral disturbances. Perhaps, this relationship can only be investigated during a polar cap event, where the precipitation is usually uniform and constant.

The atomic oxygen density also relates directly to the luminosity-height distribution of 5577Å emissions. Its variation with height in the auroral zone shows a peak at 96 km, below which the ratio of its density to that of the other principal constituents decreases very rapidly (SPLINDLER, 1966). This is clearly of importance in relation to the mechanism for production of Type B aurora, (EVANS AND VALLANCE JONES, 1965) particularly in view of the distinct border observed between the upper green region and lower red region in the artificial auroras described by BOQUIST (1967).

Particle Pitch Angle Distributions

The study of pitch angle distributions of auroral particles can provide important information on their origin and past history. Any particle acceleration mechanism which operates far out along a field line will almost certainly result in a nearly isotropic downward flux of particles just above the atmosphere (McDIARMID and BUDZINSKY, 1964). This follows from the Liouville theorem and from the unlikelihood of any such acceleration process creating initial pitch angle distributions which vary significantly over the range from zero to two degrees. Departures from complete isotropy are always observed, however, and can be attributed to the effects of particle interactions with the atmosphere, resulting in the removal or scattering of particles over some range of pitch angles. Other mechanisms may operate which through either the creation of forbidden pitch angle zones (CUMMINGS et al., 1966) or the alteration of mirror heights, can act to enhance or diminish the effects of the atmosphere on the pitch angle distributions.

Figure 3 shows two typical pitch angle distributions obtained by McDIARMID and BUDZINSKY (1964) at different times during a single rocket flight. The distribution shown at the top of the diagram is essentially isotropic over the upper hemisphere. The particles with pitch angles between 90° and 180° are due to the effects of atmospheric back-scattering of precipitated electrons.

On the other hand, the distribution at the bottom of the diagram shows a distinct peak near 90° pitch angle. The most straightforward explanation is that the electrons have undergone previous mirrorings such that those with small pitch angles have already been lost into the atmosphere. In other words, the particle pitch angle distribution has been altered by the effects of trapping and probably also of pitch angle diffusion. The isotropic distribution is typical of counting rate increases and the early phase of an event, while the anisotropic distributions are found when the rate is decreasing (McDIARMID, 1966). When the pitch angle distribution over the upper hemisphere is well known, the flux and angular distribution of back-scattered particles can be calculated and compared to the observed fluxes coming up the field line. There is good agreement between the downward and upward-going fluxes on all except two occasions. At these times anomalously high back-scattered fluxes were observed, and it has been suggested that a westward electrojet current to the south of the rocket at the time of the observation could have raised the mirror point of the particles and thus resulted in below normal loss into the atmosphere.

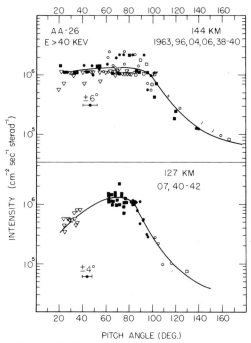

FIGURE 3. Electron pitch angle distributions during a rocket flight (courtesy I. B. McDiarmid). The isotropic distribution over the upper hemisphere as seen in the top diagram and the distribution peaked at 90° shown in the bottom are both relatively common.

EVANS (1967), CUMMINGS et al. (1966), and McDIARMID et al. (1961) have obtained results which suggest anomalies in the relative distribution and fluxes of particles traveling up and down the field lines, although care must be used in interpreting such results when the pitch angle information is incomplete. They have also suggested various mechanisms involving magnetic or electric fields which might produce anomalous pitch angle distributions.

Electron Energy Spectrum and Flux

The energy spectrum of incoming auroral electrons and their total flux are parameters fundamental to an understanding of auroral luminosity distributions and ionospheric effects, and to the ultimate task of relating the particles back to their source. Spectrum estimates are usually based on the relative rates obtained with counting systems having different energy thresholds. It is frequently convenient to characterize such results in terms of differential energy spectra of exponential form

$$\frac{dN_e}{dE} \propto e^{-E/E_0},$$

(where E_0 is referred to as the e-folding energy), or of power law form

$$\frac{dN_e}{dE} \propto E^{-\gamma}.$$

Figure 4 shows an example of such data obtained by MCDIARMID and BUDZINSKY (1966) during a recent rocket flight. The electron energy spectrum

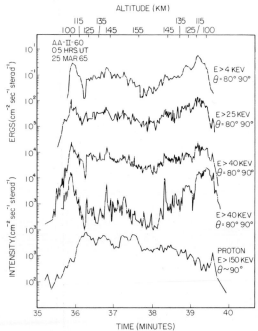

FIGURE 4. Particle fluxes at different energies and pitch angles during a rocket flight (courtesy I. B. McDiarmid).

above 4 keV obtained from the three 80–90° pitch angle channels is consistent with an e-folding energy of about 8 keV.

A remarkable example of a pure power law bremsstrahlung x-ray spectrum is shown in Figure 5. This implies a power law electron spectrum over the energy range measured (see Appendix). Spectra obtained at other times during the same rocket flight indicated an exponential electron spectrum.

Recent data of EVANS (1967) and RIEDLER (1966) have shown that there can be extreme variability in the shape of the differential energy spectrum particularly at the lower energies. HEIKKILA and MATTHEWS (1964) have obtained high resolution spectra of the lower energy end of the spectrum using an electron multiplier. Spectra showing data from this instrument combined

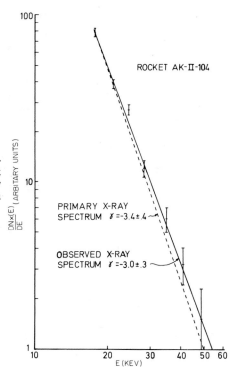

FIGURE 5. A high resolution x-ray bremsstrahlung spectrum obtained during a rocket flight by Pilkington. The pure power law x-ray spectrum implies a power law electron spectrum with $\gamma = 4.5$.

with results obtained from a scintillation spectrometer are given in Figure 6. Notable features are the turning over of some of the spectra at low energies and the completely different temporal behavior of the high and low energy electrons, in this case believed to be due to spatial variations as the rocket moved across an auroral form. Data from lower energy channels were influenced by shielding effects of the rocket itself, but are consistent with secondary electron spectra having e-folding energies in the neighborhood of 100 eV.

Other results on particle spectrum and energy flux will be discussed in the next section.

Auroral Scanner and X-Ray Measurements

Direct particle measurements sample the flux at specific points in space and time, which is one of their great advantages. However, it is usually very difficult, if not impossible, to evaluate how representative these measurements are of the particle fluxes in the surrounding region. This limitation, coupled with the practical difficulties of placing a rocket directly into an auroral form,

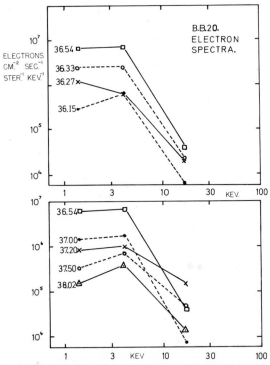

FIGURE 6. Differential electron energy spectra obtained during a rocket flight using an electron multiplier and sodium iodide scintillator (courtesy D. L. Matthews and T. A. Clark). The time corresponding to each spectrum is indicated beside it in the following form: minutes, followed by seconds. The sequence shows considerable variability in the behavior of the high and low energy electrons relative to one another.

suggests that an experimental technique which permits measurements of electron precipitation over a wide region around the rocket would be very useful — particularly when one is concerned with auroral morphology. Such a technique, which involves bremsstrahlung x-ray measurements and high speed scanning photometry — both carried out from a rocket — is described below.

Bremsstrahlung x-rays, resulting from the interaction of the more energetic precipitated electrons with the atmosphere, have been observed extensively from balloons (KREMSER, 1967). By placing a similar detector in a rocket, one can avoid problems of absorption and scattering of the x rays in the atmosphere, and thus obtain unambiguous data on x-ray intensity and spectrum as a function of azimuth angle around the rocket. These can then be related directly to the electron spectrum and average flux in the line of sight. The optical scanner described below permits a direct correlation with optical features.

The x-ray detectors are cylindrical NaI(T1) scintillators of dimensions one inch by one inch, with a 0.01–0.015 inch beryllium window. They were roughly collimated, in the experiment to be discussed here, to an angle of 60° by a hole in the rocket skin. More recent packages have employed a lead collimator, lined with a thin layer of carbon to reduce local bremsstrahlung production. Individual scintillator pulses are gated by upper and lower level discriminators, stretched and shaped, and telemetered directly. Pulse height analysis is then carried out on the ground using a multichannel analyzer. The output of a scalar giving total x-ray count rate is also telemetered. An example of a high resolution spectrum is shown in Figure 5. Reduction of an x-ray spectrum to its equivalent electron spectrum is discussed in an appendix to this paper. Accompanying the x-ray detector is a narrow angle photometer which is scanned over nearly the entire sky by combining the normal rotation of the rocket about its axis with the scanning pattern provided by a high speed rotating mirror assembly. The mirror scans through successive semicircular arcs from tail to nose of the rocket. Other components amplify the signal, and

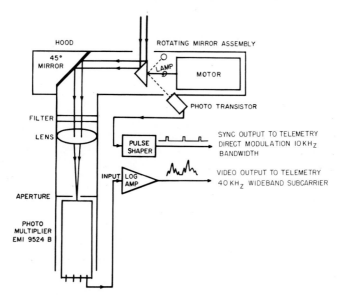

FIGURE 7. Schematic drawing of the auroral scanner, a device for producing high speed monochromatic pictures of the distribution of auroral luminosity over the sky around the rocket. More recent versions employ a dual filter housing mounted on the rotating mirror so as to provide alternate scans in 5577Å and 3914Å.

provide synchronizing pulses. A block diagram of the system appears in Figure 7.

Individual scans take place at the rate of about 100/sec. The angular resolution is 2°. The somewhat staggering quantity of data is handled by converting it into a form that can easily be interpreted visually; i.e., a similar scanning pattern is reproduced by sweeping an oscilloscope beam in synchronism with the rotating mirror, and the oscilloscope beam is intensity modulated by the telemetered video signal from the photometer. The display is photographed by a camera in which the film moves continuously at right angles to the oscilloscope scan. The result is a sequence of television-like monochromatic pictures of the distribution of auroral luminosity over the sky, which can then be compared with the x-ray data and with ground-level measurements. With this instrument it should be possible to obtain auroral heights and luminosity distributions, and to relate discrete auroral features to the auroral particle flux as determined from the x-ray data, although full utilization of its capabilities requires ground-level auroral observations with comparable time resolution (approximately 1 sec).

The instrument has been flown in two rockets, with two more flights scheduled for the immediate future. In the most recent flight the rocket failed to spin, which has made the data very difficult to interpret. In the first flight (Rocket 60), amplifier drift produced a substantial gain reduction which made the data very noisy, the picture quality rather poor, and ruled out any interpretations of the results in terms of absolute intensities. However, the flight was made into very active auroral conditions, and a preliminary analysis of the data shows much that is interesting. An illustrative scan is reproduced in Figure 8. The bright regions are due to auroral luminosity which is near the

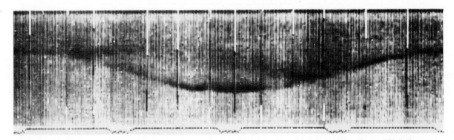

FIGURE 8. An illustrative picture from the auroral scanner showing data from slightly more than one revolution (in negative form). Scanner azimuth angle about the rocket axis is proportional to distance left and right along the picture, and elevation angle varies from down the rocket tail, at the bottom of the picture, to up along its nose at the top (some 20° is missed at each end).

horizon, and the sine wave pattern arises because the axis of the rocket is tilted some 30° with respect to the vertical. One "cycle" of the sine wave corresponds to one revolution of the rocket. An auroral band can be seen looping up from the horizon and passing through the center of the picture. (The rocket is below 100 km at this time.) The estimated position of the band is about 30 km above the rocket and about 30 km distant horizontally.

The entire flight is characterized by quite high x-ray fluxes which vary with the orientation of the rocket. Some of the time a single counting rate peak was observed, but at other times a clear double peak was apparent, as in Figure 9(D). During the entire flight, in every case except one, the x-ray flux showed a clear association with bright optical features at the appropriate azimuth angles. The counting rate increased when these features brightened and decreased when they faded. The exceptional case was an auroral arc whose brightness remained constant while the corresponding x-ray intensity decreased.

A sequence of scanner pictures and the corresponding x-ray counting rates are shown in Figure 9. Note that the rate does not go below 1000 sec^{-1} during this time. Normal background rates are 100 sec^{-1} for this counter. The high rate can be attributed to the relatively poor shielding and collimation provided by the rocket skin, together with the very high incident x-ray fluxes. It is doubted that local electrons are contributing significantly to the background intensity. Direct electrons incident on the detector will be stopped by the beryllium window, while their bremsstrahlung can account for only a few hundred counts sec^{-1}. This is deduced from the electron fluxes measured by other instruments on the same rocket (see Figure 4).

In Figure 9(A) two broad x-ray peaks are apparent from the counting rate graph, centered in the south and in the northeast. Directly above is the corresponding scanner picture, showing bright optical features at and just below the horizon. The zenith is toward the bottom of the diagrams in this sequence, and the rocket is well above the 100 km level; hence, the forms show up below the horizon. It should be noted that the angular resolution of the scanner is about twenty times better than that of the x-ray detector. The vertical light and dark bands in the picture are due to telemetry noise.

Figure 9(B) shows the situation seventeen seconds later. The bright region in the northeast quadrant has concentrated in the east, and the other bright area has faded somewhat and moved into the southwest. The x-ray counting rate shows similar changes. Somewhat later (C), the separation of the two peaks becomes more distinct. This appears to be associated with a decrease in luminosity in the region between them. The bright area in the northeast then becomes more confined in azimuth (D), and the corresponding x-ray peak narrows and intensifies, completely separating itself from the peak in the southwest, which remains at about the same level.

The x-ray spectrum during this event was approximately exponential, with an e-folding energy of about 10 keV for x-rays with energies greater than 10 keV. This is generally typical of the spectra observed during the flight. If we assume the x-rays in the northeast quadrant in Figure 9(D) are coming from the bright region in the photograph, then we can calculate the equivalent surface x-ray emission rate of the source, and from this obtain an average value for the electron flux. The optical feature has an angular height of about 12° and a width of 50°. Assuming a straight exponential electron spectrum

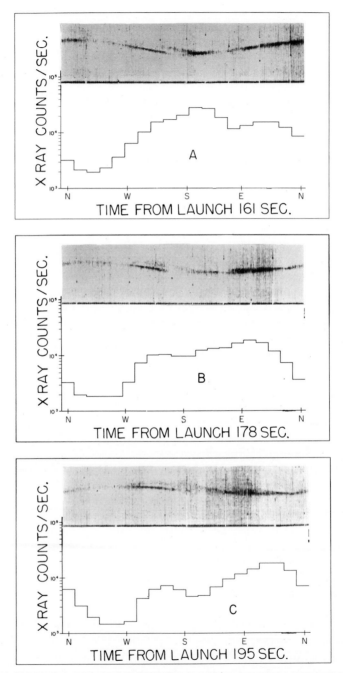

FIGURE 9. Data from the auroral scanner and x-ray detector during a rocket flight. A direct correspondence is observed between intensities and movements of regions of high luminosity (showing as dark regions in the pictures) and the position and amplitude of peaks in the x-ray flux.

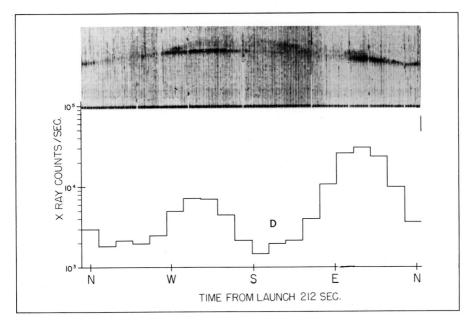

FIGURE 9. Cont.

with $\epsilon = 10$ keV (see Appendix), we obtain an equivalent average electron flux in the line of sight of 10^{10} electrons cm^{-2} sec^{-1} and a total energy flux of 10^{14} eV cm^{-2} sec^{-1}. The implied emission rate is 100 kR, if we use a figure of one photon of 3914Å emission for each keV of energy (STAIR, 1967). The e-folding energy of 10 keV implies a lower border in the neighborhood of 85 km (REES, 1963).

The vertical energy flux cannot be evaluated unless the thickness of the form in the line of sight is known. If it is at all typical of auroral band thicknesses (≈ 1 km), the vertical energy flux could easily be an order of magnitude greater than the 10^{14} eV cm^{-2} sec^{-1} quoted above.

The estimated x-ray flux which would be observed at balloon altitudes beneath the auroral form is 10^3 x-rays cm^{-2} sec^{-1}. This would be regarded as a moderately intense balloon x-ray event.

Acknowledgments The author would like to thank Drs. A. G. McNamara, D. L. Matthews, T. A. Clark, and I. B. McDiarmid, who have generously provided data for inclusion in this paper, much of it prior to publication. Valuable discussions with I. B. McDiarmid on the significance of particle measurements are also acknowledged.

Design and development of the auroral scanner and analysis of the data have been carried out by D. D. Wallis. Thanks are due to Dr. M. Wein of the National Research Council, Ottawa, for development of the scanner display and photography system. The analysis and interpretation of the rocket x-ray data were carried out by G. R. Pilkington. The x-ray instrument was designed by C. Hansen.

References

BOQUIST, W. P., 1967, this volume.
BROWN, R. R., 1966, *Space Science Rev.* 5, 311.
CRAIN, C. M., 1961, *J. Geophy. Res.* 66, 1117.
CUMMINGS, W. C., LaQUEY, R. E., O'BRIEN, B. J., and WALT, M., 1966, *J. Geophys. Res.* 71, 1399.
EVANS, D. S., 1967, this volume.
EVANS, W. F. J. and VALLANCE JONES, A., 1965, *Can. J. Phys*, 43, 697.
HEIKKILA, W. J. and MATTHEWS, D. L., 1964, *Nature* 202, 789.
KREMSER, G., 1967, this volume.
McDIARMID, I. B., 1966, Inter-Union Symposium on Solar Terrestrial Physics, Belgrade.
McDIARMID, I. B. and BUDZINSKY, E. E., 1964, *Can. J. Phys.* 42, 2048.
McDIARMID, I. B., ROSE, D. C., and BUDZINSKY, E. E., 1961, *Can. J. Phys.* 39, 1888.
MAEHLUM, B., 1966, *Radiation Trapped in the Earth's Magnetic Field* (Ed. by B. M McCORMAC).
REES, M. H., 1963, *Planetary Space Sci.* 11, 1209.
RIEDLER, W., 1966, *Arkiv Fysik* 30, 527.
SPINDLER, G., 1966, *Planetary Space Sci.* 14, 53.
STAIR, A. T., 1967, This volume.

Appendix

Bremsstrahlung X-Rays

For primary electron spectra of the simple power law or exponential form, the resultant x-ray spectra can readily be derived using the relativistic formulas for bremsstrahlung production and ionization loss. These have been reasonably valid even at the low electron energies of concern in auroral physics. The corresponding x-ray differential energy spectrum is shown beside its parent electron spectrum.

$$\frac{dN_e}{dE_e} = AE_e^{-\gamma} \qquad \frac{dN_x}{dE_x} = BE_x^{-\gamma+1}$$

$$\frac{dN_e}{dE_e} = Ce^{-E_e/E_0} \qquad \frac{dN_x}{dE_x} = \frac{D}{E_x}e^{-E_x/E_0}$$

$$\text{or} \quad \frac{E_x dN_x}{dE_x} = De^{-E_x/E_0}$$

The latter x-ray spectrum becomes essentially an exponential with e-folding energy E_0 when E_x is large compared to E_0. Alternatively, if one expresses the spectrum in terms of the amount of x-ray energy per energy interval rather than the *number* of x-rays per energy interval, the pure exponential dependence is regained.

Discussion

Heppner warns against making assumptions about the types of electric currents.

It was asked if there are differences in the energy spectra on the morning and night sides, and the reply was that there are insufficient data to determine this.

ROCKET MEASUREMENTS OF AURORAL PARAMETERS

James C. Ulwick

Air Force Cambridge Research Laboratories (OAR)
L. G. Hanscom Field, Bedford, Massachusetts

Abstract   Three Aerobee rockets were fired from Fort Churchill, Manitoba, Canada and two Nike Iroquois rockets from Fairbanks, Alaska into visible auroral forms. The rocket payloads contained a complex array of instruments to make simultaneous direct measurements of the input fluxes of auroral producing particles and the resulting ionization, heating, and luminosity. All five rockets were fired during the breakup phase of auroras. Three rockets penetrated relatively dim, diffuse auroras, and two were launched into more intense auroras with one attaining sufficient altitude to pass through several segments of an active aurora. The electron flux, electron and ion density, auroral brightness, and electron temperature measurements from the Aeorbee rockets and the preliminary results from the Nike Iroquois rockets are compared and discussed. The electron production rates and effective recombination coefficients are determined from the measurements.

Introduction

At the Air Force Cambridge Research Laboratories a rocket program is being conducted to make simultaneous direct measurements of the input fluxes of auroral producing particles and the resulting ionization, heating, and luminosity. In addition to advancing our understanding of auroral phenomena, such measurements should provide a means of determining ion production and recombination rates and photon emission rates. As part of this program five rockets carrying coordinated auroral experiments have been flown into visible auroras. Three Aerobee rockets were launched at Churchill, Canada and two Nike Iroquois (NIRO) rockets at Fairbanks, Alaska. All five rockets were flown during the breakup phase of auroras.

From the knowledge gained from the first Aerobee rocket results (ULWICK *et al.*, 1964), two very complete Aerobee payloads were designed to make simultaneous measurements of the following: energy spectrum of the electron flux, total electron energy deposition, secondary electron flux, x ray flux, auroral light, electron and ion densities, electron temperatures and positive ion composition. The results from these two rockets flown in March 1965 are

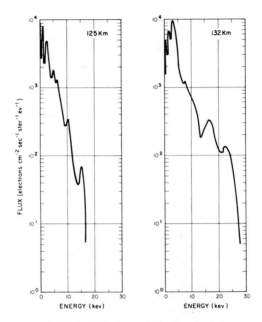

ELECTRON ENERGY SPECTRUM — AE 3.613

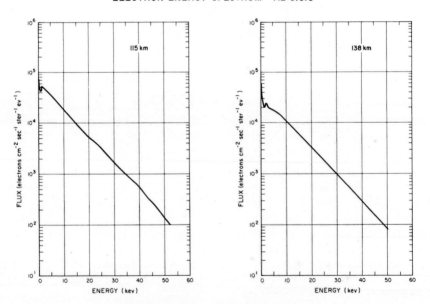

ELECTRON ENERGY SPECTRUM — AD 3.612

FIGURE 1. The differential electron flux as a function of electron energy for two altitudes on rocket ascent of rockets 3.612 and 3.613.

basically the subject of this paper. Preliminary results of the energy spectrum of the electron flux, electron density, and auroral light from the more recently fired NIRO rockets are presented and compared to the Aerobee results.

Energy Spectrum of the Electron Flux

On board the two Aerobee rockets (3.612 and 3.613) and the two NIRO rockets (7.618 and 7.619) were electronic analyzers for the measurement of differential electron flux in the energy range from 2–50 keV. Figure 1 shows the differential electron flux in electrons cm^{-2} sec^{-1} sr^{-1} eV^{-1} as a function of electron energy in keV for two altitudes on rocket ascent of rockets 3.612 and 3.613. Due to a low signal to noise ratio, it was necessary to average ten sweeps (2.5 sec.) in reducing these data. Preliminary results for NIRO's 7.618

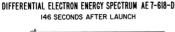

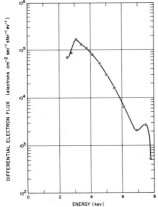

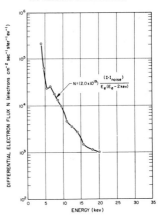

FIGURE 2. The differential electron flux as a function of electron energy from rockets 7.618 and 7.619.

and 7.619 of the differential flux measurements are shown in Figure 2 for one altitude on rocket ascent.

Rocket 3.612 passed through a discreet auroral form of medium intensity, IBC II, on rocket ascent at approximately 112 km as determined by photometer and all-sky camera data. The all-sky camera data also showed that throughout the flight the aurora was changing rapidly in intensity. Nevertheless, the slope of the primary spectrum in the energy range between 2 and 50 keV (Figure 1) was remarkably stable. The differential flux $N(E)$ can be approximated by an exponential spectrum of the type,

$$N(E) = N_0 e^{-E/E_0}$$

where the low energy flux limit N_0 and the e-folding energy E_0 are determined from the measured data. Throughout the flight the exponential distribution was very well defined and the e-folding value was close to 8.5 keV.

At the peak of the electron density, 112 km on rocket ascent, the differential flux was approximately $7 \times 10^4 e^{-E/8.5}$ electrons cm^{-2} sec^{-1} sr^{-1} eV^{-1}, which is equivalent to an energy flux of about 7 ergs cm^{-2} sec^{-1} sr^{-1}. If the flux were approximately isotropic over the upper hemisphere, the total energy would be about 20 ergs cm^{-2} sec^{-1}.

In contrast to 3.612, rocket 3.613 was fired into a diffuse and more quiet aurora of general intensity I^+. Nevertheless, the spectrum of the primary electrons appears more variable and is definitely softer. The exponential shape is not as well defined and the e-folding value appears to be between 2.7 and 4.6 keV. For the peak electron density on rocket ascent (125 km), the differential flux was approximately $1.5 \times 10^4 e^{-E/3.5}$ electrons cm^{-2} sec^{-1} sr^{-1} eV^{-1} giving a total energy flux of about 1.0 erg cm^{-2} sec^{-1}.

NIRO 7.618 was also fired into a diffuse and quiet aurora. During the flight the intensity went from a class II to a class I type aurora. A curve of differential electron flux is shown at an altitude corresponding to the peak electron density. The e-folding value is approximately 1.0 keV and the total energy flux about 5 ergs cm^{-2} sec^{-1}.

The other NIRO rocket, 7.619, was launched during a more intense aurora. Because of poor booster performance, the rocket did not penetrate the auroral form, and attained a peak altitude of approximately 97 km. Thus the spectrum shown is composed of both primary and secondary electrons with those electrons with energies greater than approximately $10 - 15$ keV considered primaries and those lower considered secondaries. The e-folding value for energies greater than 10 keV is 7 keV and for energies greater than 15 keV, about 11 keV, and the total energy flux is about 10 ergs cm^{-2} sec^{-1}.

Electron and Ion Densities

Probes for the measurement of electron density have been flown on the five auroral rockets. The smoothed results are shown in Figure 3. Also included are the results from rocket 17.606 which was flown into a daytime auroral absorption event. The electron density scales are offset by one order of magnitude for each successive rocket result and are labeled for each rocket. The ascent results (A) shown as solid curves and the descent results (D) are dashed. The 30 Mc riometer measurements during each rocket flight are shown. The e-folding values (E_0) measured by the electrostatic analyzers for rocket ascent at the peak electron density are noted.

Three of the high altitude rockets (7.618, 3.613, and 3.603) penetrated dim, diffuse auroras. The auroral layers as shown are rather thick and smooth with a maximum density of approximately 2.0×10^5 electrons/cm^3. Rocket 3.612 however, penetrated active portions of discrete auroral forms with a maximum

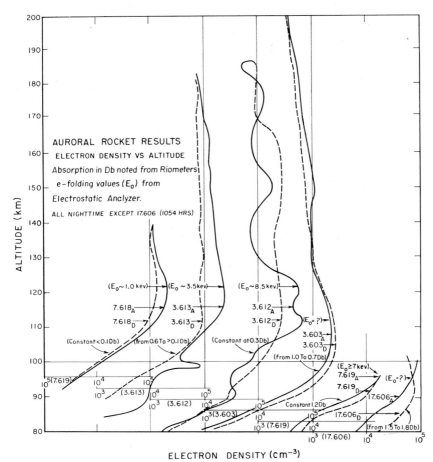

FIGURE 3. Electron density as a function of altitude from five rockets flown into visible auroras and one flown during an auroral absorption event.

density of 6.5×10^5 electrons/cm³. The e-folding values (E_0) corresponding to the peak electron density are noted in the figure. REES (1963) has shown that the height of the auroral layers becomes lower as the electron energy spectrum becomes harder. Unfortunately no flux measurements were obtained for rocket 3.603 where the E_{sa} layer was the lowest (105 km). However, a comparison of the other results shows that rocket 3.612 with the more intense and harder spectrum had higher electron density and lower altitude of the peak than the other two rockets (3.613 and 7.618) which were flown into diffuse auroras.

The auroral absorption from 30 Mc riometer data is noted for each rocket flight. For the nighttime results the photometer and all-sky camera data showed that the rockets were fired during the rapid breakup of homogeneous arcs and the magnetometer records showed negative magnetic bays. The riometer record had the sudden flash-like absorption characteristic of these conditions. In general, the results show an increase in electron density in the 90 – 100 km region with increasing absorption. In particular, examining the two extreme results, i.e., less than 0.1 dB (7.618$_A$, 7.618$_D$ and 3.613$_D$) and 1.2 dB (7.619), an increase in electron density by almost two orders of magnitude is noted at 90 km for the higher absorption distribution.

Positive ion densities were also measured on several of the rocket flights. The results show, within the uncertainty of the measurements ($\approx 15\%$), that the electron density is equal to the positive ion density above 100 km, indicating there is no significant concentration of negative ions above this altitude. However, the ascent data of 3.612 and 3.613 in the range 80 km–90 km indicate positive ion densities a factor of 2 or 3 higher than the electron densities. Tentatively this difference is interpreted as due to the presence of negative ions.

Positive ion composition measurements were made on rocket 3.613 by

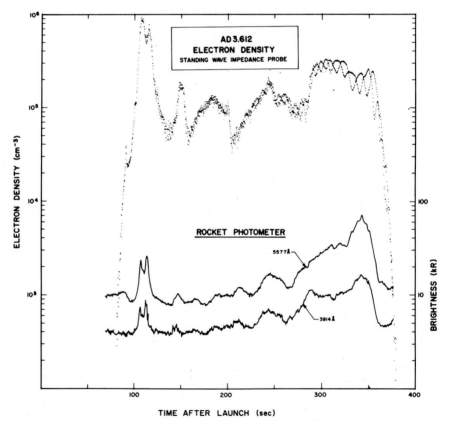

FIGURE 4. Comparison of electron density and photometer results as a function of time after launch of rocket 3.612.

Narcisi. The data show a remarkable similarity to the data by HOLMES *et al.* (1963), for a daytime flight at White Sands, New Mexico (NARCISSI, private communication). Since the aurora was widespread and diffuse, and the electron density distribution resembled a daytime ionosphere in the 100–150 km region; this could mean that the ionospheric chemistry dominates whether the ionizing source be solar radiation or auroral particles — at least in this equilibrium case.

Auroral Light Measurements

Photometers were flown on four of the rockets. On rockets 3.612 and 3.613 the photometers looked out the side whereas on 7.618 and 7.619 they were looking up. Only the data from 3.612 and 3.613 have been completely analyzed. Figures 4 and 5 show a comparison of the electron density results with the photometer data. The apparent scatter in the 3.613 electron density data, particularly on rocket descent, is correlated with the rocket spin and results

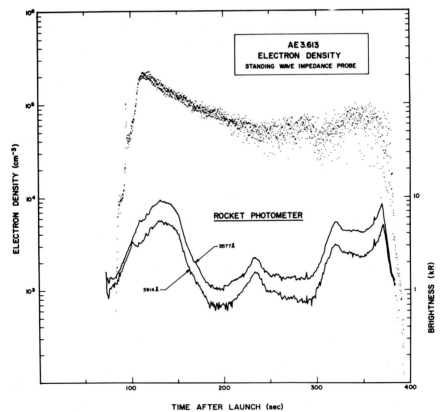

FIGURE 5. Comparison of electron density and photometer results as a function of time after launch of rocket 3.613.

from the sampling antenna falling into the rarefied wake of the vehicle. The highest values of the electron density are assumed to be the correct ones. It is even more clear in the 3.612 result that on rocket descent the antenna is falling into the rarefied wake. Here the apparent double value structure is due to the fact that the data sample period was about twice the rocket roll rate. Thus the sensing antenna falls into the rarefied wake region over per spin. The photometer data, since they are side looking, is for the direction of minimum light per scan (rocket roll). This value should be most representative of the strength of the light emission in the region surrounding the rocket.

The most interesting correlation is in the 3.612 results. On rocket ascent, at about 107 and 113 sec, the altitudes of the peaks in the brightness (approximately 25 kR) and electron density correspond very well. There is also some correspondence in the photometer results of the increases in the electron density at 150 and 250 sec. The photometer results are compatible with the general picture of the auroral development from the all-sky pictures. Also, from the all-sky pictures the buildup to the high maximum of 72 kR of 5577Å on rocket descent around 300–350 sec might have been expected. The pictures show that the rocket should have penetrated a rather quickly developing, bright auroral region in this time interval. The electron density in this region, however, remained at about 3×10^5 electrons/cm^2 which is somewhat puzzling.

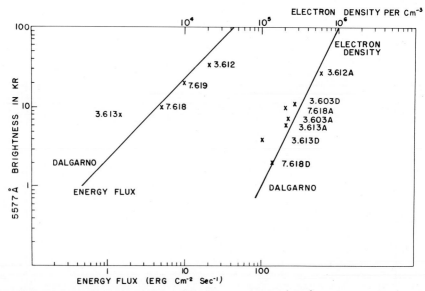

FIGURE 6. Electron density and energy flux as a function of 5577Å brightness from rocket measurements. A is for ascent and D is for descent. Electron density values are for the maximum of the E_{sa} layer. Energy flux values correspond to the peak brightness as 5577Å emission on rocket ascent.

In the other figure for the more diffuse aurora investigated, the auroral light does not appear to be as well correlated with the electron density profile. The maximum of the auroral light occurred at approximately 135 sec (140 km), whereas the electron density peak was at 117 sec (125 km). However,

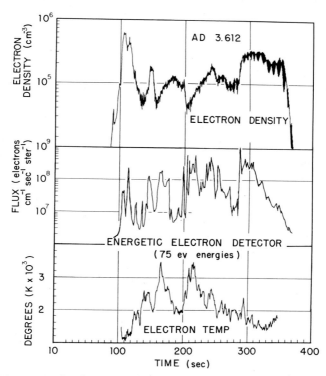

FIGURE 7. Electron density, flux of energetic electrons above 75 eV, and electron temperatures as a function of time after launch of rocket 3.612.

from the electrostatic analyzer results, an increased flux was observed at the time of maximum auroral light. Perhaps the electron density had not had sufficient time to build up. The ratio of the brightness 5577Å–3914Å emission in both rocket flights is essentially independent of altitude with a value around 2. A detailed discussion of these latter results is contained in the paper by STAIR and GAUVIN in this book.

The relationship between the brightness of the aurora and the maximum of the associated E_{sa} layer has been reported by various workers. Figure 6 shows the maximum value of the E_{sa} layer and the corresponding 5577Å brightness from the ground photometers (A is ascent, D is descent). In addition, the energy flux from electrostatic analyzer measurements corresponding to the peak brightness of the 5577Å emission for rocket ascent on four rockets is shown. The comparison of the experimental results with the straight lines from the values given by DALGARNO *et al.* (1965) is good, considering the uncertainties in the photometer measurements and the assumptions involved.

Low Energy Electrons

A retarding potential analyzer (RPA) (HINTEREGGER, 1960) was flown on rocket 3.612 as an energetic electron detector that measured the electron spectrum in the range 1–100 V. The flux for energetic electrons above 75 eV is shown in the middle of Figure 7. Also shown are the electron temperatures determined by the slope method from RPA results and the electron density results. For this flight an almost one to one correspondence between the flux from the energetic electron detector and the secondary current of the positive ion detector on this rocket was found. This secondary current is caused by the emission of secondary electrons from the tungsten cathode when bombarded with energetic electrons. The secondary electron flux should be proportional to the total electron flux between 75 eV and 2000 eV for a constant

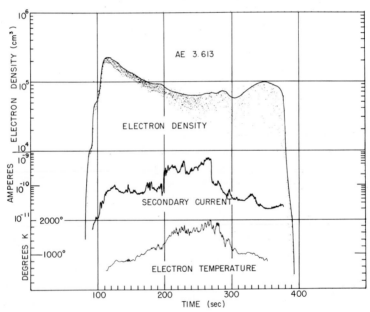

FIGURE 8. Electron density, secondary current of positive ion detector, and electron temperature as a function of time after launch of rocket 3.613.

spectral form. For rocket 3.613, the secondary current from the ion detector, the electron density, and the electron temperature are shown in Figure 8. The electron temperatures and densities measured in the active aurora (3.612) show a large degree of variation of structure compared to the results of the diffuse aurora (3.613). Spot measurements of electron temperature from a Langmuir probe on rocket 3.612 showed a temperature 800° lower but in good structural agreement with the RPA measurements. The electron temperatures show a remarkable correlation with the electron flux above 75 eV or the equivalent secondary flux from the ion detector as shown in the figures.

Electron Production Rates

Several methods are available to determine the electron production rates from measurements with rocket instruments: the primary incident spectrum, the auroral light measurements, and the flux of energetic electrons measured locally.

With respect to the primary incident spectrum, laboratory experiments carried out by GRÜN (1957) have determined the energy deposition of a monoenergetic beam between 5–54 keV as a function of distance and angular dispersion in air. REES (1963) has shown how these results can be applied to the energy deposition of primary auroral particles. Applying Rees' results to the measured flux from rocket 3.612 at the peak of the electron density distribution (112 km), and assuming isotropy, of the flux gives a maximum production rate of 2.4×10^5 electrons cm^{-3} sec^{-1}. Similarly, using the measured flux at the maximum density (125 km) for rocket 3.613 results in a calculated ion production rate of 4×10^3 electrons cm^{-3} sec^{-1}.

Theoretically, it is possible to determine the electron production rate from photometer measurements of the 3914Å line if enough stations are available to resolve the spatial distribution of the luminosity. With rocket photometers pointing upward the height dependence of a stable horizontally stratified luminosity can be resolved. Ground-based photometers pointed at the direction of the rocket give an integrated electron production rate along the line of sight. Usually a vertical thickness of 30 km is assumed for the aurora to calculate a maximum production rate. For 16 kR as found for the flight of rocket 3.612 at the peak of the electron density, this is 10^5 electrons cm^{-3} sec^{-1} according to DALGARNO et al. (1965). However, the photometers mounted horizontally in the rocket showed a thickness of the layer of only 14 km (Figure 4). Therefore, the electron production rate has to be corrected to 2.4×10^5 electrons cm^{-3} sec^{-1}. For 5 kR as found for rocket 3.613 at the peak of the electron density, the electron production rate was 3×10^4 electrons cm^{-3} sec^{-1}. For 4 kR as found for rocket 7.618 on rocket ascent at the peak of the electron density, the calculated electron production rate was 2×10^4 electrons cm^{-3} sec^{-1}. For 1 kR as found on rocket descent for 7.618 the electron production rate at the peak of the electron density was 5.7×10^3 electrons cm^{-3} sec^{-1}.

A more correct method to determine the electron production rate uses the flux of energetic electrons measured locally. The formula to be used is

$$q = 4\pi n \int \phi \, \sigma_i \, dE$$

n is the number density of air particles

E is the electron energy in eV

$\phi(E)$ is the flux of local energetic electrons in electrons cm^{-2} sec^{-1} sr^{-1} eV^{-1}

$\sigma_i(E)$ is the ionization cross section in cm^2 available from published laboratory measurements. It has a peak value of about 28×10^{-17} cm^2 at 100 eV and drops sharply at lower energies.

No assumption about the electric field in the aurora is needed in this case, but good measurements in the energy range between 100 and 2000 eV are necessary. Unfortunately the accuracy of the electrostatic analyzer is very poor at the low energies. Nevertheless, an electron production rate was calculated from the spectrum measured at the height of the maximum electron density. For rocket 3.612 this height is 114 km. The value for $\phi \sigma_i dE$ was found to be 1.8×10^{-8} electrons sec^{-1} sr^{-1} and the resulting q is 2.6×10^5 electrons cm^{-3} sec^{-1}. Similarly for rocket 3.613, a height of 125 km was chosen. In this case the value for $\phi \sigma_i dE$ was found to be 1.5×10^{-9} electrons sec^{-1} sr^{-1} with a resulting q of 7.3×10^3 electrons cm^{-3} sec^{-1}.

In studying our data we find good evidence that the electron production rate is proportional to the product of the neutral particle density and the total electron flux above 75 eV as measured by the RPA. This is to be expected when the shape of the lower part of the spectrum can be assumed to be constant. A curve of the flux of energetic electrons above 75 eV for rocket 3.612 is shown in the middle of Figure 7. The curve has to be multiplied with the neutral density in order to represent the production rate. At the peak of electron density, 114 km, we obtain with this method $q = 1.9 \times 10^5$ electrons cm^{-3} sec^{-1}.

As mentioned for 3.612, the secondary current of the positive ion detector showed an almost one to one correspondence to the curve of energetic electrons. Using this empirical calibration the production rate for rocket 3.613 (which also had ion detector secondary current results but no energetic electron detector) was calculated. Again for the peak of electron density, using the secondary current measurements, we obtained for 3.613 $q = 20 \times 10^3$ electrons cm^{-3} sec^{-1} and for 3.612 $q = 1.9 \times 10^5$ electrons cm^{-3} sec^{-1}.

The results of all the different techniques for obtaining the production rates for rockets 3.612 and 3.613 are shown in Table I. Also included are the preliminary results from photometers on 7.618 ascent and descent.

Table I.   Electronic Production Rate (cm^{-3} sec^{-1})

Rocket	Altitude	Incident Spectrum	Local Spectrum	Integr. Flux	Secondary Current	Photometer
3.612	114 km	2.4×10^5	2.6×10^5	1.9×10^5	1.9×10^5	2.4×10^5
3.613	125 km	4.0×10^3	7.3×10^3	....	2.0×10^4	3.0×10^4
7.618A	120 km	....	....	....	....	2.2×10^4
7.618D	120 km	....	....	....	....	5.7×10^3

For the brighter aurora (rocket 3.612) the results are quite consistent, and assuming the production rate to be 2.4×10^5 electrons cm^{-3} sec^{-1}, an effective recombination coefficient α for the peak of electron density (6.5×10^4 electrons/cm^3) of 5×10^{-7} cm^3 sec^{-1} is obtained. However, for 3.613 the results do not show as good a correspondence. Using the secondary current as a relatively reliable source for the production rate, an effective recombination coefficient of 5×10^{-7} cm^3 sec^{-1} is again obtained for the peak electron density (2×10^5 electrons/cm^3). Using the photometer data for 7.618 ascent and descent and the peak electron density (2.0×10^5 and 1.2×10^5 electrons/cm^3, respectively), effective recombination coefficients of 5.5×10^{-7} cm^3 sec^{-1} and 4.0×10^{-7} cm^3 sec^{-1} are obtained. It should be pointed out that in an aurora with a recombination time constant of about 10 sec the electron density is not necessarily in quasi-equilibrium, and these preliminary results should be used with some caution.

References

DALGARNO, A., LATIMER, L. D., and McCONKEY, J. W., 1965, *Planetary Space Sci.* 13, 1008.
GRÜN, A. E., 1957, *Z. Naturforsch* 12a, 89.
HINTEREGGER, H., 1960, *Space Research* 1, 304.
HOLMES, J. C., JOHNSON, C. Y., and YOUNG, J. M., 1965, *Space Research* 5.
REES, M. H., 1963, *Planetary Space Sci.* 2, 1209.
ULWICK, J. C., PFISTER, W., HAYCOCK, O. C., and BAKER, K. D., 1965, *Space Research* 5.

THE SIMULTANEOUS DETERMINATION OF ROCKET TRAJECTORIES AND RAPID AURORAL VARIATIONS

Keith Burrows

Goddard Space Flight Center
Greenbelt, Maryland

The high optical sensitivity of the Image Orthicon television system can be utilized to record rapid changes in the morphology of an auroral form, as described in the previous paper by T. Neil Davis. The value of this instrument can be greatly increased by using it as a rocket tracking facility in conjunction with a flashing light carried on board the rocket. Also, by recording simultaneously both the flashes of light and the aurora, the instantaneous relative positions of the rocket and the rapidly moving auroral forms can be inferred directly. The positions of the light flashes relative to the adjacent stars are used to determine the angular position of the rocket at the time of each light flash (Good et al., 1962).

The accuracy of each determination of rocket position is ultimately limited by the size of the image on the photographic record and by any nonlinearities in the television time bases. A typical flash has an apparent angular diameter of approximately 10 min of arc; when the rocket is at auroral altitudes this corresponds to an uncertainty in the rocket position of approximately ±50–100 meters in a plane normal to the line of sight.

To determine the rocket trajectory solely by this method it is necessary to triangulate from two or more ground stations, though it has been found that the record from a single installation can provide a useful calibration for the standard radar techniques.

The first flight test of this tracking facility was with a Nike-Tomahawk rocket which was fired from Fort Churchill, Manitoba in March 1966. The rocket carried a Xenon flash tube which produced a pulse of light, 90 BCPS in intensity and of $40 \mu sec$ duration, once every 10 sec. The unit was approximately $4'' \times 4'' \times 7''$ in size and weighed 3.6 lbs. For this flight the television camera was fitted with a RAYXAR E105/0.75 lens, and the monitor display was recorded on 16mm film at 16 frames per sec. The effective field of view (left to right) was approximately 15°.

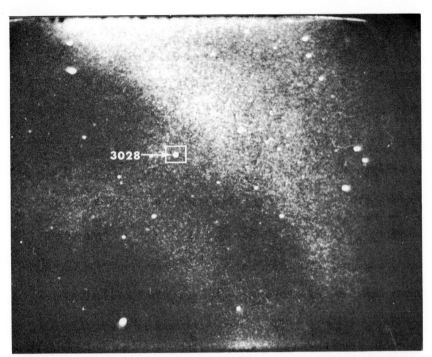

FIGURE 1. Photograph of rocket flash (indicated by arrow), Aurora and Star Field.

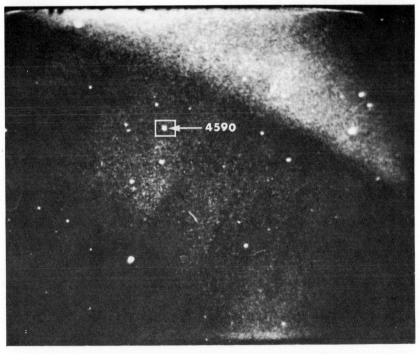

FIGURE 2. Photograph of rocket flash 60 seconds after Figure 1.

Figures 1 and 2 show two frames of the film record 60 sec apart in time. The star field can be readily identified from α-Draco, which is the lower of the two stars near the top left hand corner of Figure 1. The two flashes occurred just above and to the left of the center of the pictures and can be recognized from the change in their positions relative to the star background. The brightness of the flashes, as recorded on the film, is roughly equivalent to that of a star of magnitude 4.5. It will be noted that the form of the aurora also changed significantly during this time interval.

References

GOOD, E. W., BERBERT, J. H., and OOSTERHOUT, J. D., 1962, *Photo. Sci. Eng.* **6**, No. 6, Nov.–Dec.

ELECTRON MEASUREMENTS NEAR A WEAK AURORA

Keith W. Ogilvie, Nicholas McIlwraith

and

Don L. Lind

NASA Goddard Space Flight Center
Greenbelt, Maryland

The observations described here were made during the flight of a Nike-Tomahawk rocket launched from Fort Churchill, Canada, at 0555 UT on April 14, 1966. One purpose of this flight was to test a new electron spectrometer for the OGO-E satellite. This instrument has been described elsewhere, (LIND and MCILWRAITH, 1966), but a short description is included here. Its purpose is to determine simultaneously the energy spectra of electrons arriving at the spacecraft from three directions mutually at right angles, accomplished by means of observations made at the output of three 127° cylindrical electron analyzers by open electron multipliers of the tubular type (channeltron). The detectable electron energy range is essentially from 0–10 keV, and the measurable range of flux into the analyzer is from approximately 10^5 electrons/ sec to a maximum of greater than 10^{10} electrons/sec. The sensitive area of each detector is 0.17 cm², and the solid angle of observation is a cone with an angle of approximately 10°. The electronics associated with each electron multiplier is self-contained and independent, delivering its analog output directly to the telemetry system of the spacecraft. Each analyzer derives its deflecting potentials from the same power supply, the output of which is stepped through a sequence of values to cover the energy range referred to above. A radioactive source is used to give in-flight flux calibration.

The instrument was mounted in the rocket in the manner shown in Figure 1; a second instrument having similar characteristics but only one direction of viewing was also included in the rocket payload. The angle of view of this latter detector measured approximately 45° × 10°, centered about a line at right angles to the rocket axis, and will be referred to as the fourth unit. It contained no radioactive calibration source, but utilized the same deflection potential power supply. The lowest detectable electron energy is that of an electron just able to approach the vehicle from the plasma. Once an electron enters the analyzer, it is accelerated to 100 eV, which is above the detection threshold of the electron multiplier.

During this flight the detector pointing in the upward direction (Figure 1)

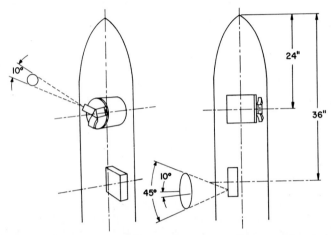

FIGURE 1. This shows the arrangement of the two detectors in the rocket with the appropriate solid angles. The horizontally pointing unit of the triaxial detector and the wide-angle detector provided most of the information discussed.

did not function properly, and the one pointing downward only worked during the latter part of the flight. Thus we shall be concerned in the most part with that detector of the triaxial unit which pointed horizontally, and with the "fourth unit," which also pointed horizontally. Furthermore, at about the peak altitude of the trajectory and for a considerable fraction of the flight afterwards, telemetry reception was poor. Nonetheless, during the ascent these two detectors obtained about 50 electron spectra, being in good agreement with each other. The electron energy band was divided into 15 steps, one of which was used for calibration. During a spectral sweep, $\frac{1}{4}$ sec was spent on each energy step, making 4 sec in all, with an additional 1 sec employed in the decay of the analyzer voltages from the top step. This 5 sec cycle was repeated continuously.

The spin period of the rocket was 0.73 sec, so more than one electron energy was sampled during each spin. Thus, azimuthal information was not obtained.

The auroral conditions during the flight may be described as follows. At the time of firing, a weak diffuse aurora covered the southern half of the field of the all-sky camera. This is illustrated in Figure 2, where the change in the position of the visible aurora is shown as a function of time during the rocket flight. The part of the trajectory above 100 km of altitude, during which measurements were made, is indicated. It will be seen that the rocket did not penetrate the brighter parts of the variable auroral forms which occurred

during its flight. The auroral photometers, whose readings will later be compared to the electron energy computed from the measurements, were trained
upon a point close to where the ascending rocket crossed the 100 km level.

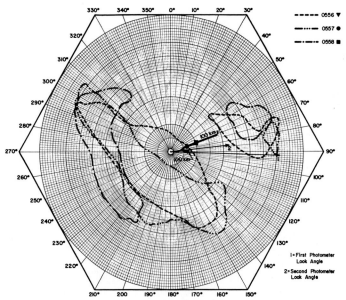

FIGURE 2. A polar plot obtained from all-sky photographs showing auroral conditions during
the rocket flight. The trace of the trajectory is also shown.

Figure 3 shows a cross section of the trajectory in its plane, showing the
projection of the photometer look cone upon it.

Some typical spectra are given in Figures 4(A) and 4(B). The results from
the triaxial instrument have been corrected for the presence of the radioactive calibration source. It will be seen from Figure 3 that at the times
when these results were obtained the detectors were well above the level
of the visible aurora and at a radial distance approximately 150 km from the
brightest area. The spectra cannot be represented by a simple exponential or
power law; they exhibit fine structure and not just changes of slope. The
absolute accuracy of calibration is approximately a factor of 2. This means
that the decrease in intensity at the lowest energy, 10 eV, may be significant.
It could result from the effects of scattering or be due to the rocket potential.

The question of how much of the observed spectra are composed of primary
and scattered radiation must be considered. McDiarmid and Budzinski (1964)
point out that if electrons in one gyration period move a distance along the
geomagnetic field line less than or equal to the distance from the nose of the
rocket to the detector, they will be scattered by the rocket before detection.

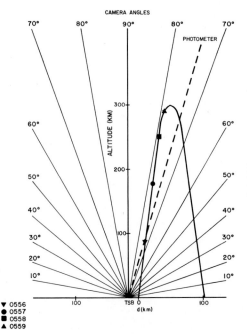

FIGURE 3. The trajectory showing the location of the rocket at the times indicated in Figure 2.

Since the rocket traveled approximately parallel to the field lines the effect apparently serves to alter the intensity of those electrons with pitch angles near 90°. Calculations show that this effect becomes serious below about 500 eV for the triaxial instrument, and below about 100 eV for the wider angle detector.

The motion of the rocket was such that while the present measurements were taken, the two detectors sampled pitch angle ranges of 90 ± 15° and of 90 ± 33°, respectively.

At 250 km, the residual atmosphere above the detectors is about 6×10^{-4} mg/cm². Neglecting scattering for the moment, and assuming the flux incident from above, this electron range corresponds to an energy of 1.5–2.0 keV at a pitch angle of 85° and to an electron energy well below 1 keV at a pitch angle of 60°. Thus we consider that the electron spectra presented are indicative of the primary spectra down to an energy of less than 1 keV, but that below this energy the effects of atmospheric absorption and atmospheric and rocket scattering have an effect upon the data.

It is of interest to compare the total energy, obtained by integrating the observed electron intensities, with the readings of the 5577Å and 3914Å photometers, the axis of whose 4° fields of view are shown in Figures 2 and 3. The result is shown in Figure 5; reasonably good correlation is found between the two peaks at 165 sec. Because of the time required to step through a spectrum correlation to better than about 5 sec is not to be expected. The energy per unit solid angle recorded by the wide-angle detector was about

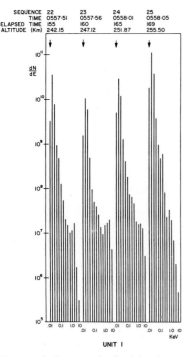

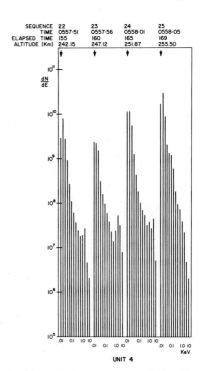

FIGURE 4. Spectra obtained by the narrow-angle and wide-angle detector, respectively. Although there is generally good agreement, the "wide-angle" spectra appear harder than the ones obtained with the narrow-angle detector. The calibration accuracy is about a factor of 2, but the relative accuracy is much better. This may be significant.

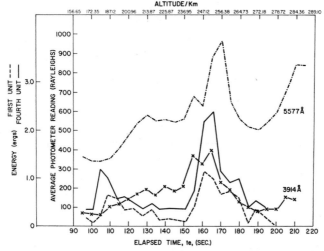

FIGURE 5. Correlation between photometer readings and integrated particle flux per unit solid angle.

twice that recorded by the narrow-angle detector, which may indicate anisotropy and reflects the different spectral shapes (Figure 4). Since the rocket was not exactly above the point at which the photometer response cone intersected the aurora, and because the photometer calibration was not especially checked for this flight, it is not possible to get a better than order-of-magnitude value of the electron energy required to produce the observed light.

If we assume isotropy in the upper hemisphere and use the average of the two peak readings of electron energy, we arrive at a figure of 11.0 ergs for approximately 970 rayleighs of $\lambda5577$. The $\lambda3914$ intensity measured at the time was 380 R. The commonly accepted figure would be about 2.0 ergs for 400 R of $\lambda3914$ (DALGARNO, 1964), but the difference can be readily accounted for by calibration and geometrical ambiguities in the photometric data. No inconsistency seems to be indicated.

References

DALGARNO, A., 1964, *Ann. Geophys.* 20, 65.
LIND, D. L. and McILWRAITH, N., 1966, IEEE trans, N. S. 13, 511.
McDIARMID, I. B. and BUDZINSKI, E. E., 1964, *Can. J. Phys.* 42, 2048.

AURORAL ZONE MICROBURSTS

Kinsey A. Anderson

Physics Department and Space Sciences Laboratory
University of California Berkeley, California

Introduction

High altitude research balloons have been used since 1957 to study the precipitation of energetic electrons into the auroral zone. Although balloon techniques permit detection of electrons only indirectly by means of their bremsstrahlung, they possess certain advantages over orbiting vehicles. The high altitude balloon remains stationary in space over characteristic times of many important geophysical phenomena. The techniques used and the results obtained from balloon studies of precipitation into the auroral zone have recently been reviewed by ANDERSON (1965a). BROWN (1966) has summarized the results on energetic particle precipitation obtained by use of ground-based riometers.

Over the past few years our group at Berkeley has made a considerable effort in the experimental design to reduce both background fluxes and atmosphere absorption of the x-ray fluxes. The largest component of background in the energy range of interest (20–100 keV) is due to the degraded secondary photons from the cosmic ray electromagnetic cascade (ANDERSON, 1961). Physical collimation of the detector reduces this component significantly. To reduce atmospheric absorption of the auroral zone x-rays, large volume balloons have been used to attain atmospheric pressure depths of 2–3 g/cm^{-2}. Such depths are a small fraction of a Compton interaction length so that a negligible fraction of the detected auroral zone x-rays have been scattered. A further consequence of reducing the Compton scattering is that the energy spectrum of the x-rays at the production layer can be accurately determined by straightforward use of photoelectric absorption corrections. These techniques have resulted in the first quantitatively reliable measurements of the size of electron precipitation regions and the energy spectrum of these particles made from balloons.

To illustrate the kind of instrumentation currently being used on balloon flights to study auroral zone electron precipitation, Figure 1 shows a directional array of four x-ray telescopes. This apparatus has been used by PARKS (1966) to study source size and motion effects in microburst precipitation.

Types of Auroral Zone Electron Precipitation

Since one of the objectives here is to compare the microbursts to other types of auroral zone electron precipitation, it is necessary to briefly discuss the present knowledge of this topic. An ideal classification would include all

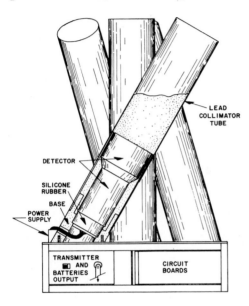

LEAD
COLLIMATOR
TUBE

DETECTOR

SILICONE
RUBBER

BASE

POWER
SUPPLY

TRANSMITTER
AND
BATTERIES
OUTPUT

CIRCUIT
BOARDS

FIGURE 1. Array of four x-ray telescopes used in 1964 and 1965 to determine the size and motions of electron precipitation regions. One result is that microburst source sizes may be as small as 20 × 20 km. This instrument is flown to atmospheric depths of 2–3 g/cm^{-2} in order to reduce Compton scattering which otherwise would prevent accurate size determinations. (Illustration courtesy of G. K. Parks.)

members of the class and group them according to fundamental causal phenomena. So far, it has not proved possible to classify auroral zone electron precipitation in this ideal way. At the present time it is possible to identify two distinct types of auroral zone electron precipitation which can be related to other magnetospheric phenomena:

(1) Nighttime precipitation associated with magnetic storm or substorm disturbance. X-rays associated with magnetic bays, recurrent and flare-induced magnetic storms all show quite similar features. Electron precipitation occurs on the night side of the earth with large fluxes near local midnight. The precipitation is intense but rather featureless over times of minutes. The precipitation takes place over a wide range of L values. For active magnetic storms having high K_p values, precipitation occurs at L values at least as low as 2.5. From their nighttime occurrence and general resemblance to electron islands (ANDERSON, 1965b) in the geomagnetic tail, it is inferred that this precipitation is related to processes in the earth's magnetic tail. An example is shown in Figure 2c.

(2) Hydromagnetic type. There are two modes of this type of particle precipitation.

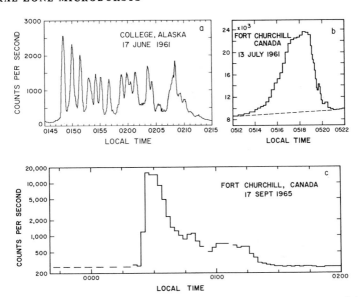

FIGURE 2. Parts a and b of the figure show examples of energetic electron precipitation in the auroral zone believed to be associated with hydromagnetic waves propagating in the magnetosphere. In part a the precipitation resembles a coherent wave. In part b the precipitation is associated with a sudden commencement. The particle effects are believed to result from the effects of the hydromagnetic impulse. (Illustration courtesy of J. R. Winckler.) In part c the intense but rather featureless precipitation at the time of a midnight bay is shown. This type is believed to be related to processes in the geomagnetic tail.

(a) Coherent wave mode. This particle precipitation shows periodic or near-periodic character over several cycles. Periods range from 1–30 min. This precipitation can be understood in terms of distant radiation zone phenomena: over large regions just inside the magnetopause, hydromagnetic waves occur nearly continuously (HEPPNER, 1965). In this region they couple very strongly to the trapped electrons producing modulations as large as a factor of 10 or 100 (LIN and ANDERSON, 1966). Infrequently at times of enhanced geomagnetic activity a train of waves originating in this region penetrates deeply into the magnetosphere. There it couples with trapped radiation resulting in precipitation. An example is given in Figure 2a.

(b) Sudden commencement mode. For about 5 min in time coincidence with ground magnetometer sudden commencement, electrons precipitate into the atmosphere in the auroral zone. Although confined in latitude the precipitation is broad in longitude. Again in this case, it is believed that a hydromagnetic disturbance propagates from the magnetopause into the auroral zone lines of force. The wave then strongly couples with the trapped particle fluxes causing precipitation. Such an event is shown in Figure 2b.

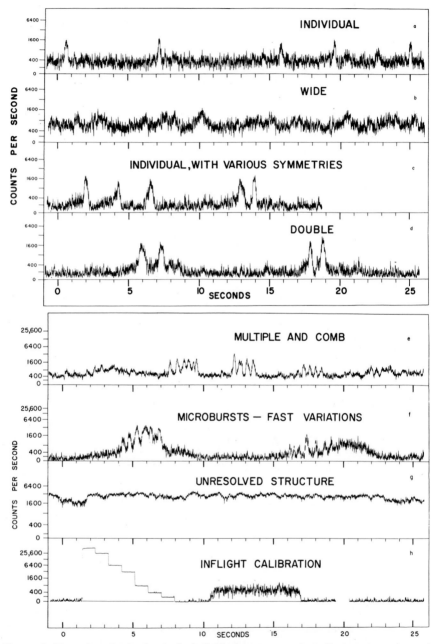

FIGURE 3. Examples of microbursts in individual patterns and small groups are shown in parts a to d. Groups of several individuals are illustrated in parts e and f. Part g of the figure shows electron precipitation in which the flux changes in times on the order of 0.1 sec but there is no clear resolution into microbursts. The apparatus used to make these measurements is calibrated in-flight every 15 min. The calibration consists of electronic checks of the count rate meters, detector gain with a radioactive source and system noise.

Other forms of precipitation occur but their causes and relationship to the above are not known at present. They may be grouped into three forms according to their temporal features:

(1) Quiescent form. Precipitation that shows no appreciable change in flux during the time it is present. The duration is from 10–100 min.

(2) Fast variations. This precipitation is characterized by large changes over times of 5–30 sec. Occasionally, the fast variations become well organized and even periodic (BARCUS et al., 1966). Temporally well-organized pulsations with characteristic times of 5–30 sec are illustrated in Figures 3 and 4.

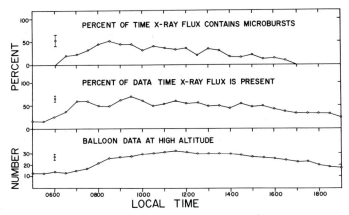

FIGURE 4. The appearance of microbursts has a strong diurnal dependence. The highest probability occurs about 0830 local time. The probability of their appearance before noon is about twice the probability of their appearance past noon.

(3) Microbursts have characteristic times of 250 msec but often occur in groups having a duration of a few seconds and spaced 5–30 sec. There is an important relationship between this form of electron precipitation and the rapid variations. Examples can be found in Figures 3, 4, and 5.

Properties of Auroral Zone Microbursts

Microburst electron precipitation into the auroral zone has been studied intensively for several years. The properties of this form of auroral zone precipitation can be summarized as follows:

(1) Microbursts have been detected in substantial numbers during the years 1962, 1963, 1964, and 1965 (ANDERSON et al., 1966). Microbursts are therefore a persistent feature of the electron precipitation into the auroral zone and represent an important means by which electrons are lost from these geomagnetic field lines.

(2) Microbursts occur in episodes of a few minutes up to 5 hours. Many episodes last about 90 min. Microbursts occur with an average rate of typically

10 per min. Thus on the order of 1000 occur during an episode. The number of episodes per day is usually two, but 1 or 3 also may occur.

(3) The peak x-ray intensity during microbursts ranged from 0.2–15 $(cm^2\text{-sr-sec-keV})^{-1}$ at 30 keV during the years 1962–1965. A representative value for the x-ray intensity is thus 3 $(cm^2\text{-sr-sec-keV})^{-1}$ at 30 keV during times of moderate geomagnetic activity. This corresponds to a parent electron flux of about $10^6(cm^2\text{-sec-sr})^{-1}$ above 20 keV.

(4) Microbursts have been observed at L values of 6 and 8. Rapid fluctuations of precipitating electron intensity having at times a periodic character have been observed at $L = 3$ during a great geomagnetic storm (WINCKLER et al., 1962). It is possible that this observation is related to the auroral zone microburst phenomenon. Our observations show the microbursts to have the same temporal characteristics at $L = 6$ and $L = 8$. At $L = 3$, the impulsive precipitation is more rapid by about a factor of 2.

(5) Microbursts appear during daytime for up to several hours on days following geomagnetic activity. If the geomagnetic disturbance is great, such as a storm with sudden commencement, the microbursts will appear every day for as many as 5 successive days. For lesser geomagnetic storms or strong but localized midnight bay activity, microbursts usually are detectable for the following 1 or 2 days. Since the detectors always have a detection threshold it may be the case that even the very weak precipitation many days following storms contains microbursts. Microbursts are present about one-third of the time when daytime electron precipitation is occurring. The fraction of the daytime electron precipitation which occurs directly in the form of microbursts is about 20%. In a sense, microburst episodes fall into the pattern of the auroral substorm (AKASOFU, 1965). These episodes have a strong tendency to appear following nights of bright auroras. Furthermore, the length of the episodes (≈ 90 min) is about the duration of an auroral substorm. Thus the microburst episode may be thought of as a daytime, high energy particle manifestation of the auroral substorm.

(6) The diurnal pattern of microburst occurrence is rather similar to the pattern of electron precipitation observed by low altitude polar orbiting satellites. The work of FRANK, VAN ALLEN, and CRAVEN (1965) shows precipitation contours for electrons >40 keV reaching their highest values between local times of 0900 and 1300 at invariant latitudes of about 66–70°. The microburst pattern actually reaches its maximum at a somewhat earlier local time, namely 0830. Considering that the observations were made at different times, this discrepancy may only be apparent. It is tempting to associate the diurnal pattern of microbursts with the high precipitation flux contours observed by satellites during midmorning and early afternoon local times.

(7) The probability of occurrence of microbursts as a function of local time has been determined. This distribution is shown in Figure 4. It can be seen that the probability microbursts occur between 1700 and 0600 local time is close to

zero. The most probable time of occurrence is 0830. The probability that microbursts occur before local noon on a given day is about twice the probability of their appearing past noon.

(8) Microbursts have a definite tendency to group into bunches of more than 4 individuals. These *combs* have a duration of typically 5 sec and have a high probability of being followed in 5–30 sec by another comb. Examples of combs are shown here in Figures 3 and 6. We have found that another form of electron precipitation also occurs in much this same manner but with microbursts absent. We have referred to these as *swells* (ANDERSON *et al.*, 1966). An example is shown in Figure 5. We also find intermediate cases in which the

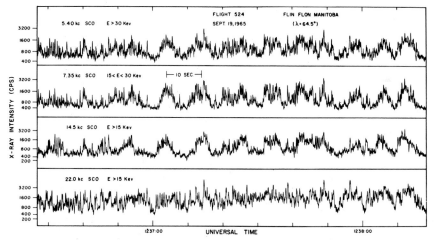

FIGURE 5. This figure illustrates the relation between microbursts and fast variations (precipitation having characteristic times of 1–30 sec). (Courtesy of G. K. Parks.)

microburst peak-to-valley ratios lie between 1 for the swells and large values (≈ 10) characteristic of the combs. The 5–30 sec time interval characteristic of the duration and spacing of the swells and combs is just the same as the fast variations most recently discussed by BARCUS *et al.* (1966). Results of PARKS (1966) confirm this relationship between the microbursts with characteristic times of 0.1–1 sec and the fast variations with characteristic times of 5–30 sec found by ANDERSON *et al.* (1966).

(9) When microbursts occur in groups the spacing between adjacent individuals is very regular and there is a striking resemblance to periodic waves. At these times the average spacing is about 0.6 sec. However, these spacings do not persist over many cycles. Furthermore the next comb may contain microbursts spaced by 0.4 sec so that under power spectrum analysis carried out over many minutes strong spectral peaks do not appear at these times. A stable periodicity is often encountered in microbursts at 1.2 sec (PARKS *et al.*, 1965) over many minutes of microburst data. Also Lampton has fired a rocket

into a microburst event and found that microbursts were very uniformly spaced at 1.2 sec.

(10) The occurrence of microbursts and fast variations may be correlated with various geophysical phenomena and with phenomena that occur in the distant geomagnetic field.

The characteristic times of particle fluctuations 0.1–20 sec agree well with the pulsations observed photometrically in pulsating auroras (CRESSWELL and DAVIS, 1965.) They find at times an average periodicity of 1.2 sec in the light fluctuations. (Figure 4, CRESSWELL and DAVIS, 1965.) This corresponds very closely with the stable periodicity observed in microbursts reported by PARKS *et al.* (1965) and in the rocket measurements of Lampton. Other light fluctuations occur with characteristic times of about 10 sec as in our *combs* and *swells*. Such a comparison hardly clarifies the situation, especially since we do not observe microbursts at the hours pulsating auroras appear in the night sky. However, Cresswell and Davis do report that the pulsating auroras often are still in progress at dawn, past which time photometric observations can no longer be carried out. We can resolve this apparent contradiction with an *ad hoc* assumption that during pulsating auroras only the soft particels (<20 keV) are being modulated so that this effect cannot be seen with balloons.

Magnetic fluctuations having characteristic times in the same range of 0.1–20 sec have been observed by satellite-born magnetometers in the magnetosheath region. HEPPNER (1965) has reported a 1.2 sec near-periodic variation in the subsolar region. The Vela magnetometer (GREENSTADT *et al.*, 1966) has found quasi-periodic and aperiodic fluctuations of up to 30 gammas with characteristic times from 5 sec (the limit of time resolution) up to 60 sec. Well developed fluctuations frequently appeared near 10 sec. Not enough is yet known about the properties of the magnetic fluctuations reported by HEPPNER (1965) and by GREENSTADT *et al.* (1966) to determine whether or not they can propagate from the magnetosheath at distances of about 12 R_e where they are observed, into the geomagnetic lines of force entering the auroral zone ($L \approx 6$) where the periodic and quasi-periodic particles effects are observed.

Recently, PARKS *et al.* (1966) have compared the occurrence times and durations of 25 x-ray microburst episodes at Flin Flon, Manitoba with riometer and micropulsation records at College, Alaska. It was found that every microburst episode was accompanied at the same Universal Time by geomagnetic micropulsation activity in the 5–40 sec period range and by cosmic noise absorption at College, Alaska. The local time difference between these sites is 4 hours. It was also found that in 24 of 25 cases of geomagnetic micropulsation activity in the 5–40 sec period range, which occurred while a balloon was in the air at Flin Flon, were accompanied by microburst activity.

Spatial Properties of Microburst Electron Precipitation Regions

By use of the directional array of x-ray detectors flown to high balloon altitudes, PARKS (1966) has obtained the first direct and quantitative measurements of microburst source size. Three x-ray telescopes pointed 30° from the zenith and were spaced uniformly in azimuth. The fourth telescope pointed toward the zenith. At the level where the electrons producing the observed bremsstrahlung stop (about 100 km), the telescopes view a circle of 20 km diameter. The full view area of all four telescopes together is roughly a circle of 70 km diameter. Several qualitative results from this experiment will be described first: It was found that during microburst episodes the response of a given telescope would be quite different from the response in the other telescopes. An example is given in Figure 6. Peak intensities of the same microburst would vary by as

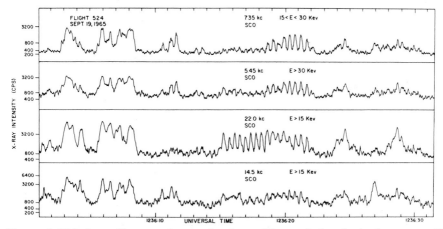

FIGURE 6. This figure illustrates the occasional wave-like regularity of microbursts as well as their small source size. The record labeled 22.0 kc comes from the detector looking at the zenith direction. The other detectors looking somewhat off the zenith see very different effects.

much as a factor of 10. Sometimes microbursts would appear in only one of the telescopes. The peak-to-valley ratio also varied greatly between the various detectors. Parks found that at Flin Flon the microburst regions in several episodes were preferentially located to the north of that site. The microburst precipitation regions were sometimes observed to move with high speed. Their speed was 10–100 km/sec, but the motion showed no preferred direction. Motion was observed to occur for about 5% of the microburst regions.

A statistical analysis of the response of the four x-ray telescopes showed that the average radius of a microburst precipitation region was 40 ± 14 km. However, for a few events the microburst source size was only half this large. On September 17, 1965 balloons at Fort Churchill and Flin Flon, which is a separation of 400 km, simultaneously observed episodes of microbursts. However, the individual microburst peaks did not coincide at the two locations. Thus the microburst precipitation resembles a rainstorm: the "storm" extends over many thousands of square kilometers, but each "raindrop" has linear dimensions of about 60 km.

PARKS (1966) has found that at times microbursts are associated with regions of electron precipitation drifting at speeds of 250–300 m/sec from west to east (Figure 7). This event consisted of two x-ray bursts each of about 6 min duration, separated in time by about 15 min. The microbursts appeared at the peaks

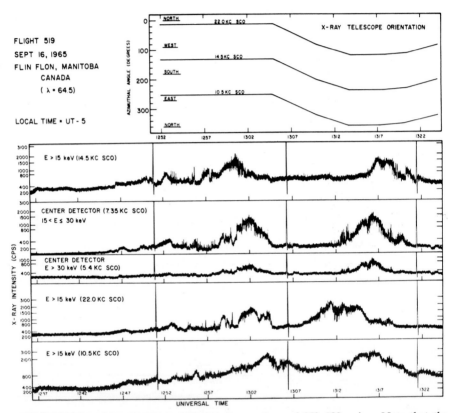

FIGURE 7. Electron precipitation event showing motions of 250–300 m/sec. Note that the peaks first appear in the detector which points to the west. Microbursts appear at the peaks of the two large bursts.

of the two bursts. The electron precipitation region was determined to be in the form of an eastward moving arc in the north-south direction and within this arc there were bright patches of x-ray emission. The microbursts occurred in these bright patches only.

Energy Spectrum of Auroral Zone Electrons

In the past, several groups have made pulse height measurements of auroral zone x-rays and have then derived approximate energy spectra for the parent electrons. Nearly all this work published to date suffers from serious sources of error, and it is not possible to use the results to draw firm conclusions about the behavior of electron energy spectra in the auroral zone. These measurements, for the most part, were obtained with omnidirectional detectors. Therefore, the amount of matter traversed by the x-rays before reaching the detector is undetermined in these experiments. Thus a soft, intense spectrum of electrons precipitating a large distance from the balloon can look like a hard, weak spectrum nearer the balloon. The problem is a two-dimensional diffusion of the x-rays undergoing both photoelectric and Compton interactions with an unknown amount of material. Since the extent of atmosphere traversed by the x-rays is greater than or much greater than the interaction lengths, it is easy to see that very large errors can result in obtaining true x-ray or parent electron energy spectra. In the gross measurement of x-ray energies no attempt was made to make in-flight or post-flight calibrations of the apparatus. The detector used had a limited range of accurate response. Examples of gross measurements of auroral zone x-ray and parent electron spectra are given by ANDERSON (1959), ANDERSON and ENEMARK (1959), BHAVSAR (1960), BARCUS and ROSENBERG (1966), and BEWERSDORFF et al. (1966). The content of these measurements can be summarized as follows:

(1) The spectral form obtained for the precipitating electrons agrees crudely with direct rocket measurements.

(2) Changes of the spectrum occur, sometimes quite rapidly. These could be due to true changes of the spectrum or by movement of the source region over the sky so that absorption and scattering effects are producing the apparent changes. Barcus and Rosenberg have claimed that on the basis of gross x-ray energy measurements there is a systematic diurnal change in the form of the particle spectrum. The same claim is made for various types of electron precipitation events. However, such changes can be equally well produced by systematic shifts of the source region over the sky.

More recently, greatly improved experiments have been carried out to determine precipitating auroral zone energy spectra. Improvements have been made in detectors by optimizing the crystal size, by providing absolute in-flight energy calibration and by using narrow-angle collimation to obtain directional intensities. This apparatus has been flown to atmospheric depths much less than a Compton interaction length so that correction for photoelectric absorption can be unequivocally made (ANDERSON, 1965a). HUDSON et al. (1965) and HUDSON (1966) used this improved apparatus to study the energy spectrum of detectors in microbursts. He found that some time prior to the onset of microburst activity the precipitating electrons had an e-folding energy of 8 keV. About 15 min before strong microburst activity began, the spectrum suddenly hardened and could be characterized by an e-folding energy of 30 keV. When the microbursts appeared the energy spectrum of the electrons underwent no further sudden change. After the microburst appearance the spectrum gradually softened to an e-folding energy of about 10 keV after about an hour. Hudson has found that electron spectra producing x-rays at balloon altitude are commonly as soft as $E_0 = 10$ keV. Spectra with e-folding energies as low as 4 or 5 keV have been observed, particularly at midnight. These results are not in agreement with the frequency distributions given by Barcus and Rosenberg, which show few if any instances of electron precipitation with $E_0 < 15$ keV. This discrepancy is easy to understand since at the large atmospheric depths that Barcus and Rosenberg flew their omnidirectional detectors the softer x-rays would be severely attenuated, and the spectrum would appear much harder. Therefore, the frequency distributions given by Barcus and Rosenberg have little meaning, either relative or absolute.

HUDSON (1966) has also studied the possibility that the energy spectrum of precipitating electrons undergoes a systematic diurnal variation. On one flight the e-folding energy of the electrons was about 10 keV at 0600 local time, increased more or less regularly until about noon, then decreased to about 12 keV at 1400 local time. It reached a value of about 30 keV at noon. In the

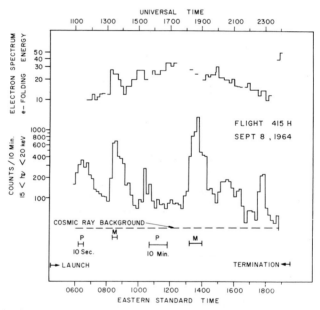

FIGURE 8. The form of the spectrum of the precipitating electrons varied systematically on this particular day. The e-folding energy rose from 10 keV early in the morning to 30 keV at noon. It then decreased to near 10 keV by 1800 local time. The bars marked P indicate the presence of pulsating electron events. M denotes microbursts. (Illustration courtesy of H. S. Hudson.)

morning hours during a microburst episode the e-folding energy did increase abruptly, then returned to a lower value within an hour. This result is shown in Figure 8.

Hudson has also determined the energy spectrum of electrons precipitating during an intense midnight bay event at Fort Churchill ($L = 8$). The temporal form of the event resembled electron islands as observed in the geomagnetic tail. The electron flux appeared very suddenly and slowly decayed away. Initially,

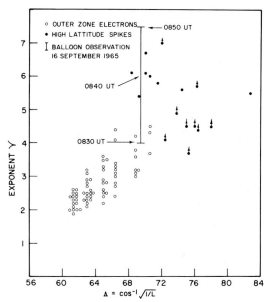

FIGURE 9. The spectrum of precipitating electron events obtained during a midnight bay event at $L = 8$ underwent a systematic softening. The spectral form parameter changed from a value characteristic of outer zone electrons to a value characteristic of its high latitude spikes of McDiarmid. (Illustration courtesy of H. S. Hudson.)

the energy spectrum was rather hard ($\gamma = 4$) and then progressively softened to about $\gamma = 7$ (Figure 9). This behavior is in good agreement with the spectral measurements made on electron islands by KONRADI (1965).

Acknowledgements This work was supported by the National Science Foundation and by the National Aeronautics and Space Administration. The Office of Naval Research provided logistic and administrative assistance.

References

AKASOFU, S. I., 1965, *Space Science Reviews* **4**, 498–540.
ANDERSON, K. A., 1961, *Phys. Rev.* **123**, 1435–1439.
ANDERSON, K. A., 1960, *J. Geophys. Res.* **65**, 551–564.
ANDERSON, K. A., 1965a, *Auroral Phenomena* (Ed. by M. WALT), Stanford Press.
ANDERSON, K. A., 1965b, *J. Geophys. Res.* **70**, 4741–4763.
ANDERSON, K. A. and ENEMARK, D. E., 1960, *J. Geophys. Res.* **65**, 3521–3538.
ANDERSON, K. A., CHASE, L. M., HUDSON, H. S., LAMPTON, M. L., MILTON, D. W., and PARKS, G. K., 1966, *J. Geophys. Res.* **71**, 4617–4626.

ANDERSON, K. A. and MILTON, D. W., 1964, *J. Geophys. Res.* **69**, 4457–4479.
BARCUS, J. R., BROWN, R. R., and ROSENBERG, T. J., 1966, *J. Geophys. Res.* **71**, 125–140.
BEWERSDORFF, A., DION, J., KREMSER, G., KEPPLER, E., LEGRAND, J. P., and RIEDLER, W., 1966, *Ann. Geophys.* **22**(1).
BROWN, R. R., 1966, *Space Science Reviews* **5**, 311–387.
CRESSWELL, G. R. and DAVIS, T. N., 1965, Goddard Space Flight Center Preprint Series, X-612-65-485.
EDWARDS, P. J., MCCRACKEN, K. G., STEINBACK, M., OLIVER, M., and VENKATESAN, D., 1966, *Trans. Am. Geophys. Union* **47**, 139.
EVANS, D. S., 1963, *J. Geophys. Res.* **68**, 395.
FRANK, L. A., VAN ALLEN, J. A., and CRAVEN, J. D., 1964, *J. Geophys. Res.* **69**, 3155–3167.
GREENSTADT, E. W., INOUYE, G., GREEN, I., and Judge, D., 1966, *Trans. Am. Geophys. Union* **47**, 143.
HEPPNER, J. P., 1965, Goddard Space Flight Center Preprint Series, X-612-65-490.
HUDSON, H. S., 1966, Ph.D. Thesis, University of California, Berkeley.
HUDSON, H. S., PARKS, G. K., MILTON, D. W., and ANDERSON, K. A., 1965, *J. Geophys. Res.* **70**, 4979–4982.
KONRADI, A., 1965, Goddard Space Flight Center Preprint Series, X-611-65-465.
LIN, R. P. and ANDERSON, K. A., 1966, *J. Geophys. Res.* **71**, 1827–1835.
PARKS, G. K., 1966, *J. Geophys. Res.* **72**, 215–226.
PARKS, G. K., HUDSON, H. S., MILTON, D. W., and ANDERSON, K. A., 1965, *J. Geophys. Res.* **70**, 4976–4978.
PARKS, G. K., MCPHERRON, R. L., and ANDERSON, K. A., 1966, *J. Geophys. Res.* **71**, 5743–5745.
WINCKLER, J. R., BHAVSAR, P. D., and ANDERSON, K. A., 1962, *J. Geophys. Res.* **67**, 3717–3736.

Discussion

K. Anderson discussed an overall magnetospheric picture of the distribution of energetic charged particles based mainly on satellite measurements. Spikes of energetic electrons are found near the bow shock and many weaker ones are found upwind. The skirt is situated between the magnetopause and the stable trapping zone. In this latter region the radiation is triply periodic (possesses all three adiabatic invariants). Its outer boundary usually occurs at 8.5 ± 1 R_e. The particle spectra in the skirt are soft and the fluxes are perpetually modulated by long wave length (~ 20 R_e) hydromagnetic waves. Because of the weak radial gradient and the large changes in the magnetic field imposed by the wave activity the particles have only the first two adiabatic invariants. Their azimuthal motion is predominantly random walk. The skirt has a distinct termination at the 2000 and 0400 local time meridian. Behind the antisolar portion of the stable trapping zone is the particle *cusp*. It is much flattened in latitude compared to the skirt. It extends to 12 or more earth radii geocentric distance. The high density of particles in the cusp produces a large diamagnetic effect (inflation). The relation of the cusp to the auroral zone is a key problem.

Impulsive acceleration processes in the geomagnetic tail give rise to *island* fluxes of electrons and protons. Their outstanding characteristic is a rapid buildup of intensity followed by a slow decay. At these times the β of the plasma is close to unity. Vela measurements show this process is related to the entire plasma energy spectrum suddenly being heated. The electron energy spectrum progressively softens with time. Initially the e-folding energy is about 12 keV and softens to about 6 keV near the end. According to Konradi the protons show a constant e-folding energy of about 30 keV. Experiments by Lin and Anderson using solar flare electrons as tracers have shown that some of the geomagnetic tail field lines connect directly to the interplanetary field. An upper limit of 0.2 A.U. to the length of the tail has been given by them. This rules out the long tail proposed by Dessler. It was asked if the solar flare electron fluxes perturb or load the interplanetary field. Anderson said that the effect is very small.

P. Rothwell stated that her attempts to correlate the electron islands with magnetic bays were unsuccessful. This requires an assumption that magnetic bays are related to reconnection of magnetic lines. L. Harang and others objected to this assumption. There was also an objection to attempting to correlate electron islands with magnetic bays. She also stated that resolution of spatial and temporal variations with one satellite is difficult. However, if the islands move much faster than the satellite, the islands should look the same on the outbound leg as on the inbound. She could not find any experimental evidence that the islands move inward.

Axford would like to see the correlation of islands of >40 keV electrons with low altitude >40 keV electron events and with riometer absorption as measured from the surface.

Session

3

THEORY I

Dr. Liev Harang

Norwegian Defence Research Council

THE AURORAL OVAL AND THE
INTERNAL STRUCTURE OF THE MAGNETOSPHERE
S.-I. Akasofu

Geophysical Institute University of Alaska
College, Alaska

Abstract The auroral and polar magnetic substorms are a manifestation of interactions between the magnetospheric plasma near the outer boundary of the trapping region and the neutral atmospere underneath. Two kinds of interaction, dynamical and atomic, occur in a narrow belt along the intersecting line between the outer boundary of the trapping region and the ionosphere, the auroral oval. Both interactions occur most violently in the E region of the ionosphere, which is a rather thin transition region between the magnetospheric plasma and the neutral atmosphere. The atomic interaction is either collisional excitation or ionization which results in the auroral light. The dynamical interaction is a frictional interaction between the plasma and the neutral atmosphere and causes an intense polar electrojet.

Our main concern here is why such interactions tend to occur most violently along the narrow oval belt and why this auroral oval shifts toward the equator during intense geomagnetic storms.

The Auroral Oval as a Natural Coordinate

Recent studies of the aurora have revealed an important fact that auroral arcs tend to lie in a narrow oval belt encircling the geomagnetic pole. The oval is eccentric with respect to the dipole pole and its center is appreciably ($\sim 3°$) displaced towards the dark hemisphere (FELDSTEIN, 1963, 1966; KHORO-SHEVA, 1963) (Figure 1). The auroral zone is simply the locus of the midnight part of the oval where intense auroral displays are most frequently seen. It may be noted in this connection that spectral studies by SANDFORD (1964 and this volume) indicate that another type of auroral luminosity extends approximately along a zone in the morning sector at constant dipole latitude. This may be caused by energetic electrons which "drizzle" after drifting eastward from the midnight sector (BRICE and HARTZ, 1966). The behavior of this mantle aurora will not be considered here.

The eccentricity of the oval is closely related to the day-night asymmetry of the internal structure of the magnetosphere. The outer radiation belt has a marked asymmetry, and the line of intersection between its outer boundary and the ionosphere coincides approximately with the auroral oval (PID-DINGTON, 1965; AKASOFU et al., 1965; FELDSTEIN, 1966); (Figure 1). The concept of the auroral oval has thus a basic foundation.

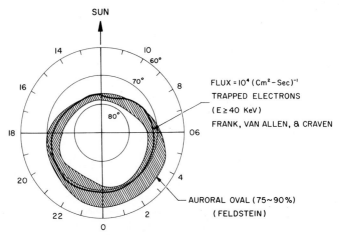

FIGURE 1. Location of the auroral oval obtained by FELDSTEIN (1963) and of iso-intensity (the flux = $10^4/cm^2sec$) contour line of the trapped electrons of energies greater than 40 keV (FRANK, VAN ALLEN, and CRAVEN (1964)).

AKASOFU et al. (1965) have shown recently that the polar electrojet flows westward all around the auroral oval. FELDSTEIN (1966) has recently arrived at the same conclusion.

Therefore, two major polar geophysical phenomena, auroral and magnetic, occur along the auroral oval. The oval can thus be considered to be the natural frame of reference to which some major polar geophysical phenomena can be referred. The dipole coordinate is not necessarily the most suitable coordinate in describing these polar geophysical phenomena because of the eccentricity of the oval center with respect to the dipole pole.

In fact, this eccentricity of the auroral oval, together with the lack of a close network of stations, has obstructed studies of polar geophysical phenomena. Two different methods have been used to study magnetic disturbances in the polar regions: by SD analysis and by polar plots of the maximum magnetic deviations. The SD analysis (along dipole circles) was unable to reveal this fundamental pattern of the oval and its eccentric nature. Polar plots of the maximum disturbance vectors, which have been extensively used (particularly by Russian workers), have revealed M and N "spirals," but these workers have failed to recognize that the spirals show only segments of the oval.

It is not difficult to identify Nikolsky's "M-spiral" as the forenoon part of the oval. Figure 2 shows the location of the forenoon part of the oval at 0,

6, 12, and 18 UT by solid curves and Nikolsky's spirals at the same UT hours by dotted curves.*

The "N-spiral" can be identified as the afternoon part of the oval. AKASOFU, CHAPMAN, and MENG (1965) and AKASOFU, MENG, and KIMBALL (1965) have

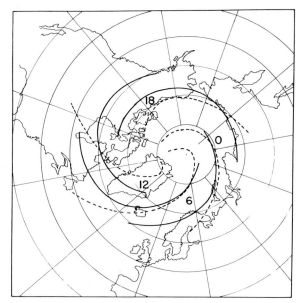

FIGURE 2. Location of the forenoon part of the auroral oval at 0, 6, 12, and 18 UT (solid curve) and of Nicolsky's spirals at the same UT hours (dotted curve).

shown that westward traveling auroral surges generated in the midnight sector of the oval travel westward along the preexisting arcs, namely, the oval, and are accompanied by an intense (westward) polar electrojet; therefore, an intense magnetic disturbance occurs along the afternoon part of the oval.

Other geophysical phenomena, such as the sporadic E layer, spread F layer, Hα emission, and radio auroras, are also known to occur approximately along spiral curves (NAGATA, 1963). They are, however, essentially the oval phenomena.

The polar cap (or the auroral cap) has been defined as the region inside the classical auroral zone: namely, the region beyond dipole latitude (dp lat) 67°. We propose here that the polar cap should be defined as the region inside the

*In general, Nikolsky's spiral curves tend to curl less tightly than the solid curves. However, it is not difficult to show that the solid curves represent a more accurate location of intense magnetic disturbances. For example, the K indices at Eskdalemuir (England; geographic lat. 55°19′N, long. 3°12′W) Agincourt (East Canada; geographic lat. 43°47′N, 79°16′W), Meanook (West Canada; 54°37′N, 113°20′W) tend to peak at 21–24 UT, 0–3 UT, and 6–9 UT, respectively. Furthermore, Nikolsky's curves in the very high latitudes do not seem to be realistic.

auroral oval. Again, this definition has a basic foundation, since the geomagnetic field lines originating in the auroral cap cross the equatorial plane
in the tail region of the magnetosphere or are connected to interplanetary
magnetic field lines; on the other hand, the field lines originating equatorward of the oval lie in the trapping region of the magnetosphere.

By the early definition, a station at dp lat 70° is permanently in the polar
cap. However, by the new definition, the station is outside the polar cap in
the daytime and inside the polar cap in the midnight hours. The station is
not unique when compared with other stations in lower latitudes in the day
sector. For example, low energy galactic cosmic rays (≈ 1 MeV) penetrate
into the newly defined polar cap, so that they cannot reach the 70° station in
the day sector as well as lower latitude stations (STONE, 1964).

The auroral oval is not a fixed coordinate. Figure 1 shows only the average
location of the oval. Its "radius" varies greatly with solar activity. Figure 3

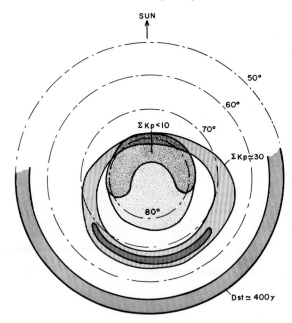

FIGURE 3. Distribution of the aurora for different geomagnetic activities. When ΣK_p is of
the order of 30, the aurora tends to be distributed along the average location of the oval shown
in Figure 1.

shows the locations of the auroral oval for different geomagnetic activity.
During great magnetic storms, the oval descends to as low as dp lat 50° in
the midnight sector (AKASOFU and CHAPMAN, 1963); this is associated with
an equatorward shift of the outer boundary of the outer belt. Therefore, a
station at dp lat 65°, like College, Alaska, becomes temporarily a polar cap
station.

Such a flexible coordinate system can aid the explanation of a number of complicated features of geophysical phenomena. For example, it is well known that there exists an excellent correlation between the K index and auroral activity at an auroral zone station; however, this correlation apparently breaks down for large K values. This is simply because the oval descends below dp lat 60° during great magnetic storms and thus a station at 65° becomes temporarily a polar cap station. An example of this situation is studied by AKASOFU and CHAPMAN (1962).

Further, it is well known that at 18 hours local time at an auroral zone station, the sky is dark enough to see overhead auroras in midwinter, but auroras are rarely seen there; in the dusk hours (16 $\sim$ 20 hours), intense auroral activity is seen well poleward of the station: namely, at about dp lat 72° (Figure 1). As the night progresses, however, auroras appear near the poleward horizon and draw gradually closer to the station, indicating that the station is approaching the oval since the earth rotates under the eccentric oval. However, during great magnetic storms, the oval descends toward the equator, resulting in an abnormally early appearance of auroras in the evening sky. It is also associated with an abnormally early appearance of negative (magnetic) bays, since the westward electrojet flows along the auroral oval. These complications can be simply ascribed to the changing oval. In other words, some of apparent complications or confusion can be greatly reduced when the location of each station is considered with respect to the changing oval (inside, within, or outside).

Apparent daily variation of the occurrence frequency of the aurora, geomagnetic disturbances, and other associated geophysical phenomena can also be understood in terms of changing distance between a station and the oval. A station at dp lat 72° observes two maxima in the occurrence of the aurora and magnetic disturbances simply because it crosses the oval twice in a day, from outside to inside in the evening and inside to outside in the morning. An auroral zone station has a simple maximum occurrence of these phenomena, since it comes under the oval once a day in the midnight hours.

We have now established that some major polar geophysical phenomena occur along an oval band (the auroral oval), and that the oval lies close to the line of intersection between the outer boundary of the trapping region and the ionosphere. Taking this to be a coordinate, the description of these polar geophysical phenomena can be greatly simplified. *Our problem is now reduced to finding why these major geophysical phenomena occur along such a unique oval band*, one in each hemisphere, and also why the auroral oval shifts toward the equator during geomagnetic storms. We will first consider the latter problem in the next section.

2. The Equatorward Shift of the Auroral Oval

As mentioned earlier, there exists a striking resemblance in geometry of the auroral oval with the intersection line between the outer boundary of the trapping region and the ionosphere. A detailed study made by satellites indicates that auroral particles are detected just *outside* the trapping boundary (FRITZ and GUNETT, 1965), suggesting that they originate in the equatorial region of the magnetospheric tail and penetrate into the polar ionosphere along the boundary of the trapping region. Therefore, the auroral oval delineates the internal structure of the magnetosphere on the polar ionosphere.

From the above consideration, we may infer that the equatorward shift of the auroral oval indicates the equatorward movement of the outer boundary of the trapping region. This was first observed by MAEHLUM and O'BRIEN (1963), and later by WILLIAMS and PALMER (1965) and NESS and WILLIAMS (1965).

Since such an equatorward shift of both the auroral oval and the boundary of the trapping region occurs during the main phase of geomagnetic storms, one may infer that it is due to changes of the internal structure of the magnetosphere, which are caused by the growth of storm-time electric current systems in and around the magnetosphere. In order that the boundary of the trapping region near the earth's surface shifts toward the earth, the field lines which had been constituting the outer part of the trapping region must be stretched outward to the tail region, so that they no longer can trap durably 40 keV electrons. The storm-time radiation belt has been known to have the

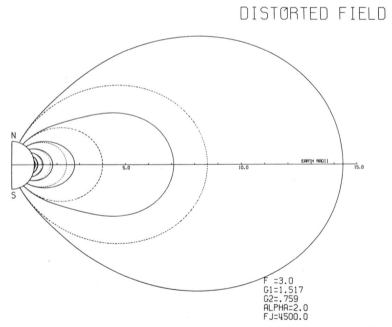

DISTORTED FIELD

F =3.0
G1=1.517
G2=.759
ALPHA=2.0
FJ=4500.0

FIGURE 4. Distortion of the geomagnetic field caused by a model ring current belt. The distorted field lines are shown by the solid lines and the corresponding dipole field lines by dotted lines. For the model ring current, see the text.

stretching effect (DESSLER and PARKER, 1959; AKASOFU and CHAPMAN, 1961; APEL, SINGER, and WENTWORTH, 1962). For the first time its existence has been definitely confirmed by CAHILL (1966); the belt is formed deep in the trapping region ($r_e = 3.0 \frown 3.5$). Figure 4 shows an example of a model calculation; the six parameters defining the belt are $r_{eo} = 3.0$, $g_1 = 1.517$, $g_2 = 0.759$, $\alpha = 2.0$ and $n_0E = 4500.0$ (keV/cm³): for details, see AKASOFU and CHAPMAN (1961). This particular model produces a magnetic field which is perpendicular to the equatorial plane at the earth's surface, where its magnitude is $-320\ \gamma$. It can be seen from Figure 4 that the dipole field line crossing the equatorial plane at $r_e = 4.0$ can be stretched to as far as $r_e = 7.1$. The stretching action reduces the magnetic field intensity from $3.2 \times 10^4\ \gamma/(4.0)^3 = 500\ \gamma$ to about $180\ \gamma$; in other words, the ring current greatly redistributes the magnetic flux in the inner magnetosphere. It is immediately clear, however, that such a ring current alone is unable to stretch low latitude field lines to the tail region of the magnetosphere. But we should recognize that the sheet current in the tail region is also very efficient in the stretching, since it reduces the flux everywhere in the inner magnetosphere. It will further reduce the above value of $180\ \gamma$.

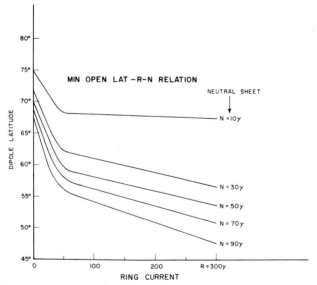

FIGURE 5. Relationship between the minimum latitude exposed to auroral particles and the ring current intensity (R) at the equator on the earth's surface. The magnetic field intensity (N) of the sheet current is taken as the parameter.

Figure 5 shows the relationship between the minimum latitude (ϕ) exposed to auroral particles from the equatorial region of the magnetospheric tail and the ring current intensity (R), taking the magnetic field intensity (N) of the sheet current to be the parameter; for details of the model, see AKASOFU (1966). It can be seen in Figure 5 that the sheet current of intensity, $N = 50\ \gamma$ alone can open the field lines beyond dp lat 70°, but the growth of the ring current decreases considerably the minimum latitude ϕ. For an extreme case of the ring current intensity $R = 300\ \gamma$ and $N = 90\ \gamma$, dp lat 47° 30′ can be exposed to auroral particles. This latitude is a little less than the minimum dp lat attained by quiet auroral arcs during the IGY.

3. The Auroral Substorm

In addition to the equatorward shift, the auroral oval rapidly repeats expansions and subsequent contraction of its width, particularly in the midnight sector. The expansion and the contraction occurs during the expansive phase and the recovery phase of the auroral substorm, respectively.

In the midnight sector, during the expansive phase, quiet arcs lying in the oval first become bright and advance rapidly polewards, resulting in an explosive expansion of the oval width. This initiates a planetary-scale activity of auroras that lie in the rest of the oval (Figure 6). In the evening sector of

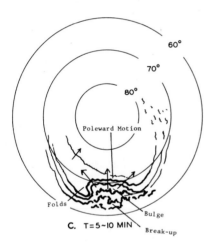

FIGURE 6. Schematic illustration of the explosive phase of the auroral substorm.

the oval, a surge-type motion of auroras (the westward traveling surge) is generated by the expansion which travels along preexisting arcs, namely along the oval toward the evening twilight sector. In the morning sector, particularly to the equatorward side of the oval, arcs disintegrate into patches, and the resulting patches drift eastward. In this way, the whole auroral system in the oval is progressively activated from its midnight portion. For details of the auroral substorm, see AKASOFU (1964, 1965). In the following, we list some of the important features of the aurora and the auroral substorm and consider the basic physics involved.

1. The ribbon-like form of the aurora suggests a thin electron (or plasma) sheet beam injected along the outer boundary of the trapping region.

2. The mechanism that causes the sheet beams is multiple in nature, rather than singular, so as to produce several arcs, with the most common separation distance of order 30–40 km.

3. The mechanism must be able to supply a very weak plasma sheet beam into the polar ionosphere (10 ergs/cm² sec) and should not spontaneously be activated by itself (or there is an accompanying mechanism that tends to check the spontaneous activation to a certain extent), since homogeneous arcs can remain fairly quiet for a few hours. However, when it is activated, it should increase the output (particle flux) at least by two orders of magnitude over a wide range of energies (less than 500 eV to perhaps more than 100 keV), suddenly within several minutes. The center of the activation is located in the midnight sector. Since there is no visible indication that the substorm is preceded by any auroral motion, and since an enhanced solar plasma does not initiate the substorm, the substorm is most likely to be an internal process within the magnetosphere (AKASOFU, 1964).

4. Since the auroral substorm has a sudden onset, an explosive energy release (the explosive phase) and a slow relaxation (the recovery phase), the activation must be caused by an instability.

5. The activation of the mechanism must be associated with the poleward shift of the plasma sheet beams.

From these considerations we are led to conclude that the auroral substorm is most likely to be due to a plasma instability. Here we try to specify characteristics of the instability.

1. The instability must occur in a confined region of the magnetosphere. The confined region must be stable against the instability to a certain extent, in order to give rise to a stable homogeneous arc.

2. The growth rate of the instability must be rapid, the e-folding time being of the order of $10^2 \sim 5 \times 10^2$ sec.

3. The instability should be nonlinear and explosive in the sense described by STURROCK and COPPI (1966) in their discussion of mechanisms of solar flares. This is because a stable homogeneous arc, which can remain inactive for hours, becomes activated in a matter of a few minutes, so that the non-linear process must promote the instability.

4. The instability must be such as to cause a rapid poleward shift of the plasma sheet beams.

The specification of the characteristics given in the above section greatly limits a number of possible candidates for the required instabilities. So far, two kinds of instabilities have been examined as possible mechanisms. The first is an instability which takes place in the neutral sheet and the other an interchange instability which takes place in the vicinity of the outer boundary of the ring current.

The neutral sheet could have three kinds of instabilities, the rippling mode, tearing mode, and gravitational mode. Our particular interest is concerned with the tearing mode. This is essentially a disintegration of a sheet current into a number of filaments by the pinch effect. Further, since the medium has a finite resistance, a decoupling between the field lines and plasma occurs, and the field energy can be converted into the thermal energy by the Ohmic heating mechanism. FURTH (1964) also studied the growth of the tearing instability in a collisionless plasma, since effects of collisions (leading to the resistivity) can be replaced by electron inertia. He examined the stability of the neutral sheet configuration for a perturbation (exp (ωt + ikz)) and showed that the stability condition is analogous to Bennett's pinch condition.

A more detailed examination of the growth rate by using the Vlasov equation approach has been made by LAVAL and PELLAT (1964), based on Harris' solution of the plasma-magnetic field configuration in the vicinity of the neutral sheet. The application of their results to auroral phenomena was discussed by COPPI, LAVAL, and PELLAT (1966). Their study shows that the growth time τ of the instability is of the order of 5 sec for electrons of 1 keV.

As mentioned earlier, the tearing mode is essentially the pinch of a sheet current, resulting in the disintegration of the sheet current into a number of filamentary currents. Each filament produces its own magnetic field around it. Figure 7 schematically shows the situations before and during the insta-

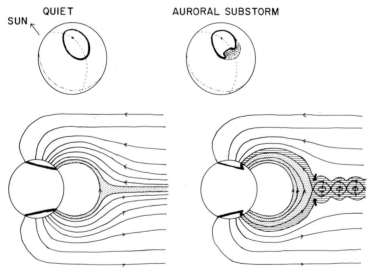

FIGURE 7. Schematic illustration of the relationship between the auroral substorm and changes in the magnetospheric tail suggested by COPPI, LAVEL, and PELLAT (1966).

bility. PIDDINGTON (1966) has discussed the possibility of this instability becoming a substorm and has considered its consequences.

One of the important features of this instability is that some of the field lines which had been "opened" by the tail current before the onset of the instability tend to close. This closure forces the hot plasma produced by the instability to flow toward a higher latitude. This may be identified with the expansive phase of the auroral substorm.

Since one of the basic processes of this particular instability is the conversion of the magnetic energy to the thermal energy of the plasma, a transient decrease of the magnetic field in the tail is inevitable. In fact, BEHANNON and NESS (1966) observed such a transient decrease by Imp I.

Suppose that the intensity of the neutral sheet is suddenly decreased. As is clear from Figure 5, a decrease of the intensity of the neutral sheet must indicate an increase of the minimum open latitude ϕ. For the ring current intensity $R = 100\,\gamma$, a decrease of the neutral sheet intensity from $N = 50\,\gamma - 10\,\gamma$ can cause the closure of the field lines which anchor between dp lat $57°-68°$. During geomagnetic storms of a medium intensity $R \simeq 100 \sim 150\,\gamma$, the auroral oval descends from its average location (dp lat $67°$) to about $57° \sim 60°$; then during auroral substorms, the poleward boundary of the oval moves rapidly to about dp lat $70°$. The brightest auroral bands are seen at the advancing boundary, and the region swept by such bands is covered by irregular bands or patches.

An extremely intense substorm observed at about 1030 UT on February 11, 1958 could be explained if the intensity of the neutral sheet decreased from $N = 90\,\gamma$ to $N = 10\,\gamma$ if the intensity of the ring just prior to the substorm was of the order of 300 γ. This will result in a temporal widening of the oval, extending from about dp lat $50°$ to dp lat $70°$. This agrees well with the extent of the poleward motion observed during an extremely intense substorm which occurred about 1030 UT on February 11, 1958. In fact, such a drastic substorm occurs only during geomagnetic storms with a large main phase decrease.

One important problem to be examined in this connection is whether or not the transportation of the fusing field lines from the dayside to the nightside occurs. If this is the case, what are the firm evidences to support such a conjecture? So far, although different mechanisms have been proposed by different authors, it seems to be that the SD current system is the basis of their conjecture (DUNGEY, 1966; PIDDINGTON, 1966; AXFORD, PETSCHEK, and SISCOE, 1965). However, AKASOFU, CHAPMAN, and MENG (1965) have proposed an important revision on the flow pattern of the auroral electrojet. They propose that the polar electrojet flows westward along the oval and that the so-called eastward electrojet is the return current from it. HEPPNER (this volume) argues against such a proposal.

In order to obtain an accurate distribution of the polar electrojet, it is necessary to have a fine distribution of disturbance vectors over the polar cap. Unfortunately, however, it is quite clear that the distribution of the presently available stations is far from satisfactory to make such an attempt on an instantaneous basis (even allowing the condition that div i = 0 in the ionosphere). Therefore, it is necessary to find some statistical methods to overcome such a serious lack of magnetic observatories beyond dp lat 70° (where more than half of the oval lies) or to find another geophysical phenomenon associated with the jet. FELDSTEIN (1966) could successfully overcome the difficulty statistically and concluded that the polar electrojet flows westward along the oval. AKASOFU, CHAPMAN, and MENG (1965) based their argument on a detailed study of magnetic disturbances associated with various types of auroral activity. Their current system also agrees well with an extensive statistical analysis made by Nikolsky and others: their "spirals" are a part of the auroral oval (see Figure 2). It may be noted also that it is unlikely to have a unique phenomenon like an eastward electrojet flow along the auroral zone which has no physical meaning on an instantaneous basis.

Acknowledgments The research reported in this paper was supported in part by a grant from the National Science Foundation (GP-2721) and in part by a grant from the National Aeronautics and Space Administration (NsG 201-62).

References

AKASOFU, S.-I., 1964, *Planetary Space Sci.* **12**, 275–282.
AKASOFU, S.-I., 1965, *Space Sci. Rev.* **4**, 498–540.
AKASOFU, S.-I., 1966, *Planetary Space Sci.* **14**, 587–595.
AKASOFU, S.-I. and CHAPMAN, S., 1961, **66**, 1321–1350.
AKASOFU, S.-I. and CHAPMAN, S., 1962, *Atmospheric Terrest. Phys.* **24**, 735–796.
AKASOFU, S.-I. and CHAPMAN, S., 1963, *J. Atmospheric Terrest. Phys.* **25**, 9–12.
AKASOFU, S.-I., CHAPMAN, S., and MENG, C.-I., 1965, *J. Atmospheric Terrest. Phys.* **27**, 1275–1305.
AKASOFU, S.-I., MENG, C.-I., and KIMBALL, D. S., 1965, *J. Atmospheric Terrest. Phys.* **27**, 173–187.
APEL, J. R., SINGER, S. F., and WENTWORTH, R. C., 1962, *Advance In Geophysics*, vol. 9, (Ed. by H. F. Landsberg), Academic Press, New York, pp. 131–189.
AXFORD, W. I., PETSCHEK, H. E., and SISCOE, G. L., 1965, *J. Geophys. Res.* **70**, 1231–1236.
BEHANNON, K. W. and NESS, N. F., 1966, *J. Geophys. Res.* **71**, 2327–2352.
CAHILL, L. J., Jr., 1966, *J. Geophys. Res.* **71**, 4505–4520.
COPPI, B., LAVEL, G., and PELLAT, R., 1966, *Phys. Rev. Letters* **16**, 1207–1210.
DESSLER, A. J. and PARKER, E. N., 1959, *J. Geophys. Res.* **64**, 2239–2252.
DUNGEY, J. W., 1966, Dept. of Phys. Imperial College, London.
FELDSTEIN, Y. I., 1963, *Geomagnetism and Aeronomics* **3**, 183–226.
FELDSTEIN, Y. I., 1966, *Planetary Space Sci.* **14**, 121–130.
FRANK, L. A., VAN ALLEN, J. A., and CRAVEN, J. D., 1964, *J. Geophys. Res.* **69**, 3155.
FURTH, H. P., 1963, *Phys. Fluids* **6**, 48–57.
KHOROSHEVA, O. V., 1962, *Geomagnetism and Aeronomics* **2**, 696–838.
LAVEL, G. and PELLAT, R., 1964, *C. R. Acad. Sci. Paris* **259**, 1706–1709.
MAEHLUM, B. and O'BRIEN, B. J., 1963, *J. Geophys. Res.* **68**, 997.
NAGATA, T., 1963, *Planetary Space Sci.* **11**, 1395–1430.
NESS, N. F. and WILLIAMS, D. J., 1965, Pub. Goddard Space Flight Center, NASA.
PIDDINGTON, J. H., 1965, *Planetary Space Sci.* **13**, 565–577.
PIDDINGTON, J. H., 1966, *Geophys. J.* (to be published).
STONE, E. C., 1964, *J. Geophys. Res.* **69**, 3557–3582.
STURROCK, P. A. and COPPI, B., 1966, *Ap. J.* **143**, 3–22.
WILLIAMS, D. J. and MEAD, G. D., 1965, *J. Geophys. Res.* **70**, 3017.

Discussion

Dr. Akasofu stated that we should study the aurora with respect to the trapping boundary rather than a fixed geographic or geomagnetic latitude.

Dr. Akasofu stated that our knowledge of magnetic field variations is insufficient, simply because there is a lack of observing stations in the most important regions. We used to think the auroral zone was the most important region, and some stations were set up accordingly. It now appears that the inner region of the auroral zone is important, and there should be some stations at latitudes $> 70°$ if we wish to perform accurate studies.

Craven stated that he had compiled some new observations that clearly demonstrate that as the electron energy is lowered the trapping boundary extends out to greater L values. The trapping boundary for electrons > 40 keV may decrease to L of 3.5–4 during a storm. The auroral electrojet is always north of the 40 keV trapping boundary.

THE SIGNIFICANCE OF THE MULTIPLE
STRUCTURE OF THE AURORAL ARC

S.-I. Akasofu,* S. Chapman,** and P. C. Kendall***

*Geophysical Institute, University of Alaska, College, Alaska
**National Center for Atmospheric Research
Boulder, Colorado, and Geophysical Institute, College, Alaska
***University of Sheffield.

The aurora often has multiple arc structure, that is, there is often more than one arc in the field of view of an observer (four or five are not uncommon). Photographic or visual records from more than one place sometimes show that as many as 10 may be included within 10° of latitude. A single arc is more rare than multiple arcs.

Individual arcs have (north-south) widths of the order of a few or several hundred meters (ELVEY, 1957; AKASOFU, 1961), and an east-west dimension often of thousands of kilometers. The most common separation distance between two arcs is of the order of 30–40 km (AKASOFU, KIMBALL, and MENG, 1966). The lifetime of an arc is not accurately known. By studying many all-sky camera records, Akasofu, Kimball, and Meng noted that auroral arcs grow and fade continually within a narrow band, the auroral oval. It is difficult to follow their life for more than 30 min unless they are extremely bright. The multiple structure is common to both quiet and active periods; the arcs tend to be more nearly parallel during quiet periods.

There is a striking similarity between the form and location of the auroral oval and the line of intersection of the outer boundary of the trapping region with the ionosphere. This suggests that auroral particles penetrate the polar ionosphere along and from beyond the outer boundary of the trapping region. (PIDDINGTON, 1965; AKASOFU, CHAPMAN, and MENG, 1965; AKASOFU, 1966; FELDSTEIN, 1966). Further detailed satellite studies have detected auroral particles just outside the trapping boundary (FRITZ and GUNETT, 1965). This suggests that they originate near the equatorial plane of the tail region of the magnetosphere (PIDDINGTON, 1960; NESS, 1965) (Figure 1). For more than a decade the possibility of reconnection of field lines in this type of configuration has been discussed (DUNGEY, 1953, 1958, 1963; SWEET, 1958; PARKER, 1957, 1963 PETSCHEK, 1964). An electric current in that region is supposed to collapse into a sheet so thin that dissipative effects become important. This implies the existence of an electric field in the sheet, and energizing of charged particles in the sheet. Neither effect is understood at the present, but SPEISER (1965, 1966) has made illuminating studies of particle motions in such a situation.

Such a magnetic configuration could guide auroral particles into a narrow strip of the ionosphere oriented east-west. COPPI, LAVAL, and PELLAT (1966), taking the diameter of the tail cross section (normal to the sun-earth line) to be 20a (a = earth radius), and the thickness of the equatorial current region in the tail to be 50 km, inferred theoretically an auroral latitudinal width of the order of 0.3 km in the polar ionosphere.

Their suggestion, like those of others (cf. PIDDINGTON, 1960), provides only a single arc. However the frequent multiple arc structure of the aurora indicates that even during quiet periods the magnetic configuration is not as simple as that suggested in Figure 1. The hot plasma in the equatorial region must be

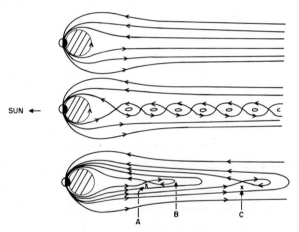

FIGURES 1 (top) and 2 (middle). The magnetic field configuration in the tail region of the magnetosphere and an instability developed there, proposed by COPPI, LAVAL, and PELLAT (1966).
FIGURE 3 (bottom). The magnetic field configuration in the magnetospheric tail proposed in the present paper.

divided and focused into at least a few discrete strips. The cause may be the pinch effect acting on accidental irregularities in the equatorial sheet current, as COPPI, LAVAL, and PELLAT (1966) have suggested (Figure 2). But they show a single field line connecting a number of irregularities — neutral points or lines — in the field. It seems highly improbable that one field line would connect a series of singularities, and Figure 3 shows what we consider to be a more likely configuration. Thus we suggest that the equatorial region of the tail contains, in general, at least a few neutral lines (not all associated with the same field line) as in Figure 3, which shows the suggested noon-midnight meridian cross section of the magnetosphere. Each meridian cross section of a neutral line is indicated by x. The very small auroral thickness (0.5 km) compared with the mean separation distance (40 km) between arcs suggests that auroral particles are discharged from a series of strips in the tail, relatively small compared with their separation distance. We suggest that the neutral lines correspond to such a structure.

The great distorted extension of the geomagnetic field lines in the tail implies that an electric current sheet exists in its equatorial region. The configuration shown in Figure 1 suggests that the current intensity is fairly uniform, or changes monotonically, over a great radial distance, perhaps 1000a. Our suggestion modifies that conception by proposing that the current intensity is not uniform, and that the regions of intense current are enclosed in magnetic loops. Such a configuration is rather similar to the one proposed by AKASOFU and CHAPMAN (1961, 1962) in their neutral line discharge theory, except that in the present model, the region of such a field configuration is located beyond 10a (instead of around 6a), and the configuration extends over a far greater distance, about 1000a; moreover, the neutral lines are not here associated with the Van Allen belt or belts of trapped particles, but instead with the tail current sheet. Figures 4 and 5 illustrate the magnetic field configuration

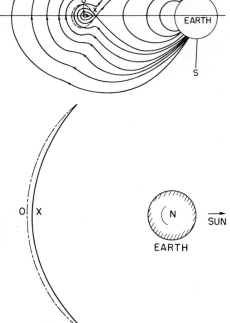

FIGURE 4(A). Lines of force in geomagnetic meridian plane of Earth, when magnetic field is disturbed by a ring current. The circular cross section of this current is shown by broken lines. Points O and X are the points where the resulting O and X neutral lines cross plane of diagram. Line NS is Earth's magnetic axis.

FIGURE 4(B). Typical loop formed by an O- and X-type neutral line in geomagnetic equatorial plane, during magnetic storm. Radiation belt protons and electrons travel from vicinity of X neutral line and produce an auroral arc as shown on plan of Earth.

associated with the neutral lines and their corresponding auroras (AKASOFU and CHAPMAN, 1961). The theory of Akasofu and Chapman was criticized on the ground that the trapped particles in the Van Allen belts could never produce such a reversed field configuration (cf. PARKER, 1962), and that trapped particles would at most nullify the field and would not reverse it, since $\beta(=8\pi p/B^2)$ cannot be greater than unity for the trapped particles. In the

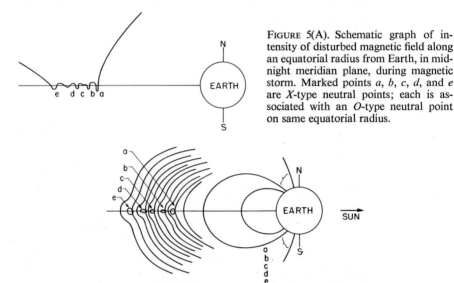

FIGURE 5(A). Schematic graph of intensity of disturbed magnetic field along an equatorial radius from Earth, in midnight meridian plane, during magnetic storm. Marked points a, b, c, d, and e are X-type neutral points; each is associated with an O-type neutral point on same equatorial radius.

FIGURE 5(B). Schematic diagram of magnetic field lines in midnight meridian plane of Figure 4(A). Protons and electrons travel along the lines from X-type neutral lines a, b, c, d, and e and produce parallel auroral arcs in Earth's ionosphere, as indicated in diagram.

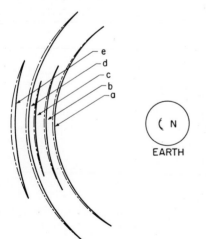

FIGURE 5(C). Schematic diagram of the five loops formed by X-type neutral lines a, b, c, d and e of Figures 4(A) and 4(B), and by associated O-type neutral lines (broken lines). All these lines lie in or close to Earth's magnetic equatorial plane. Auroral arcs associated with the X-type neutral lines are indicated on Earth.

tail region, however, such a criticism may not be applicable, because the sheet current may arise by other mechanisms than simply magnetostatic drift and diamagnetism. FURTH (1963), COPPI, LAVAL, and PELLAT (1966), and PIDDINGTON (1966) have discussed the "pinch" effect in such a current sheet, and have suggested that when the pinch becomes strong enough the sheet current disintegrates into a number of filaments. Each filamentary current may then produce closed magnetic field lines. Such closed loops have been observed (BODIN 1963; EBERHAGEN and GLASER, 1964) in a thermonuclear vessel (the θ pinch). Therefore it seems that the configurations shown in Figures 2 and 3 are possible.

To sum up, the multiple structure of auroral arcs suggests that:

(1) The equatorial sheet current in the tail is nonuniform, even during a quiet period.
(2) The region of strong current tends to produce closed magnetic loops and neutral lines.
(3) The sheet current is not due simply to magnetostatic drift and diamagnetism.
(4) Even during quiet periods, the distribution of the sheet current is continuously changing, causing growth and decay of the neutral lines, with a lifetime on the order of less than 30 min.

The order of magnitude of the minimum distance between two neutral lines can be tentatively inferred from the mean separation distance of two arcs. Consider the magnetic flux through a horizontal north-south strip in the auroral ionosphere, of latitudinal width 1 cm, extending between two arcs 40 km apart: let $B = 0.55$ gauss there. The magnetic flux through this area is 5.5×10^4 (gamma) $\times 4 \times 10^6$ (cm) $\times 1$ cm $= 2.2 \times 10^{11}$ gamma cm². Suppose that this flux crosses the equatorial plane in a strip that is radially broadened from 1 cm in the ionosphere to a width 10 cm in the tail (assuming that the current sheet has a minimum distance of the order of 10a), and that the component of B normal to the plane is 1 gamma. Then for equality of the flux, the length of the strip must be 2.2×10^{10} cm or about 35a. This distance corresponds to BC in Figure 3, and the distance AC between the neutral lines will be still greater.

Acknowledgments The research reported here in this paper was supported in part by a grant from the National Aeronautics and Space Administration (NsG 201-62) and in part by a grant from the National Science Foundation (GP-2721). One of us (P. C. K.) is very grateful to the High Altitude Observatory for the opportunity to visit there during the summer of 1966.

References

AKASOFU, S.-I., 1961, *J. Atmospheric Terrest. Phys.* **21**, 287.
AKASOFU, S.-I., 1966, *Planetary Space Sci.* **14**, 587.
AKASOFU, S.-I. and CHAPMAN, S., 1961, *Phil. Trans. Roy. Soc.* **253**, 359.

AKASOFU, S.-I. and CHAPMAN, S., 1962, *J. Phys. Soc. Japan* 17, Supp'l.A.-I. 169.
AKASOFU, S.-I., CHAPMAN, S., and MENG, C.-I., 1965, *J. Atmospheric Terrest. Phys.* 27, 1275.
AKASOFU, S.-I., KIMBALL, D. S., and MENG, C.-I., 1966, *J. Atmospheric Terrest. Phys.*
BODIN, H. A. B., 1963, *Nucl. Fusion* 3, 215.
COPPI, B., LAVAL, G., and PELLAT, P., 1966, *Phys. Rev. Letters* 16, 1207.
DUNGEY, J. W., 1953, *Phil Mag.* 44, 725
DUNGEY, J. W., 1958, *Cosmical Electrodynamics*, Cambridge University Press.
DUNGEY, J. W., 1963, *Geophysics, The Earth's Environment*, Gordon and Breach, New York.
EBERHAGEN, A. and GLASER, H., 1964, *Nucl. Fusion* 4, 296.
ELVEY, C. T., 1957, *Proc. Nat. Acad. Sci.* 43, 63.
FELDSTEIN, Y. I., 1966, *Planetary Space Sci.* 14, 121.
FRITZ, T. A. and GUNETT, D. A., 1965, *J. Geophys. Res.* 70, 2485.
FURTH, H. P., 1963, *Phys. Fluids* 6, 48.
NESS, N. F., 1965, *J. Geophys. Res.* 70, 2989.
PARKER, E. N., 1957, *J. Geophys. Res.* 62, 509.
PARKER, E. N., 1962, *Space Sci. Rev.* 1, 62.
PETSCHEK, H. E., 1964, *AAS-NASA Symposium on the Physics of Solar Flares* (Ed. by W. N. Hess).
PIDDINGTON, J. H., 1965, *Planetary Space Sci.* 13, 565.
PIDDINGTON, J. H., 1960, *J. Geophys. Res.* 65, 93.
SPEISER, T. W., 1965, *J. Geophys. Res.* 70, 4219.
SPEISER, T. W., 1966, *J. Geophys. Res.* (submitted).

PENETRATION OF ELECTRONS
INTO THE ATMOSPHERE

Martin Walt
Lockheed Palo Alto Research Laboratory
Palo Alto, California

Introduction

It is now well established that an immediate cause of the luminosity in discrete auroras is the influx of energetic electrons into the atmosphere. However, it is not understood whether this bombardment process is accompanied by plasma instabilities, local electric fields, or other phenomena which will also lead to luminosity. Hence, it is of interest to determine whether the optical phenomena observed in the aurora can be fully attributed to the bombarding electrons or whether additional mechanisms such as those mentioned above must be invoked.

The primary purpose of this article is to examine the available experimental data on electron precipitation to see if the electron behavior can be understood on the basis of binary collisions with atmospheric constituents and guidance by the geomagnetic field. At present the most pertinent experimental information bearing on this question are energetic electron fluxes measured as a function of altitude and angle by instruments in rockets and satellites. As will be seen, these data are far from satisfactory at present, but experiments in the near future should enable a definitive test to be obtained.

Computational Method

The earliest comprehensive calculation of electron diffusion into matter is that of SPENCER (1955) who utilized an expansion in moments of the energy deposition. However, the moments method and the calculations of REES (1963), which were based on experimental data of GRÜN (1957), give only the energy deposit as a function of position and are therefore not adequate for comparison with observed electron flux distributions. The calculations of MAEDA (1965) and of STADSNES and MAEHLUM (1965) were made by Monte Carlo techniques and result in detailed flux values for the cases considered. However, in all the work described above, the mirroring effect of the converging geomagnetic

287

field was neglected, and no estimates were made of the horizontal diffusion of the electrons across the magnetic field lines.

The method developed for the present work consists of solving the time-independent-diffusion equation by implicit finite difference techniques. The electron distribution function is retained as the dependent variable, and the electron flux as a function of position, angle with respect to the magnetic field, and energy is obtained. Diffusion perpendicular to magnetic field lines is neglected, but an analytical solution to an approximate diffusion equation indicates that this process is not important except for extremely thin auroras. A shortcoming of the present method is that the straggling caused by variations in the discrete energy loss during individual collisions is neglected. It has been shown by Maeda and by Stadsnes and Maehlum that for a monoenergetic source the neglect of energy loss straggling has a pronounced influence on the number of particles reaching extreme ranges. However, if the source distribution has a broad energy spread, the effect of extreme penetration by electrons of a given energy is dominated by the penetration of large numbers of electrons of slightly greater initial energy. The method given here is particularly useful for treating problems with broad energy and angular distributions, as rapid calculation of the result is possible. However, since derivatives of the electron distribution are obtained numerically, the method is not easily applied to fluxes which are strongly peaked in either energy or angle.

The time-independent-diffusion equation describing the distribution function of electrons in the atmosphere is derived by the Fokker-Planck method assuming the electrons interact with constituents of the atmosphere by Coulomb collisions, energy loss collisions being described by the usual dE/dx relations. The resulting equation is

$$\alpha\frac{\partial}{\partial s}\left(\frac{f}{r}\right) = \frac{3(1-\alpha^2)}{2R}\frac{\partial}{\partial\alpha}\left(\frac{f}{r}\right) + \frac{3r\alpha}{2R}\frac{\partial}{\partial r}\left(\frac{f}{r}\right)$$

$$+ A_1\frac{(T+1)^2}{T^2(T+2)^2}\frac{\partial}{\partial\alpha}\left[(1-\alpha^2)\frac{\partial}{\partial\alpha}\left(\frac{f}{r}\right)\right]$$

$$+ 2A\frac{T+1}{T^{1/2}(T+2)^{1/2}}\frac{\partial}{\partial T}\left[\frac{T+1}{T^{1/2}(T+2)^{1/2}}\left(\frac{f}{r}\right)\right]$$

$$+ \frac{A_1}{2}\left(\frac{mc}{Be}\right)^2\frac{(T+1)^2}{T(T+2)}(1-\alpha^2)\frac{1}{r}\frac{\partial}{\partial r}\left[r\frac{\partial}{\partial r}\left(\frac{f}{r}\right)\right]$$

where

$$A_1 = 2\pi R_0^2\sum_i Z_i^2 n_i \ln \eta_i^{-1}$$

$$A = 2\pi R_0^2 \sum_i Z_i n_i \ln \sigma_i$$

In the equation $f(\alpha, T, s, r)\,\Delta s\,\Delta\alpha\,\Delta T\,\Delta r$ is the number of electrons between

s and $s + \Delta s$, with energy in rest mass units between T and $T + \Delta T$, with pitch angle cosine between α and $\alpha + \Delta\alpha$ and whose guiding center lies between r and $r + \Delta r$. The other quantities are:

r = radial coordinate giving distance of guiding center from arbitrary axis of symmetry

s = distance along field line as measured downward from some arbitrary altitude

R = distance to center of earth

$R_0 = e^2/mc^2$

n_i = number density of atmospheric constituent i

Z_i = atomic number of atmospheric constituent i

η_i = minimum effective scattering angle

$\sigma_i = \dfrac{Tmc^2 \sqrt{(T + 2)\, 2.718}}{2\, I_i}$

I_i = average excitation energy for constituent i.

The first two terms describe the mirroring properties of the magnetic field, which is assumed to vary as $1/R^3$. The second line represents diffusion in pitch angle, and the third line introduces the energy loss processes. The last term is required to allow for diffusion perpendicular to the magnetic field.

If the first, second, and third terms on the right hand side of Equation (1) are neglected, as these should not lead to appreciable cross field diffusion, the resulting equation can be solved by the method of characteristics giving an estimate of the extent of the diffusion perpendicular to B. This horizontal spreading is relatively insignificant for auroras of width greater than 100m, so that in the following sections the last term in Equation (1) will be neglected, a procedure equivalent to treating an incident beam of infinite horizontal extent.

Under these conditions, the second term is also zero since $\dfrac{f}{r}$ = constant.

The finite difference equations are obtained by integrating Equation (1) (neglecting the second and the last terms) over a cuboid in α, s, and T space. The values of f on the half plane $s = 0$, $0 \leq \alpha \leq 1$ specify the input flux for each problem and are the given boundary conditions.

Because the electron "flow" is always in the negative T direction, T is used as the stepping variable and the computation proceeds from some chosen T_{max} to T_{min}. Since the complete boundary conditions are not specified, the problem must be treated by iteration on each T = constant plane. The sweep through each α, s plane is repeated until further iteration has negligible effect on the result. The computation is then shifted to the next lower T plane.

Results

Some of the earliest experimental data on electron interactions with the atmosphere were obtained by O'BRIEN (1964) with Injun III. From a number of measurements taken during the oscillating phase of the satellite, he calculated the ratio of the electrons backscattered at angle θ to those incident at angle (180-θ). These measurements were made for a large number of auroras, and therefore, do not represent a single case in which the angular distribution was known. However, allowing for the scatter of the points, a crude estimate of a typical auroral angular distribution can be obtained. The results and comparison with theory are shown in Figure 1. Although there appears to be

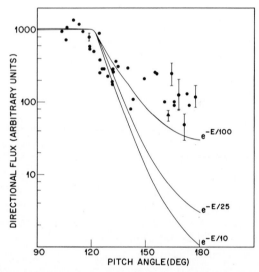

FIGURE 1. Comparison of observed angular distribution of precipitating electrons with theoretical expectations. Experimental data are from O'BRIEN (1964). Solid lines show expected distributions for an incident flux which is isotropic in the downward direction and which has the differential energy flux distributions indicated on the figure.

more backscattered electrons than expected, the quality of the data are such that no definite discrepancy can be identified.

Further backscatter measurements and an attempt to account for them theoretically were reported by CUMMINGS et al. (1966). In the experiment, the counting rates of two oppositely directed geiger counters were compared to obtain a gross ratio of the upward and downward moving electron flux. No other information of the angular or energy distribution were available. Calculations utilizing a number of different incident energy spectra and angular distributions indicated that between 8% and 22% of the incident electrons could be reflected, compared to experimental values ranging from about 10–100%. These high experimental values cannot be accounted for by the reflection model used here.

Experiments by MCDIARMID and BUDZINSKI (1964) and by MCDIARMID, ROSE, and BUDZINSKI (1961) have provided a number of angular distributions for auroral electrons at various altitudes. Unfortunately, complete energy spectrum information is not available, and possible fluctuations of the incident beam during the time of the measurements are a concern. Nonetheless, the comparison of the data with calculations is of interest. Figure 2 shows the

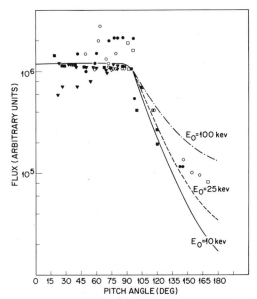

FIGURE 2. Comparison of the angular distribution of auroral electrons with energy >40 keV observed by McDiarmid and Budzinski (1964) with theoretical expectations. Lines give theoretical distributions for differential energy spectra of the form exp (E/E_0).

comparison of theory and experiment for a case in which the incident flux appeared to be isotropic within the errors of the measurement. The calculation was done assuming an exponential energy distribution, $F(E) = \exp(-E/E_0)$, for the incident electrons, and the backscattered flux above 40 keV is shown for three characteristic energies E_0 of the incident flux. Satisfactory agreement can be obtained, although the characteristic energy must be somewhat higher than that usually attributed to auroral electrons.

Another case reported by McDiarmid et al. (1961) has caused greater difficulty. Over the angular range observed, about 40–150°, more electrons were moving upward than downward. The authors proposed that this feature might be explained by an electric field in the atmosphere below the rocket. On the other hand, Stadsnes and Maehlum (1965) suggested that the downflux might have occurred over a small angular region near zero pitch angle and was therefore missed by the detectors. Their calculations, done with a monoenergetic source, lent support to this contention. Calculations with the method described here utilizing an exponential energy spectrum indicate that this latter explanation seems possible. However, it should be recognized that the incident flux required is very strongly peaked at 0°, a distribution which has never been observed directly.

It is concluded from the meager data now available that some cases exist in which the electron data cannot be explained on the basis of the bombardment of the atmosphere by a beam of electrons in a converging magnetic field. However, the experimental information is incomplete in most of these cases and further experiments are badly needed.

References

CUMMINGS, W. D., LaQUEY, R. E., O'BRIEN, B. J., and WALT, M., 1966, *J. Geophys. Res.* **71**, 1399.

GRÜN, A. E., 1957, *Z. Naturforsch.* **12a**, 89.

McDIARMID, I. B. and BUDZINSKI, E. E., 1964, *Can. J. Phys.* **42**, 2048.

McDIARMID, I. B., ROSE, D. C., and BUDZINSKI, E. E., 1961, *Can. J. Phys.* **39**, 1888.

MAEDA, K., 1965, NASA Technical Note, NASA TN D-2612.

O'BRIEN, B. J., 1964, *J. Geophys. Res.* **69**, 13.

REES, M. H., 1963, *Planetary Space Sci.* **11**, 1209.

SPENCER, L. V., 1955, *Phys. Rev.* **98**, 1597.

STADSNES, J. and MAEHLUM, B., 1965, Intern Rapport E-53, Norwegian Defense Research Establishment, Kjeller, Norway.

Discussion

Axford believes that the old McDiarmid and O'Brien backscatter data should be ignored; then there is only an occasional doubling of reflection which can be explained by an increase in the magnetic field.

It was noted that to obtain the reflection coefficient, which is a ratio of the charged particles going out of the atmosphere to those coming in, it is necessary to integrate over the angular distribution. If one considered an angular distribution strongly peaked at 90°, then it might be possible for the observed reflectivities to agree with theoretical predictions. There appears no obvious reason why such a skewed path angle distribution should occur, but available experimental evidence apparently does not rule this out. Considerably more experimental data are needed in this area.

AURORAL ELECTRIC FIELDS

Rolf Boström

Royal Institute of Technology
Department of Plasma Physics, Stockholm, Sweden

1. Electric Fields in the Magnetosphere

Introduction

A theory of the aurora must include a description of the electric fields in the magnetosphere, because such fields are important for a number of auroral phenomena. As yet, these fields have not been mapped. Information on the electric fields may be obtained from theoretical studies of the interaction of the solar wind with the magnetosphere and from processes caused by this interaction, such as plasma motions within the magnetosphere. However, these difficult problems have not been solved completely. An alternative approach is to start from the other end by considering the observed auroral phenomena and finding the electric fields that would produce these phenomena. Then one has to find the process by which the fields are produced.

This paper is devoted to a discussion of the production of electric fields in the magnetosphere and some effects of these fields, viz. motion of visual and radio aurora and currents in the ionosphere. Especially, we will consider the conclusions that may be drawn about the fields from observations of these phenomena. Only static fields are considered; however, some auroral phenomena may be related to oscillating and transient fields.

Choice of Frame of Reference

Upon discussing electric fields in space, we must remember that the field will depend on which frame of reference we use. The field E' in a frame moving with the velocity V relative to a frame where the field is E is given by

$$E' = E + V \times B \qquad (1.1)$$

V is assumed to be small compared to the velocity of light. The magnetic field B is then independent of the choice of frame of reference.

It may be suitable to use frames fixed to the earth, moving with the local neutral gas velocity, or fixed to the sun-earth line. The electric field may be quite different in these various frames.

Production of Electric Fields

Electric fields in the magnetosphere may be produced by several mechanisms. Different auroral theories make different assumptions as to their relative importance.

In the theories by AXFORD and HINES (1961) and DUNGEY (1961) a plasma motion within the magnetosphere driven by the solar wind induces a field. In the hydromagnetic approximation the electric field and the plasma velocity are related by the equation

$$E + v \times B = 0 \qquad (1.2)$$

i.e., $E = 0$ in a frame moving with the plasma. In this approximation, which often is used, a discussion of the plasma motion (convection) is equivalent to a discussion of the electric field distribution. Then Equation 1.2 may be used to derive E *if* v *is known.*

However, if we want to derive theoretically the electric field distribution *and* the plasma motions we must use more accurate approximations. Magnetic field gradients and other effects cause the electrons and ions to move with slightly different velocities, which may bring them into different regions. Then charge separation electric fields are produced, which in turn affect the motions. FEJER (1961) and KERN (1962) have suggested that charge separation of the trapped energetic particles is the primary mechanism which produces electric fields and motions. In the auroral theory by ALFVÉN (1950) the magnetospheric electric field was supposed to be the field induced within a magnetized solar-plasma beam. KARLSON (1963) and BLOCK (1966a) have modified this theory by introducing charge separation fields. A problem, which remains to be solved, is to determine to which extent the separating charges are discharged and the plasma motions braked by currents flowing to the ionosphere.

Electric fields are also induced in the ionosphere by the winds blowing there, and polarization fields are produced when electric currents in the ionosphere flow through regions of varying conductivity. In the theories by COLE (1960) and SWIFT (1963) the ionospheric winds have been assumed to produce the auroral electric fields, but the winds are probably too weak to be of major importance (BOSTRÖM, 1964).

As seen from the sun, electric fields are also induced by the rotation of the ionosphere. It has been suggested by FEJER (1963) and TAYLOR and HONES (1965) that the magnetospheric convection (or electric field) is primarily established by the earth's rotation, but modified by the solar wind-magnetosphere interaction.

Electric Fields Along the Magnetic Field Lines

Depending on the properties of the plasma in the outer magnetosphere, various mechanisms may produce electric fields, $E_{||}$, along the magnetic field lines. ALFVÉN and FÄLTHAMMAR (1963) have introduced the terms "low-density plasma" and "medium-density plasma" to distinguish between plasmas where the mean free path of the electrons is longer than the characteristic length of the region considered or shorter than this (but still longer than their gyroradius).

1. ALFVÉN and FÄLTHAMMAR (1963) have suggested that the magnetospheric plasma is of "low density". Then a considerable electric field must exist along the field lines in this "ion-exosphere" to preserve the electrical neutrality, if the pitch-angle distributions of electrons and ions are different (PERSSON, 1963). BLOCK (1966b) has recently applied Persson's theory to auroral problems.

2. Currents must flow along the field lines to drive the auroral electrojets (see Section 5). If the plasma is of "medium density" the ohmic resistance will produce an electric field. It is difficult to estimate this field, since the geometry of the current system is unknown.

3. SWIFT (1965) has suggested that the currents along the field lines may generate ion acoustic waves by a two-stream instability. Such waves may give a high effective resistivity and a high voltage drop along the field lines. The resistivity proposed by Swift is a factor 5×10^3 higher than the ohmic resistivity of a highly ionized medium-density plasma at 1500°K.

In any case the total voltage drop along the field lines cannot be larger than about 10 kV, otherwise the precipitating particles would have too high energy.

Coupling of Electric Fields Between the Outer Magnetosphere and the Ionospheric E and F Layers

We should expect that any large-scale fields transverse to the magnetic field, which are produced in one region, will be mapped onto other regions by conduction along the magnetic field lines. Since a finite voltage drop does exist along the field lines, this is not necessarily true for small-scale fields. In the ionosphere the transverse field is about 10–100 mV/m. If the voltage drop is different along different magnetic field lines, but less than 10 kV, fields of a scale < 10 kV (100 mV/m)$^{-1} = 100$ km at E layer heights are not necessarily images of the magnetospheric fields. On a large scale, however, the distribution of electric fields in the E layer and in the equatorial plane of the magnetosphere must be related.

2. Motion of Auroral Primary Particles and Visual Aurora

The Source of the Visual Aurora and Its Motion

The light emission from ordinary polar auroras is produced by precipitating electrons which excite the atmospheric constituents. The lifetime of the excited states is generally very short. However, it is about 0.75 sec for the important green oxygen line (5577Å). Since the neutral gas velocity is at most about 100 m/sec, the light is emitted within about 100 m from magnetic field lines along which electrons precipitate.

Thus the location and motion of the visual aurora are related to the position and motion of the source of the primary electrons. The source may be visualized as a group of primary particles in the outer magnetosphere drifting in the electric and magnetic fields, as will be described below. However, it must be noticed that motions also may be produced by "switching" on and off various stationary sources. Some very rapid motions (>10 km/sec) are probably related to some kind of wave motion.

Motion of Auroral Primary Electrons

The auroral primary particles have a mean free path much larger than the linear scale of the magnetosphere, but a small radius of gyration. We may use the guiding center approximation to study their motion. If the aurora occurs on closed dipole-like field lines, the guiding center has a rapid bounce motion along the field lines between the mirror points (if it does not precipitate) and a slow drift transverse to the magnetic field. The latter has two components, one due to the electric field and one due to the gradients of the magnetic field.

To find the time it takes for a particle to drift from one field line to another, the velocities are projected along the field lines onto the ionospheric E layer and integrated over one bounce period. The projected drift velocity U_E produced by E is independent of where along the field line the particle is (if curl $E_{||} = 0$). It is given by

$$U_E = E_i \times B_i/B_i^2 \qquad (2.1)$$

where E_i and B_i are the fields at E layer heights. The ∇B drift in a dipole field has been studied by HAMLIN et al. (1961). For particles which reach the E layer of the auroral zone

$$U_B(\text{m/sec}) = 0.03 \ W(\text{eV}) \qquad (2.2)$$

directed eastward for electrons and westward for protons. W is the total kinetic energy of the particle.

If the source is a blob of enhanced particle density, the ∇B drift will separate the electrons and ions. A charge separation field is produced which will push the blob in the direction of decreasing magnetic field. The general magnetospheric electric field can bring the blob into a stronger magnetic field to the point where the charge separation field cancels the general field at the blob. To some extent the space charges may be neutralized by particles from the ionosphere. An upper limit of this neutralizing effect may be obtained by assuming a perfect coupling to the ionosphere, but taking into account the finite transverse conductivity in the ionosphere (KERN, 1964). The motion of blobs is evidently dependent on the unknown coupling to the ionosphere. However, we are not going to deduce the motion, but deduce the electric field from the observed motion. Then we obtain the field at the source region, which may differ from the general magnetospheric field.

Conclusions About the Electric Fields

The ∇B drift given by Equation 2.2 is not negligible. If we know that the aurora occurs on closed field lines and if the energy W of the primary particles is known, we may compute U_B. Since the observed velocity $U_0 = U_E + U_B$, we may then deduce the electric field from U_0 using Equation 2.1. An estimate of the energy of the electrons which produce the visible aurora may be obtained by studying the luminosity profile (BELON *et al.*, 1966). Most of the luminosity is produced by electrons with $W < 10$ keV, i.e. $U_B < 300$ m/sec.

The primary particles will in general have an energy distribution, and according to Equation 2.2, various ∇B drifts. The observations that auroral forms never overtake each other and that all parts of rays (which are produced by particles of various energies) move at the same velocity (COLE, 1963) suggest that the ∇B drift is not important. This may be the case if the primary particles come directly from the neutral sheet in the tail of the magnetosphere or if the particles are energized by electric fields along the magnetic field lines.

Auroral forms are generally seen to move westward before midnight and eastward after midnight on the equatorward side of the auroral belt. The velocities are of the order of 1 km/sec, while the velocities in the north-south direction are an order of magnitude smaller (COLE, 1963). An eastward drift velocity of 1 km/sec corresponds to a southward field of about 50 mV/m at E layer heights measured in a frame of reference fixed to the earth. Before midnight the field should be in the opposite direction.

However, it has been pointed out by AKASOFU (1965) that the motions in the evening and morning are different in many ways. The westward motions in the evening are characterized as propagation of deformations along the auroral forms, while in the morning, patches drift as a whole eastward. Akasofu suggests that only the latter motions are related to the electric fields.

3. Effects of Ionospheric Electric Fields

Electric Currents

Since the conductivity along the magnetic field lines is much higher than transverse to these, we may in general neglect voltage drops along the field lines in the E and F layers. The coupling between various levels above 100 km is almost perfect for fields of a scale larger than a few kilometers (REID, 1965). Thus $E_\perp$ is independent of height, and if the neutral gas velocity v_n is also independent of height or small, we have the following expression for the height integrated current density $I_\perp$ in terms of the height integrated conductivities Σ

$$I_\perp = \Sigma_P(E_\perp + v_n \times B) + \Sigma_H B \times (E_\perp + v_n \times B)/B \tag{3.1}$$

For a nighttime ionosphere, the Pedersen conductivity $\Sigma_P^N \approx 1$ mho and the Hall conductivity $\Sigma_H^N \approx 0.5$ mho, and for an auroral excited region (maximum electron density 10^6 cm^{-3}), $\Sigma_P^A \approx 30$ mho and $\Sigma_H^A \approx 50$ mho (MAEDA and MATSUMOTO, 1962; KIM and KIM, 1963; BOSTRÖM, 1964). Previously it has often been assumed that $\Sigma_P \ll \Sigma_H$, which does not seem to be correct.

Motion of Irregularities

The auroral ionization irregularities are generally field aligned. It has been shown (CLEMMOW et al., 1955; KATO, 1965) that such irregularities will propagate with the velocity

$$V = v_n + (1 + \nu_e \nu_i/\omega_e\omega_i)^{-1}(E + v_n \times B) \times B/B^2 \tag{3.2}$$

This expression is strictly valid only if the collision and gyrofrequencies, ν and ω, do not vary with the height. However, above 100 km, V is very close to $E \times B/B^2$, and there the formula may be used for extended irregularities. In this expression the electric field at the irregularity should be used. In general this is different from the external field due to polarization effects; it may be determined by applying the condition div $I_\perp = 0$. Then we neglect currents parallel to B above the F layer. This may be correct for small-scale irregularities and in any case it will give an upper limit for the polarization effects.

Expressions for the internal field in a slab irregularity (a model of a homogeneous auroral arc) have been discussed by BOSTRÖM (1964). Using the conductivities given above and assuming the external field E^N to be parallel to the irregularity we find that a polarization field $E^A \approx 2 E^N$ is produced transverse to the irregularity. The transverse motion of the irregularity will not be affected by this field, neither will it be affected by motions of the neutral gas if the irregularity is located above a height of 100 km.

The corresponding expressions for a cylindrical irregularity have been given by HAERENDEL et al. (1966). For the conductivities given above we find that the internal field $E^A \approx 0.03 E^N$. E^A is inclined at an angle of 60° relative to E^N in the direction of $E^N \times B$. Such a strong irregularity, with a finite extension in all directions transverse to B, moves with a speed much less than E^N/B. If $v_n \neq 0$, this will give a contribution to the velocity of the irregularity, which is almost equal to v_n.

Since the internal field is homogeneous in these two cases, the irregularities may move without changing their shape.

In the absence of any source of auroral ionization the irregularities will decay due to dissociative recombination. In the E layer the recombination coefficient is about 3×10^{-7} cm^3 sec^{-1}. An irregularity of initial density 10^6 electrons/cm^3 is reduced by a factor 2 in a time of about 3 sec. However, the density is more than twice the density of the undisturbed ionosphere for about 1000 sec, if the latter density is assumed to be 2×10^3 electrons/cm^3.

4. Motion of Auroral Ionization

Introduction

The precipitating electrons that produce visual aurora will also produce regions of enhanced ionization, "radio aurora." Although the visual and radio auroras are produced at the same place, their motion may be different. The lifetime of the ionization is considerable, thus its motion is not only due to motions of the source, but also to the effect of electric fields in the ionosphere.

Correlation With Visual Aurora

If the ionization source (which coincides with the visual aurora) does not move with the same velocity as ionization irregularities, the regions of enhanced ionization may separate from regions of visual aurora. If we consider only strong irregularities the separation will not be great, since they decay in a few seconds and the observed velocities are of the order of 1 km/sec. For weak irregularities a considerable separation may occur, and such irregularities may remain for a considerable time after a visual aurora has disappeared.

If the following conditions are fulfilled the source and the irregularity will move synchronously with the velocity $E \times B/B^2$, and no separation occurs. (1) $E_{||} = 0$ or curl $E_{||} = 0$, i.e., good coupling of the electric fields between the ionosphere and magnetosphere. (2) The ∇B drift is negligible. (3) The height of the irregularity > 100 km (otherwise it moves with a speed $< E/B$ and E is reduced). (4) v_n must be small.

If the irregularity is an auroral arc (thickness ≈ 10 km, length $\gtrsim 1000$ km), i.e., a slab irregularity, it is only velocities transverse to the arc which can produce a separation. No velocities in this direction occur if (1) the arc is aligned in the direction of the ∇B drift (in general the east-west direction on the earth), if such drifts are important, (2) $E_\perp$ is perpendicular to the arc, and (3) v_n is small or the arc is located at a height > 100 km. If condition (2) is not fulfilled, but the arc is above a height of 100 km, the visual aurora and the region of enhanced ionization will have the same velocity transverse to the arc. We must expect a good coupling to the source region, since the field along the arc extends over distances of the order of 1000 km. In general we should expect a good correlation between visual auroral arcs and regions of enhanced ionization.

Conclusions About the Electric Fields

The radio auroras are observed to move with about the same speeds and in the same directions as visual auroras (COLE, 1963). If the conditions discussed above are fulfilled, the motions should be interpreted as $E \times B/B^2$ drift velocities. The general conclusions about the electric fields should be the same as in Section 2. The field computed from the motion of radio aurora is the field within ionospheric irregularities, which is different from the external field but may be related to this, cf. Section 3.

If the coupling between the ionosphere and magnetosphere is not perfect, small-scale irregularities may be expected to move with a velocity different from that of the visual aurora. Due to observational difficulties (absorption and aspect sensitivity of radio observations) it has not been possible to show whether this is the case. Experiments where the motion of artificially injected ion clouds (which are visible) are observed (HAERENDEL et al., 1966) may be used to study the coupling. If such experiments are carried out in or above a region where visual auroral irregularities occur, and the velocities of the ion cloud and the aurora are compared, it may be possible to draw some conclusions about the coupling between the ionosphere and magnetosphere.

5. Ionospheric Currents

The DS Current System

The ionospheric currents, which produce local magnetic disturbances in the auroral zone, must be driven by electric fields. Since the conductivity in the ionosphere is fairly well known, the electric field may be computed if the current density is known.

The magnetic disturbances are usually represented by an *equivalent* current system, the DS system, which is assumed to flow horizontally in an ionospheric shell. The *real* current system must include currents along the magnetic field lines, because the currents are driven by a "dynamo" in the outer magnetosphere. Thus, *the DS system is not the true current system.* It cannot be used directly for a derivation of the electric fields, although this has been done sometimes, for example by TAYLOR and HONES (1965). The present author does not agree with Taylor and Hones when they call their field "a carefully derived representation of the electric field."

The motions of the visual aurora generally proceed in a direction opposite to that of the DS currents. If the motions are interpreted as $E \times B/B^2$ drift velocities this implies that the DS currents flow in the direction of the Hall currents. Either the Hall conductivity dominates over the Pedersen conductivity, or the Pedersen currents do not produce any magnetic disturbances observable on the ground. Since all recent estimates of the height integrated Hall and Pedersen conductivities show that they are of the same order of magnitude, we would prefer the latter explanation, although many theorists have used the former.

A model of the auroral current system which has the required properties is shown in Figure 1(A). A radial electric field is produced in the equatorial plane

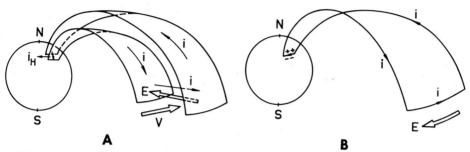

A   **B**

FIGURE 1. Two different auroral current systems which produce similar magnetic disturbances, DS, on the ground.
(A) Only the Hall current contributes to DS.
(B) Both the Hall and Pedersen currents contribute to DS.

by an azimuthal plasma motion. The field is transferred to the auroral ionosphere, where it is directed equatorward and drives a westward Hall current (the electrojet). The Pedersen current and the current along the field lines form a current system that will produce a westward magnetic disturbance *within* the current system but no disturbance on the ground. The current transverse to the magnetic field in the outer magnetosphere brakes the motion, i.e., the dynamo is loaded. The $\mathbf{i} \times \mathbf{B}$ force is balanced by the inertia force $nm(\mathbf{v} \cdot \nabla)\mathbf{v}$.

The main effect of the currents along the field lines is to turn the magnetic field vector without changing its magnitude. To detect these currents it is necessary to perform directional magnetic field measurements from satellites. Recently ZMUDA et al. (1966) have found local disturbances at a height of about 1000 km over the auroral zone which may be related to the currents discussed here.

According to some observations, the magnetic disturbances are proportional to the maximum electron density in the auroral sporadic E layers (NAGATA, 1963). This indicates that variations in the magnetic disturbance are produced mainly by varying amounts of precipitation, which produce variations in the conductivity, while the electric field is approximately constant.

The Auroral Electrojets

The most intense part of the DS current system, the auroral electrojets, is probably confined to regions of enhanced ionization such as auroral arcs. It has been shown in a number of investigations that the magnetic disturbance vector often is perpendicular to auroral arcs. There are often several parallel arcs present. The current that must flow along each arc to produce a moderate disturbance is of the order of 3×10^4 A. Assuming that the ionospheric currents in the model of Figure 1(A) are confined to a 10 km thick arc and using the conductivities given in Section 3 , we find that an equatorward electric field of about 60 mV/m must exist in the ionosphere to drive the westward electrojet. This model requires a good coupling between the ionosphere and the magnetosphere.

However, there also exist other possibilities to drive the electrojets. We may apply a westward field to the auroral zone from outside (i.e., an azimuthal field in the equatorial plane) as in Figure 1(B). This tends to drive a westward Pedersen current and a northward Hall current. The latter is prevented from flowing since the conductivity outside the auroral region is much smaller. A secondary southward directed polarization electric field is produced as described in Section 3. The total field is directed so that the total current flows westward. If the secondary field is confined to such narrow features as auroral arcs, it is possible that it is not transferred to the outer magnetosphere. These and other models of the auroral current systems have been discussed by BO-STRÖM (1964, 1966).

6. Concluding Remarks

Obviously many problems remain to be solved before it is possible to make a detailed derivation of the electric fields from auroral observations.

The motion of visual and radio auroras are probably primarily $E \times B/B^2$ drifts of the source region and the auroral ionization. However, for the visual auroras, ∇B drifts may also be important, and some kinds of motions are probably produced by other mechanisms. The auroral ionization may be affected by motions of the neutral gas, and below a height of 100 km the velocity of irregularities is less than $E \times B/B^2$.

The ionospheric currents cannot be used for a detailed derivation of the electric field, since we do not know the real current systems. Only order of magnitude estimates can be made.

We must also notice that the field derived from auroral observations may be characteristic only for regions affected by the auroral particles. An unsolved problem of major importance for the dynamics of the aurora and the interpretation of the observations is to determine the coupling between the outer magnetosphere and the auroral ionosphere.

However, it is encouraging to find that the order of magnitude estimates of the electric field derived from different kinds of observations agree. They also agree with the order of magnitude of the magnetospheric field deduced theoretically by BLOCK (1966a) and the ionospheric field used by MEGILL and CARLETON (1964) to explain the excitation in high red arcs.

The order of magnitude of the auroral electric field is 50 mV/m in the E layer or a few millivolts per meter in the outer magnetosphere measured in a frame of reference fixed to the earth.

We expect that experiments, where the electric fields in space are measured directly or where ion clouds are injected, will contribute much to our understanding of the phenomena discussed in this paper.

References

AKASOFU, S.-I., 1965, *Space Sci. Rev.* **4**, 498.
ALFVÉN, H., 1950, *Cosmical Electrodynamics*, Clarendon Press.
ALFVÉN, H. and FÄLTHAMMAR, C.-G., 1963, *Cosmical Electrodynamics, Fundamental Principles*, Clarendon Press.
AXFORD, W. I. and HINES, C. O., 1961, *Can. J. Phys.* **39**, 1433.
BELON, A. E., ROMICK, G. J., and REES, M. H., 1966, *Planetary Space Sci.* **14**, 597.
BLOCK, L. P., 1966 a, *J. Geophys. Res.* **71**, 855.
BLOCK, L. P., 1966 b, *Space Sci. Rev.* (to be published).
BOSTRÖM, R., 1964, *J. Geophys. Res.* **69**, 4983.
BOSTRÖM, R., 1966, *Space Sci. Rev.* (to be published).
CLEMMOW, P. C., JOHNSON, M. A., and WEEKS, K., 1955, *Rep. Phys. Soc. Conf. Phys. Ionosphere*, London, p. 139.
COLE, K. D., 1960, *Australian J. Phys.* **13**, 484.
COLE, K. D., 1963, *Planetary Space Sci.* **10**, 129.
DUNGEY, J. W., 1961, *Phys. Rev. Letters* **6**, 47.
FEJER, J. A., 1961, *Can. J. Phys.* **39**, 1409.
FEJER, J. A., 1963, *J. Geophys. Res.* **68**, 2147.
HAERENDEL, G., LÜST, R., and RIEGER, E., 1966, 7th COSPAR Symposium, Vienna, May 1966 (to be published).
HAMLIN, D. A., KARPLUS, R., VIK, R. C., and WATSON, K. M., 1961, *J. Geophys. Res.* **66**, 1.
KARLSON, E. T., 1963, *Phys. Fluids* **6**, 708.
KATO, S., 1965, *Space Sci. Rev.* **4**, 223.
KERN, J. W., 1962, *J. Geophys. Res.* **67**, 2649.
KERN, J. W., 1964, in *Physics of Geomagnetic Phenomena* (Ed. by S. MATSUSHITA and W. H. CAMPBELL), Academic Press (to be published).
KIM, H. Y. and KIM, J. S., 1963, *J. Atmospheric Terrest. Phys.* **25**, 481.
MAEDA, K. and MATSUMOTO, H., 1962, *Rep. Ionosph. Space Res. Japan* **16**, 1.
MEGILL, L. R. and CARLETON, N. P., 1964, *J. Geophys. Res.* **69**, 101.
NAGATA, T., 1963, *Planetary Space Sci.* **11**, 1395.
PERSSON, H., 1963, *Phys. Fluids* **6**, 1756.
REID, G. C., 1965, *Radio Sci. J. Res. Natl. Bur. Std.* **69D**, 827
SWIFT, D. W., 1963, *J. Geophys. Res.* **68**, 2131.
SWIFT, D. W., 1965, *J. Geophys. Res.* **70**, 3061.
TAYLOR, H. E. and HONES, E. W., 1965, *J. Geophys. Res.* **70**, 3605.
ZMUDA, A. J., MARTIN, J. H., and HEURING, F. T., 1966, *J. Geophys. Res.* **71**, 5033.

Discussion

The implications of electric fields are hampered by not having any experimental measurements of field strengths. In spite of the overall uncertainties involved, a number of unanswered questions were asked. For example: how are the red emissions explained which seldom occur although the ionospheric currents flow every night? Why won't F region height observations help resolve E field strengths? Can the F region effects be seen with ionosondes or other instruments? Can E fields help explain radio aurora?

There were several comments directed at the implication of electric fields on the ionosphere. Mozer stated his opinion that the electric fields are useful in summarizing the particle measurements, but that the existence of such fields should be determined by electric field measurements.

Blamont pointed out that the anti-correlation between protons and electrons can be seen with optical measurements of the 3914Å, 5577Å and Hβ lines. In previous observations, the first two were seen to increase when the Hβ decreased; the variations were about 10%. It is assumed that the Hβ is related to protons and the other two to electrons, so this implies an anti-correlation of electron and proton fluctuations.

INTERPRETATION OF TWILIGHT EMISSIONS

M. Gadsden

Institute for Telecommunication Sciences and Aeronomy
Environmental Science Services Administration
Boulder, Colorado

Introduction

A preceding paper has dealt with the techniques and results of optical observations made during twilight. Generally, two things can be learned from these
observations: the solar irradiance of the atmosphere in a specified spectral
region or the concentration of a species at a known height in the atmosphere.
For many of the resonance lines, the solar irradiance determination is trivial.
The determination of the abundance of the species, on the other hand, can
lead to an improved understanding of the physical state of the upper atmosphere. Three of the many aspects of twilight have been selected for detailed
discussion because of the immediate interest in the physical processes involved
and personal interest. These three will be discussed in the following order:
(I) orthohelium (II) dust and aerosols in the high atmosphere, and (III)
metallic atoms.

Orthohelium in the Outermost Atmosphere

SHEFOV (1962, 1963a) and McELROY (1965) have examined in considerable
detail the resonant scattering of sunlight from helium in the lowest triplet
(orthohelium) state. The process is the straight forward absorption of 10830Å
by the $2^3S - 2^3P$ transition, followed by emission of the 10830Å line from the
2^3P atoms. The 2^3S state of helium is the lowest level of helium above the 1^1S
ground state. Since the triplet-singlet radiative transition is forbidden, 2^3S
helium is metastable. The concentration high in the atmosphere can be obtained
from the twilight observations. Because of the large-scale height associated with
helium, the twilight scattering continues to relatively large angles of solar
depression. The computed radiance begins to fall at about 15° solar depression
and, depending on the assumed atmospheric temperature, becomes small
between 30° and 40° solar depression.

There seem to be two main processes for the production of 2^3S helium, in the absence of auroral electron precipitation. The first of these is by direct excitation from 1^1S helium by electrons with energies exceeding 19.8 eV:

$$He(1^1S) + e \rightarrow He(2^3S) + e.$$

In practice, the electron energy should exceed approximately 25 eV and such electrons are produced in photoionization of atmospheric constituents by the extreme ultraviolet radiation of the sun, particularly, by the He^+ emission line at 304Å and by radiation at shorter wavelengths. McELROY (1965) shows that production of 2^3S helium by He^+ recombination is lower than the production by electron impact by a factor of 10^2 or more.

Another possible process involves the metastable 2^1S level. Resonant absorption of the solar emission lines at 584Å and 537Å takes helium up to the 2^1P level, from which it can drop to the metastable 2^1S level with the emission of a quantum ($\lambda 20581$Å). The probability of this occurring is 10^{-3} that of reradiation of the 584Å line. Collision of helium in the 2^1S level with an ambient electron can yield 2^3S. Therefore, the production process can be summarized:

$$He(1^1S) + h\nu \; (\lambda 584\text{Å}) \rightarrow He(2^1P).$$

$$He(2^1P) \rightarrow He(2^1S) + h\nu \; (\lambda 20581\text{Å}).$$

$$He(2^1S) + e \rightarrow He(2^3S) + e.$$

SHEFOV (1963b) suggests that this process will be important only at heights above about 1000 km. The fairly short radiative lifetime of the 2^1S state, combined with the small electron concentration at these heights, indicates that electron impact at lower heights will be dominant and for most purposes may be considered to be the only operative process (McELROY, 1965).

Given the production rate and the deactivation rate of 2^3S, the radiance of the 10830Å line as a function of time after sunset can be computed for given models of atmospheric helium. Since the scale height of helium is proportional to the assumed atmospheric temperature, a determination of the behavior of the radiance during twilight can, in principle, yield a temperature for the atmosphere in the 300–1500 km region. This method is not useful if the atmospheric temperature changes appreciably during the observations.

Assuming that the total abundance of helium remains constant, the radiance of the 10830Å line gives a way of monitoring the solar irradiance in the extreme ultraviolet region. SHEFOV (1963) shows some plots of the radiance measured at Zvenigorod as a function of sunspot number and area, and area of calcium flocculi. The expected increase in 10830Å radiance with solar activity cannot be described as striking. Many more observations are desirable before this measurement can be claimed to be a good monitor of the extreme ultraviolet.

Dust in the 80–100 KM Region

The measurements of HEMENWAY, SOBERMAN, and WITT (1964) show that the total dust content of this region is extremely variable. Under noctilucent cloud conditions, the total content between 75 and 95 km can be 8×10^6 cm^{-2} and at other times less than 8×10^3 cm^{-2}. The size distribution of the particles for the noctilucent cloud conditions is expressed by

$$n(r) \propto r^{-P} \ (r > 5 \times 10^{-6} \text{ cm})$$

where r = radius in cm of the particles, n = number of particles, cm^{-2}, of radius greater than r, and P lies between 3 and 4. The value of $n(r)$ remains constant as r decreases below 5×10^{-6} cm, indicating very few particles with radii less than this. From ground-level twilight observations, DIVARI (1964) finds that the dust concentration at 90 km is 4×10^{-4} cm^{-3} and that the variation of concentration with height follows a (-7.2)th-power law. This corresponds to a scale height of a little over 10 km in the 90 km region, and a total abundance of 2×10^4 cm^{-2} in the height range 75–100 km. MIKIROV (1963), from daytime rocket firings, finds an aerosol layer that has a peak scattering coefficient of about 15×10^{-12} cm^{-1} at 85–92 km (depending on latitude), and a thickness of about 20 km.

HEMENWAY et al. (1964) find that the size distribution of the particles in a noctilucent cloud peaks markedly at about 5×10^{-6} cm. If we assume that Mikirov's measurements refer to metallic spheres with radii about 5×10^{-6} cm, his scattering measurements yield a peak concentration in the neighborhood of 0.1 cm^{-3} and a total abundance of about 6×10^4 cm^{-2}.

Thus, the column abundance in the region being considered seems to be of the order of $1 - 10 \times 10^4$ cm^{-2} in the absence of noctilucent clouds and one hundred times higher than this in their presence. Divari and Mikirov disagree about the height distribution of the dust or aerosol, the former finding no layering at twilight and the latter, a definite layer in daytime; therefore, the disagreement may be apparent only. WEBB (1965) has drawn attention to unusual meteorological conditions that are probable in the mesosphere at high latitudes in the summer due to the divergence of a strong meridional air movement in the stratosphere. He suggests that upward movements of the atmosphere can halt the settling of particles smaller than about 10^{-5} cm.

The relevance of the existence of dust or aerosols to physical problems in the high atmosphere lies in the possibility that the dust can provide a solid surface for attachment of electrons and increased recombination of ions. In addition, DONAHUE (1966), HUNTEN, and WALLACE (1966) and MEIER (1966) invoke the possibility of meteoric dust, confined to a thin layer, as a source of atomic sodium. AIKIN, KANE, and TROIM (1964) found a definite valley in the height distribution of electron density at about 82 km, which they tentatively ascribed to increased recombination on the surface of dust particles.

NATANSON (1960) has considered, theoretically, the capture of ions onto dust or aerosol particles. At the heights being considered, the dust particles will probably be negatively charged, and the capture cross section for positive ions is thus increased. With dust concentrations in the 80 km region as high as 1 cm^{-3}, the effective recombination coefficient is increased very little, according to PARTHASARATHY and RAI (1966).

For the case of attachment of neutrals to dust, a first approximation (ignoring the dipole moment in the neutral induced by the Coulomb field of the charged dust particle) is obtained from classical kinetic theory. Taking a dust concentration of 0.1 cm^{-3}, and a typical particle radius of 10^{-5} cm, the total surface area in 1 cm^3 of the atmosphere is approximately 10^{-10} cm^2. The mean velocity of the neutrals at 90 km is close to 3.5 × 10^4 cm sec^{-1}, so the collision frequency with a dust particle is 10^{-6} sec^{-1} *per neutral*. It seems improbable, therefore, that attachment of neutrals to dust particles is an important loss process in the 80–100 km region, except, perhaps, for dense noctilucent cloud conditions.

DONAHUE (1966), HUNTEN, and WALLACE (1966) and MEIER (1966) suggest that detachment of sodium atoms from dust particles in sunlight is an important source of free sodium in the daytime. It is unlikely to be reattached in as short a period as twelve hours of darkness, so the dust is required to be renewed each day for the detachment to occur shortly after each sunrise. Taking 6 × 10^4 dust particles cm^{-2} in the region of interest, 10^{-5} cm as the typical radius (which is probably an overestimate), and 2.5 gm cm^{-3} for the density, this renewal rate demands an influx to the Earth of about 3 × 10^9 grams per day — which is similar to estimates derived from several different lines of reasoning (MILLMAN and MCKINLEY, 1963). For this process to be important the permissible fractional increase in sodium due to each day's solar irradiation must be approximately the reciprocal of the residence time (in days) of sodium in the region.

It will be recalled that GADSDEN (1964) has estimated a residence time above the tropopause of 100 years for sodium. (It is worth noting that a misprint appears in that paper: the total sodium content above the tropopause is printed as 10^{11} cm^{-2}, instead of 10^{14} cm^{-2}.) For that estimate, the downward flux of sodium was taken to be 10^{12} sodium atoms cm^{-2} yr^{-1}, as used by JUNGE, OLDENBURG, and WASSON (1962), and Gadsden noted that the deduced residence time was four to five times higher than that derived from Rh^{102} tracer measurements. Such a flux implies a net replacement time of the observable (atomic) sodium of only three to four days. If the flux itself is underestimated by a factor of 4–5, as appears possible by comparison with the radioactive tracer measurements, then the replacement time of sodium at the upper levels comes down to less than a day — and evaporation of sodium from fresh dust particles each day becomes an attractive hypothesis to account for the rapid rise in abundance after sunrise. On this hypothesis, a thin layer can be accounted for by a process similar to that invoked by WEBB (1965) for the creation of noctilucent clouds. The vertical wind need be only a sporadic phenomenon. Out of three rocket flights to date, only one has shown the presence of a thin layer.

Metallic Atoms between 80 and 100 km

Three alkali metals (sodium, potassium, and lithium) and two alkaline earth metals (calcium and magnesium) have been observed in the 80–100 km altitude region. The alkali metals and ionized calcium are observable optically from the ground, the ions of sodium, calcium, and magnesium being found from the *in situ* mass spectrometer observations reported by NARCISSI and BAILEY (1965). (At a higher altitude, ISTOMIN (1963) found ions of calcium, magnesium, iron, and possibly a few silicon ions.) Typical concentrations of these atoms and ions are given in Table I and seem to be the most precise data available for the 80–100 km region of the atmosphere.

Table I. Abundances of metallic atoms and ions in the height interval 85–105 km

Species	Abundance, Number per sq. cm. Column.	Notes
Li	6×10^6 (spring)	1
Na	3×10^9 (summer), 8×10^9 (winter) 1.4×10^{10} (day)	2,3,4
K	6×10^7 (spring)	1
Na^+	6×10^9 (day)	5
Mg^+	3×10^{10} (day)	5
Ca^+	9.5×10^8 (day)	5

1. The lithium and potassium abundances are from the data of SULLIVAN and HUNTEN (1964); the lithium abundances are taken away from times of "artificial" enhancements.
2. The sodium abundances are representative of a large body of twilight data.
3. The daytime sodium abundance is taken from the modified data of Blamont and Donahue (GADSDEN, BLAMONT, and DONAHUE, 1966).
4. HUNTEN and WALLACE (1966) find a daytime abundance equal to the twilight abundance from a rocket flight in summer, and increased 40% in spring.
5. The ion data are taken from the results of NARCISI and BAILEY (1965) of an autumn daytime flight of a mass spectrometer. The twilight data of VALLANCE JONES (1958) for Ca^+ are similar.

First, there is the question of the origin of these metals in the high atmosphere. (See VALLANCE JONES (1966) for the most recent review of this question.) Seawater has been suggested for sodium and potassium (SULLIVAN and HUNTEN, 1964), but this has been questioned by GADSDEN (1964). The ratios of the abundances should give a reasonable identification of the origin, bearing in mind the likelihood of having differing proportions of the metals in ionic and chemically combined forms. Table II summarizes the relative abundances of the elements in the sun and meteorites (MINNAERT, 1957), together with the analysis of bulk seawater (FORSYTHE, 1959), and tropospheric aerosol droplets (WILSON and HOUSE, 1965; KOMABAYASI, 1962). In the sixth column, the rela-

Table II. Abundances Relative to Sodium

Element	Sun	Meteorites	Seawater	Seawater Aerosol	Upper Atmosphere
Na	10^4	10^4	10^4	10^4	10^4
Li	4.9×10^{-2}	2.3×10^1	3.2×10^{-1}	(8×10^{-3})	1.2×10^1
K	5.4×10^2	7.2×10^2	2.1×10^2	5.9×10^2	1.2×10^2
Mg	1.3×10^5	2.1×10^5	1.1×10^3	1.3×10^3	2.1×10^5
Ca	1.2×10^4	1.1×10^4	2.2×10^2	6.3×10^2	6.8×10^2

tive abundances in the upper atmosphere are listed for comparison. These should not be taken too literally without individual discussion.

The lithium/sodium ratio agrees very well with the meteoritic ratio; however, there are two qualifications. First, lithium is known to be seriously contaminated by debris from thermonuclear explosions, so that the quoted atmospheric abundance may or may not refer to the natural level, depending on what residence times are appropriate for the thermonuclear material. Second, of the nineteen elements for which Minnaert, *loc. cit.*, gives relative abundances in both meteorites and the sun, lithium is the only one to show a significant difference. Therefore, it is possible that the meteoric abundance is not representative of fine dust, and should be decreased 100–1000 times. As SULLIVAN and HUNTEN (1964) have pointed out, because the lithium is observed at a lower level than the two other alkali metals, a correction based on the assumption of a constant mixing ratio should be applied. This reduces the relative atmospheric abundance to 2, which is still greater than the solar and the aerosol abundances. GADSDEN (1964) suggests, on the contrary, that the relative abundance of lithium should be increased one hundred times, to take account of the high photoionization rate of lithium. The great excess of lithium then occurring is ascribed entirely to thermonuclear contamination and a residence time of several years.

It is noted that the potassium/sodium ratio is more or less independent of the source, and that the observed ratio is consistent, within the likely errors of observation and interpretation, with the predicted ratios.

Therefore, it is believed that the ratios of the abundances of the alkali metals are not, for one reason or another, good indicators of the origin of the sodium.

Looking now at the abundance of magnesium and calcium, we see that the predicted ratios show a clear distinction between an extraterrestrial and an aerosol origin — the distinction being a factor of 100. From mass-spectrometer results, we find that the magnesium/sodium ratio shows clear evidence of an extraterrestrial origin, while the calcium/sodium ratio is equally clearly in favor of the aerosol origin. Additional understanding requires much more data.

Consideration of the chemistry and ionization of sodium in the 80–100 km region is hampered by the lack of thermochemical data on the oxides of sodium. Thus it is difficult to estimate the rates of the chemical processes that control the concentration of free atomic sodium. Two recent observations with rocket-borne photometers (HUNTEN and WALLACE, 1966) have shown that, on one day (April 7, 1964), the sodium abundance had risen nearly 50% in approximately two hours from the morning twilight observation. On the other day (June 19, 1964), a similar increase was not found — instead, a decrease in concentration occurred at all altitudes between 80 and 106 km.

BLAMONT and DONAHUE (1961, 1964) have published a considerable amount of data on the variation during daylight of the sodium abundance. Modification of the original results has been found to be necessary (GADSDEN, BLAMONT, and DONAHUE, 1966), and it appears that the average abundance of sodium in daytime shows little systematic seasonal variation. The abundance is approximately twice (winter) or four times (summer) what is found in twilight, and is of the order of 14×10^9 cm^{-2}. There is good evidence for the sporadic occurrences of high abundances in November and April. Furthermore, the abundance three hours after noon is, on the average, 30% higher than that three hours before noon.

The photoionization rate of sodium at the 80–100 km level is 2×10^{-5} sec^{-1}. Photoionization continues throughout the day, without self-absorption, until the shadow of the ozonosphere falls on the sodium during early twilight. Therefore, during a period of six hours of daylight, the concentration of atomic sodium can be expected to fall by 35% due to photoionization, whereas the abundance is observed to rise by 30% over the same period of time. Thus, there are sodium-liberating processes occurring during the day which have an overall specific rate of about 4×10^{-5} sec^{-1}. If the sodium influx to the Earth is 10^{13} atoms cm^{-2} yr^{-1} (see previous section), i.e. 3×10^5 cm^{-2} sec^{-1}, and with an atomic abundance in the neighborhood of 10^{10} cm^{-2}, the specific rate associated with the influx is 3×10^{-5} sec^{-1}.

HUNTEN and WALLACE (1966) find a "scale height" of only 2 km on the upper side of one of their observed profiles. DONAHUE (1966) refers to a similar finding from a rocket flight, the details of which are given by MEIER (1966). As DONAHUE, *loc. cit.*, points out, this demands a rapid rate of combination of atomic sodium to maintain such a steep gradient against the diffusion current. Taking a diffusion coefficient of 5×10^6 cm^2 sec^{-1} at these altitudes, the required time for the disappearance of a sodium atom is of the order of 3×10^3 sec. We have seen above that the sodium concentration changes during the day more slowly than this, therefore we have to look for production and loss processes of roughly equal rates, with specific rates of the order of 3×10^{-4} sec^{-1}.

Let us assume that the upper limits of the rates of chemical two- or three-body processes are 10^{-11} cm^3 sec^{-1} and 10^{-31} cm^6 sec^{-1}, respectively. The lower limit of reactant concentration for a two-body process is thus 3×10^{-1} cm^{-3} and, taking 3×10^{13} cm^{-3} as the total number density in the region of interest, a three-body process is unlikely to be sufficiently fast. Referring to the calculations of HUNT (1966) we are restricted to N_2, O_2, $O(^3P)$, H, or O_3 as possible reactants. BARTH (1966) finds that the concentration of NO is 4×10^7 cm^{-3}, so this is an additional possibility. Furthermore, there is probably sufficient O_2 ($^1\Delta$g) available (c.f. SCHIFF and MEGILL, 1964). If we assume a constant mixing ratio throughout the atmosphere, then CO_2 is also present in sufficient concentration. Taking the heats of formation of NaO and NaO_2 to be the same as OH and HO_2, respectively, the only oxidation process that is likely to be exothermic is the familiar

$$Na + O_3 \rightarrow NaO + O_2. \tag{1}$$

The NaO can be destroyed by any of the following:

$$NaO + O \rightarrow Na + O_2 \tag{2}$$

$$NaO + O_3 \rightarrow NaO_2 + O_2 \tag{3}$$

$$NaO + NO \rightarrow Na + NO_2 \tag{4}$$

$$NaO + H \rightarrow Na + OH \tag{5}$$

$$NaO + O_3 \rightarrow Na + O_2 + O_2 \tag{6}$$

Reaction (2) is likely to be predominant in reactions (2) through (6) because the concentration of O exceeds those of O_3, NO, and H by least 10^3, and because the analogous hydrogen reaction is known to be very fast (KAUFMAN, 1964).

By a process of reduction, therefore, we are left with the familiar reactions (1) and (2) as the probable processes, and it follows that the concentration of atomic sodium at a particular height is given by

$$[Na] = \frac{k_2}{k_1} \cdot \frac{[O]}{[O_3]} \cdot [NaO].$$

Taking the analogous hydrogen rates (KAUFMAN, 1964), and allowing for the decreased collision frequency for Na and NaO relative to H and OH, $\frac{k_2}{k_1} \approx 6.6$. At 95 km, $[O_3] \approx 4 \times 10^8$ cm^{-3}, $[O] \approx 3 \times 10^{11}$ cm^{-3} (COLEGROVE, HANSON, and JOHNSON, 1965) and so

$$[Na]_{95km} \approx 5 \times 10^3 [NaO].$$

There is then a negligible concentration of sodium oxide. However, we need a fairly rapid removal process for atomic sodium at these heights in order to maintain an observed steep gradient. The photoionization rate is known to be too low, and charge transfer from positive ions to sodium atoms is unlikely to be much faster than photoionization with a positive ion density of only 10^5 cm^{-3}.

The above analysis depends critically on the assumption that the rates of reactions (1) and (2) are the same as the analogous hydrogen rates. For reaction (2) to be exothermic, there is an implicit assumption that the dissociation energy of NaO does not exceed that of OH (4.39 eV) by more than one-sixth. If this is not the case, then reactions (2) and (6) become endothermic, and sodium must be regenerated by either (4) or (5). The rate of destruction will therefore be down approximately 10^3 times since the concentrations of NO and H are only about 10^{-3} that of O. Thus the atomic sodium concentration now becomes

$$[Na] = \frac{k_4[NO] + k_5[H]}{k_1[O_3]} \cdot [NaO],$$

and the ratio [Na]/[NaO] will be of the order of unity. Its direction of variation through a day will depend on how [NO] or [H] change relative to $[O_3]$.

The concentration of sodium in the ionized form is comparable with that of the atomic form (see Table I). One should not lose sight of the possibility of dissociative recombination processes such as

$$Na^+ + CO_3^- \rightarrow NaO + CO_2 \tag{7}$$

$$Na^+ + NO_2 \rightarrow NaO + NO. \tag{8}$$

If, during daytime, there is a negative ion/electron ratio of 0.01, and the rate coefficients of (7) and (8) are in the neighbourhood of 10^{-7} cm^3 sec^{-1}, the rates of (7) and (8) could well be as high as 0.1 sec^{-1}, giving a specific rate for the production of NaO in the vicinity of 10^{-4} to 10^{-5} sec^{-1}.

Summary

It has been shown that there are many problems associated with the search for a full understanding of the processes in the 80–100 km region of the atmosphere. The specific rates of the reactions are typically sufficiently fast that twilight observations have much to contribute.

The three topics treated here — orthohelium, dust, and the alkali metals — are to some extent the result of an arbitrary choice. Even so, the interpretations of these observations involve important conclusions about the atmosphere and its environs. The orthohelium measurements may eventually provide a simple ground-based method of monitoring the extreme ultraviolet region of solar radiation. In the 80–100 km region, consideration of dust and alkali metal concentrations, which are related to some extent, must inherently involve processes governing the ionic constitution of the D region. Understanding the daily and seasonal variations of the abundances undoubtedly involves meteorological information. The region is not accessible for study on a regular basis other than by either an extension of the Meteorological Rocket Network observations upward by about 35 km, or by ground-based optical observations. Thus there is a good case for continuing observations in twilight in the classical optical manner.

Acknowledgments   It is with pleasure that I offer my thanks to Drs. T. M. Donahue and D. M. Hunten for sending prepublication information used in guiding this, and the preceding review.

References

AIKIN, C. A., KANE, J. A., and TROIM, J., 1964, *J. Geophys. Res.* **69**, 4621.

BARTH, C. A., 1966, *Ann. Geophys*, **22**, 198.

BLAMONT, J.-E. and DONAHUE, T. M., 1961, *J. Geophys. Res.* **66**, 1407.

BLAMONT, J.-E. and DONAHUE, T. M., 1964, *J. Geophys. Res.* **69**, 4093.

COLEGROVE, F. D., HANSON, W. B., and JOHNSON, F. S., 1965, *J. Geophys. Res.* **70**, 4931.

DIVARI, N. B., 1964, *Geomagnetism and Aeronomics* **4**, 688.

DONAHUE, T. M., 1966, *J. Geophys. Res.* **71**, 2237.

FORSYTHE, W. E., 1959, *Smithsonian Physical Tables*, Smithsonian Institution, Washington, D. C.

GADSDEN, M., 1964, *Ann. Geophys.* **20**, 383.

GADSDEN, M., BLAMONT, J.-E., and DONAHUE, T. M., 1966, *J. Geophys. Res.* **71**, 5047.

HEMENWAY, C. L., SOBERMAN, R. K., and WITT, G., 1964, *Tellus*, **16**, 84.

HUNT, B. G., 1966, *J. Geophys. Res.* **71**, 1385.

HUNTEN, D. M. and WALLACE, L., 1967, *J. Geophys. Res.* (to be published).

ISTOMIN, V. G., 1963, *Planetary Space Sci.* **11**, 173.

JUNGE, C. E., OLDENBURG, O., and WASSON, J. T., 1962, *J. Geophys. Res.* **67**, 1027.

KAUFMAN, F., 1964, *Ann. Geophys.* **40**, 106.

KOMABAYASI, M., 1962, *J. Met. Soc. Japan*, **40**, 25.

McELROY, M. B., 1965, *Planetary Space Sci.* **13**, 403.

MEIER, R. R., 1966, *Ph.D. Thesis*, Pittsburgh University, Pittsburgh.

MIKIROV, A. YE., 1963, *Planetary Space Sci.* **11**, 417.

MILLMAN, P. M. and McKINLEY, D. W. R., 1963, in *The Moon, Meteorites and Comets*, (Ed. by B. M. Middlehurst and G. P. Kuiper), Univ. of Chicago Press, Chicago.

MINNAERT, M. G. J., 1957, *Monthly Notices Roy. Astron. Soc.* **117**, 315.

NARCISI, R. S. and BAILEY, A. D., 1965, *J. Geophys. Res.* **70**, 3687.

NATANSON, G. L., 1960, *Soviet Phys. — Tech. Phys*, 5, 538.

PARTHASARATHY, R. and RAI, D. B., 1966, *Radio Science* 1, 1401.

SCHIFF, H. I. and MEGILL, L. R., 1964, *J. Geophys. Res.* **69**, 5120.

SHEFOV, N. N., 1962, *Aurorae and Airglow*, No. 9, 55.

SHEFOV, N. N., 1963 a, *Aurorae and Airglow*, No. 10, 56.

SHEFOV, N. N., 1963 b, *Planetary Space Sci.* **10**, 73.

SULLIVAN, H. M. and HUNTEN, D. M., 1964. *Can. J. Phys.* **42**, 937.

VALLANCE JONES, A., 1958, *Ann. Geophys.* **14**, 179.

VALLANCE JONES, A., 1966, *Ann. Geophys.* **22**, 189.

WEBB, W. L., 1965, *J. Geophys. Res.* **70**, 4463.

WILSON, A. T. and HOUSE, D. A., 1965, *J. Geophys. Res.* **70**, 5515.

INTERPRETATION OF THE DAYGLOW

J. F. Noxon

Blue Hill Observatory, Harvard University, Cambridge, Massachusetts

In 1954 Bates and Dalgarno discussed how and to what extent solar radiation could be transformed into an emission spectrum in the dayglow; where the information then available permitted, they gave estimates or upper limits on the intensity of the features to be expected. Although predictions of the intensity of specific emissions appeared in one or two other papers, the majority of theoretical work has come after 1960, when observation of the dayglow spectrum commenced. In reviewing this work we begin by mentioning those excitation processes which appear to be important; we then discuss the way in which individual emission features have been interpreted.

I. Sources of Excitation

The major excitation processes appear to be chemical reactions, fluorescent and resonant scattering, electron impact, and photodissociation. These all occur as a result of sunlight incident upon the atmosphere; with such a variety of energetic processes available during the day no demand has yet arisen for significant excitation of dayglow emission by an energetic particle flux.

Chemical reactions, in which the participants may be neutral particles, ions, or electrons, all moving with near thermal velocity, can often yield excited products; the night airglow is almost entirely due to such reactions. Their contribution is probably the most difficult of all to evaluate. Even when a reaction rate has been measured in the laboratory, the probability of producing a certain excited product may be completely unknown. Several successive reactions must often be considered together and it may have to be assumed, without justification, that there exists a local equilibrium at all steps. If this is not the case, then transport effects in the atmosphere can make any quantitative predictions valueless. Yet it is often possible at least to set upper limits on the production of excited species; in other cases, observation can show that a certain reaction scheme must be of either limited or negligible importance. Since many of the dayglow emissions come from long lived metastable states, quenching reactions are very important (HUNTEN and McELROY, 1966).

In contrast, it is often possible to calculate accurately the efficiency of resonant or fluorescent scattering. With a knowledge of the solar intensity, the scattering cross section, and ground albedo, one may evaluate a quantity "g" which expresses the scattering rate per particle. In those cases where scattering can be shown to be the dominant excitation process, dayglow observation serves as a powerful and passive means of determining the distribution of scatterers with altitude. This is particularly important when the scattering species is a minor constituent in the atmosphere, as is often the case.

Although the vast majority of electrons in the ionosphere have energies below 1 eV, there are sufficient numbers at higher energy to make electron excitation important in the dayglow. Above $\approx$ 5 eV, the electrons present are the result of direct production by photoionization processes, and their distribution with energy may be calculated with some accuracy (DALGARNO, MCELROY, and MOFFETT, 1963). Below $\approx$ 2 eV, the mutual interaction of electrons is strong and the energy distribution tends towards Maxwellian; heating of the low energy electron gas can lead to an effective temperature several times that of the ambient atmosphere. The excitation rate of dayglow emission by electron impact depends strongly in certain cases upon the number of electrons present in the intermediate energy range of 2–5 eV; it is in this range that the energy distribution is hardest to calculate. Thus, while the contribution of photoelectrons to dayglow excitation can be reliably estimated, the overall importance of electron excitation remains uncertain in some cases.

Since the cross section for continuous absorption by many atmospheric constituents has been accurately determined in the laboratory, it is possible to calculate their rate of photodissociation by sunlight. However, the nature of the product states may not be well known, and so it is sometimes only possible to estimate an upper limit on the production of dayglow by this process. The excited products may not only produce dayglow emission directly but may also contribute significantly as a result of their subsequent chemical reactions.

II. Interpretation of Individual Emissions

For convenience we group the emissions according to whether they arise predominantly from above or below 130 km. In the lower region, the important features are the sodium D lines, NO γ bands, infrared bands of O_2, OH vibration-rotation bands, and the lower of the two "layers" emitting the OI 5577Å line. Although the height of the OH and O_2 emission has not been measured, there is little doubt, on energy grounds alone, that they must arise from well below 130 km.

A. Sodium D Lines

There is no longer doubt that the sodium dayglow arises from the resonant scattering of sunlight by sodium atoms whose abundance in the daytime may be several times greater than at twilight. The relationship between the abun-

dance and the emission intensity has been discussed by BRANDT and CHAMBER-
LAIN (1958) and BLAMONT and DONAHUE (1961, 1964); ground reflection of the
incident sunlight must be allowed for, as well as attenuation and multiple
scattering by sodium atoms in the dayglow layer. The central problem in the
sodium dayglow is how to account for the magnitude and height distribution of
the enhanced daytime abundance of free sodium atoms. Blamont and Donahue
indicated that an enhancement might result from the photodissociation of
sodium oxides. But the resulting dayglow emission was predicted to come from
lower altitude than in twilight, in conflict with the identical heights measured
by rockets. More recently, DONAHUE (1966), HUNTEN and WALLACE (1966),
and GADSDEN (this volume) have suggested that the daytime excess might be
due to sodium liberated by sunlight from meteoric dust.

B. NO γ Bands

The NO bands observed in the dayglow by BARTH (1966) have a relative
intensity appropriate to that expected from resonance fluorescence; Barth has
used the observations to show that the daytime abundance of NO above 80 km
must be much greater than had been anticipated. As with sodium the excitation
process seems clear; the problem is to account properly for the abundance and
distribution with height of the minor constituent involved. In order to raise the
predicted NO abundance, NICOLET (1965) introduced ion-molecule reactions
which create NO through the destruction of O_2^+. Because NO is easily ionized,
the effects of additional NO on the ionization equilibrium in the D region have
had to be reexamined; recent work is that of DONAHUE (1966) and FERGUSON et
al. (1965).

C. O_2 Infrared Atmospheric Bands

The only source of $O_2(^1\Delta g)$ adequate to account for the large dayglow intensity appears to be photodissociation of ozone by sunlight (2000–3000Å) as
discussed by GATTINGER and VALLANCE JONES (1966). The emission thus must
come from the 40–80 km region where this process is important, and the theory
of the dayglow must be related intimately to the larger problem of mesospheric
ozone. The dayglow intensity and the decay at twilight can be predicted when
certain assumptions are made concerning the quenching of $O_2(^1\Delta g)$ by collision;
yet there has been only limited progress in accounting for the fact that dawn
twilight intensity is much weaker than in the evening and for a pronounced
seasonal variation in twilight intensity. The theory presented by Gattinger and
Vallance Jones is restricted to a pure oxygen atmosphere and ignores transport
effects; a less restricted approach seems necessary here as well as in the ozone
problem itself. The difficulties are formidable but attempts are in progress
(HAMPSON, 1964, 1965; HESSTVEDT, 1965; HUNT, 1966). Presumably there
should be some dayglow emission from the $O_2(^1\Sigma_g^+)$ state also, but no observations have been reported as yet.

D. OH Bands

Since the OH emission is apparently the result of a reaction between ozone and atomic hydrogen, one might anticipate some relationship with the O_2 emission. The impressive sudden drop in the OH intensity at dawn observed by LYTLE (1966) resembles a similar change expected when photodissociation begins in the ozone layer. The subsequent rise during the morning presumably reflects an expected increase in the concentration of H atoms resulting from reactions which consume atomic oxygen (HAMPSON, 1964, 1965; HESSTVEDT, 1965; HUNT, 1966). A characteristic of these theoretical discussions is their prediction of a significant extension of the ozone-hydrogen reaction zone to lower altitude during the day with an appreciable increase in the expected OH intensity. The reactions are so numerous and complex, however, that even qualitative prediction is very difficult at present. It is certainly worth making a continued effort to investigate the diurnal variation of the OH emission since any theory of the mesosphere must be able to account for the effects observed. Measurements of the height distribution in the dayglow would be of particular interest.

E. [OI] 5577Å

The rocket observations reported by WALLACE and MCELROY (1966) show the lower of the two dayglow "layers" to occur near 90 km, where the majority of the 5577Å nightglow radiation arises. Although the total intensity from below 130 km is several times larger than at night, the authors note that a relatively small increase in the atomic oxygen concentration would increase the rate of the Chapman reaction considerably. They do not rule out the possibility of a contribution to the production of $O(^1S)$ by photodissociation of O_2 near 100 km.

III. Dayglow Arising Above 130 km

A. Lyman α (1216Å)

The theory of Lyman α dayglow has been recently discussed by DONAHUE (1966); the emission is considered to be due to resonant scattering of solar Lyman α by atomic hydrogen, but the problem is complicated by the effects of multiple scattering in an optically thick medium. The interpretation appears to support the existence of a significant diurnal variation in the abundance of H atoms above 100 km.

B. OI (1304Å)

Both resonant scattering and excitation by photoelectrons have been considered (DONAHUE and FASTIE, 1963; TOHMATSU, 1964; DONAHUE, 1965; BARTH, 1966). As with Lyman α the problem is complicated by the effects of multiple scattering, but there appears at present to be no particular conflict between the observations and these modes of excitation.

C. N_2 Second Positive Bands

NAGY and FOURNIER (1965) have calculated the intensity to be expected from photoelectron excitation of N_2; they can account for the observed intensity above 170 km and predict a total zenith intensity of 2 kR above 100 km.

D. N_2^+ 3914Å

Except at lower altitude, where the intensity is small, the 3914Å dayglow appears to be due to resonant scattering of sunlight by preexisting N_2^+ ions (WALLACE and McELROY, 1966; ZIPF, 1966). The N_2^+ densities required are not greatly different from the concentrations measured directly with rocket-borne mass spectrometers (HOLMES et al., 1965); as a result, much of the theoretical work has been concerned with explaining the observed height distribution of the ions. In addition to photoionization, there may be a significant creation of N_2^+ by reaction of $O^+(^2D)$ with N_2 (DALGARNO and McELROY, 1966). Below 150 km there appears to be an important contribution to the dayglow from fluorescent scattering in which neutral N_2 is simultaneously ionized and excited by solar ultraviolet. The additional excitation is significant because the N_2^+ ions are rapidly removed by reactions with oxygen at these heights. Further observation might well include a simultaneous measurement of ion density and dayglow intensity; the remarkable amount of emission above 300 km reported by NAGATA et al. (1965) might also bear further investigation.

E. [NI] (5200Å)

WALLACE and McELROY (1966) find that no clear decision is possible on the source of excitation; dissociative recombination of N_2^+ or NO^+ may be important, but so also might a reaction of N_2^+ with O atoms. The major problem is a lack of knowledge of the efficiency of these reactions in producing the $N(^2D)$ state. However, they do find that quenching of the state by collisions with neutral particles must be important; were it not, the transition from day to night intensity would be slower than is observed.

F. [OI] (5577)Å

Although excitation of $O(^1S)$ by photoelectrons seems adequate to explain the green line dayglow above 130 km (WALLACE and McELROY, 1966), a very similar distribution of intensity with height can result from dissociative recombination of O_2^+. This is shown in Figure 2 of the review of dayglow observations in this volume. As is so often the case, there is uncertainty as to how efficiently the reaction yields the required excited product. To produce the required intensity, the efficiency must exceed 10% and the rate coefficient has to be about 5×10^{-8} cm³/sec. One consequence of this would be that a weak 5577Å emission would be expected above 200 km at night; Wallace and McElroy suggest 5–10 rayleighs. In the past, rocket measurements of the nightglow could only set an upper limit of this same magnitude, but a new measurement now shows that just such a weak high altitude component does exist in the nightglow (GULLIDGE and PACKER, 1966). Although this might suggest that the dissociative recombination reaction is highly efficient, the possibility of excitation at night by a weak flux of low energy electrons may yet have to be considered. The limits on the flux imposed by 3914Å nightglow intensity have recently been lowered again (BROADFOOT and HUNTEN, 1966), but it may still be possible to reconcile this with a few rayleighs of green line arising at 250 km.

G. [OI] 6300Å

The most extensive theoretical discussions of this emission are by DALGARNO and WALKER (1964) and WALLACE and MCELROY (1966). Other references are BRANDT (1958), NOXON (1964), ZIPF (1966), and NAGATA *et al.* (1965). Two of the three individual rocket intensity profiles can be satisfactorily interpreted by a combination of O_2 photodissociation, dissociative recombination of O_2^+, and photoelectron excitation. It has been necessary, however, to assume a very large quenching rate for the excited $O(^1D)$ state at low altitude if the photodissociation contribution is not to become too large. Figure 2 in the dayglow observational review in this volume shows the rocket measurements and theoretical curves calculated by Wallace and McElroy for two different values of S_D, the rate coefficient for quenching by N_2.

When the red line is observed over a period of time (NOXON, 1964) there appear to be variations in the intensity which are difficult, if not impossible, to explain by means of the mechanisms already mentioned. It has therefore been proposed that additional excitation may sometimes occur through collisions between low energy quasi-thermal electrons and O atoms; this would be expected to be most important in the 200 km region. For such excitation to be of significance it is necessary that the effective temperature of the electrons between 2 and ≈ 5 eV exceed 3000°K; measurements in this energy range are not yet generally available. The electron temperatures usually quoted are derived from the energy distribution of electrons below 1 eV; these temperatures are usually considerably less than 3000°K. There is no assurance, however, that the two energy ranges can in fact be described by a common temperature; thus the role of quasi-thermal electrons remains unclear.

The rocket measurement by NAGATA *et al.* (1965) seems to show that on that occasion the majority of 6300Å emission came from above 300 km. This disagrees both with the other rocket observations and with theoretical expectation. Although one might suspect the presence of background contamination, it would be important in any case to obtain further measurements of the intensity at high altitude.

IV. Other Predicted Emissions

There are a number of interesting features whose intensity has been estimated, although no observations have yet been reported. These include emission from helium, the O_2 atmospheric bands, lines from the $O^+(^2D)$ state near 7300Å, the Meinel bands of N_2^+, and the O_2^+ First Negative system. The latter three result from simultaneous photoionization and excitation (DALGARNO and MCELROY, 1965); the intensity will directly follow the solar extreme ultraviolet causing the excitation. Since a comparison with observation is not yet possible we shall not review these further.

Acknowledgment This work has been partly supported by the Atmospheric Sciences Section, National Science Foundation, NSF grant G-24903 to Harvard University.

References

BARTH, C. A., 1966, *Ann. Geophys.* **22**, 198.
BATES, D. R. and DALGARNO, A., 1964, *J. Atmospheric Terrest. Phys.* **5**, 329.
BLAMONT, J. E. and DONAHUE, T. M., 1961, *J. Geophys. Res.* **66**, 1407.
BLAMONT, J. E. and DONAHUE, T. M., 1964, *J. Geophys. Res.* **69**, 4093.
BRANDT, J. C., 1958, *Astrophys. J.* **128**, 718.
BRANDT, J. C. and CHAMBERLAIN, J. W., 1958, *J. Atmospheric Terrest. Phys.* **13**, 90.
BROADFOOT, L. and HUNTEN, D. M., 1966, *Planetary Space Sci.* **14**, 1303.
DALGARNO, A. and MCELROY, M. B., 1965, *Planetary Space Sci.* **13**, 947.
DALGARNO, A. and MCELROY, M. B., 1966, *Planetary Space Sci.* **14**, 1321.
DALGARNO, A., MCELROY, M. B., and MOFFETT, R. J., 1963, *Planetary Space Sci.* **11**, 463.
DALGARNO, A. and WALKER, J. C. G., 1964, *J. Atmos. Sci.* **21**, 463.
DONAHUE, T. M., 1965, *Planetary Space Sci.* **13**, 871.
DONAHUE, T. M., 1966, *Ann. Geophys.* **22**, 175.
DONAHUE, T. M., 1966, COSPAR meeting.
DONAHUE, T. M., 1966, *Planetary Space Sci.* **14**, 33.
DONAHUE, T. M. and FASTIE, W. G., 1963, *Space Res.* **4**.
FERGUSON, E. E., FEHSENFELD, F. C., GOLADAN, P. D., and SCHMELTEKOPF, A. L., 1965, *J. Geophys. Res.* **70**, 4323.
GATTINGER, R. L. and VALLANCE JONES, A., 1966, *Planetary Space Sci.* **14**, 1.
GULLIDGE, I. and PACKER, D. M., 1966, *Trans. Am. Geophys. Union* **47**, 74.
HAMPSON, J., 1964, 1965, CARDE Tech. Note 1627, 1690.
HESSTVEDT, E., 1965, *Geofys. Publikasjoner* **23**, No. 1.
HOLMES, J. C., JOHNSON, C. Y., and YOUNG, J. M., 1965, *Space Res.* **5**, 756.
HUNT, B. G., 1966, *J. Geophys. Res.* **71**, 1385.
HUNTEN, D. M. and MCELROY, M. B., 1966, *Rev. Geophys.* **4**, 303.
HUNTEN, D. M. and WALLACE, L., 1967, *J. Geophys. Res.* **72**, 69.
LYTLE, E. A., 1966, private communication.
NAGATA, T., TOHMATSU, T., and OGAWA, T., 1965, *Planetary Space Sci.* **13**, 1273.
NAGY, A. F. and FOURNIER, J. P., 1965, *J. Geophys. Res.* **70**, 5981.
NICOLET, M., 1965, *J. Geophys. Res.* **70**, 691.
NOXON, J. F., 1964, *J. Geophys. Res.* **69**, 3245.
TOHMATSU, T., 1964, *Rep. Ionos. Space Res. Japan* **18**, 425.
WALLACE, L. and MCELROY, M. B., 1966, *Planetary Space Sci.* **14**, 677.
ZIPF, E. C., 1966, *J. Geomag. and Geoelectricity.*

Session

4

ARTIFICIAL AURORA AND AIRGLOW

Dr. Roland Meyerott

Lockheed Palo Alto Research Laboratory

CONJUGATE AURORAL MEASUREMENTS FROM THE 1962 U. S. HIGH ALTITUDE NUCLEAR TEST SERIES

Wallace P. Boquist
EG&G, INC., Boston, Massachusetts

John W. Snyder
DASA, Washington, D. C.

I. Introduction

In the summer and fall of 1962 the United States detonated a number of high altitude nuclear tests from which there were induced auroras in both the northern and southern geomagnetic conjugate regions of the burst. The tests were conducted over the vicinity of Johnston Island in the Central Pacific Ocean for which the northern conjugate region occurred between Johnston Island and the upper Hawaiian Islands, and for which the southern conjugate region occurred within the triangle formed by the Samoa, Fiji, and Tonga Islands. This paper summarizes some of the pertinent measurements of auroral position, motion, and brightness history as measured by EG & G for the U. S. Defense Atomic Support Agency. The data was obtained from stations located on Johnston Island, two KC-135 jet aircraft, and Mauna Loa, Hawaii in the northern conjugate region, and from Tutuila, Samoa, and Tongatapu, Tonga in the southern conjugate region.

Table I. 1962 U.S. High-Altitude Nuclear Events

Name	Date/Time (UT)	Height	Yield	Optical Aurora
Star Fish	July 9/0900	400 km	1.4 megatons	Beta, debris aurora; >30 min duration
Check Mate	October 20/0830	Tens of km	<20 kilotons	Beta aurora; 10 min duration
King Fish	November 1/1210	Tens of km	<1 megaton	Beta aurora; ≈5 min duration
Blue Gill	October 26/1000	Tens of km	<1 megaton	Beta aurora; >50 min duration
Tight Rope	November 4/0730	Tens of km	<20 kilotons	Very weak aurora; short lived — sec

Measurable auroras occurred in both the northern and southern conjugate regions for all of the high altitude events except Tight Rope, although some limited data were obtained by DANIELS (1964). Table I summarizes the available pertinent parameters of these events. In the northern conjugate region, the auroras were observed by one or more of the EG & G optical stations for Star Fish, Check Mate, Blue Gill, and King Fish. In the southern conjugate region, the same was true with the exception of King Fish, which was not observed because of weather conditions. Figure 1 shows the relative locations of the optical stations and the initial positions of three of the beta auroras.

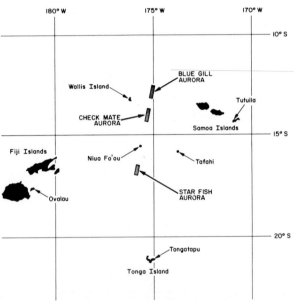

FIGURE 1. Initial location of several southern conjugate auroras from the 1962 U. S. test series. EG & G optical stations were located on Tutuila, Ovalou, and Tongatapu.

II. Background

Auroras induced by high altitude nuclear detonations were first observed during the Teak and Orange events of the 1958 summer U. S. nuclear test series in the Central Pacific. The Teak event was a megaton range yield, detonated at 77 km altitude. The Orange event was of similar yield and was detonated at 43 km. Auroral effects were reportedly observed from Western Samoa for both events. Three low yield (1–2 kilotons) events were also detonated during late summer of 1958 at altitudes near 500 km in the middle Atlantic. Auroral effects were observed along the geomagnetic field lines in the vicinity of the bursts.

Auroras resulting from such detonations have been generally categorized as either a beta aurora or a debris aurora. The former is that caused by electrons from the nuclear source and decaying fission products. The debris aurora is caused by the debris ions being guided to the conjugate regions with the resultant atmospheric excitation and auroral emission. In addition, late time (many minutes) field aligned visually luminescent emissions are also characteristic of the higher detonations. It has been found that the beta aurora is generally most intense in the 50–100 km altitude regime, and the debris aurora most intense in the 100–200 km altitude regime. The beta aurora will occur first in the conjugate regions because of the much faster velocity of the electrons compared to the debris ions. It should be noted that remote conjugate beta auroras will occur for detonations above about 40 km altitude, whereas debris auroras will occur for detonation altitudes only above the order of 300 km.

It has been established that the initial radial expansion of the beta aurora results from the weapon fission debris expansion, and that the horizontal (north/south) motion of the centroid of this aurora results from the rise of the fireball or debris cloud in the atmosphere. The auroral brightness-time history data indicate the effective source of escaping electrons or debris ions which are trapped and guided to the conjugate regions. This effective source is primarily a function of the actual source strength, the field line trapping efficiency, and the atmospheric attenuation of the emitted electrons or debris ions.

III. Results

A. Auroral Position and Correlation with Geomagnetic Field Line Models

The geographical location of the artificially induced auroras was determined from measurements on photographic records. In the northern conjugate region, the occurrence of both the nuclear burst image and the auroral image on the same photographic frame enabled the camera pointing angle and hence, the angular position of the aurora, to be determined. In the southern conjugate region, stars and the moon were used to determine camera pointing angles. Triangulation of results from two or more stations then permitted a determination of the position of the aurora.

The location of the Star Fish auroral end points for the northern and southern conjugate regions are presented in Table II, for altitudes of 50 and

Table II. Star Fish Auroral Positions and Deduced Injection Altitude

	Latitude	Longitude
Northern Conjugate Region	21°36′N	168°35′W
Southern Conjugate Region	17°13′S	175°57′W
	Jensen-Cain Field Model	Centered Dipole Field Model
Injection Altitude	385 km	440 km

44 km, respectively. These heights represent the lowest observable penetrations due to limitations of camera field of view in the northern conjugate region and cloud obscuration in the southern conjugate region. The location of the burst point at 400 km altitude was 16° 28.1′ N and 169° 37.8′ W.

In order to check the accuracy of the geomagnetic field line models used to predict conjugate auroral locations, the observed southern conjugate auroral locations were used to "determine" the altitude of several bursts over the known ground zeros. A mapping of projected field lines onto actual photographs of a given aurora was made using a centered dipole model (modified to better fit the magnetic measurements in the Pacific area) and the JENSEN-CAIN (1962) model of the earth's magnetic field.

The results of this method to determine the field line model accuracy are included in Table II. Here it is seen that the Jensen-Cain field model suggests an injection altitude to within about 3% of the actual 400 km detonation altitude whereas the centered dipole model differs by 10%. At considerably lower altitudes — as in the case of the Check Mate and Blue Gill events — deduced injection altitudes using the Jensen-Cain field model were also on the order of 3% variation with actual detonation altitudes. The centered dipole model, on the other hand, became increasingly inaccurate at lower altitudes, indicating as much as a factor of 3 difference in the projected and the actual detonation altitudes.

B. Auroral Deposition Characteristics

The average beta energy associated with a fission product spectrum is about 1 MeV, with higher energies extending to about 8 MeV. The penetration depths associated with beta auroras of the type considered here would be expected to exhibit a general consistency and, indeed, did for the four observed events. Although the high yield Star Fish event produced auroras which penetrated to an altitude of 44 km, almost all of the other events exhibited penetration values of the order of 50 km. It has been shown (BOQUIST et al., 1964) that the electron energy corresponding to this 50-km penetration depth is 3.5 MeV.* The northern conjugate penetration for the Blue Gill event also corresponds to 3.5 MeV* electron energy (BOQUIST et al., 1964). It is interesting to note that the observed penetration depth of the southern conjugate aurora of Blue Gill remained essentially constant as the brightness decreased with time, indicating

Table III. Auroral Altitude Characteristics

Event	Altitude of Maximum Radiance	Altitude of Color Boundary
	(km)	(km)
Star Fish	66	85
Check Mate	..	84
Blue Gill	63	87

a constant electron decay energy with decreasing flux. The altitude of the maximum observed radiance of the Star Fish and Blue Gill auroras is given in Table III, and is seen to be of the order of 65 km (initially) for both events. The electron energy corresponding to these penetration depths is about 1 MeV.*

C. Late Time Debris Aurora

Late time debris induced effects were observed throughout the geomagnetic field line system following the Star Fish event, and in the general vicinity of the burst area for Check Mate and King Fish events. Figures 2 and 3 illustrate

FIGURE 2. Star Fish aurora between 2 and 3 min as seen from Canton Island looking north.

photographically the striking magnitude of the appearance of the debris induced aurora many minutes after the burst of the Star Fish event. The Star Fish auroras shown in these and similar photographs were reconstructed and depicted on a Jensen-Cain geomagnetic field line model in Figure 4.

Between the times of occurrence of the initial rapidly changing Star Fish beta auroras and the relatively stabilized debris induced aurora shown in

*Electron energy of an electron incident at 30° (nominal magnetic field inclination) and zero injection pitch angle.

FIGURE 3. Star Fish aurora at 11 min as seen from Tongatapu looking north. Vertical extent of aurora at this time was between 600 and 2200 km above the equator.

Figure 4, a gross upward distortion of the geomagnetic field lines above and towards the equator from the burst point was observed between 10 and 100 sec. The distortion appears to have extended significantly to the east as well, as seen in Figure 2.

The aurora at later times was observed by other investigators in the south as being associated with field lines corresponding to 7000 km altitude at the equator. It is clear from Figure 4, however, that reflected sunlight could not have been an influencing factor in the aurora below 2500 km.

Both the Check Mate and King Fish debris induced auroras developed slowly as a result of deformation and extension of the residual debris cloud following the burst in contrast to Star Fish, wherein the debris was spread over hundreds of kilometers within a second. As the luminous clouds rose, the

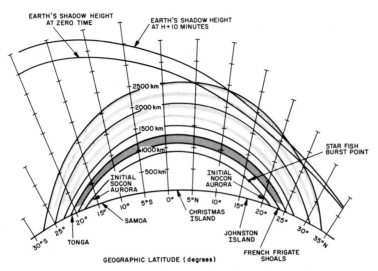

FIGURE 4. Composite diagram of Star Fish aurora between 10 and 15 min as projected on Jensen-Cain geomagnetic field line model.

developing aurora spread increasingly to the south along the geomagnetic field lines as typified by the photograph of the late time Check Mate aurora in Figure 5.

FIGURE 5. Check Mate aurora at 8 min as seen from Mauna Loa, Hawaii looking west.

D. Auroral Motion

Star Fish. The north-south expansion of the southern conjugate beta aurora is shown in Figure 6, relative to the center of the initial ray. This plot illustrates some interesting aspects of the auroral expansion. The initial radial

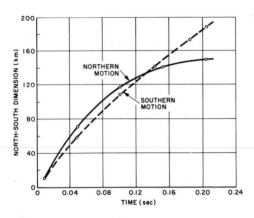

FIGURE 6. Radial expansion of Star Fish beta aurora in southern conjugate region.

expansion rate is essentially symmetrical and about 1600 km/sec. However, as the beta-emitting debris in the burst area expands downward, it is slowed by the increasingly dense atmosphere, causing a nonsymmetrical change in the auroral expansion. Data for the average radial east-west expansion of the southern conjugate beta aurora in the 0.1–0.2 sec time regime was found to agree with the average (nonsymmetrical) north-south expansion in this same time period.

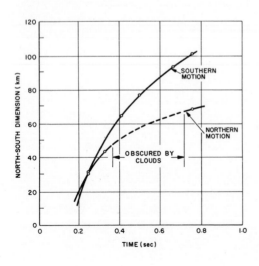

FIGURE 7. Radial expansion of Star Fish debris aurora in southern conjugate regions.

In the southern conjugate region, a debris aurora was observed to appear within a fraction of a second after the appearance of the beta aurora. Figure 7 shows the time history of the expansion of this debris aurora along a north-south longitude. By the time the debris had arrived at this conjugate, its expansion rate was observed directly to be about 200 km/sec at about 0.3 sec. Distortion of the initially symmetric expansion is seen to be similar to that shown in Figure 6. During the same period, measurements were also made on the apparent vertical growth of this debris aurora (see Figure 8). The possible

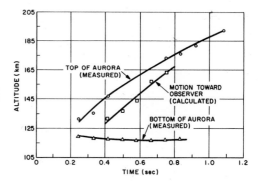

FIGURE 8. Vertical motion of Star Fish debris aurora in southern conjugate region.

apparent vertical motion due to the horizontal motion of the aurora towards the observer is shown to be less than that observed and, therefore, of no consequence here.

Blue Gill. The aurora from the Blue Gill event was observed in the southern conjugate region from Samoa and Tongatapu, and in the burst area from Johnston Island and a KC-135 aircraft. Because of the much lower detonation altitude of this event, debris was unable to escape and therefore, a beta aurora alone was observed. In the conjugate region, the beta aurora appeared between 50 and 100 km; however, in the burst region the aurora occurred as low as 45 km.

Figure 9 is a long exposure (2 min) photograph of the southern conjugate Blue Gill aurora as seen from Samoa. The initial aurora is the single striation seen to the right of the integrated image, and was about 3 km in diameter. As the debris cloud rose in the burst region the aurora progressed south (to the left) as would be expected. It is uncertain, however, what caused the very definite striations evident in this integrated exposure. These striations, separated by 8 km, increased and faded slowly in brightness at about 25 sec intervals.

FIGURE 9. Blue Gill aurora from 0–2 min as seen from Tutuila, Samoa looking west. Southward motion of aurora in this integrated photograph is to left.

The north-south expansion of the Blue Gill southern conjugate aurora is shown in Figure 10 for the first 200 sec after zero time. The initial rate of motion of the southern expanding edge of the aurora in the first minute is

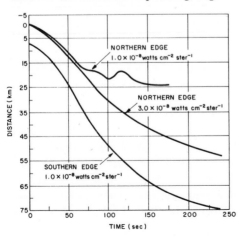

FIGURE 10. Southward motion of Blue Gill aurora in southern conjugate region.

about 0.53 km/sec. This rate is a result of the combined effect of the upward motion (primarily) and expansion of the Blue Gill debris cloud in the burst area.

For a somewhat longer time period, data were also obtained on the east-west expansion of the aurora by viewing the aurora end-on. In this instance shown in Figure 11, the radial growth is a function of the Blue Gill lateral expansion

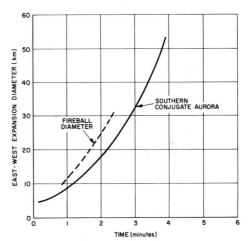

FIGURE 11. Comparison of east-west expansion of Blue Gill aurora and debris cloud.

only, independent of the rise rate of the debris cloud. Also presented in Figure 11 is the measured apparent debris-cloud diameter from Johnston Island data. The agreement here is not as good as for the longitudinal case, but is consistent and reasonable, considering that the data were obtained from a distance of over 800 km.

E. Auroral Brightness

Star Fish. Typical radiance time histories of the Star Fish conjugate auroral column are shown in Figure 12, for the first 15 sec after zero time as observed

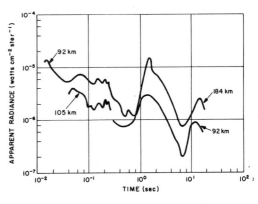

FIGURE 12. Star Fish auroral radiance-time history in the southern conjugate region.

from Samoa. These particular curves, obtained from cinemagraphic records, represent the brightness history at altitudes 72, 105, and 184 km. Similar curves are obtained from other altitudes, but with significant differences occurring in the relative intensity of the beta induced peaks in the 0–0.1 sec time period and the debris induced peak at about 1.5 sec. The maximum intensity of the beta aurora was found to occur in the vicinity of 66 km.

Prior to 0.3 sec, several enhancements occur in the observed brightness which are not altitude dependent. For example, between 0.2–0.3 sec one observes a very distinct pair of peaks in both altitude plots. At about 1.5 sec, the first probable debris maximum occurs, with a small fraction of the debris being of considerably higher velocity than the rest. As mentioned earlier with regard to Figure 8, this debris aurora was distinctly observed to occur above 115 km altitude. Beginning at about 8 sec, an enhancement of this debris aurora is observed.

In the northern conjugate region, a brightness-time history for a 60 km altitude was obtained and is presented in Figure 13. The geomagnetic-field line

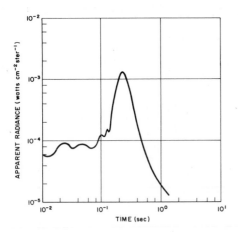

FIGURE 13. Star Fish auroral radiance-time history in the northern conjugate region.

path length from the burst to the 60-km altitude of the aurora is about 600 km. Because of this relatively short distance with respect to the 0.003 sec time resolution of the northern conjugate data, the initial beta peaks are not discernible. The first distinguishable brightness peaks occur at 2.4×10^{-2} sec and 4.5×10^{-2} sec. At 2.3×10^{-1} sec, the major debris peak is seen to occur. Comparing the derived velocities from the southern and northern conjugate regions, a reasonably good correspondence was found to exist throughout the times examined, with the notable lack of a slower debris component in the northern conjugate data. This effect is believed definitely attributable to device asymmetry.

Blue Gill. The peak radiance-time history of the Blue Gill beta aurora in the southern conjugate region exhibited a moderate initial peak and a peculiar broad maximum peaking in the vicinity of 70 sec as illustrated in Figure 14. Although this broad maximum appears similar to the debris maximum found in Star Fish, appreciable debris cannot be present here, and the enhancement is attributed entirely to the rise of the Blue Gill debris cloud to an altitude at

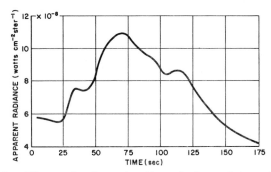

FIGURE 14. Blue Gill auroral radiance-time history in the southern conjugate region.

which the betas achieve a mean-free-path sufficient for vertical escape. The decrease in intensity of the observed radiance beyond 70 sec is due mainly to the $t^{-1.2}$ decay of the beta emitting fission debris and, to a lesser extent, the continuing expansion of the debris cloud. Table IV summarizes some of the

Table IV. Blue Gill Southern Conjugate Auroral Intensities

Wavelength	Atom or Molecule	Intensity 40–160 sec	Intensity 3.5–8.5 min
3914	N_2^+	6.5 kR	0.77 kR
4278	N_2^+	8.6	3.8
4709	N_2^+	7.5	1.2
5228	N_2^+	4.8	1.46
5577	OI	25	7.4
5854	N_2	8.5	1.9
5890	NaI	10.4	. . . .
6014	N_2	16.7	3.4
6624	N_2	17.2	. . . .
6705	N_2	. . . .	7.2

prominent spectral emissions observed in the south during two exposure periods within the first 10 min after the detonation.

Check Mate. Because of the scarcity of observations pertinent to the auroral phenomena in both the northern and southern conjugate regions, only limited comparisons of the brightness data is possible. The radiance versus time of the aurora as observed in the northern-conjugate region from a KC-135 aircraft is plotted in Figure 15. The radiance is seen to fall off as $t^{-1.26}$ until about 4.5 sec, at which point it decays somewhat more rapidly. At approximately the same time (about 4 sec), the southern conjugate aurora as observed

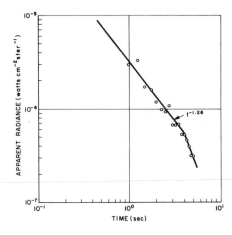

FIGURE 15. Check Mate auroral radiance-time history in the northern conjugate (burst) region.

from Samoa at 55- and 100-km altitudes exhibited a similar change in decay rate.

King Fish. A well-documented radiance-time history of the aurora from King Fish is available only from the northern conjugate region. These data were taken from records obtained at Johnston Island. A decay rate varying as $t^{-1.4}$ is found to exist for approximately the first 40 sec after which a more rapid decay occurs. This change is thought to be due to a spatial motion of the expanding auroral column after 40 sec.

An approximate, relative-radiance-time history of the early southern conjugate aurora was obtained by CHESNUT (1963) from a color cinemagraphic record. These data also show that the bright portions of the southern aurora decays at approximately a $t^{-1.2}$ rate beyond 10 sec to about 1 min.

IV. Discussion

Observations have shown that a unique correspondence exists between the history of the radioactive debris from a high altitude nuclear detonation and the induced aurora in both the northern and southern conjugate regions. Extensive data from detonations as high as 400 km (Star Fish) down to about 40 km (Orange) have formed a coherent picture of the characteristics of these aurora as a function of burst altitude and other parameters. In general, it has been found that the auroras will exhibit characteristics indicative of one of three detonation altitude regimes; an uncontained* detonation above 300 km, a contained detonation between 300 and 65 km, and a contained detonation below 65 km, where 65 km represents the altitude above which energetic electrons can freely escape the earth's atmosphere.

As brought out in the discussion of this lecture, there are several facets of these artificial aurora measurements which are of special interest to those concerned with the study of related natural phenomena. The unusual brightness of the artificial auroras as compared to natural aurora permitted observation of the detailed temporal changes of the structure and general development of the aurora. This brightness-time history was shown to relate approximately to the t^{-102} decay law for the fission product source of the beta type aurora.

The very explicit color boundary change in the beta aurora at 84–87 km altitude was thought to be an important measurement in that this seemed to isolate the altitude at which the natural red type B aurora exhibits a similar color change, previously unmeasured to this accuracy. Moreover, the altitudes within which debris ions traveling at 3000 km/sec interact is evidenced by the Star Fish data, which show the ions slowing significantly as high as about 300 km and essentially stopped as low as 115 km altitude.

The discussion further made note of the fact that the measured accuracy of the Jensen-Cain geomagnetic field line model in the Central Pacific was within approx. 3% from tens of km to 400 km. This was of interest to those concerned with conjugate measurements of natural phenomena such as airglow, particularly for possible simultaneous conjugate measurements between Haleakala, Hawaii, and Rarotonga in the Southern Pacific.

*By atmospheric interaction.

References

BOQUIST, W. P., HALL, W. N., PASCOE, T. E., and DOHERTY, S. H., 1964, EG&G Report No. B-2819, DASA Report No. 1534, June.

BOQUIST, W. P., HALL, W. N., PASCOE, T. E., and DOHERTY, S. H., 1964, EG&G Report No. B-2833, DASA Report No. 1545, June.

CHESNUT, W., 1963, private communication.

DANIELS, G. and NEWMAN, P., 1965, *J. Geophys. Res.* **70,** 23, 5861.

JENSEN, D. and CAIN, J., 1962, unpublished, presented at April meeting of American Geophysical Union, Washington, D. C.

CLARIFICATION OF AIRGLOW PROCESSES
BY NUCLEAR EXCITATION*

Irving L. Kofsky

Technical Operations Research
Burlington, Massachusetts

Introduction

Widespread, persistent glows in the upper atmosphere are among the geophysical perturbations that were observed to follow nuclear detonations in the Pacific in 1958 (CULLINGTON, 1958; MALVILLE, 1959; STEIGER and MATSUSHITA, 1960) and 1962 (GREGORY, 1962; KEYS, 1964; ODENKRANTZ et al., 1962). These afterglows are excited by the various outputs of the exploding bomb, which we might consider as a nuclear analog of chemical explosions and releases in the atmosphere. Not unexpectedly, the emissions have been found to consist principally of the same lines and bands that are observed in the natural airglow and aurora. The sources of air-stimulating energy from the detonation include a very intense pulse of soft thermal (≈ 1 KeV) x rays emitted from the hot bomb surface (this radiation has been used for measuring air fluorescence efficiencies (WESTERVELT et al., 1959)); both prompt and delayed beta and gamma rays, and neutrons, associated with the nuclear reactions, which can induce auroral glows at great distances from the burst (including the region conjugate in the earth's magnetic field to the explosion); shocks strong enough to excite the high atmosphere to luminescence; fast-moving ions (which, like electrons, can become magnetically trapped) and atoms; and of course, visible, infrared, and ultraviolet light. We have pointed out how in particular these last radiations, with their high intensity and narrow pulse width, induce perturbations in the airglow/auroral layers that can provide useful information about the excitation mechanism of most of the principal natural airglows (KOFSKY, 1962a).

We have made a series of measurements on the afterglows that occurred in the lightly disturbed air outside the intensely irradiated, heated "fireballs" of the Pacific nuclear explosions. The observations were made from two jet aircraft operating at 37,500 ft altitude (11.4 km), a ground station near the bursts, and the 10,025-ft Haleakala mountaintop station about 1500 km away at

*Supported by the Defense Atomic Support Agency through the Air Force Cambridge Research Laboratories, OAR.

Maui, Hawaii. The principal instruments used were multichannel photoelectric photometers and radiometrically calibrated cameras, the photographs from which we reduced with our automatic-scanning isophotometer (MILLER *et al.*, 1964). Many different glow effects were observed, the characteristics of which vary systematically with detonation altitude because of changes in both the mix of the aforementioned radiations escaping the central fireball region and the pressure- and concentration-dependence of atmospheric chemilumines-cence and fluorescence.

In this article I discuss those of our measurements that bear on the interpre-tation of natural upper-atmospheric glow phenomena. The artificial glows I shall describe include a persistent, apparently chemiluminescent continuum following ionization of the D- and E-regions; air fluorescence excited by the

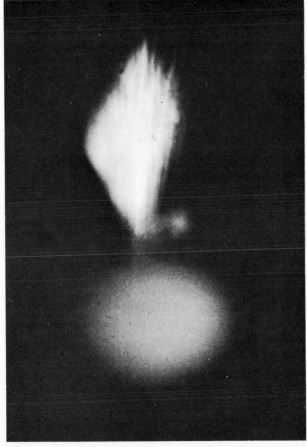

FIGURE 1. A yellow-green afterglow. The oval area is produced by the hard radiations from the detonation, and the two smaller patches by the magnetically confined beta rays. The (blue-white) streaked area above it is an unrelated phenomenon. (From a color photograph.)

fission-decay radiations; and the red and green forbidden lines of atomic oxygen, which are readily excited in both aerochemical reactions and collisions with free or shock-associated energetic particles.

The Glows

The Yellow-Green Afterglow

An extremely persistent, stationary afterglow appears in the altitude region between 50 and 110 km (and perhaps even higher) whenever sufficient ionization has been produced there. A photograph of such a glow, created by one of the high-altitude detonations, is shown in Figure 1. The photograph of this glow from another station (Figure 2) is accompanied by its isophotometric

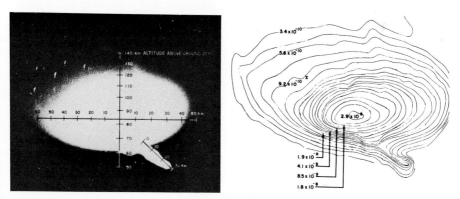

FIGURE 2. Photograph and isophot diagram of the afterglow, from a lower and more easterly viewing angle. (Surface brightness units are watts/cm² sr.)

plot, which shows the surface brightness quantitatively. The large (≈ 150 km across) oval region has been excited by thermal x rays and other hard quanta from the early phase of the nuclear burst; the smaller patches — which lie within the altitude range occupied by the oval, as shown by triangulation between Figures 1 and 2 (and other views) — can be seen on earlier photographs evolving from the local "artificial auroras" produced by the magnetically guided beta rays. Photographs show a similar stationary yellow-green cloud near the position of an intense auroral flash produced in the magnetic conjugate region by charged particles from this detonation; this southern glow was centered at an altitude variously reported as 65 and 85 km. The surface brightnesses of similar appearing glows made by other bursts have been above the threshold of practical photographic detectability, while in another case a glow with essentially the same spectrum was detected with photometers; indeed, this afterglow is a ubiquitous feature of high-altitude nuclear detonations.

The yellow-green oval is $\approx 30°$ above the horizon in Figure 2; its point of maximum surface brightness intersects the line of view at an altitude of about 70 km, and appears to rise slowly (a few meters per second) in photographs taken in the first 200 sec. The surface radiance of the emitting volume depends, of course, on the distribution of deposition of ionizing energy from the detonation and the angular depression of the observing station, as well as on the quantitative aerochemistry for each altitude at which energy is absorbed. Unfolds of the surface brightness of the glow (which is optically thin) show that its emission per unit volume decreases toward the edges and extends as low as 50 km (the upper boundary of ≈ 110 km is uncertain because of the viewing angle).

The irradiances from the afterglow of Figures 1 and 2 decrease roughly exponentially, with the same halflife of about 1500 sec at each wavelength. Those from the glow produced by another detonation, which had peak surface brightness a few kilometers lower (near 65 km), decrease with a halflife near 500 sec. A typical low-resolution spectrum compiled from the irradiances recorded by wide-angle ($\approx 55°$ circular field), narrow-wavelength band photometers is shown in Figure 3 (the data have been corrected for Rayleigh scattering by the

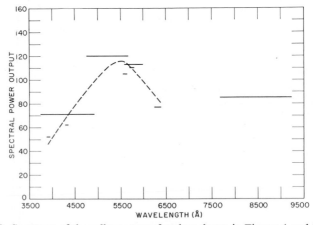

FIGURE 3. Spectrum of the yellow-green afterglow shown in Figures 1 and 2.

atmosphere). The emission in the visible gives evidence of being a continuum, although the data certainly do not permit the presence of bands to be ruled out. The spectrum of the glow does not change with time or altitude; the relative irradiances in each wavelength band stay about constant during the two-hour measurable lifetime, and no spatial color gradient is detectable on the photographs.

There appears to be a second maximum in the emission in the near-infrared, as evidenced by the radiances recorded by a 3°-field multiple-channel radiometer that was manually tracked on the visually brightest region of the glowing cloud. These infrared surface brightnesses can be compared directly with the visible brightnesses measured from the photographic negatives, and indirectly with the irradiances measured by the photometers (with the help of the iso-photometric plots). The energy emitted at wavelengths between 1.0 and 2.2μ (again considering the emission to be a continuum) is about four times as great as that emitted between 0.4 and 1μ (this ratio is somewhat uncertain because of the low ratio of signal to the high natural background of the sky in the infrared); the power emitted per unit wavelength in bands centered at 1.6, 1.8, and 2.2μ decreases in the ratio 1.0:0.6:0.1. In the visible, the spectrum appears to peak between 5500Å and 6000Å. For the afterglow shown in Figures 1 and 2, some emission is observed at wavelengths as low as 3950Å; for those produced by other detonations, the spectrum is often contaminated in the blue and violet by air fluorescence, making its shape at short wavelengths difficult to determine.

These afterglows show no hydrodynamic motions other than the aforementioned slow rise of the point of maximum surface brightness. (After $\frac{1}{2}$ hr, however, the glow of Figure 1 becomes broken up by high-altitude winds, taking on a herringbone structure reminiscent of noctilucent clouds.) They also show no tendency to align with the earth's magnetic field, and indeed have too low an electron density to be detected by even the lowest-frequency radars and riometers that were monitoring the postdetonation ionosphere. These observations lead to the conclusion that the glow must arise from reactions among neutral species at ambient atmospheric temperatures. The long persistence of the emission and its color-photographic and spectral similarity to the yellow-green afterglow so well known in laboratory discharges in low-pressure air, immediately suggest that the visible phenomenon results from the cyclic chemiluminescent reaction sequence usually represented as $NO + O \rightarrow NO_2^*$, $NO_2 + O \rightarrow NO + O_2$.

This identification is quantitatively supported by the observed energy balance and persistence of the afterglows; however, there are discrepancies among the spectra of the laboratory glow, the nuclear-induced glow, and other afterglows ascribed to the NO-O reaction. The surface brightness of the glow shown in Figures 1 and 2 has been computed (CARPENTER, 1965) from the deposition in the atmosphere of the pulse of thermal radiation from the nuclear explosion that produced it; the calculation assumes that the nitric oxide is generated in a reaction sequence involving ionization of N_2 to N_2^+ by the prompt hard radiations, followed (on a slower time scale) by dissociative recombination of electrons with N_2^+ (or NO^+) to form N atoms that then react with ambient O_2 (the sequence is $h\nu + N_2 \rightarrow N_2^+ + e$, $e + N_2^+ \rightarrow N + N$, $N + O_2 \rightarrow NO + O$). The calculation then sums the emission per unit volume along lines of sight, taking the laboratory (FONTIJN et al., 1964) rate constant for the chemiluminescent reaction ($\approx 3 \times 10^{-17}$ cm^3/sec for the emission of quanta actinic to panchromatic film). The computed surface radiances are quite consistent with those measured with the isophotometer on photographs taken in the first few hundred seconds; and similar calculations are in satisfactory accord with the measurements made at other detonations. Furthermore, the observed decrease of the irradiance from the glow can be explained on the assumption that O atoms are removed by the usual ozonospheric mechanism of third-body-stabilized reaction with O_2 molecules to form O_3 (followed by two-body reaction of O and O_3); this process eliminates atomic oxygen much more rapidly than does the chemiluminescent reaction sequence with oxides of nitrogen that actually causes the afterglow. At the 70-km mean altitude of the glow shown in Figure 1, the calculated halflife of O against reaction with O_2 is about 1000 sec, which is very near the measured lifetime of 1500 sec. This oxygen-consumption mechanism also explains the more rapid etching away of the bottom edge of the glowing volume, which results in the rise of its point of maximum surface radiance; the shorter halflife (≈ 500 sec) of the glow that was centered at a few kilometers lower altitude; and the failure to observe the yellow-green luminescence below ≈ 50 km, even though the air at these altitudes was strongly irradiated at other detonations.

The spectrum of this nuclear-induced afterglow is qualitatively similar to that from excited NO_2 formed in the laboratory reaction of NO with O, to that of the glow observed when nitric oxide is released at E-region altitudes, and to the continuum component of the natural glow of the night sky. Quantitatively, however, there are differences in the short-wavelength cutoff, the wavelength of maximum emission, and the halfpower wavelengths of the spectra of the four phenomena; these are compared in Table I. The short-wavelength cutoff of both kinds of artificially induced high-altitude glow (and occasionally of the nightglow) appears to lie below that of the laboratory glow, which is anomalous because the laboratory cutoff corresponds to the 71 kcal/mole heat of reaction of NO with O. The irradiances from the glow of Figure 3 measured by the photometer channels monitoring the 3880–3950Å band at all stations have about the same time dependence as those in the channels monitoring the other wavelengths; consequently, it is improbable that this excess of short-wave radiation is contamination from air fluorescence (which is discussed in the next section). The observation that the readings in the blue and violet photometer channels closely follow those in the other channels suggests that if these excess short-wavelength radiations result from some other reaction — for example, one populating the A state of O_2 to produce the forbidden Herzberg bands — then that reaction follows the main reaction producing the glow at longer wavelengths. The wavelengths of peak intensity of all the glows, except that from the chemical releases, are nearly the same; the spectra of the NO releases show a rather serious discrepancy, one spectrum (SPINDLER, 1966) having only a secondary maximum in the yellow. The wavelengths at which the intensity of the emitted light has dropped to one-half its peak value are generally not in good accord, but there is a reasonably good fit here between the nu-

Table I. Comparison of the Spectra of the Continuum Glows

Glow	Short-Wavelength Cutoff	Wavelength of Peak Intensity	Half Power Wavelengths	Infrared Emission
Nuclear (ionization) induced	<3950Å	5500–6000Å	≈4200– ≈6500Å	Several times stronger than visible; decreases beyond 1.6μ
Intense natural night sky* (including astronomical component and perhaps Herzberg bands)	≪4000Å	6200Å	4350–6750Å	
Normal natural night sky† (including astronomical component)	(∼4000Å**)	5700–5900Å	–6500Å	
Chemical release of NO; prompt and afterglow††	<3850Å	5000–5400Å	4600–6000Å	
Chemical release of NO; prompt glow***	≪4200Å	Subsidiary at 5800Å, then an increase to beyond 6400Å	5300– Å	
Laboratory NO + O††† (at ≈1 mm pressure; all others in this table at ≈10⁻⁴ mm)	3975Å	6000Å	4800–8300Å	Extends beyond 2μ, but intensity/μ much less than in the visible****

*SHEFOV, 1961.
†CHAMBERLAIN, 1961.
**KRASSOVSKIY et al., 1962.
††GOLOMB et al., 1965.
***SPINDLER, 1966.
†††FONTIJN et al., 1964.
****STAIR, 1965.

clear-induced afterglow and the broad, intense nightglow continua occasionally observed by SHEFOV (1961). The spectrum of the glow produced by nuclear explosions appears to lie at generally shorter wavelengths than that of the laboratory glow, which is obtained at considerably higher gas pressure; a possible source of the excess energy is vibrational excitation of the NO molecules (for $v = 1$ the short-wavelength cutoff drops to 3620Å). In addition, the afterglow made by the detonation contains an infrared component that is not observed in the laboratory (STAIR, 1965) or detected in the natural airglow.

Differences such as these in the chemiluminescence spectrum of the NO_2 molecule are usually ascribed to differences in the excitation mechanism (see, for example, SPINDLER, 1966). Banded radiation is occasionally observed, and the afterglow may be kinetically complex (BROIDA et al., 1961); furthermore, a second series of wavelengths, lying to the red of 5900Å, and consisting of a group of unresolved bands overlying an apparent continuum, can be excited by heating NO_2 or forming it in the reaction of NO with O_3. Consequently, the discrepancies in the emission spectra summarized in Table I cannot be considered as constituting strong evidence that the yellow-green afterglow is not coming principally, if not wholly, from NO_2 molecules excited in the reaction between NO and O. More positive evidence in favor of this process is provided by the aforementioned model for the energy deposition and the aerochemical reactions, the results of which are consistent with the observed surface brightness of the glowing cloud; and by the observed lifetime of the afterglow, which can be explained by the usual ozonospheric process of removal of the free oxygen atoms.

Let us now compare the radiation-generated glow with the natural nightglow continuum, which has also been ascribed to the NO-O reaction (with perhaps an auxiliary mechanism in the blue region of the spectrum). The peak and upper halfpower wavelengths of the nuclear glow match quite well those of the normal nightglow; on nights of particularly intense emission (when Herzberg bands, which are difficult to separate from the true continuum, are also strong), the spectra also match at the short-wavelength end. The infrared emission of the artificial glow could not be detected in the natural night sky against the much stronger infrared radiations (the continuum in the visible is only $\approx 3 \times 10^{-3}$ as intense as the hydroxyl system, for example). Most of the nuclear-induced emission comes from altitudes below 85 km (where most of the energy of the ionizing radiation is absorbed), with the emitting region extending down to 50 km and up to at least 110 km; the natural glow, which presumably is excited by less penetrating radiations, has been found to come principally from altitudes between 90 and 120 km (KOOMEN et al., 1963). Apparently the reactions following ionization favor the emission of the yellow-green radiation over a wide range of atmospheric densities. The spectrum of the artificially generated radiation appears to stay constant with time and altitude; the spectrum of the natural continuum has not been reported as changing during the night (no data exist on the variations of its color with altitude other than edge-on sightings of the glowing layer by astronauts (CARPENTER et al., 1962) who reported only an unspatially resolved "buff-white"). If the nightglow continuum is indeed caused by the same reactions as the artificial glow, its failure to fade as the night progresses is readily explained by the slower removal of O atoms at its higher altitude.

In conclusion, it appears that the yellow-green afterglow radiation from those high-altitude regions that have absorbed ionizing energy from nuclear bursts can be identified in the main with the familiar NO_2 continuum excited in the reaction of NO with O. Like the laboratory glow, the nuclear-induced glow has spectral (and lifetime) similarities to the natural continuum of the airglow, the spectra matching particularly well when the nightglow continuum is enhanced. The critical point of the observations at the nuclear explosions is, that this persistent afterglow appears whenever air at altitudes above about 50 km has been ionized; in persistence and intensity, it is the principal chemiluminescent relaxation process in the D- and E-regions.

Fluorescence of Air

The atomic fragments remaining after nuclear fission decay radioactively, emitting beta and gamma rays that excite fluorescence in the ambient air. An appreciable amount of energy is carried off in these delayed nuclear radiations, the power emitted at time t seconds after the detonation being $7 \times 10^{10} t^{-1.2}$ watts/kiloton of fission yield (about equally divided between the betas and gammas). If the location of the fission debris in the atmosphere is known, it is, in principle, possible to compute fluorescence efficiencies by calculating the amount of energy deposited in each volume of air (using the absorption characteristics of the two kinds of decay radiation) and then comparing the energy summed along the line of sight of the photometer with the measured surface radiance of the glow.

In practice, several factors introduce complications in this procedure when the burst is at high altitude. The location of the radioactive debris is not always well known; the ionization by the beta rays, which are more or less confined to the local magnetic field lines, is very nonuniform; and the range of the gamma rays is extremely long, their downward-going component being principally absorbed in a "pancake" centered near 30 km altitude. Consequently, we made our measurements on the fluorescence with wide-angle photometers that contain within their fields of view either substantially all the ionization, or (for gamma-ray sources above the pancake layer) a fraction of the energy deposition that can be estimated with reasonable accuracy. (The wavelength band passed by each photometer channel was kept constant over the broad field of view by a lens system that compressed the bundle of rays before they passed through the interference filter.)

We took late-time irradiance data on two fluorescent glows stimulated by sources that remained at low enough altitude to keep the fission debris atoms contained within a known volume. The glow shown in Figure 4 was centered at 32 km ($\rho/\rho_0 = 1.07 \times 10^{-2}$); at the other glow (not shown), the fluorescence spectrum of which was overlaid by the yellow-green continuum described in the last section, the debris was centered near 65 km. Calculations of the ion density showed that in neither case was the stimulation intense enough to produce so great a population of excited and ionized molecules that correction was needed for self-absorption or pumping (which often distort the air spectrum excited by the very intense "prompt" pulse of ionization). The fluorescence efficiencies are for a spectrum of beta rays with mean energy about 1-1/2 MeV (but also containing many low-energy beta particles), plus the Compton electrons from the gamma rays, which have average energy somewhat less than 1 MeV.

Several observations show that the persistent glow pictured in Figure 4 indeed results from stimulation of air by the fission product radiations, and not from some other process connected with the nuclear detonation. First, intense

FIGURE 4. Air fluorescence from the fission beta rays (bright ring) and gamma rays (blue circle) at 32 km altitude. The difference in exposure through the ends of the calibration wedge at the bottom is 3-½ stops. (From a color photograph.)

irradiances were measured in those narrow-band-pass photometer channels monitoring the (0, 0) and (0, 1) bands of the N_2^+ First Negative system (which have heads at 3914Å and 4278Å, respectively), while very low readings were recorded in those channels not sensitive to the blue and violet. Second, the irradiances decreased following the (time)$^{-1.2}$-law characteristic of the radioactive decay of the distribution of fission nuclei, as Figure 5 shows. Third, the measured decrease in surface brightness toward the edges of the large blue disk of Figure 4 is consistent with the expected distribution of energy deposition by the gamma rays, which at 32 km altitude have a mean absorption length of 30 km in the horizontal direction (with faster attenuation downward and slower upward, since the mean free path is greater than an atmospheric scale height); and the mean end-point range of the fission beta ray spectrum, $\sim$1 km, is less than the distance across the bright inner torus ring (which contains the decaying atoms). Fourth, the power emitted from the ring and the circle are very nearly equal, as we found by integrating the isophotometrically measured surface radiances with a planimeter (the ring/circle ratio was measured as 0.87 on a negative taken at 6 min after burst, and 0.88 at 8 min). These last two observations show that the outer blue spheroid is stimulated by the gamma

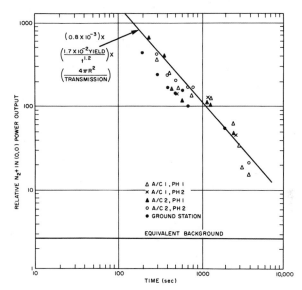

FIGURE 5. Time dependence of the fluorescent power from the source of Figure 4.

rays, and the brighter torus (which is overexposed in Figure 4 and is actually blue) principally by the beta rays.

Isophotometric plots from the photographs show that under favorable pointing conditions only a small correction — about 15% — is needed for the tail of the gamma-ray energy deposition that lies outside the fields of view of the photometers on the two aircraft and at the nearby ground station. Figure 5 gives the irradiances in the 3914Å band corrected back to the source for geometrical divergence of the beam and transmission by the atmosphere; the ordinate is proportional to the power emitted by the air in the N_2^+ 1N(0, 0) band. The calibration of the absolute sensitivity of the photometer channel to the (0, 0) band involved folding the rotational structure of the P and R branches (as observed in the natural aurora (CHAMBERLAIN, 1961)) into the transmission of the interference filter. The predetonation background reading from the sky, which was illuminated by a half moon, has been subtracted from the data. At the aircraft stations, the attenuation of the light signal by the atmosphere is due almost solely to Rayleigh out-scattering, and besides being readily calculable, it is quite small (about 15%). At the ground station, however, scattering by aerosols must be taken into account; we used a figure of 0.6 for the transmission of blue light along the slant path to the glow, which was measured by another experimental group using the irradiances of standard stars. (On the basis of previous data on scattering in maritime atmospheres this figure appears somewhat high; this is corroborated by the low readings in Figure 5 for the ground station.) The data taken from the aircraft stations show scatter because of errors in correction for the variations in range (the aircraft flew chords of a circle around the glow, with the navigational data used in computing the ranges) and small mispointings of the photometers (which were fixed to the airframe).

The straight line with slope -1.2 fitted by hand to the experimental points of Figure 5 gives 0.8×10^{-3} for the fluorescence efficiency of air near 32 km altitude in the N_2^+ First Negative (0, 0) band, under stimulation by the beta and gamma rays from the fission products. The energy of the beta rays is deposited within a fraction of a scale height of this altitude; the deposition of the half carried by the gamma rays, however, although peaked between 22 and 35 km, is spread over a wide range of altitudes. Considering the uncertainty in the definition of the density of the air to which this fluorescence efficiency applies, and all the errors in the measurement (as evidenced by the scatter of the data), we estimate the accuracy of the figure as $+60\%$, -40%.

Other observations on the air fluorescence, taken from similar photometer data, are:

1) $$\frac{\text{Fluorescence efficiency in the (0, 0) band of the } N_2^+ \text{ First Negative system}}{\text{Fluorescence efficiency in the (0, 1) band of } N_2^+ \text{ 1N}}$$
$$= 3.3 \pm 0.4$$

2) Relative fluorescence efficiencies (the wavelengths correspond to halfpower points of steep-sided pass bands)

$$N_2^+ \text{ 1N (0, 0)} + \text{(0, 1)} : 3800\text{–}4870\text{Å} : 4750\text{–}5675\text{Å} : 5570\text{–}6050\text{Å}$$
$$1 \qquad : \quad 2 \quad : \quad 0.2 \quad : \quad 0.025$$

3) No radiation was detected over the moonlit-sky background in 0.2μ-wide wavelength bands centered at 0.8, 1.6, 1.8, and 2.2μ.

4) A very faint signal was seen over the sky background at 5577Å, but none was detectable at 6300Å.

The ratio (1) of the two principal First Negative bands is consistent with the laboratory figure, $3.7 (\pm 0.5)/1$ (DAVIDSON and O'NEIL, 1964). About one-half the blue and violet fluorescence energy appears (2) in these two bands (most of the energy in the important Second Positive system lies to the ultraviolet of our photometer channels). Little radiation is observed beyond 4750Å; some of this emission is the forbidden oxygen green line, but the red line is certainly quenched at these extremely low altitudes (4); the (long-wavelength) First Positive system of N_2 is also weak at these high air pressures. The faint long-wavelength radiations have about the same time dependence as the N_2^+ bands, so they probably result from fluorescence; at altitudes near 32 km, little or none of the afterglow chemiluminescence discussed in the last section is observed.

Fluorescence yield data similar to those of Figure 5 for a source of radiation centered at an altitude of 65 km ($\rho/\rho_0 = 1.6 \times 10^{-4}$) are shown in Figure 6. In this case virtually none of the upward-going gamma rays and only

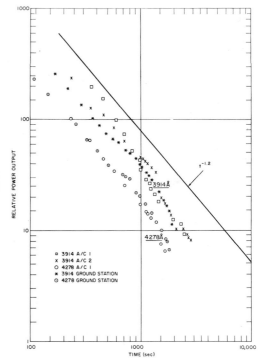

FIGURE 6. Time dependence of the fluorescent power from the source at 65 km altitude.

a fraction of the upward-directed betas are absorbed by the atmosphere; furthermore, the downward-going gammas excite air near 30 km, largely outside of the instrument fields of view. Only the downward-directed component of the beta rays contributes appreciably to the signal, exciting air over a range of altitudes extending down to about 42 km. Making corrections for the loss of effective source strength, we get for the fluorescence efficiency in the N_2^+ (0, 0) band $4(+3,-2) \times 10^{-3}$. The large error estimate figure arises in part from uncertainties in the actual range from the observing stations to the "centroid" of the irradiated air. Measurement of the (0, 0)/(0, 1) band ratio is made difficult by the overlay of yellow-green chemiluminescence; this continuum afterglow fades more rapidly than the fluorescence, however, and at late times (≈ 2500 sec) the ratio approaches a value near 3.0. The background of chemiluminescent radiation also makes it impossible for us to identify any fluorescence bands at wavelengths greater than 5000Å, or oxygen forbidden lines, in the data taken with the photometers.

The fluorescence efficiency figure of $4(+3, -2) \times 10^{-3}$ is in satisfactory agreement with the $\geqslant 5 \times 10^{-3}$ inferred from measurements near 80 km altitude (WESTERVELT et al., 1959) and the 3.3×10^{-3} measured at $10^{-2} - 10^{-1}$ mm Hg pressure in the laboratory (HARTMAN, 1965). At the high altitudes where most of the beta ray energy is absorbed, there is little collisional quenching of the $B^2\Sigma_u^+$ state of N_2^+, which has a lifetime of 6.6×10^{-8} sec. When air is stimulated at the pressures prevailing near 32 km, however, the measured fluorescence efficiency is reduced by a factor 5; taking for this altitude a particle density of $2.7 \times 10^{17}/cm^3$ and a mean molecular speed of 4×10^4 cm/sec, we compute a quenching cross section of $3/4 \times 10^{-14}$ cm²/air molecule. This figure is very near that recently measured by HIRSH et al. (1965) in air excited in a large tank by electrons from a Van de Graaff accelerator.

In summary, we find that the fluorescence efficiency of atmospheric air at two different pressures in the N_2^+ First Negative (0, 0) and (0, 1) bands is close to that measured under laboratory conditions. In the absence of collisional quenching, the efficiency in the 3914Å band under bombardment by 1 MeV radiation is 4×10^{-3}; at 32 km altitude, it is 0.8×10^{-3}, with roughly 1/4 of all the energy between 3800Å and 6000Å being emitted in this band. When air near 32 km is ionized, the chemiluminescent afterglow described in the last section is weak or absent.

The Oxygen Green Auroral Line

The intense "prompt" pulse of thermal x-rays and other hard radiations from the nuclear detonation also excites fluorescence in the surrounding air. Emission in the permitted lines and bands is very short-lived, with the shape of the irradiance curve being determined principally by the transit time of the radiations; the rate of arrival of energy in the (electric-dipole) forbidden lines, on the other hand, depends mainly on the natural lifetimes of the excited states. The familiar oxygen airglow-auroral line at 5577Å happens to have the right combination of moderately long lifetime and high excitation probability to produce a bright, smooth-surfaced green skyglow that persists for several seconds after a high-altitude burst. Color photographs of one such widespread green afterglow, which followed the 400-km "Starfish" detonation on the night of July 9, 1962, have even appeared in LIFE magazine (1962); the green skyglow surrounding another detonation in the upper atmosphere is shown in Figure 7.

The wide-angle photometers view the bright fireball as well as this green glowing sky; consequently, to find the time dependence of the emission of the 5577Å line from the sky we measured surface radiances in the green-sensitive layer of the radiometrically calibrated photographic films. The brightness of the sky just after three high-altitude detonations, taken from the image of a narrow cone passing the central fireball at about one diameter from its limb, is

FIGURE 7. Green glow of the sky, from the 5577Å line of oxygen. The (blue) streaks are a beta ray aurora, and the rough-edged area is the fireball. Vignetting by the camera lens reduces the intensity of the image near the edge of the frame. (From a color photograph.)

shown in Figure 8. The radiance decreases exponentially in the first few seconds following each of the three bursts; the measured lifetimes are 0.8, 0.75, and 0.7 sec ± 15% (the error arises from uncertainties in the film radiometry). These lifetimes are in good agreement with the theoretical figure of 0.74 sec for the natural lifetime of $^1S_0$ state of atomic oxygen; they are somewhat higher than the apparent lifetimes measured from auroral emissions by Omholt's method and its variations (PAULSON and SHEPHERD, 1965). The long lifetime suggests that little collisional quenching of the ^1S state takes place in that range of altitudes over which is absorbed the broad spectrum of hard radiations from the three nuclear explosions. We may interpret the experimental figure of 0.7 ± 0.1 sec as a lower limit for the natural lifetime of this state.

After about 5 sec, the radiance curves from the detonations labeled II and III begin to decrease as (time)$^{-1}$ (data from detonation I were complicated by the passage of the debris of the explosion across the imaged cone of sky). This

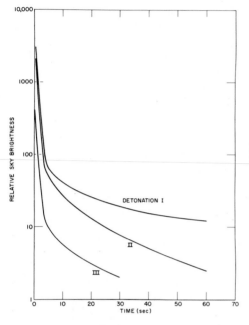

FIGURE 8. Time dependence of the surface radiance of the green skyglows.

second-order time dependence implies that the upper state of the green-line transition is being excited in a bimolecular reaction; the reaction is most probably dissociative recombination of oxygen molecular ions, $e + O_2^+ \rightarrow O(^1S) + O(^1D)$. This interpretation requires that the concentration of O_2^+ be controlled by the reaction with slow electrons in the time period 5–60 sec; specifically, the removal of O_2^+ by dissociative recombination must dominate its production by charge transfer to O_2 from O^+ and N_2^+ (which also are directly produced by the prompt ionizing pulse from the nuclear burst). The laboratory rate constants for these two interchange reactions are 2×10^{-12} cm^3/sec (FITE, 1962) and $\approx 2 \times 10^{-10}$ cm^3/sec (LANGSTROTH and HASTED, 1962), respectively. Since there are about 10^{12} O_2 molecules/cm^3 at the approximately 100 km altitude of the glow, the transfer of charge to O_2 molecules is indeed essentially complete before the t^{-1}-dependence becomes established.

This model for the excitation of the second phase of the green afterglow is only semiquantitative, as it neglects both the other ionospheric reactions (notably, $e + N_2^+$ and those that form NO^+) and the fact that the glow must be excited over a wide range of altitudes. Nevertheless the second-order time dependence of the measured sky radiances is certainly suggestive of the fast dissociative recombination reaction causing the excitation. At altitudes above ≈ 110 km, the continuum afterglow excited in the NO-O reaction is weak, and the principal chemiluminescent reactions in the first minutes after intense ionization are those that produce the forbidden green line of oxygen.

The Oxygen Red Nebular Lines

The $^1D_2$ state of atomic oxygen, besides being the lower state of the green-line transition, is also directly excited by the various outputs from high-altitude bursts. However, its long natural lifetime makes the irradiances in the red oxygen lines small compared with the others in the first minute or so; then at later times, the nebular doublet may become the strongest individual afterglow feature.

The Starfish detonation of 1200 kilotons at 400 km provided a classic example of excitation of the two low-lying states of O. The widespread green skyglow mentioned above gradually turned to red (the LIFE pictures showed the glows extending to beyond the zenith at Oahu, 800 miles from burst), with the irradiances from the two forbidden transitions being equal at about 15 sec. Photometer data taken at the Maui, Hawaii mountaintop station (1580 km from burst, with a 130 km horizon above ground zero) are most suitable for analysis of the skyglow since they were less contaminated by radiation from the hot fireball than the readings at the nearby aircraft and ground stations, and in addition the irradiances are biased toward emission from higher altitudes where collisional de-excitation is unimportant; they are shown in Figure 9 (the data are somewhat irregular because of variable clouds). During the

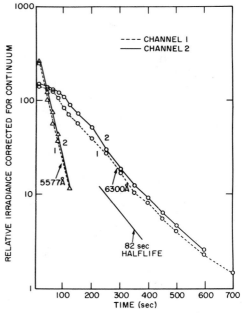

FIGURE 9. Irradiance in the green and red forbidden lines at the Maui mountaintop station, 1580 km from Starfish.

first 100 sec the irradiances in $\approx 70\text{Å}$-halfwidth wavelength bands are still dominated by emission from the fireball itself. (These irradiance data, which were taken with the wide-angle photometer, should not be confused with the photographically measured surface radiances discussed in the last section.) After 100 sec, the signal in the 6300Å-sensitive channel shows a near-exponential decay with about the expected 82 sec natural halflife of the ^1D state of oxygen; a patrol spectrogram (MARKHAM, 1962) showing intense emission at 6300Å and 6364Å corroborates that we are seeing the depopulation of this state in the large ($\approx 10^{10}\text{km}^3$) volume of red-glowing air.

At about 400 sec after burst the red irradiance curve begins to show upward curvature (this change in slope is seen in the data from all four stations, and is also evident in the radiances measured at various points on the photographs), indicating that some aerochemical reaction is persistently repopulating the ^1D state. The most probable mechanism for this excitation is the dissociative recombination reaction $e + NO^+ \rightarrow N + O(^1D)$, which is believed to be the source of the well known post-twilight glow in the red lines. The shape of this very-late-time red signal from the air excited by Starfish can be roughly fit to the irradiance curve of the natural post-twilight glow (CHAMBERLAIN, 1958); furthermore, the magnitudes of the two irradiances agree reasonably well if an "initial" (≈ 500 sec) electron density near $10^6/\text{cm}^3$ for the "artificial ionosphere" produced by Starfish is assumed. It is believed that the NO^+ ions are formed at F-layer altitudes in the ion-atom interchange reaction of O^+ with N_2; atomic oxygen ions for this reaction are of course directly produced by the prompt hard radiations from the nuclear explosion.

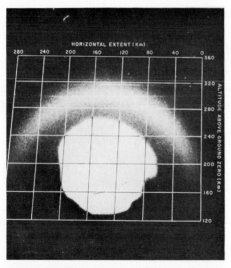
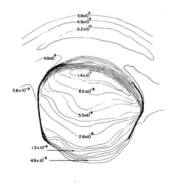

FIGURE 10. Photograph and isophot diagram of the red air shock. The large bright area underneath the shock is the glowing remains of the heated fireball air. (Surface brightness units are watts/cm² sr.)

Excitation by these hard radiations has not proved suitable for measuring the natural radiative lifetime of the ^1D state of atomic oxygen. We have, however, been able to make a measurement of this lifetime by observing the decrease of emission from O atoms following the passage of the upward-going luminous air shock that is generated by detonations in the $\approx 80–200$ km altitude range. One such red-line-emitting shock was seen at the 1958 "Teak" explosion (STEIGER and MATSUSHITA, 1960); a photograph of one from the 1962 series is given in Figure 10. The photographs show decreasing emission below 180 km altitude, undoubtedly because of collisional de-excitation. The mean upward shock speed of 4 km/sec shows that the kinetic temperature behind the shock front is near 1 eV; consequently the ^1D state of atomic oxygen, which lies only 1.96 eV above the ground state, is strongly populated. Unfolds of the surface brightness of the shocked air (starting from isophot diagrams such as in Figure 10) show that the emission per unit volume peaks just behind the front of the diverging shock, which supports this model of thermal excitation of ambient O atoms.

The irradiances recorded from the luminous shock at the Maui station by the two narrow-band photometer channels sensitive to the red doublet are shown in Figure 11. The data are corrected for the predetonation sky background, and for Rayleigh scattering and absorption by ozone (which after 125 sec remain nearly constant at only $\sim 30\%$). By 180 sec after burst, the surface radiance of the shock front has dropped below the threshold of the 25-sec exposure, f/2 photographs; furthermore, after 150 sec the only part of the

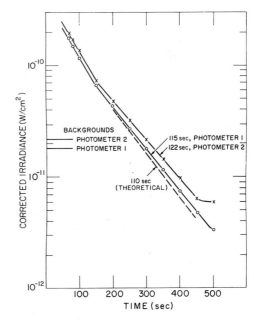

FIGURE 11. Time dependence of the irradiance from the air shock in the red oxygen doublet.

volume of glow remaining photographically detectable is at altitudes above 250 km, where collisional de-excitation is small. Consequently most of the red-line emission after, say, 200 sec should come from the natural radiative depopulation of the ^1D state of previously excited oxygen atoms. This argument is borne out by the irradiance data in Figure 11, which show an essentially exponential decay between 200 and 450 sec, with measured lifetimes of 115 and 122 sec. The readings of the two channels differ because of both a 15% difference in calibration and the fact that the irradiances lie very near the background from the night sky.

We interpret the exponential decrease of irradiance between 200 and 450 sec, following the passage of the weakening shock, as the natural radiative depopulation of the ^1D state of O atoms. The measured lifetime of 118 sec (with an estimated error of $+10$, -15 sec) is in satisfactory agreement with the theoretical figure of 110 sec; to our knowledge, this is the first direct measurement of this quantity. This lifetime also fits closely the long straight portion of the red-line irradiance from the airglow excited by the hard radiations from the Starfish burst (see Figure 9). In addition to these two relatively straightforward collisional mechanisms for populating the ^1D state of atomic oxygen, we observe also a slower, persistent excitation, which we assign to the dissociative recombination of electrons with NO^+ ions.

Cyclic Rebrightenings

I shall describe this last afterglow only briefly, as it is excited by magnetically-trapped heavy ions and therefore is less related to the natural airglows than the others I have discussed. Long-period cyclic skyglows have been observed after several high-altitude nuclear bursts; but good data exist for only one event, which had both high ion injection efficiency and local glows so dim that the weak oscillatory signals were not appreciably obscured.

The center of this diffuse, roughly circular glow feature was found by triangulation on the photographs to lie at an altitude of 300 ($+20, -40$) km; its edge appeared to move northward at about $\frac{1}{2}$ km/sec during the first rebrightening cycle. Emission from the glow was detected only by those photometer channels that were sensitive to the red and green forbidden lines of oxygen; no departure from a monotonically decreasing signal (coming from the local afterglows) was observed in the N_2^+ First Negative bands, in a wide-band blue-sensitive channel, or in the infrared-sensitive channels. The irradiances recorded in the 5577Å and 6300Å channels at three stations are shown in Figure 12; the data have been corrected for predetonation sky background, but not for atmospheric attenuation (which is sensibly the same at both wavelengths) or relative range of the glow from the stations. First evidence of enhancement over the decreasing signal from the local glow is at 410 ± 15 sec, with a second minimum of the green-line irradiance at 830 ± 10 sec (this minimum occurs about 90 sec later in the red lines, which lag the excitation because of the long natural lifetime of the ^1D state); there is also a hint of a third minimum near 1200 sec. Consequently the leading edge of the re-brightening pulse has a period of 410 sec. The times at which the irradiances increase correlate with those at which signals were observed on various radars and magnetometers, and with a rebrightening of the sky in the southern magnetic conjugate region.

The kinetic energy of ions that travel in 400–700 sec the 8000 km round trip to the southern conjugate region, spiraling along the geomagnetic field lines, is of the order of 50 eV, which is in the range expected for those ions that escape the early hot fireball cloud. Such an energy is also consistent with the observed interaction altitude, 300 km, where the atmospheric depth of $\approx 10^{16}$ atoms/cm^2 column is one mean free path for large-energy-loss collisions. Some small fraction of these ion-atom (or ion-molecule) collisions are inelastic and result in the eventual emission of the red and green forbidden lines of oxygen atoms.

To find the relative number of quanta emitted in the two oxygen transitions, we integrated the irradiances of Figure 12 between 400 and 1200 sec; the aver-

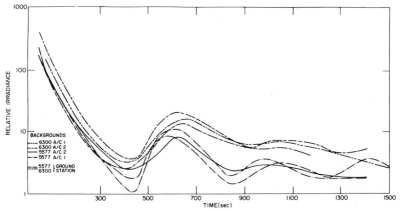

FIGURE 12. Time dependence of the irradiance from the cyclic glow in the oxygen forbidden lines.

age ratio of number of red to number of green photons received at the three stations is $2\frac{1}{2}$. Since the lower state of the green-line transition is the upper state of the red line (and collisional deactivation is negligible), the ratio of excitation (^1D-state/^1S-state) is $1\frac{1}{2}$, with an estimated accuracy of $\pm30\%$.

There are no experimental data or specific theories on the excitation of the forbidden lines in collisions of oxygen with slow ions (some of which may be O^+ or O_2^+); however, there exists an empirical theory due to ÖPIK (1958) for the over-all inelastic ion-atom cross section under these near-adiabatic conditions. The theory is based on observations of He^+ and K^+ in He and Ne, and is in accord with the measurements of light emission from meteor trails (meteors have speeds comparable to that of our oscillatory beam of ions); it predicts that the excitation cross sections vary as (projectile kinetic energy/target excitation energy)$^{1/2}$. The predicted ratio of excitation cross sections for the two states of atomic oxygen is therefore $(4.17 \text{ eV}/1.96 \text{ eV})^{1/2} = 1.47$, which is in very good agreement with our measurement of the excitation ratio in the cyclic glow.

In summary, we find that the forbidden lines of OI are excited as magnetically-mirrored ions with energies near 50 eV strike the atmosphere near 300 km altitude. The measured ratio of probability of excitation to the two low-lying states is $1\frac{1}{2}$; this ratio is in accord with Öpik's empirical theory of inelastic collisions between ions and atoms.

Summary and Conclusions

I have described here those of the afterglows induced by atmospheric nuclear detonations that are analogous or otherwise closely related to the natural airglow and aurora. The major source of these long-lived glows is the chemiluminescent reactions that occur during the slow return toward species equilibrium following the original ionization of the air; the reactions result in a persistent yellow-green infrared glow that we have identified with the continuum from excited NO_2 molecules, and in emission of both the red and green forbidden lines of O atoms. Other sources of excitation of skyglows are the nuclear radiations from the radioactively-decaying fission products, air shocks, and ions that have become trapped in the earth's magnetic field. We have made use of this artificial stimulation of the upper atmosphere to measure the lifetimes of the ^1S and ^1D states of atomic oxygen, and some fluorescence efficiencies (and a collisional quenching cross section) of air.

Nuclear excitation, as I pointed out in earlier publications (KOFSKY, 1962a and b), can also be used to investigate natural aerochemical phenomena other than those discussed here: — the kinetics of hydroxyl emission and ozone formation (the prompt ultraviolet quanta dissociate the O_3 at high altitudes, quenching the OH glow); red/green line excitation ratios and the altitude dependence of quenching; the altitude variation of relative excitation of OI and N_2; the mechanism of excitation of the NaD lines in the airglow; resonant scattering; and oxygen recombination processes. In the event of future atmospheric nuclear explosions, it would be advantageous to observe the perturbed sky with those instruments normally used to study the airglow and aurora, and we suggest that some procedure be instituted for encouraging interested scientists to make measurements on the various nuclear-induced afterglows.

Acknowledgments I wish to record my indebtedness to Mr. Carlton S. Miller, who contributed immeasurably to the design and implementation of the experiments on which this article is based. The valued collaboration of Mr. R. H. Johnson, Dr. G. G. Mannella, and others of the Tech/Ops staff is also gratefully acknowledged. Thanks are due to Messrs. T. P. Markham, R. O'B. Carpenter, and A. T. Stair for permission to use unpublished data. It is a pleasure also to thank Messrs. H. P. Gauvin (Director), J. Grenier, J. P. Cahill, and their associates of the Radiation Effects Branch of AFCRL, and Mr. J. Snyder of DASA, for initiating and supporting this work.

References

BROIDA, H. P., SCHIFF, H. I., and SUGDEN, T. M., 1961, *Trans. Faraday Soc.* **57**, 259.
CARPENTER, M. S., O'KEEFE, J. A., and DUNKELMAN, L., 1962, *Science* **138**, 978.
CARPENTER, R. O'B., 1965, private communication.
CHAMBERLAIN, J. W., 1958, *Astrophys. J.* **127**, 54.
CHAMBERLAIN, J. W., 1961, *Physics of the Aurora and Airglow*, Academic Press, New York, (data from N. N. Shefov) p. 360.
CULLINGTON, A. L., 1958, *Nature* **182**, 1365.
DAVIDSON, G. and O'NEIL, R., 1964, "The Fluorescence of Air and Nitrogen Excited by 50 keV Electrons," AFCRL Report 64-466.
FITE, W. L., RUTHERFORD, J. A., SNOW, W. R., and VAN LINT, V. A., 1962, *Discussions Faraday Soc.* **33**, 264.
FONTIJN, A., MEYER, C. B., and SCHIFF, H. I., 1964, *J. Chem. Phys.* **40**, 64.
GOLOMB, D., ROSENBERG, N. W., AHARONIAN, C., HILL, J. A. F., and ALDEN, H. L., 1965, *J. Geophys. Res.* **70**, 1155.
GREGORY, J. B., 1962, *Nature* **196**, 508.
HARTMAN, PAUL L., March 30, 1965, Los Alamos Scientific Laboratory, Report LA-3147-MS.
HIRSH, M. N., EISNER, P. N., and SLEVIN, J. A., 1965, Report R-190-2, G. C. Dewey Corp., New York.
KEYS, J. G., 1964, *J. Atmospheric Terrest. Phys.* **26**, 979.
KOFSKY, I. L., 1962a, *J. Atmospheric Terrest. Phys.* **24**, 797.
KOFSKY, I. L., 1962b, *J. Geophys. Res.* **67**, 739.
KOOMEN, M. J., GULLEDGE, I. S., PACKER, D. M., and TOUSEY, R., 1963, *Science* **140**, 1087.
KRASSOVSKIY, V. I., SHEFOV, N. N., and YARIN, V. I., 1962, *Planetary Space Sci.* **9**, 883.
LANGSTROTH, G. F. O. and HASTED, J. B., 1962, *Discussions Faraday Soc.* **33**, 298.
Life, July 20, 1962, **53**, No. 3, 26-35.
MALVILLE, J. M., 1959, *J. Geophys. Res.* **64**, 2267.
MARKHAM, T. P., 1962, private communication.
MILLER, C. S., PARSONS, F. G., and KOFSKY, I. L., 1964, *Nature* **202**, 1196.
ODENKRANTZ, F. K., ST. AMAND, P., and MOORE, J. G., 1962, *J. Geophys. Res.* **67**, 4091.
ÖPIK, E. J., 1958, *Physics of Meteor Flight in the Atmosphere*, Interscience, New York, Chapter 7.
PAULSON, K. V. and SHEPHERD, G. G., 1965, *J. Atmospheric Terrest. Phys.* **27**, 831.
SHEFOV, N. N., 1961, *Fourth Section of IGY Program*, Report (*Sbornik*), USSR Academy of Sciences, Moscow, **5**, 29.
SPINDLER, G. B., 1966, *Planetary Space Sci.* **14**, 53.
STAIR, A. T., 1965, private communication.
STEIGER, W. R. and MATSUSHITA, S., 1960, *J. Geophys. Res.* **65**, 545.
WESTERVELT, D. R., BENNETT, E. W., and SKUMANICH, A., 1959, *Proceedings of the Fourth International Conference on Ionization Phenomena in Gases*, Uppsala, **1**, North-Holland, Amsterdam, p. 225.

RESEARCH ON OPTICAL INFRARED CHARACTERISTICS OF AURORA AND AIRGLOW (ARTIFICIAL AND NATURAL)

A. T. Stair, Jr. and H. P. Gauvin

Optical Physics Laboratory
Air Force Cambridge Research Laboratories
L. G. Hanscom Field, Bedford, Massachusetts

I. Introduction

For some years the AFCRL has maintained a research program through partial assistance from the Defense Atomic Support Agency designed to measure and understand the long time afterglows produced by high altitude nuclear detonations. Some of the phenomena are closely related to the naturally occurring airglow and aurora; consequently, pursuit of either aids in the understanding of both. The paper in this volume by Dr. Kofsky on the field observations and interpretations is part of the overall program. This paper will cover some of the most recent work and will be divided into three sections: 1) electron excitation of nitrogen and air, 2) the $NO + O \rightarrow NO_2^*$ and $OH\ddagger$ airglows, and 3) late time spectra of a high altitude nuclear burst in which the infrared spectrum of NO^+ is observed for the first time. Other investigators besides the authors have contributed to the work reviewed here and will be identified with the various areas discussed.

II. Excitation of Nitrogen and Air by Energetic Electrons

A knowledge of absolute cross sections and fluorescent efficiencies is basic to understanding excitation phenomena in gases. The excitation of nitrogen molecules and ions is particularly applicable to the natural phenomena of auroral and ionospheric processes. In the present paper absolute cross sections are presented for the (0-0) band of the N_2^+ First Negative system ($B^2\Sigma_u^+ \rightarrow X^2\Sigma_g^+$) and the (0-0), (1-0), and (2-0) bands of the N_2^+ Meinel system ($A^2\pi_u \rightarrow X^2\Sigma_g^+$) for production by electrons with energies from 3–60 keV. The cross sections are absolute effective values for production of the radiation observed, independent of the excitation path, but due to single collisions of the energetic electron with the neutral ground state molecule of nitrogen. The fluorescent efficiency of the (0-0) band of the N_2^+ First Negative is presented for various combinations of incident electron energy and gas pressure from 10–60 keV and 22–800 Torr. In addition, the rotational temperature dependence of the 3914Å band on electron energy is discussed. Finally, rocket-borne measurements of auroral light at 3914Å (N_2^+), 5577Å (OI), and 6300Å (OI) are presented.

A. Thin Target Cross Section Measurements

Absolute cross sections for the production of the N_2^+ First Negative (0-0) band at 3914Å by electron impact have been measured in various energy regions from threshold to 20 keV by STEWART (1956), by SHERIDAN et al. (1961), by HAYAKAWA and NISHIMURA (1964), and by McCONKEY and LATIMER (1965). The results of all but the last set of measurements agree within 20% in overlap regions. The cross sections of McConkey and Latimer are 2.5 times that of the other observers. To date, the absolute cross sections for electron production of the Meinel bands of N_2^+ have not been reported. Relative excitation functions for the Meinel bands excited by electrons with energy less than 140 eV have been given by STEWART (1955).

The system used to measure absolute cross sections is a modification of a system previously used to measure thick target fluorescent efficiencies for electrons stopping in gases. An electron gun provides electrons with energy variable from 3–60 keV. The electrons pass through a series of differentially

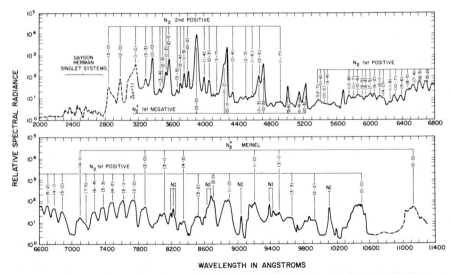

WAVELENGTH IN ANGSTROMS

FIGURE 1. Relative spectral radiance of nitrogen at 5×10^{-2} Torr excited by 50 keV electrons. The effective spectral slit width was 18Å and the total scanning time approximately 90 min. The dashed regions indicate the relative intensity is less certain.

pumped nozzles into a target chamber. The electron gun and system of differentially pumped chambers are described in detail in an earlier report (DAVIDSON and O'NEIL, 1964). The target gas pressure is variable from 10^{-4}–$8 \times 10^{+2}$ Torr.

A spectrogram of the emission from N_2 as recorded by the monochromator with an effective spectral slit width of 18Å is presented in Figure 1. The pressure was 5×10^{-2} Torr (equivalent to an altitude of 68 km). The data presented are the emission spectrum from the first few centimeters of the range of the 50 keV electron (a small fraction of the total range). The 2,000–11,000Å wavelength interval was recorded with a series of photomultipliers and gratings and normalized to a single relative radiance by a comparison of the overlapping wavelength regions. The spectrogram of Figure 1 is corrected for the relative response of the monochromator system, which is less certain in the dashed regions of the spectrogram. The integrated intensities of the spectral components in Figure 1 are not simply related to absolute cross sections, since at 5×10^{-2} Torr many of the components have contributions from other than primary interactions.

The absolute cross sections for the (0-0) band of the N_2^+ First Negative system and the (0-0), (1-0), and (2-0) bands of the N_2^+ Meinel system are

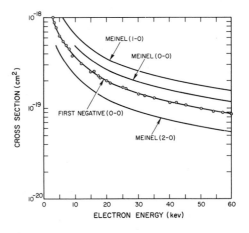

FIGURE 2. Absolute cross sections for production of N_2^+ bands by electrons.

presented in Figure 2 for excitation by energetic electrons. The estimated probable errors for the absolute cross sections are $\pm 12\%$ for the 3914Å band, $\pm 15\%$ for the (2-0) and (1-0) Meinel bands, and $\pm 20\%$ for the (0-0) Meinel bands. There is no measurable difference in the energy dependence of the Meinel bands and the 3914Å band. The ratios of the (2-0), (1-0), and (0-0) Meinel band cross sections to the 3914Å band can be found more accurately than the absolute values of the cross sections. The ratios are 0.60 ± 0.06, 1.40 ± 0.14, and 1.20 ± 0.18, respectively.

SCHRAM et al. (1965) has analyzed a measured cross section for the ionization nitrogen by electrons of from 0.6–20 keV energy in terms of the Born approximation. The resulting expression has the form

$$\sigma_{N_2^+} = \frac{A}{E'} \log_e CE'$$

where $\sigma_{N_2^+}$ is the cross section in cm² per molecule, $E' = \frac{1}{2} m_0 v^2$ (m_0 = rest mass of the electron) and A and C are constants. Schram found the Born approximation to be an accurate description of the nonrelativistic energy dependence. The constants A and C are $(1.84 \pm 0.01) \times 10^{-14}$ eV cm² and 0.078 ± 0.001 eV⁻¹, respectively.

For analysis of the excitation cross section for the 3914Å band by electrons of from 3–60 keV energy, where relativistic effects become significant, the expression

$$\sigma_{3914\text{Å}} = \frac{A}{E'} [\log_e CE' - \log_e(1 - \beta^2) - \beta^2]$$

is used where β is the ratio of the electron velocity to the velocity of light. Figure 3 shows ($\sigma_{3914} E'$) plotted as a function of the quantity [$\log_e E' - \log_e$

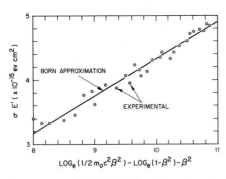

FIGURE 3. Comparison of the measured energy dependence of the (0-0) First Negative band with the Born approximation.

$(1 - \beta^2) - \beta^2]$. The linear relationship indicates that the use of the Born approximation gives an accurate description of the energy dependence of the 3914Å band cross section in this energy range. A least squares analysis of the data presented in Figure 3 was performed to determine the best linear fit. The analysis yields values of A and C of $(5.80 \pm 0.15) \times 10^{-16}$ eV cm² and $\left(0.08^{+0.04}_{-0.02}\right)$ eV⁻¹, respectively. An additional estimated error of $\pm 12\%$ exists in the value of A due to the error in the absolute cross section measurements. Schram's value of A is 32 times the value presented for the 3914Å band, while the values of C agree within experimental error.

The measurements of 3914Å band cross sections and total ionization cross sections of N_2^+ indicate that a constant ratio exists between the two values for excitation by electrons with energy in excess of approximately 100 eV. All experimental evidence confirms that this ratio is a constant. Much additional evidence indicates that energetic electrons incident on nitrogen lose an average

35 eV per ion pair produced (VALENTINE and CURRAN, 1958). The average energy lost is independent of electron energy for electrons with energy in excess of approximately 100 eV. Based on the ratio of 32 ion pairs per 3914Å photon and 35 eV lost per ion pair produced, a fluorescent efficiency of 2.8×10^{-3} is indicated via excitation of the 3914Å band by electrons. The fluorescent efficiency is independent of electron energy for electrons with energy in excess of 100 eV. This value for the efficiency applies at pressures where collisional deactivation is an insignificant depopulating process.

B. Thick Target Fluorescent Efficiency Measurements

The fluorescent efficiency of the 3914Å band has been measured for many combinations of incident electron energy and nitrogen gas pressure from 10–60 keV and 22–800 Torr. In this pressure range the 3914Å fluorescence is diminished by collisional deactivation. Figure 4 presents the reciprocal fluorescent

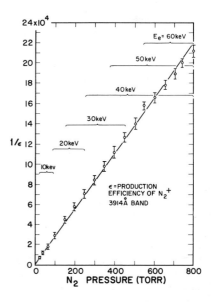

FIGURE 4. Reciprocal fluorescent efficiency for the production of 3914Å emission by electrons. For a series of incident electron energies the nitrogen pressure was varied to change the electron range from approximately 3–10 cm. The pressures used for each electron energy are indicated.

efficiency as a function of pressure. The data points presented summarize and indicate the range of many more experimental points. For a given electron energy, the fluorescent efficiency was measured with the target gas pressure varied to change the electron range from approximately 3–10 cm. The linear relationship of Figure 4 suggests both that the fluorescent efficiency is independent of electron energy and that the Stern-Volmer mechanism describes the quenching process of the 3914Å emission. Figure 4 may be analyzed in terms of the Stern-Volmer expression of the form

$$\frac{1}{\epsilon} = \frac{1}{\epsilon_0}(1 + 2.2 \cdot 10^{21}\sigma\tau p)$$

where ϵ is the fluorescent efficiency at any pressure, ϵ_0 the fluorescent efficiency at low pressure where quenching is an insignificant depopulating process, σ the deactivation cross section of the neutral nitrogen molecules in cm², τ the lifetime (BENNETT and DALBY, 1959) of the 3914Å band (6.5 $\times$ 10⁻⁸ sec) and p the pressure in Torr. Assuming ϵ_0 is 2.8 $\times$ 10⁻³, as indicated from cross section measurements, Figure 4 yields a value of σ of 5.4 $\times$ 10⁻¹⁵ cm² for N₂. For air, the value of σ_a is approximately 6.5 $\times$ 10⁻¹⁵ cm², which compares favorably with a value of 7.5 $\times$ 10⁻¹⁵ cm² recently reported by HIRSH et al. (1965).

Figures 5 and 6 present the emission from air and nitrogen at 22 Torr

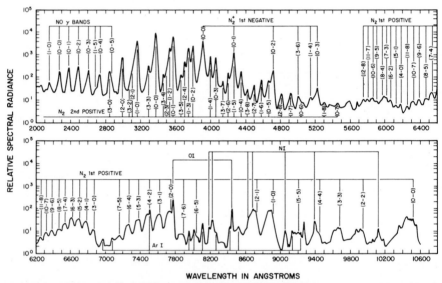

FIGURE 5. Relative spectral radiance of air at 22 Torr excited by 10 keV electrons. The effective spectral slit width was 18Å and the total scanning time approximately 90 min. Below 3200Å the relative intensity is less certain.

(equivalent to an altitude of 24 km) excited by 10 keV electrons. The spectra have been corrected for the monochromator response function and the integrated intensity of each spectral feature is proportional to its fluorescent efficiency. The fluorescent efficiency for production of 3914Å radiation by 10 keV electrons in nitrogen and air is 1.6 $\times$ 10⁻⁴ for nitrogen and 8.3 $\times$ 10⁻⁵ for air. The total fluorescent efficiency over the wavelength interval 3200–10,800Å is 2.2 $\times$ 10⁻³ for N₂ and 6.0 $\times$ 10⁻⁴ for air.

As is well known, the thermal x-radiation from the detonation of an un-shielded nuclear weapon accounts for a considerable part of the total yield. At high altitudes these x rays can escape to large distances and produce fluorescent radiation spectra akin to those presented in Figures 1 and 5. For detonations which occur near 24 km, the spectrum presented in Figure 5

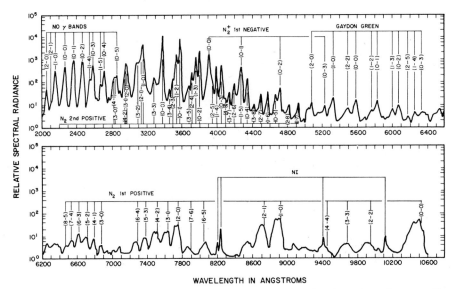

FIGURE 6. Relative spectral radiance of nitrogen at 22 Torr excited by 10 keV electrons. The effective spectral slit width was 18Å and the total scanning time approximately 90 min. Below 3200Å the relative intensity is less certain.

will be produced due to excitation by gamma rays and β rays from the radioactive decay of the fission debris component of the weapon.

C. Rotational Temperature Dependence of the 3914Å Band on Electron Energy

The effective rotational temperature of N_2^+ has been determined as a function of electron energy for energies from 19–300 eV by CULP and STAIR (1966). Temperatures were obtained by analysis of relative line intensities in the R branch of the resolved 3914Å band spectrum. Pure N_2 gas in a collimated beam was crossed with a nearly monoenergetic electron beam; excitation was by single electron impact. All data were corrected for fluctuations in electron beam current and gas pressure by monitoring the 3914Å band intensity. In addition, observed temperatures were found to be independent of beam current. Figure 7 shows the dependence of rotational temperature on electron energy.

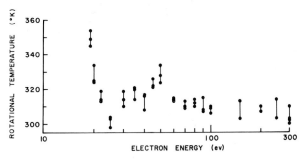

FIGURE 7. Rotational temperature of N_2^+ (3914Å) as a function of electron energy. Each datum point (connected by vertical lines) represents a measured rotational temperature determined from an independently obtained spectrum at the same electron energy.

Observed rotational energies of N_2^+ closely approximated a Boltzmann distribution. The results are significant for the excitation process and in the study of electron induced auroras. Rotational temperatures obtained from the auroral radiation have been generally assumed to be valid measures of the gas temperature and, consequently, the altitude of the aurora. This assumption is valid only if there is negligible rotational excitation of the molecule by the bombarding particle during the ionization-excitation collision which creates the excited N_2^+ ion.

Results from the crossed beam experiment tend to substantiate measurements of the N_2^+ rotational temperature made recently by DAVIDSON and O'NEIL (1965). They bombarded room temperature air with 50 keV electrons and found an appreciable increase in rotational temperature as the target pressure was increased, independent of beam current. Their results are shown in Figure 8. The effect of low energy secondary electrons at the higher pressures is

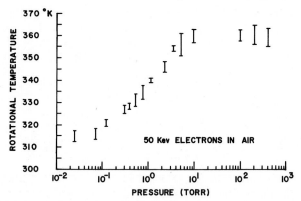

FIGURE 8. Rotational temperature of N_2^+ (3914Å) as a function of pressure for 50 keV electrons in air.

suggested as a contributor to the rotational temperature increase. However, collisional quenching affects the N_2^+ rotational energy distribution at these higher pressures and it is difficult to assess the contributions of each effect.

D. Rocket-Borne Measurements of Auroral Light

Auroral light measurements at several wavelengths were made aboard two Aerobee rockets flown into auroral forms from Churchill, Canada, during March, 1965 (K. BAKER, 1966). These flights probed auroral regions of low to medium intensity (IBC I - IBC II) during the breakup phase. The photometers used were Utah State University Model WT-1 with EMR 541A multiplier phototubes preceded by a narrow bandpass Schott interference filter with a bandwidth of about 40Å. These instruments viewed the same volume of emission centered in a direction normal to the longitudinal axis of the rocket with a field of view of 9°. On rocket AE 3.613, the two brightest emissions in the visible range, the bandhead of the (0, 0) transition of N_2^+ at 3914Å and the atomic oxygen green line at 5577Å, were measured. These two emissions and the 6300Å line of atomic oxygen were measured on rocket AD 3.612.

The flight results showed large variations as the photometers scanned spatially due to the rocket roll. Figures 9 and 10 show the radiance data

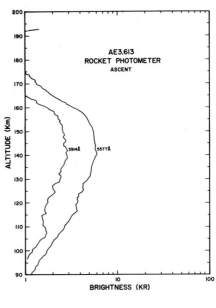

FIGURE 9. "*In situ*" measurements of auroral light at 3914 and 5577Å for Aerobee AE 3.613 (ascent) launched 0131:46 CST, March 6, 1965 from Churchill, Canada.

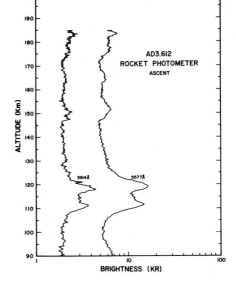

FIGURE 10. "*In situ*" measurements of auroral light at 3914 and 5577Å for Aerobee AD 3.612 (ascent) launched 0142:17 CST, March 13, 1965 from Churchill, Canada.

from these two flights for the upward portion of the rocket trajectories. The brightness values shown are for the direction of minimum intensity. It was thought that these values would be most representative of the emission of the region surrounding the rocket. The half-intensity thickness of the auroral emitting region probed on rocket AE 3.613 was about 40 km in altitude; while on AD 3.612, it was only about 15 km. The two peaks apparent from the latter measurement are well correlated with a double-peaked structure of electron density measured by other instruments on board the rocket.

The relative intensity of the N_2^+ (3914Å) and $[OI]_{32}$ (5577Å) emissions measured from the ground typically give a ratio $R(5577)/R(3914)$ of from 1 to 2 for auroras (CHAMBERLAIN, 1961; REES, 1959). The value of this ratio and its altitude dependence are important in understanding the auroral excitation processes and the relationships between aurora and airglow. Theoretically, the ratio of $R(5577)/R(3914)$ in aurora might be expected to be quite large, as it is in the night airglow. O'BRIEN et al. (1965) recently measured "in situ" this ratio for the night airglow at a value of about 80. Also, since this ratio must depend on the relative abundance of N_2^+ and O, as well as collisional deactivation of the O, it might be expected to show a large altitude dependence.

The rocket measurements reported here provide good altitude resolution and avoid the corrections for atmospheric extinction, etc., that are necessary

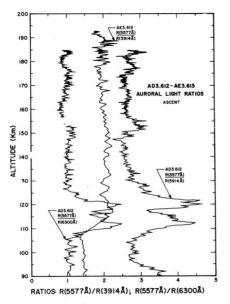

FIGURE 11. Ratios of the auroral brightness at 5577, 3914, and 6300Å from data measured with rockets AD 3.612 and AE 3.613.

in the ground-based measurements. The results from the ascent portion of the two rocket flights are shown in Figure 11. The data from AE 3.613 show a ratio between 1 and 2 throughout the flight which penetrated a rather dim, diffuse auroral region. These data again are plotted for the minimum 5577Å light seen per rocket roll. As the rocket rolled, the ratio remained between 1 and 2 but did show much more variation than the data shown. These variations might be due to a time delay between the rapid emission of the N_2^+ and the relatively long lifetime of the parent state of $[OI]_{32}$ or to a different volume of emission for 3914Å and 5577Å as has been reported by ROMICK and BELON (1964).

The "in situ" measurements of auroral light showed the ratios of 5577Å to 3914Å and 6300Å to be relatively altitude independent from 90–180 km. The value of $R(5577)/R(3914)$ was found to be near 2 for these flights which probed dim to medium intensity auroras. The ratio of 5577Å to 6300Å emission was found to be near unity except in the brightest portions of the aurora where it increased to a factor of 3.

III. The NO + O → NO₂* and OH‡ Airglows

A. The NO + O → NO*₂ Airglow

1. Infrared Laboratory Studies of the NO + O Reaction. The longest lived visible phenomenon of some high altitude nuclear detonations is a large volume yellow-green glow which lasts for hours. The color is very close to that of the air afterglow, so familiar in the laboratory and produced by the nitric oxide-oxygen atom reaction which creates nitrogen dioxide in an excited electronic state. The yellow-green visible chemiluminescence is the result of a radiative transition from that state. In addition, one of the spectral features of the natural airglow in the upper atmosphere is a continuum with a spectral distribution very similar to the "air afterglow," and attempts are being made to relate that emission to the NO-O reaction. Also, rocket releases of nitric

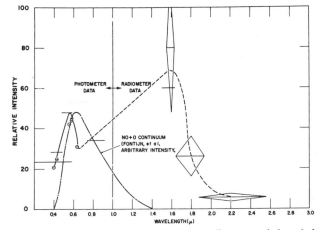

FIGURE 12. Spectra of the nuclear induced yellow-green infrared glow.

oxide are being actively pursued as a technique for measuring the atmospheric distribution of atomic oxygen. In this paper we will compare the visible and infrared spectra obtained on a late time nuclear glow with recent laboratory data extending to 7μ (STAIR and KENNEALY, 1966) and present a recent rocket measurement of the altitude profile of the normal airglow continuum (D. BAKER, 1966).

Figure 12 presents spectral radiometric data of the yellow-green glow resulting from a high altitude nuclear detonation obtained many minutes after burst. The visible photometer data were obtained by Kofsky (GAUVIN, 1963), and the infrared data were obtained by R. L. Morgan of AFCRL (GAUVIN, 1963). Also plotted in Figure 12 are the laboratory data of the NO + O reaction at 1 Torr as given by FONTIJN et al. (1964). The data appear to peak at shorter wavelengths than the laboratory spectra, a result also obtained on rocket-borne releases of NO (SPINDLER, 1966). From the amount of energy radiating beyond 1μ, one would be justified in calling this phenomenon the "infrared glow."

Using an f/9 Ebert monochromator with 2-inch square gratings and a cooled lead sulphide detector, FONTIJN et al. (1964) were unable to get data beyond 1.25μ due to low signal-to-noise. To extend the spectral measurements into the infrared it was necessary to maximize the signal-to-noise. This was accomplished by the use of an infrared integrating sphere as the reaction vessel and by the use of an interferometer spectrometer for the spectral observations. The experimental arrangement is shown in Figure 13. The integrating sphere reaction cell is a 1 liter Pyrex flask, the surface of which has been dimpled from the exterior with a hot carbon rod to provide a macroscopically diffuse surface (MORRIS, 1966). A film of gold about 2000Å thick is evaporated onto the

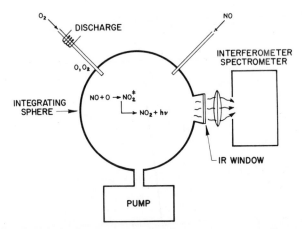

FIGURE 13. Schematic of the steady-state chemiluminescent setup. The discharge was created by a 100 watt 2450 MH$_z$ generator.

interior surface. The sphere is attached to a section of 4 inch glass pipe which is connected through a large cold trap to a 100 cfm double-stage mechanical vacuum pump. The high pumping speed and correspondingly low residence time help minimize wall recombination problems and assist the observation of any nonequilibrium vibrational-rotational distributions.

The signal-to-noise advantages of Fourier Spectroscopy over monochromators in the infrared are now well known. A recent review article by LOEWEN-STEIN (1966) discusses the field very well. For the NO + O system, which exhibits an apparent continuum emission, the multiplex gain (FELLGETT, 1951) is particularly advantageous. A Michelson interferometer with 2 cm diameter end mirrors was used. An interferogram produced by the 5461Å line of mercury was used to monitor the mirror position and command the digitizing system.

Figure 14 shows one of the measurements of the spectral distribution of the NO-O continuum from 1.8–3.3μ (5400–3000 cm⁻¹). There is some minor

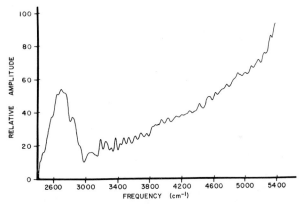

FIGURE 14. Infrared spectra of the NO + O reaction at 1 Torr total pressure. At the present time it is unknown whether any of the apparent structure from 5400–3000 cm⁻¹ is real or just noise.

structure superimposed on the continuum which is also observed in spectra obtained from 1.2–1.8μ. Some of the structure may possibly be real, and in the near future, using improved techniques, we expect to be able to unambiguously identify any real structure. However, there are definitely no gross deviations from a continuum between 1 and 3.3μ. The presence of a broad band centered at about 3.7μ (2700 cm⁻¹) and about 600 cm⁻¹ wide has prevented determination of the continuum distribution any further than 3.3μ. By joining the spectral curves of Figure 14 and shorter wavelength data and drawing a smooth line through them, Figure 15 is obtained. The spectral distribution represented in

Figure 15 is accurate to about 10% and accounts for roughly 5% of the quanta emitted on the continuum. It is evident that there is no structure observed in the laboratory spectrum corresponding to the large signals observed around

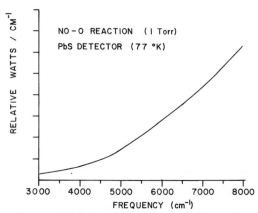

FIGURE 15. A spectral curve of the NO + O emission made by drawing a purposely smoothed curve through Figure 14 and a similar spectrum obtained in the region 5000–8000 cm⁻¹. The relative response of the instrument has been removed from the data.

1.6μ in Figure 12. This implies that the physical phenomena occurring in the disturbed atmosphere must be more complicated than the reaction as measured in the laboratory. This could be the result of other mechanisms being involved such as NO + O_3, or it could be a result of the unreproduced kinetic conditions.

The longer wavelength emissions and dependence on relative nitric oxide concentration is shown in Figure 16. The four bands present are, going from left to right in any one spectrum, the ν_3 fundamental of NO_2 at 6.3μ, the fundamental of NO at 5.4μ, the ν_3 fundamental of N_2O at 4.5μ, and again the anomalous broad band at 3.7μ.

The nitric oxide-oxygen atom reaction has been the subject of studies by many other groups in the past (BROIDA et al., 1961; CLYNE and THRUSH, 1962; DOHERTY and JONATHAN, 1964; REEVES et al., 1964; and KAUFMAN and KELSO, 1965). However, no agreement has been reached on whether or not a third body is required for the reaction (a very fundamental question), and infrared emission past 1.2μ has not previously been studied (or observed) at all. Another result of this study has been the discovery of the broad band at 3.7μ (shown in Figures 14 and 16), whose intensity varies with that of the continuum (vs. P, [O], and [NO]). This band may be due to a transition to or from a very low-lying state of NO_2. Other data indicate that its intensity is also proportional to the intensity of the ν_3 fundamental of NO_2 at 6.3μ. This would be a very significant finding and might help answer the third body question if one could assume that the reaction, NO + O (+ M ?) → NO_2 (+ M ?), was the only source of vibrationally excited NO_2. However, this study has shown that NO_2 can also be vibrationally excited by a near-resonant collisional transfer process:

$$O_2\ddagger + NO_2 \rightarrow O_2 + NO_2\ddagger.$$

Unfortunately, the vibrationally excited O_2 may be produced by one or both of two things; the discharge used to produce atomic oxygen may also produce some vibrationally excited oxygen, and the fast reaction

$$O + NO_2 \rightarrow O_2\ddagger + NO\ddagger,$$

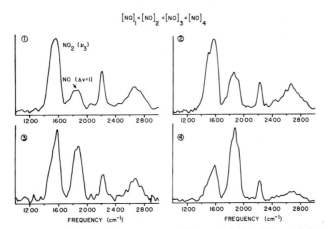

$$[NO]_1 < [NO]_2 < [NO]_3 < [NO]_4$$

FIGURE 16. Spectra of the NO + O reaction at different relative NO partial pressures. The band at approximately 2500 cm^{-1} is due to N_2O resulting from a trace of N_2 in the discharged oxygen. Later work with pure O_2 gave no sign of the N_2O emission and its presence did not affect the results shown here. The band at 2700 cm^{-1} is the same one shown in Figure 14.

which occurs following production of NO_2, appears to produce both NO and O_2 vibrationally excited. Initial studies indicate that this second mechanism is the most likely source of the $O_2\ddagger$ which excites NO_2. However, the relative efficiencies of

$$NO + O\,(+\,M\,?) \rightarrow NO_2\ddagger\,(+\,M)$$

or

$$NO^*_2 \rightarrow NO_2\ddagger + h\nu$$

and

$$O_2\ddagger + NO_2 \rightarrow O_2 + NO\ddagger$$

are not yet known.

2. Rocket Measurements of the Altitude Profile of the Night Sky Airglow Continuum. A radiance versus altitude profile of the night sky airglow continuum was obtained from a rocket flight at White Sands, New Mexico (D. BAKER, 1966). Utah State University radiometers (Model WT-1C) were flown on Aerobee rocket AD3.723 (Sidewinder II) launched at 20:49 hours MST on April 28, 1966 as shown in Figure 17. The spectral bandpass of the radiometer is given in Figure 18, and the altitude profile of the continuum

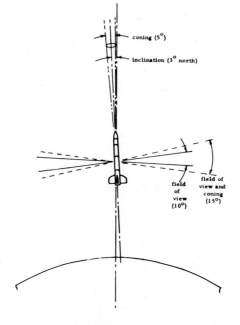

FIGURE 17. Aerobee Sidewinder II aspect at approximately 100 km.

profile of the continuum airglow in the 5700–5850Å spectral region (Figure 18) is given in Figure 19. A pronounced layer of 6 or 7-km thickness is evident at about a 90 km altitude.

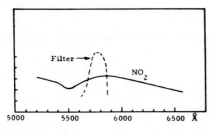

FIGURE 18. Night-sky continuum according to SHEFOV (1959) with integrated 5775Å filter and photomultiplier response overlay.

The atomic oxygen green line ($^1D_2{}^1S_0$) at 5577Å was also measured at the same look angle and field of view on the same flight. The radiance profile of this familiar airglow line is shown in Figure 20. The maximum radiance occurred at an altitude of about 98 km.

This altitude distribution measurement of the continuum agrees very well with earlier measurements made at different spectral regions by TOUSEY (1958). The possibility of two emitting layers was suggested by PACKER (1961).

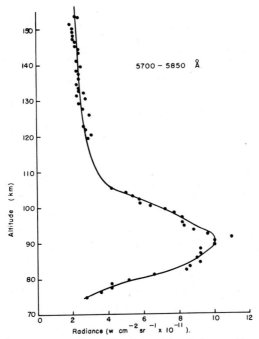

FIGURE 19. Altitude profile of the night airglow continuum.

FIGURE 20. Altitude profile of the night-sky oxygen green line airglow.

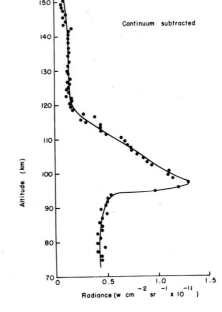

3. Conclusion. In conclusion, it appears that the NO + O reaction scheme is certainly involved in the long-lived afterglow of high altitude nuclear detonations, but comparison of the laboratory spectra and field data demonstrates that we do not adequately understand the atmospheric mechanisms. Further experimental studies should improve our understanding of this very interesting upper atmospheric airglow phenomena.

The OH‡ Airglow

The strongest emissions in the normal airglow are the Meinel bands; i.e., the vibrational-rotational bands of the ground electronic state of the excited hydroxyl radical. These bands extend through the visible and infrared spectrum and are several orders of magnitude stronger than other airglow phenomena, with the possible exception of emission due to O_2 ($1\Delta_g$). There have been many investigations of the Meinel bands in the chemosphere, some of which have provided good data on the relative intensities of the various overtone vibrational-rotational bands (CHAMBERLAIN, 1961). However, the source of excited hydroxyl radicals in the upper atmosphere remains undetermined, partially due to lack of knowledge of the OH dipole moment. Without information on the dipole moment, attempts to obtain vibrational populations, which will help determine the primary excitation step, are doomed to failure.

FERGUSON and PARKINSON (1963) have shown that to uniquely determine the dipole moment one must simultaneously obtain data on the fundamental and overtone sequences of OH. The first observations of this kind at moderate spectral resolution have been accomplished by studying the emission from hydroxyl radicals produced by the H + O_3 reaction in a steady-state flow system at 4 Torr pressure (STAIR *et al.* 1965). To enhance signal-to-noise, the emission spectra were observed with an interferometer spectrometer. The instrument was a typical Michelson design with 2 cm diameter end mirrors. A cooled lead sulphide detector (77°K) was used in obtaining the spectra from 1.4–4μ. The OH emission spectrum, which contains most of the $\Delta v = 1$ and $\Delta v = 2$ sequences, is shown corrected for the instrument response in Figure 21.

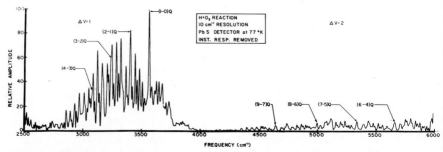

FIGURE 21. OH emission spectra from H + O_3 reaction. Q branches of observed vibrational transitions are indicated.

It is apparent that the resolution is not sufficient to resolve the $\Delta v = 1$ sequence well enough to obtain the integrated intensities of the various vibrational transitions. However, the resolution is sufficient to assign almost all of the observed structure to OH. The $\Delta v = 2$ sequence was stronger by a factor of about 10 before removing the instrument response; consequently, the identification in this region was also unambiguous. It is of interest that under these conditions there is no apparent intensity structure in the spectra at 3.3μ as observed in the airglow (LYTLE and HAMPSON, 1964). The spectra discussed here represented the first observation of the OH $\Delta v = 1$ sequence from the $H + O_3$ reaction. Data will soon be available at 1 cm^{-1} resolution which will be sufficient to define the dipole moment.

Inability to carry out vibrational state population analysis has been one of the major reasons for the lack of agreement on the primary excitation mechanism of OH in the upper atmosphere. The dispute over which of the competing chemical reaction mechanisms is responsible is still unresolved. Until recently the consensus among western scientists has favored the reaction, $H + O_3 \rightarrow OH\ddagger + O_2$, as the most likely mechanism. Supporting this hypothesis are the airglow observations which show OH excited only up through the ninth vibrational level, corresponding to an excitation energy of 3.23 eV. The hydrogen atom-ozone reaction releases 3.32 eV, enough to populate only $v = 9$ and lower. Laboratory spectral measurements (Figure 21) confirm that only levels with $v \leq 9$ are populated (GARVIN, 1959). Additionally, the airglow of OH frequently exhibits a striking covariance with that of Na D during the night. This suggests something common in the excitation mechanism, a role perhaps played by atomic hydrogen. Russian scientists have often criticized this mechanism and have suggested many alternate possibilities (KRASSOVSKY et al., 1961), most of which have not been readily accepted by many atmospheric physicists.

There are, however, serious objections to the ozone mechanism. Rocket flights have indicated that the maximum intensity of the OH emission occurs around 90 km or higher (HEPPNER and MEREDITH, 1958; PACKER, 1961; LOWE, 1960; and TARASOVA, 1961), an altitude where the ozone and hydrogen atom concentrations appear to be too small to be capable of producing the OH intensities observed (KRASSOVSKY et al., 1961; HEPPNER and MEREDITH, 1958; and PACKER, 1961). The most recent rocket measurement of the radiance versus altitude profile of the hydroxyl emission was obtained, as part of this research program, on the same Aerobee rocket previously discussed. The spectral bandpass of the radiometer (Utah State University Model WT-1C) used to obtain the measurement was 7210–7450Å as shown in Figure 22. The absolute radiance profile during ascent is given in Figure 23. The maximum radiance of the OH(8, 3) night airglow occurred at an altitude of about 98 km, and the thickness (50% brightness) of the emission layer appeared to be about 16 km. The profile is very similar to one obtained from a November 6, 1959

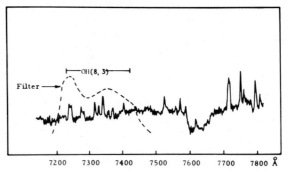

FIGURE 22. Microphotometer tracing of nightglow spectrum with integrated 7325Å filter and photomultiplier response overlay.

rocket flight by PACKER (1961). Unfortunately, all of the rocket data to date have been obtained at night. Altitude measurements as a function of the zenith angle of the sun will aid considerably in determining the responsible

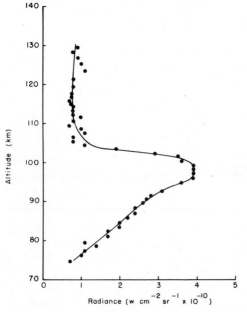

FIGURE 23. Altitude profile of night-sky OH(8, 3) airglow.

mechanism(s). The other major objection to the ozone mechanism results from the first daytime observations of OH emission using a balloon-borne spectrometer, wherein the intensity was observed to be approximately the same as at night (LYTLE and HAMPSON, 1964). Since the sun dissociates ozone so strongly, calculations show that there should be almost an order of magnitude decrease in daytime intensity of the OH emission compared to that at night (WALLACE, 1962).

The kinetics of the OH emission are so complex, there are so many possible OH sources, and we know so little concerning either laboratory or atmospheric parameters, that analysis at present is almost pure mental gymnastics. There is a definite trend to accept multiple, concurrent mechanisms for the airglow explanations. Since so little is known about critical atmospheric parameters such as [H], [$O_2\ddagger$], [HO_2], etc., many more atmospheric observations are needed to establish such things as diurnal, seasonal, and latitudinal effects on both intensities and spectral distributions. Similarly, continued laboratory work is required on rate constants, energy distribution, and the OH dipole moment.

IV. Infrared Spectra of Hot Air Resulting From a

High Altitude Nuclear Detonation

Another important late time ($t > 1$ sec) afterglow of nuclear bursts is due to radiation from the heated air itself. Typical infrared spectra of such a low density hot gas are shown in Figures 24 and 25. Figure 24 is data obtained in the region 1300–3800 cm^{-1}, and the fundamental bands ($\Delta v = 1$) of nitric oxide

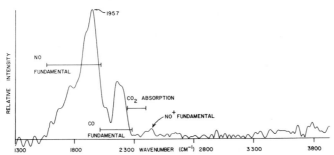

FIGURE 24. Relative infrared late time spectra of a high altitude nuclear detonation in the 1300–3800 cm^{-1} region.

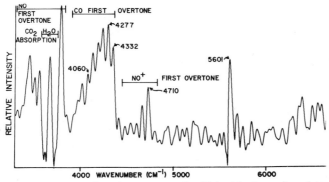

FIGURE 25. Relative infrared late time spectra of a high altitude nuclear detonation in the 3800–6500 cm^{-1} region.

and carbon monoxide are easily identifiable. At high temperature ($T > 2000°K$) and low densities, the only molecular species with dipole moments expected to be present in equilibrium air in significant concentrations are NO, CO, and NO+. The band at 2400 cm^{-1} is the fundamental of NO+, and in Figure 25, the first overtones ($\Delta v = 2$) of NO, CO, and NO+ are observed. This is the first unambiguous observation of the vibrational-rotational spectra of NO+ in the ground electronic state. This free radical is a particularly important one for electron density determinations of hot air and auroral produced ionization. These data indicate that the reported observations of NOXON and JONES (1960) of emission at 2.15μ during an aurora were very possibly due to NO+. It is of fundamental value to establish, if possible, the dipole strength of NO+ since one could then, by spectral radiometric measurements, determine the concentration of NO+ in the atmospheric phenomena of interest.

Since the radiative lifetimes of infrared vibrational-rotational transitions are typically 10^{-1}–10^{-3} sec and the collision frequency at $\rho/\rho_0 = 10^{-4}$ is on the order of 10^6 per sec, one can possibly assume kinetic and radiative equilibrium. Under these conditions, relative specie concentrations as a function of temperature and density can be obtained from tables of equilibrium hot air (GILMORE, 1964; HILSENRATH and KLEIN, 1965). Figure 26, for example,

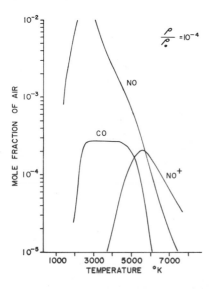

FIGURE 26. Molecular concentrations of NO, CO, and NO+ in equilibrium air at a density ratio of 10^{-4} versus temperature.

shows curves of NO, CO, and NO+ concentrations versus temperature for a density ratio of 10^{-4}. In the following discussion kinetic, radiative, and chemical equilibrium will be assumed. To obtain relative concentrations from this spectral data it is necessary to know the transition probabilities of the molecules of interest. Since these are not known for the high vibrational-rotational levels involved in high temperature gases, a useful approximation is followed. At room temperature there are a number of methods (PENNER, 1959) of obtaining the integrated band intensity, S. The integrated intensity of the experimental data, I, can then be expressed as

$$I_{NO} \approx [NO]\left(\frac{\bar{\nu}_{NO}{}^3}{\exp{(hc\nu/kT)} - 1}\right)S_{NO}$$

and, therefore:

$$\frac{[NO]}{[CO]} \approx \frac{I_{NO}}{I_{CO}}\left\{\frac{\bar{\nu}_{CO}}{\bar{\nu}_{NO}}\right\}^3 \left[\frac{\exp{(hc\nu_{NO}/kT)^{-1}}}{\exp{(hc\nu_{CO}/kT)^{-1}}}\right]\frac{S_{CO}}{S_{NO}}$$

where $\bar{\nu}$ represents an average wave number of the band, ν is the band center, and the brackets [ ] represent concentration. Since the bands are adjacent and at the temperatures under consideration, the $\bar{\nu}^3$ and the exponential terms represent corrections on the order of only 100°K, they can be neglected in the first approximation. Thus, from measured values of I and knowledge of the integrated band intensities, S, one can obtain relative concentrations of the species which for a known density determines the temperature. Conversely, from knowledge of temperature and density (equivalent to knowing specie concentration) the measured intensities can be used to determine the relative S's.

A summary of the information available on the integrated band intensity of the CO fundamental is given by BENEDICT et al. (1962). There is relatively good agreement, and 258 cm^{-1}/atm-cm at 273°K from PENNER and WEBER (1951) is taken as the most probable value. There are some nine known measurements on the CO overtone band intensity which range in value from 1.66–2.50. However, there seems to be reasonable current agreement on a value between 2 and 2.5, with BREEZE and FERRISO (1964) reporting 2.3 ± 0.3 and SCHURIN and CLOUGH (1965) reporting 2.15 ± 0.10 cm^{-1}/atm-cm. There also seems to be fairly good agreement on the value for the NO overtone band intensity. A value of 2.11 cm^{-1}/atm-cm is adopted (SHEPHARD and CLOUGH, 1965). The situation, unfortunately, is not so clear in regard to the band intensity of the NO fundamental. The current status is summarized by CARPENTER and FRANZOSA (1965). The range in reported values is from 69–145 cm^{-1}/atm-cm. However, the most serious controversy seems to be between a value of about 70 and 120.

Ratios of the measured integrated intensities of comparable portions (same band intervals) of the fundamental bands of NO and CO are presented in Figure 27. Since CO$_2$ absorption at 2300 cm^{-1} interferes with part of the CO band, the entire band ratios were not used. There is considerable scatter in the data, but the best fit smoothed curve is shown. From these data one can obtain the relative specie concentrations and, therefore, the temperature, provided the density is known. Similarly, the ratios of the integrated value of the NO$^+$ band relative to NO and CO have been obtained. Unfortunately, the atmospheric absorption due to CO_2 at 2300 cm^{-1} permits only a small portion of the NO$^+$ band to be reliably used. Even so, a very rough estimate of 500 cm^{-1}/atm-cm is obtained for the NO$^+$ fundamental integrated intensity relative to the value 258 cm^{-1}/atm-cm for CO.

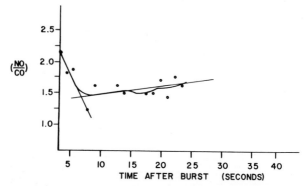

FIGURE 27. Integrated intensity ratio of the fundamental bands of NO and CO versus time following a high altitude nuclear detonation (t_p in this figure and Figure 28 represent the same time).

Figure 28 is a plot of the NO$^+$/CO integrated intensity ratio obtained at various times from spectra similar to that shown in Figure 25. The NO overtone can be seen from Figure 25 to be severely distorted by the atmospheric H_2O

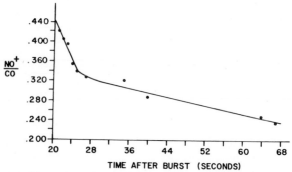

FIGURE 28. Integrated intensity ratio of the first overtone bands of NO$^+$ and CO versus time following a high altitude nuclear detonation (t_p in this figure and Figure 27 represent the same time).

and CO_2 absorption and, consequently, there was considerable scatter in its integrated values. However, since the value of the CO overtone integrated intensity is well known, a relatively reliable value of 3.0 cm^{-1}/atm-cm is obtained for the NO$^+$ overtone (subject, of course, to the equilibrium assumptions).

In conclusion, the use of infrared techniques can be seen to be one of the most powerful methods for determining the kinetic state of a gas. Not only can one obtain relative concentrations of important species but also the degree of internal excitation, which is an important parameter affecting the reaction rates of the subsequent atmospheric chemical history.

References

BAKER, D. J., 1966, Final Report Contract AF19(628)-251, Utah State University, Logan, Utah.

BAKER, K. D., 1966, *Direct In Situ Measurements of Auroral Parameters*, Sci. Report No. 4, Contract AF19(628)-4995, University of Utah, Salt Lake City, Utah.

BENEDICT, W. S., HERMAN, R., MOORE, G. F., and SILVERMAN, S., 1962, *Astrophys. J.* **135**, 277.

BENNETT, R. G. and DALBY, F. W., 1959, *J. Chem. Phys.* **31**, 434.

BREEZE, J. C. and FERRISO, C. C., 1964, *J. Chem. Phys.* **41**, 3420.

BROIDA, H. P., SCHIFF, H. I., and SUGDEN, T. M., 1961, *Trans. Faraday Soc.* **57**, 259.

CARPENTER, R. O'B. and FRANZOSA, M. A., 1965, *J. Quant. Spectr. Radiative Transfer* **5**, 465.

CHAMBERLAIN, J. W., 1961, *Physics of the Aurora and Airglow*, Academic Press, New York.

CLYNE, M. A. A. and THRUSH, B. A., 1962, *Proc. Roy. Soc. (London).* **A269**, 404.

CULP, G. and STAIR, A. T., Jr., 1966, paper presented at the 16th Annual Meeting of the Societe de Chimie Physique, Paris, France, May 1966; (to be published) *Fr. J. de Chimie Physique* (January 1967).

DAVIDSON, G. and O'NEIL, R., 1964, *J. Chem. Phys.* **41**, 3946.

DAVIDSON, G. and O'NEIL, R., 1965, Abstr. of 4th Intern. Conf. Phys. Electronic and Atomic Collisions, Quebec, Canada, 428.

DOHERTY, G. and JONATHAN, N., 1964, *Discussions Faraday Soc.* **37**.

FELLGETT, P. B., 1951, Thesis, Univ. of Cambridge, Cambridge, England.

FERGUSON, A. F. and PARKINSON, D., 1963, *Planetary Space Sci.* **11**, 149.

FONTIJN, A., MEYER, C. B., and SCHIFF, H. I., 1964, *J. Chem. Phys.* **40**, 64.

GARVIN, D., 1959, *J. Am. Chem. Soc.* **81**, 3173.

GAUVIN, H. P., 1963, *High Altitude Nuclear Detonation Optical-Infrared Effects (U)*, Operation Dominic Project Officers Interim Report — Project 8A.1, DASA (January 1963).

GILMORE, F. R., 1964, *Approximate Radiation Properties of Air Between 2000 and 8000°K*, Rand Corporation, Report RM-3997-ARPA.

HAYAKAWA, S. and NISHIMURA, H., 1964, *J. Geomagnetism and Geoelectricity (Japan)* **16**, 72.

HEPPNER, J. P. and MERIDITH, L. H., 1958, *J. Geophys. Res.* **63**, 51.

HILSENRATH, J. and KLEIN, M., 1965, *Tables of Thermodynamic Properties of Air in Chemical Equilibrium Including Second Virial Corrections from 1500°K to 15,000°K*, Arnold Engineering Development Center, USAF, AEDC-TR-65-58.

HIRSH, M. N., EISNER, P. N., and SLEVIN, J. A., 1965, G. C. Dewey Corporation, Report R190-2, New York.

KAUFMAN, F. and KELSO, J. I., 1965, paper presented at Symposium on Chemiluminescence, Durham, North Carolina.

KRASSOVSKY, V. I., SHEFOV, N. N., and YARIN, V. I., 1961, *J. Atmospheric Terrest. Phys.* **21**, 46.

LOEWENSTEIN, E. V., 1966, *Appl. Opt.* **5**, 845.

LOWE, R. P., 1960, CARDE Tech. Memo No. 291/59, Canadian Armament Research and Development Establishment, Valcartier, Quebec, Canada (May 1960).

LYTLE, E. A. and HAMPSON, J. 1964, *Nature* **202**, 76.

McCONKEY, J. W. and LATIMER, I. D., 1965, *Proc. Phys. Soc. (London).* **86**, 463.

MORRIS, J. C., 1966, *Appl. Opt.* **5**, 1035.

NOXON, J. F. and JONES, V. A., 1960, *J. Atmospheric Terrest. Phys.* **18**, 342.

O'BRIEN, B. J., ALLUM, F. R., and GOLDWIRE, H. C., 1965, *J. Geophys. Res.* **70**, 161.

PACKER, D. M., 1961, *Ann. Geophys.* **17**, 67.

PENNER, S., 1959, *Quantitative Molecular Spectroscopy and Gas Emissivities.* Addison-Wesley Publishing Company, Inc., Reading, Massachusetts.

PENNER, S. and WEBER, D., 1951, *J. Chem. Phys.* **19,** 807, 817.

REES, M. H., 1959, *J. Atmospheric Terrest. Phys.* **14,** 325.

REEVES, R. R., HARTECK, P., and CHACE, W. H., 1964, *J. Chem. Phys.* **41,** 764.

ROMICK, G. J. and BELAN, A. E., 1964, Geophysical Institute Report UAG-R149, Univ. of Alaska, College, Alaska.

SCHRAM, B. L., DEHEER, F. J., VAN DER WIEL, M. J., and KISTEMAKER, J., 1965, *Physica* **31,** 94.

SHEFOV, N. N., 1959, *Spectral Electrophotometrical, and Radar Researchers of Auroral and Airglow.* Publ. House, Academy of Sciences, Moscow, USSR, No. 1, p. 25.

SHERIDAN, W. F., OLDENBERG, O., and CARLETON, N. F., 1961, Abstr. of 2nd Intern. Conf. Phys. Electronic and Atomic Collisions, Boulder, Colorado.

SCHURIN, B. and CLOUGH, S. A., 1965, Air Force Cambridge Research Laboratories, L. G. Hanscom Field, Bedford, Massachusetts, private communication.

SPINDLER, G. B., 1966, *Planetary Space Sci.* **14,** 53.

STAIR, A. T., Jr. and KENNEALY, J. P., 1966, paper presented at the 16th Annual Meeting of the Societe de Chimie Physique, Paris, France, June 1966; (to be published) *Fr. J. de Chimie Physique* (January 1967).

STAIR, A. T., JR., KENNEALY, J. P., and STEWART, S. P., 1965, *Planetary Space Sci.* **13,** 1005.

STEWART, D. T., 1955, *Proc. Phys. Soc.* (*London*) **68,** 404.

STEWART, D. T., 1956, *Proc. Phys. Soc.* (*London*) **69,** 437.

TARASOVA, T. M., 1961, *Astr. Circ.* Academy of Sciences, Moscow, USSR, No. 222, p. 31.

TOUSEY, R., 1958, *Ann. Geophys.* **14,** 186.

VALENTINE, J. M. and CURRAN, S. C., 1958, *Rept. Progr. Phys.* **21,** 1.

WALLACE, L., 1962, *J. Atmos. Sci.* **19,** 1.

USE OF ARTIFICIAL BARIUM CLOUDS TO STUDY MAGNETIC AND ELECTRIC FIELDS IN THE ATMOSPHERE

L. Haser

Max-Planck-Institut für Physik und Astrophysik
Institut für extraterrestrische Physik,
Garching bei Müchen.

Dedicated to Professor L. Biermann
for his 60th anniversary.

The exploration of magnetic fields in space has become a routine procedure for sounding rockets, satellites, and space probes. On the contrary, the measurement of electric fields has met many difficulties since the fields are weak and the perturbations created by a space probe and its measuring equipment are considerable (ALFVEN, 1965; BOYD, 1965; FAHLESON, 1965; GDALEVICH, 1964; KAVADAS and JOHNSON, 1964). The smallest perturbation of an existing field would probably be the injection of a visible plasma cloud and the observation of its movement under the influence of the fields.

Since 1951 BIERMANN (1951, 1952, 1953) investigated the possibility of using the ion tails of comets to probe the interplanetary plasma. Later it was proposed to use artificial plasma clouds to probe interplanetary space, since good comets are rare events and cometary ions (essentially CO^+ and N_2^+) have low oscillator strengths in the visible band systems.

The most promising elements are Ba and Sr and, probably Eu. They have resonance lines in the visible spectrum both for the neutral and the ionized atoms. This is a great simplification for the observations. On the other hand, the photoionization efficiencies seem to be high. One could hope that solar light is sufficient to ionize the atoms and that the only thing to do is the release of the elements in neutral form. An artificial ionization would have needed very high energies and a correspondingly complicated payload.

Before exploring interplanetary magnetic and electric fields and the movements of neutral and ionized clouds, the techniques of evaporation and the physics of ionization and interaction of plasma with fields had to be investigated with releases in the high atmosphere using sounding rockets. Since 1963 our group produced a large number of vapor clouds in the high atmosphere ranging from 130–2000 km. Both Ba and Sr were tested. In the following we present some of the results obtained.

Payload and Launchings

The first experiments were made to test the efficiency of different chemicals in respect to evaporation efficiency. Barium and Strontium were tried in the following reactions (Föppl et al., 1965):

$$3BaO_2 + 4Al \rightarrow 3Ba + 2Al_2O_3$$

$$BaO_2 + 2Mg \rightarrow Ba + 2MgO$$

$$Sr(NO_3)_2 + 6Mg \rightarrow Sr + 6MgO + N_2$$

$$Ba(NO_3)_2 + 6Mg \rightarrow Ba + 6MgO + N_2$$

More recently, we used a mixture of Ba and CuO with an excess of Ba (Föppl et al., 1966). In some mixtures, Ba is the product of the reaction. In others, part of the Ba is burned, and the heat created by the reaction is used to evaporate the excess Ba. By the use of collodion or silicon gum binder, the speed of the reaction could be changed. The mixtures were pressed into steel containers equipped with timing and igniting devices. The experiments were done at the launching sites in Sardinia and in the Algerian Sahara using British Skylark rockets and French Centaure, Dragon, and Rubis vehicles. It immediately became evident that the evaporation of Sr was much more efficient than that of Ba (Föppl et al., 1965). On the contrary, we never observed Sr ions but did observe good ionization efficiency for Ba. Therefore, the experiments were continued with Ba releases, Ba/CuO being the most efficient until now. Fortunately, Sr is always present in our Ba metal as an impurity, and because of its good evaporation efficiency, we also get a Sr cloud.

A typical Ba vapor release has two distinct phases. In the initial phase, the Ba vapor expands with a speed of about 1.2 km/sec until the vapor reaches equilibrium with the ambient atmosphere after some seconds.

The further expansion is governed by diffusion. Approximately at the time of transition between free expansion and the diffusion phase, a cigar-shaped Ba ion cloud becomes visible superposed on the neutral cloud, the length of the cigar-shaped cloud approximately equaling the diameter of the spherical Ba cloud. The ion cloud is aligned with the earth magnetic field lines and the further development of the two clouds is different. The ion cloud expands along the field lines and shows relatively small displacements in a perpendicular direction. The neutral Ba/Sr cloud generally moves in a different direction and has a higher speed. It separates from the ion cloud following atmospheric winds and is often sheared into an elliptical form.

The intensity in the Ba I resonance line 5535Å decreases with a time constant of about 100 sec, whereas the Sr I line at 4607Å maintains its intensity. This means that neutral Ba is continuously destroyed. The only processes known are ionization and oxidation by atmospheric oxygen. Since our spectrograms show very strong BaO bands at 130 km and no trace of BaO at 180 km, the limit of oxidation is near 150 km. For clouds above this level the only process for destruction of Ba is its ionization by solar light. Fortunately, Sr remains as a tracer for the displacement of the neutral cloud.

Spectra of Ba Clouds

Early spectral observations revealed only the resonance lines of the atoms present.

$$\text{Ba I} \quad 5535,484\text{Å} \quad 6s^2\ {}^1S_0 \ - 6p\ {}^1P_1{}^0$$

$$\text{Ba II} \quad 4934,088\text{Å} \quad 6s\ {}^2S_{1/2} - 6p\ {}^2P_{1/2}{}^0$$

$$4554,033\text{Å} \quad 6s\ {}^2S_{1/2} - 6p\ {}^2P_{3/2}{}^0$$

$$\text{Sr I} \quad 4607,331\text{Å} \quad 5s^2\ {}^1S_0 \ - 5p\ {}^1P_1{}^0$$

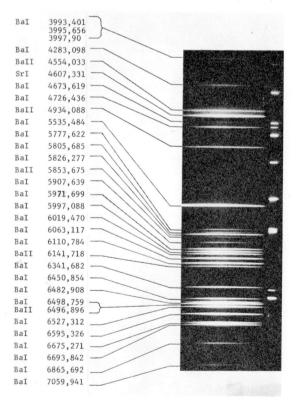

BaI	3993,401
	3995,656
	3997,90
BaI	4283,098
BaII	4554,033
SrI	4607,331
BaI	4673,619
BaI	4726,436
BaII	4934,088
BaI	5535,484
BaI	5777,622
BaI	5805,685
BaI	5826,277
BaII	5853,675
BaI	5907,639
BaI	5971,699
BaI	5997,088
BaI	6019,470
BaI	6063,117
BaI	6110,784
BaII	6141,718
BaI	6341,682
BaI	6450,854
BaI	6482,908
BaI	6498,759
BaII	6496,896
BaI	6527,312
BaI	6595,326
BaI	6675,271
BaI	6693,842
BaI	6865,692
BaI	7059,941

FIGURE 1. Spectrum of the initial phase of a Ba vapor release.

With the use of spectrographs with more powerful optics (camera $f/0.75$) and high-sensitivity films, together with a greatly increased brightness of the recent clouds, we obtained much better spectrograms (HASER, 1966) for the initial phase of a release (Figure 1). The relevant spectral data are contained in Table I.

Table I. Spectral Data

λ cloud (Å)	Int.	Emitter	Transition	λ Lab. (Å)
3995	1	Ba I	$5d\,^3D_3 \;-4f\,^3F_4^\circ$	3993,401
			$-4f\,^3F_3^\circ$	3995,656
			$-4f\,^3F_2^\circ$	3997,90
4284	2	Ba I	$5d\,^1D_2 \;-4f\,^1F_3^\circ$	4283,098
4554	5	Ba II	$6s\,^2S_{1/2} \;-6p\,^2P_{3/2}^\circ$	4554,033
4608	10dd	Sr I	$5s^2\,^1S_0 \;-5p\,^1P_1^\circ$	4607,331
4675	1	Ba I	$5d\,^3D_3 \;-7p\,^3P_2^\circ$	4673,619
4726	6	Ba I	$5d\,^1D_2 \;-7p\,^1P_1^\circ$	4726,436
4934	6	Ba II	$6s\,^2S_{1/2} \;-6p\,^2P_{1/2}^\circ$	4934,088
5535	10dd	Ba I	$6s^2\,^1S_0 \;-6p\,^1P_1^\circ$	5535,484
5778	3	Ba I	$6p\,^3P_2^\circ \;-6d\,^3D_3$	5777,622
5806	3	Ba I	$5d\,^3D_3 \;-6p'\,^1F_3^\circ$	5805,685
5826	10d	Ba I	$5d\,^1D_2 \;-6p'\,^1P_1^\circ$	5826,277
5854	1	Ba II	$5d\,^2D_{3/2} \;-6p\,^2P_{3/2}^\circ$	5853,675
5908	3	Ba I	$5d\,^3D_1 \;-6p'\,^3P_2^\circ$	5907,639
5971	10d	Ba I	$5d\,^3D_2 \;-6p'\,^3P_2^\circ$	5971,699
5997	10d	Ba I	$5d\,^3D_1 \;-6p'\,^3P_1^\circ$	5997,088
6019	10d	Ba I	$5d\,^3D_1 \;-6p'\,^3P_0^\circ$	6019,470
6063	10dd	Ba I	$5d\,^3D_2 \;-6p'\,^3P_1^\circ$	6063,117
6111	10dd	Ba I	$5d\,^3D_3 \;-6p'\,^3P_2^\circ$	6110,784
6142	8	Ba II	$5d\,^2D_{5/2} \;-6p\,^2P_{3/2}^\circ$	6141,718
6342	9	Ba I	$5d\,^3D_2 \;-6p'\,^3D_3^\circ$	6341,682
6451	9	Ba I	$5d\,^3D_1 \;-6p'\,^3D_2^\circ$	6450,854
6483	8	Ba I	$5d\,^1D_2 \;-6p'\,^1F_3^\circ$	6482,908
6498	10dd	Ba I	$5d\,^3D_3 \;-6p'\,^3D_3^\circ$	6498,759
		Ba II	$5d\,^2D_{3/2} \;-6p\,^2P_{1/2}^\circ$	6496,896
6527	10d	Ba I	$5d\,^3D_2 \;-6p'\,^3D_2^\circ$	6527,312
6595	10d	Ba I	$5d\,^3D_1 \;-6p'\,^3D_1^\circ$	6595,326
6675	10	Ba I	$5d\,^3D_2 \;-6p'\,^3D_1^\circ$	6675,271
6693	10	Ba I	$5d\,^3D_3 \;-6p'\,^3D_2^\circ$	6693,842
6866	2	Ba I	$5d\,^1D_2 \;-6p'\,^3P_2^\circ$	6865,692
7060	1	Ba I	$5d\,^3D_3 \;-6p'\,^3F_4^\circ$	7059,941

d = overexposed
λ Lab taken from Russell and Moore, 1955

The observed transitions are included in the energy level diagram of Ba I and Ba II (Figures 2 and 3).

The identification of the lines is not based only on the wavelength coincidence since the spectra have a dispersion of 190Å/mm and the measured values may be in error by ±2Å. Because a cloud in the shadow of the earth is invisible, the emissions of the cloud must be excited by fluorescence. In that case only low lying energy levels with long lifetimes can be involved as lower states for the different transitions.

The inspection of the energy level diagram reveals the great importance of the two metastable levels. Grating objective streak camera observations show that the level $5d\ ^1D_2$ is populated by some pumping mechanism starting about 0.5 sec after release and maintaining its population for about 5 sec. The triplet level

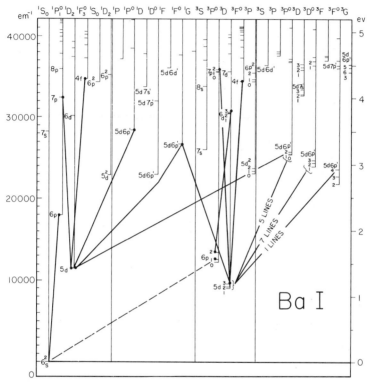

FIGURE 2. Energy level diagram of Ba I, extracted from NORRIS (1955).

$5d\ ^3D$ also starts to be populated at 0.5 sec but stays so until about 100 sec after release.

In spite of the similarity of the energy level diagrams of Ba I and Sr I, no other Sr line has been observed. We have the peculiar situation that the absence of Sr ions is correlated with the absence of any Sr I line, except in the case of the resonance line. On the other hand, the strong ionization of Ba is correlated with numerous spectral lines, all of which involve metastable levels (except the resonance line). Furthermore, the time constants for the population of the metastable levels coincide with the rapid initial ionization (producing the cigar-shaped cloud) and the disappearance of neutral Ba.

The difference in the behavior of Ba and Sr comes from the different constellations of low lying terms in the two atoms. For Sr the $4d\ ^3D$ level is not metastable; permitted transitions lead to the $5p\ ^3P^0$ level and an intercombination leads from $^3P^0$ to the ground state $5s^2$ $^1S_0$. This explains the absence of any triplet line in the fluorescence spectrum. The $4d$ ^1D level in Sr is quite near the $^1P^0$ level, and the pumping mechanism does not seem to be sufficient to populate it appreciably.

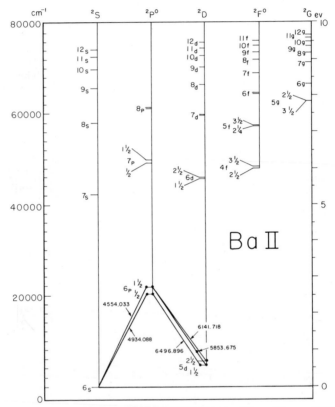

FIGURE 3. Energy level diagram of Ba II, extracted from NORRIS (1955).

We conclude that there is a correlation between the population of metastable levels and the efficiency of ionization for Ba. In fact the observed ionization times are much shorter than those calculated from known photoionization cross sections (FÖPPL et al., 1965). This discrepancy may be solved by a two step process leading to ionization:

(1) Resonance absorption and subsequent population of a metastable level by spontaneous transitions.
(2) Photoionization by absorption in the metastable state.

This process is possible for both metastable states of Ba I.

The singlet state is populated by absorption of 5535Å, 3071Å, 3501Å, and subsequent emission of 15,000Å, 4726Å, and 5826Å, respectively.

Photoionization including the transition to the autoionized level $5d\ 8p^1\ {}^1P^0$ requires less energy (3266Å) and is a one electron jump, whereas ionization from the ground state needs 2380Å and a two electron jump, which probably has a much lower transition probability than a one electron jump. Since the solar intensity is higher by a factor of 30 at the longer wavelength, compared to the shorter one, photoionization from the $5d\ {}^1D$ level should be highly efficient. The same mechanism works for the ${}^3D$ state. Pumping is done by the intercombination line 7911Å, and ionization requires approximately 3000Å. Here the efficiency should be lower than for the singlet levels.

During a recent experiment a cloud was produced near the shadow of the earth at a height of 154 km. The ultraviolet solar light near 3000Å was strongly absorbed by the earth's atmosphere (eight times less than normal), and the Ba vapor produced no observable ion cloud. We consider this as a test in favor of the above mentioned two step process.

It is of special importance for the measurement of electric fields that the ion clouds are produced in a short time (some seconds) and have a small extension perpendicular to the magnetic field. This allows a good measurement of its movement in that direction. Four intense emission lines in the visible spectrum facilitate the observations. The long persistence of the Sr I line allows good measurements of the neutral wind.

Theory of Electric Field Measurements

The equation of motion of charged particles in a neutral atmosphere is given by (HAERENDEL, 1966):

$$m_j n_j \frac{d\mathbf{v}_j}{dt} = -\nabla p_j + m_j n_j \mathbf{g} + n_j e_j \left(\mathbf{E} + \frac{\mathbf{v}_j}{c} \times \mathbf{B} \right) - \sum_l m_j n_j \nu_{jl} (\mathbf{v}_j - \mathbf{v}_l) \qquad (1)$$

The indices j and l stand for e = electrons, i = ions, n = neutral molecules, and m_j is the mass, n_j the number density, v_j the velocity; p_j the pressure, g_j the gravitational acceleration, e_j the charge, E the electric field, B the magnetic field and ν_{jl} the collision frequency between components j and l.

For our application we consider a stationary state $\frac{d\mathbf{v}_j}{dt} = 0$, and we neglect the influence of gravitation ($g = 0$), this term considered by HAERENDEL (1966) with respect to sedimentation of Ba clouds. We further assume

$$\text{curl } \mathbf{E} = 0$$

and all processes are considered to be isothermal

$$p_j = n_j kT; \qquad T_e = T_i = T_n = T = \text{const.}$$

We further postulate charge neutrality $n_l = n_i$ which means

$$\text{div } \boldsymbol{j} = 0$$

where $\boldsymbol{j} = e\, n(\mathbf{v}_i - \mathbf{v}_e)$ is the current density.
With these simplifications we are left with a simpler expression

$$n_j e_j\left(\mathbf{E} + \frac{\mathbf{v}_j}{c} \times \mathbf{B}\right) - \sum_l m_j n_j \nu_{jl}(\mathbf{v}_j - \mathbf{v}_l) - \nabla n_j kT = 0 \tag{2}$$

one for electrons and one for ions.
We transform on a frame where the neutral particles are at rest

$$\mathbf{v}^*_j = \mathbf{v}_j - \mathbf{v}_n$$

$$\mathbf{E}^* = \mathbf{E} + \frac{\mathbf{v}_n}{c} \times \mathbf{B}$$

and use the definitions

$$\mathbf{e}_B = \frac{\mathbf{B}}{|B|} \qquad \varkappa_j = \frac{\omega_{gj}}{\nu_{jn}} = \frac{e_j|B|}{m_j c \nu_{jn}}$$

ω_{gj} being the gyrofrequency of j particles. We get:

$$\mathbf{v}^*_j + \varkappa_j^2 \mathbf{e}_B \times (\mathbf{v}_j^* \times \mathbf{e}_B) = \varkappa_j \mathbf{U}_j + \varkappa_j^2(\mathbf{U}_j \times \mathbf{e}_B) \tag{3}$$

with

$$\mathbf{U}_j = \frac{c}{B}\left(\mathbf{E}^* - \mu_j \frac{\nabla n}{n}\right)$$

$$\mu_j = \frac{kT}{e}$$

and by separation of $\mathbf{v}^*_j$ into components perpendicular ($\mathbf{v}^*_{j\perp}$) and parallel ($\mathbf{v}^*_{j\parallel}$) to $\mathbf{B}$

$$\mathbf{v}^*_{j\perp} = \frac{\varkappa_j}{1 + \varkappa_j^2}\mathbf{U}_{j\perp} + \frac{\varkappa_j^2}{1 + \varkappa_j^2}(\mathbf{U}_j \times \mathbf{e}_B) \tag{4}$$

$$\mathbf{v}^*_{j\parallel} = \varkappa_j \mathbf{U}_{j\parallel}. \tag{5}$$

In writing these equations for electrons and ions and by introducing the velocities into $\boldsymbol{j} = e\, n(\mathbf{v}_i - \mathbf{v}_e)$, we get by comparison with the equation

$$\boldsymbol{j} = \overset{\leftrightarrow}{\sigma}\mathbf{E}^* - \overset{\leftrightarrow}{\delta}\mu_j\frac{\nabla n}{n}$$

the conductivity tensor and $\overset{\leftrightarrow}{\sigma}$ the tensor of the differences of the diffusion coefficients $\overset{\leftrightarrow}{\delta}$.

Since in the following we are only interested in the displacement of the ion cloud as a whole, we neglect diffusion terms (deformation of the cloud) and retain the conductivities:

$$\sigma_P = \frac{nec}{|B|}\left(\frac{\varkappa_i}{1+\varkappa_i{}^2} - \frac{\varkappa_I}{1+\varkappa_I{}^2}\right) \text{ Pedersen conductivity}$$

$$\sigma_H = \frac{nec}{|B|}\left(\frac{\varkappa_I{}^2}{1+\varkappa_I{}^2} - \frac{\varkappa_i{}^2}{1+\varkappa_i{}^2}\right) \text{ Hall conductivity}$$

$$\sigma_{||} = \frac{nec}{|B|}(\varkappa_i - \varkappa_2) \text{ parallel conductivity}$$

Because $\sigma_{||}$ is much larger than δ_P and δ_H, the electric field parallel to **B** should be small, and we concentrate on the perpendicular field only.

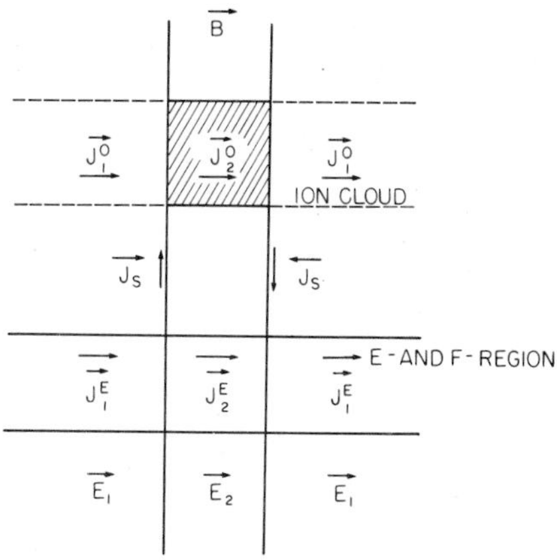

FIGURE 4. Definition of currents in the vicinity of an ion cloud.

Figure 4 contains a diagram of the currents near an ion cloud including the E and F regions below. The continuity of the total current leads to

$$n(J_1{}^0 + J_1{}^E) = n(J_2{}^0 + J_2{}^E) \tag{6}$$

where **n** is normal to **B** and

$$J_{1,2} = \int j_{1,2}{}^{\perp}dl$$

integrated along the lines of force.

The continuity equation may be expressed in terms of the electric field outside (E_1) and inside the cloud (E_2) by introducing

$$J = \Sigma \cdot E$$

$$\Sigma_{P,H} = \int \sigma_{P,H}dl$$

and we get:

$$n(\overset{\leftrightarrow}{\Sigma}_1 E_1 - \overset{\leftrightarrow}{\Sigma}_2 E_2) = 0. \tag{7}$$

In cylindrical coordinates r, ϑ this means

$$\Sigma_{P_1}E_{r_1} - \Sigma_{H_1}E_{\vartheta_1} - \Sigma_{P_2}E_{r_2} + \Sigma_{H_2}E_{\vartheta_2} = 0.$$

By curl $E = 0$ we have $E_{\vartheta_1} = E_{\vartheta_1}$ and with the definition

$$\lambda^* = \frac{\Sigma_{P_2}}{\Sigma_{P_1}} \qquad \zeta = \frac{\Sigma_{H_2}}{\Sigma_{H_1}} \qquad \xi = \frac{\Sigma_{H_2}}{\Sigma_{P_1}},$$

we get:

$$E_{r_1} = \lambda^* E_{r_2} - (\xi - 1)\zeta E_{\vartheta_2}. \tag{8}$$

From an equation given by DUNGEY (1958) we find a relation between the field at infinity (E_0) and inside the cloud (E_2)

$$E_0 = \tfrac{1}{2}(\lambda^* + 1)E_2 - \tfrac{1}{2}(\xi - 1)\zeta(E_2 \times e_B) \tag{9}$$

and solved for E_2,

$$E_2 = \alpha E_0 + \beta\left(E_0 \times \frac{B}{|B|}\right) \tag{10}$$

$$\alpha = \frac{2(1 + \lambda^*)}{(1 + \lambda^*)^2 + (1 - \xi)^2\zeta^2}; \qquad \beta = \frac{2(\xi - 1)\zeta}{(1 + \lambda^*)^2 + (1 - \xi)^2\zeta^2}.$$

We are interested in E_0, but we can measure only the velocity U of the boundary of an ionized cloud. Since the current along the field lines is carried by electrons, we may establish a continuity equation for the horizontal ion current only.

$$nU(n_2 - n_1) = n(n_1 v_{i_2} - n_1 v_{i_1}) \tag{11}$$

with $\lambda = \dfrac{n_2}{n_1}$ and the expression for $v^*_{i_\perp}$ [Equation (4)] we get:

$$nUn_1(\lambda - 1) = \frac{\varkappa_i}{1 + \varkappa_i^2}\frac{c}{B}n_1 n(\lambda E_2 + \lambda\varkappa_i E_2 \times e_B - E_1 - \varkappa_i E_2 \times e_B). \tag{12}$$

We replace E_1 by Equation (8), and consider that Equation (12) is true for all directions of n around the cylinder. We get:

$$U = \gamma\frac{c}{B}E_2 + \delta c\frac{E_2 \times B}{B^2} \tag{13}$$

$$\gamma = \frac{\varkappa_i}{1 + \varkappa_i^2}\frac{\lambda - \lambda^*}{\lambda - 1}; \qquad \delta = \frac{\varkappa_i}{1 + \varkappa_i^2}\left(\varkappa_i + \frac{\xi - 1}{\lambda - 1}\zeta\right).$$

Into that we introduce Equation (10) and find

$$U = ac\frac{E_0}{|B|} + bc\frac{E_0 \times B}{B^2} \tag{14}$$

$$a = \alpha\gamma - \beta\delta \qquad b = \alpha\delta + \beta\gamma.$$

Since in general the neutral component of the atmosphere is not at rest we transform by

$$\mathbf{U} = \mathbf{V}_\perp - \mathbf{v}_{n_\perp}$$

$$\mathbf{E}_0 = \mathbf{E}_\perp{}^0 + \frac{1}{c}(\mathbf{v}_{n_\perp} \times \mathbf{B})$$

and take the component perpendicular to **B**

$$V_\perp = a\left(c\frac{\mathbf{E}_\perp{}^0}{|B|} + \mathbf{v}_{n_\perp} \times \mathbf{e}_B\right) + b \cdot c\,\frac{\mathbf{E}_\perp{}^0 \times \mathbf{B}}{B^2} + (1-b)\mathbf{v}_{n_\perp} \qquad (15)$$

and solved for $\mathbf{E}_\perp{}^0$

$$\mathbf{E}_\perp{}^0 = \frac{|B|}{c}D^{-1}[a(\mathbf{V}_\perp - \mathbf{v}_{n_\perp}) + b(\mathbf{e}_B \times V_\perp) + (b - D)(\mathbf{v}_{n_\perp} \times \mathbf{e}_B)] \qquad (16)$$

$$D = a^2 + b^2.$$

A simplification results from the fact that for heights above the E layer $\varkappa_i \gg 1$ and consequently,

$$a \approx \frac{1}{\varkappa_i}\frac{2}{1 + \lambda^*}; \qquad b \approx \frac{2}{1 + \lambda^*},$$

and Equation (16) becomes

$$\mathbf{E}_\perp{}^0 \approx \frac{1 + \lambda^*}{2}\frac{|B|}{c}\left[\mathbf{e}_B \times V_\perp + \frac{1}{\varkappa_i}(\mathbf{V}_\perp - \mathbf{v}_{n_\perp}) + \frac{\lambda^* - 1}{\lambda + 1}(\mathbf{v}_{n_\perp} \times \mathbf{e}_B)\right]. \qquad (17)$$

This is the basic equation for measurements of electric fields. To deduce $\mathbf{E}_\perp{}^0$ we need: the velocity $\mathbf{v}_\perp$ of the ion cloud; the velocity $\mathbf{v}_{n_\perp}$ of the neutral atmosphere and the value of K_i and Σ, which imply the knowledge of the electron density in the cloud and in the ionosphere. The best data are the velocities which are presented in Table II. The first column is flight number and the last

Table II. Velocities

Flight No.	Element	$v_{\|\|}$ (m/sec)	$\|V_\perp\|$ (m/sec)	φ
i 1	Ba+	35.7	22.6	+5°
	Sr, Ba	17.8	73.0	
i 2	Ba+	22.4	47.6	+3°.4
	Sr, Ba	26.8	75.0	
i 3	Ba+	63.7	53.9	−14°.2
	Sr, Ba	64.9	117.0	
i 4	Ba+	27.7	39.7	+28°
	Sr, Ba	62.9	113.5	
i 7	Ba+ tail	−39.0	90.7	+25°
	Sr, Ba, Ba+	−41.1	47.1	
i 8	Ba+	27.7	28.1	−8°
	Sr, Ba	90.5	54.5	

column is the angle between the displacements of Ba and Ba⁺. The electron density inside the cloud may be deduced from the brightness of the ion cloud. The least known data are the conductivities which change appreciably during twilight when these experiments are made. Since the conductivities are not

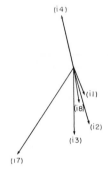

10^{-3} VOLTS/m

FIGURE 5. Electric fields measured by ion cloud experiments.

known very well, the data (Table II) were reduced by using $\lambda^* = 1$ and $a = K_i(1 + K_i)^{-1}$; $b = 1$. As a result, we present a diagram of measured fields (Figure 5). It seems that the field points south in the evening and north in the morning at the latitudes of Sardinia and the Sahara.

References

ALFVEN, H., ESRO Colloquium, November, 1965, Stockholm.
BIERMANN, L., 1951, *Z. Astrophys.* **29**, 274.
BIERMANN, L., 1952, *Z. Naturforsch* **7 a**, 127.
BIERMANN, L., 1953, *La Physique des Cometes, Mem. Soc. Roy. Sci. Liege*, **13**, 251.
BIERMANN, L., LÜST, R., LÜST, RH., and SCHMIDT, H. H., 1961, *Z. Astrophys.* **53**, 226.
BOYD, R. L. F., ESRO Colloquium, November, 1965, Stockholm.
DUNGEY, J. W., 1958, *Cosmic Electrodynamics*, Cambridge Univ. Press.
FAHLESON, M., ESRO Colloquium, November, 1965, Stockholm.
FÖPPL, H., HAERENDEL, G., HASER, L., LOIDL, J., LÜTJENS, P., LÜST, R., MELZNER, F., MEYER, B., NEUSS, H., and RIEGER, E., 1966, *Planetary Space Sci.* (to be published).
FÖPPL, H., HAERENDEL, G., LOIDL, J., LÜST, R., MELZNER, F., MEYER, B., NEUSS, H., and RIEGER, E., 1965, *Planetary Space Sci.* **13**, 95.
GDALEVICH, G. L., 1964, *Space Research* **4**, 452–453.
HAERENDEL, G., in preparation.
HAERENDEL, G., LÜST, R., and RIEGER, E., 1966, *Planetary Space Sci.* (to be published).
HASER, L., in preparation.
KAVADAS, A. and JOHNSON, D. W., 1964, *Space Research* **4**, 365–370.
MOORE, E., 1958, *Atomic Energy Levels, Natl. Bur. Std. Circ.* **467**.
RUSSELL, H. N. and MOORE, C. E., 1955, *J. Res. Natl. Bur. Std.* **55**, 299.

Discussion

The velocity of ions parallel to B is difficult to measure; therefore, only the velocity perpendicular to B is being investigated. Thus, by measuring the displacement of ions in the cloud perpendicular to B an expression for getting the E field perpendicular to B is obtained. Several millivolts per meter is the strength of the E field. Some very preliminary results from Fort Churchill show the opposite vector directions for the E field as Sahara and Sardinia, but with a ten times greater strength.

The dense ion clouds show much internal structure. One had eight bands. The clouds do not seem to rise, but just to expand along the magnetic field lines. These bands indicate that the initial expansion was broken up by the development of instabilities.

These experimental techniques can be used to measure the direction of the magnetic field lines. They should also have application for investigations in the auroral region.

Session

5

OBSERVATIONS II

Dr. Anders Omholt

The Auroral Observatory, Tromsø

AIRGLOW OBSERVATIONS NEAR THE EQUATOR

G. M. Weill

Institut D'Astrophysique, Paris, France

Summary

Few observations of airglow in equatorial regions are available, due partly to overcast skies. A review of the main visible radiation groups shows that:

(a) The emissions in the lowest group (Na D and OH bands) exhibit distinct seasonal variations. Their behavior is still practically unexplored.

(b) The intermediate layer which accounts for the continuum, Herzberg bands, and a major part of 5577 OI emission, has a smooth structure and a major trough (about one half of middle latitude intensities) near the magnetic equator. The position of this trough, not yet observed directly, probably varies seasonally by $\pm 5°$. Intensity maxima occur shortly after the equinoxes.

(c) The high altitude layer, in close relation to the so-called ionospheric "equatorial anomaly," is characterized by two arclike regions of enhanced 6300 OI radiation. Midway between these world-round belts, the region of the magnetic dip equator is one of relative minimum. The variations of the system, as observed optically and inferred from the ionograms, are recalled. The arc system appears to be severely altered during magnetic storms.

I. Introduction

A. The Equator of Airglow

Airglow radiations in the visible portion of the electromagnetic spectrum have been extensively studied on the basis of ground-based observations obtained from middle northern latitude stations in most cases. Until recently, the behavior of these emissions in low latitude regions has received very little attention. It is the purpose of the present paper to review the structure and variations of the main nightglow emissions in the vicinity of the airglow equator.

This particular equator coincides with the magnetic dip equator, i.e., the locus of the magnetic field line and perpendicular gravity force at 300 km altitude. Many features of the airglow emissions are controlled by magnetic dip latitude. In the strictest sense, equatorial observations from the ground can only be obtained within belts of ±8° of dip latitude since the earth's curvature and atmospheric scattering normally prevent observations from greater distances. A list of low latitude airglow stations is given in Table I, including previous, present,

Table I

Station	Country	Latitude	Longitude	Dip Latitude At 300 Km
Mount Abu	India	24.60°	72.70°	23.5°
Haleakala	U.S.A.	20.80°	−156.50°	21.6°
Tamanrasset	Algeria	22.80°	5.52°	15.4°
Poona	India	18.05°	73.12°	11.1°
Agadez	Nigeria	17.00°	7.93°	08.8°
Zamboanga	Philippines	6.54°	122.04°	06.3°
Kodaikanal	India	10.23°	77.48°	01.2°
Huancayo	Peru	−12.05°	−75.33°	−00.5°
Jicamarca	Peru	−11.95°	−76.87°	−00.3°
Addis Ababa	Ethiopia	9.03°	38.77°	−00.4°
Chacaltaya	Bolivia	−16.32°	−68.15°	−02.6°
Arequipa	Peru	−16.35°	−71.57°	−03.0°
Gilgil	Kenya	−0.48°	36.32°	−13.2°
Makatea	Fr. Polynesia	−16.20°	−148.20°	−14.1°
Lwiro	Congo	−2.25°	−28.80°	−15.5°
Rarotonga	Cook Isl. (N.Z.)	−21.20°	−159.75°	−21.5°

and planned stations. Stations with latitudes greater than 20° have not been included, although in many cases they have yielded major results in the global study.

Around the world, the dip equator crosses the geographic equator in the middle of the Pacific, curves down to the vicinity of Lima, Peru, then up across Brazil and the Atlantic to Ghana, Nigeria, Ethiopia, continues to Southern India, to Malaya and to the Philippines. Extreme geographic latitudes are reached in the South American sector (−12°) and in East Africa and India (+9°) (Figure 1).

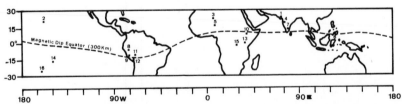

F<small>IGURE</small> 1. A map of tropical and equatorial regions (Mercator projection). The dip equator at 300 km in the Jensen and Cain field for 1960 (J<small>ENSEN</small> and C<small>AIN</small>, 1962) is shown together with the position of existing or planned airglow stations as mentioned in Table 1.

Climatic conditions in those regions are generally unfavorable for ground-based observations; high rainfalls prevail everywhere at least through part of the year because of the intertropical fronts or monsoon regime. Two notable exceptions exist in the south western American coast and in East Africa. Many of the available results have been obtained by means of air or ship-borne equipment. Observations by rockets and satellites have not yet been attempted, and high thunderstorm activity which typifies these regions may prove a serious contaminant for satellite-borne photometers.

B. Available Data

The first measurements on equatorial airglow were made by Lord Rayleigh and his associates who carried out a world-wide program of visual photometry of the green line, between 1924 and 1933. By means of carefully intercompared photometers equipped with filters about 200Å wide, they observed for several months at such stations as Kodaikanal and Arequipa. Tropical observations were made at Hawaii and Gilgil. This early work was recently brought together and reanalyzed by HERNANDEZ and SILVERMAN (1964).

Great progress was made with the development of photoelectric photometry. A network of observatories was set up for the International Geophysical Year, covering middle and lower latitudes. The oxygen and sodium lines were observed with a zenithal photometer at Huancayo, close to the dip equator, and a few measurements of the oxygen green line were made at Zamboanga (Philippines). Data tables covering the IGY and IGC period were published (YAO I.G. 1962).

By the end of the IGY the potential value of mobile stations was recognized. Airglow photometers were operated on the "Soya" during traverses from Japan to Antarctica; similar surveys were later made in the American sector with the "Eltanin." Airborne surveys were initiated by Barbier over Africa. An attempt to observe optical effects of the South American magnetic anomaly has been reported by MARKHAM et al. (1966).

II. Review of Observations

A. The Spectrum of Equatorial Airglow

The early work of BAPPU (1950) and the excellent spectra more recently obtained by BLACKWELL et al. (1960a, b) have shown that the airglow spectrum is essentially the same at the equator as at middle latitudes. There is no reason to believe that the weak, unidentified line reported by the latter authors at 6437,6Å does not occur at other latitudes. The same authors report observing the forbidden doublet of NI at 5199Å, not only during twilight, but also throughout the night. I have evidence which I shall discuss elsewhere that 5199 radiation is greatly enhanced in intertropical arcs over the regular nightglow level. This fact may account, at least in part, for the interesting finding of Blackwell and Ingham.

B. Behavior of the Main Airglow Groups

Airglow emissions fall into three groups of different covariance and altitude (BARBIER, 1960a). Group A of 5577Å includes the Herzberg bands and the continuum. These radiations have a peak altitude between 95 and 105 km. Group B includes sodium and OH, with a peak altitude between 80 and 95 km. Group C contains the red line at 6300Å and originates in the 200–400 km range. The radiations of any one group covary, while the correlation is poor between two different groups.

An exception to this classification comes from the double-peaked distribution of 5577 emission altitude. This line has a high altitude component which varies with 6300, essentially arising from the electronic recombination of O_2^+ which can yield an oxygen atom in either of two excited states, ($1D$) and ($1S$).

1.) OH Bands and the Sodium D Lines. Although some measurements of the "B Group" have been made at low latitudes, they have yielded few notable results. Data from Tamanrasset (BARBIER et al., 1961) indicate that, while the correlation between instantaneous values of the two emissions is as good here as in middle latitudes, the monthly mean values of the D lines observed at two stations 21° apart in latitude are quite similar. This remark does not apply to the OH bands and may be an indication of a world-wide control of sodium in the upper atmosphere, as might be expected if that metal originates in meteors or interplanetary dust. The seasonal variations for the OH bands and Na D lines are shown in Figure 2. The diurnal variation of the Na D lines at the

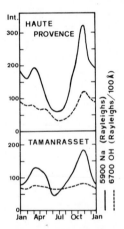

FIGURE 2. Seasonal variations of the OH bands and of the sodium D lines at Tamanrasset and Haute-Provence in the period 1957.

equator (SILVERMAN, 1965) is very regular and shows a midnight minimum. BLACKWELL et al. (1960 b) measured an OH rotational temperature of 293°K from Chacaltaya; this value is not appreciably different from middle latitude values.

Basic research is needed to establish the excitation processes for the airglow B group, and experimental work must proceed in order to clarify the physical and chemical processes which govern the atmospheric region 80–100 km.

2.) The Oxygen Green Line 5577, Herzberg Bands, and the Continuum. Within this group of radiation, the green line of oxygen has naturally been more extensively observed. As mentioned earlier, caution is required to interpret ground-base measurements since at least two different processes are operative. The Chapman triple collision process $O + O + M \rightarrow O^* + OM$ contributes a thin layer around 100 km, and radiative recombination processes in the F region, mainly $O^+ + O_2 \rightarrow O_2^+ + O$, followed by $O_2^+ + e^- \rightarrow O + O^*$, can yield the green as well as the red line. The contributions of the upper layer to global zenithal intensities are of the order of 25 and $< 10\%$ in low and middle latitudes, respectively. At high altitude where quenching of the $(1D)$ state is negligible, the ratio of transition rates $5577/6300$ is about $1/4$; the constancy of this experimentally measured ratio enabled CHRISTOPHE (1965) to study the lower altitude component from Tamanrasset and Agadez.

At low latitudes, 5577 intensities are systematically weaker than at middle latitudes. In Tamanrasset during the IGY and IGC, where the photometer had been carefully intercompared to that of Haute-Provence, the mean corrected intensity ratio at the two stations was about 40%, a crude estimation considering the difficulties inherent in the obtention of accurate photometric calibrations. An analysis of the intensity gradient with latitude from a number of stations (CHRISTOPHE, 1965) confirms the existence of an equatorial "trough" of 5577; the trough has also been observed during ship-borne traverses (DAVIS and SMITH, 1965), although no correction was made for upper altitude emission. The intensities decrease regularly between 25 and 10° geographic latitude in the Sahara. The world's minimum intensities must lie along a "5577 Equator," the exact position of which has not yet been measured directly. The position and movement of the equator can be roughly inferred (Figure 3) from the above

FIGURE 3. The seasonal movement (tentative) of the zone of maximum and minimum intensities of 5577Å at middle latitudes (maxima) and near the equator (minimum). The northern curve is deduced from an analysis of European and African data (CHRISTOPHE, 1965). The southern curve is supposed to be symmetrical with respect to the dip equator with a time shift of six months. The airglow equator is supposed to be half-way between the northern and southern middle latitudes maxima.

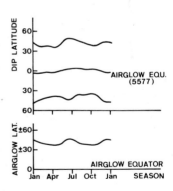

mentioned analysis of intensity gradients with latitude, knowing that the variations with local season in both hemispheres are quite similar at similar latitudes (BARBIER et al., 1963a).

The seasonal movement of the airglow equator so deduced resembles that of the meteorological equator. It varies on a 12 month cycle by $\pm 5°$ about the dip equator, and its latitude follows the declination of the sun with a one month delay. The maximal zones at middle latitudes vary on a semiannual cycle as the polar aurora does; also as the aurora, they are closest to the poles at solstices. An additional annual variation of the world-wide 5577 intensity is necessary to reconcile the low latitude annual intensity variation (Figure 5) with the simplified picture above. This variation is marked by two maxima, one month after solstices, and minima in January–February, and August–September (less marked).

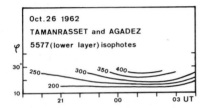

FIGURE 4. A typical set of isophotes of 5577Å radiation (lower layer) versus time and latitude, from observations at Tamanrasset and Agadez. To convert geographic latitudes to dip latitudes in that longitude sector, subtract 8° (CHRISTOPHE-GLAUME, 1965).

The equatorial 5577 lower layer exhibits very smooth variations in space and time. Enhancement cells (ROACH, 1961; BARBIER, 1964a) typical of middle latitudes do not appear, and at any one time, the intensity decreases regularly between 25 and 10° (Figure 4). At low latitudes, the amplitude of the diurnal

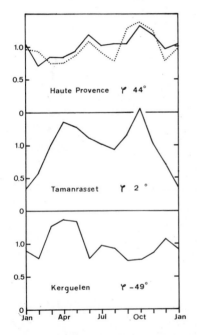

FIGURE 5. The seasonal variation of 5577Å at northern, tropical, and southern latitude stations. At an equatorial station two similar intensity maxima would be observed shortly after the equinoxes.

variation is only about 30%. The shape of the diurnal curve is a function of latitude and possibly longitude (SILVERMAN, 1965). North of Tamanrasset a weak maximum occurs in the morning hours ($\phi = 25°$), the curve is flat at

$\phi = 10°$, and at $\phi = -3°$ (Lwiro) there is a midnight minimum similar to that observed at Huancayo.

3.) High Altitude Emissions. The high altitude optical emission at 6300Å, which exhibits quite regular distribution and variation features at middle latitudes, undergoes abrupt and intense variations in the tropics closely related to the "magnetic anomaly" in the F region (APPLETON, 1954; BARBIER, 1963 b,c,d). The most spectacular global feature (BARBIER, 1960) was initially called "arc intertropical" (northern or southern). It is referred to under several names in the literature. This phenomenon shows various aspects according to longitude and season and frequently appears in the form of finely structured airglow intensity enhancements (BARBIER *et al.*, 1962 a); their observation from Haleakala Observatory is covered by W. R. Steiger elsewhere in this volume, and observations from India were described by CHIPLONKAR *et al.*, (1961). The present description pertains to the general features of the arcs and is based essentially on airglow observations in the African sector by the Barbier group and on some currently available ionospheric data.

Two regions of maximum enhancement occur symmetrically with respect to the dip equator around magnetic dip latitudes $\pm 12°$. The regions are statistically aligned on a world-wide (BARBIER *et al.*, 1962 a) and local (STEIGER *et al.*, 1966) scale, along the magnetic isoclines. Under favorable conditions of season and solar cycle, the maximum zenith brightness is of the order of 1000 rayleighs, while it is only about 80 R in middle latitudes and at the equator (Figure 6).

From Tamanrasset during periods of solar maximum activity, the inter-

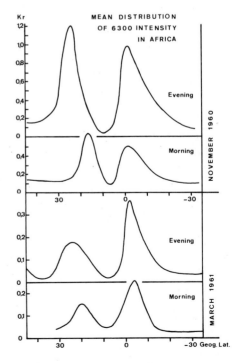

FIGURE 6. The mean distribution of 6300Å zenithal intensities in Africa after airborne surveys in 1960–61 (BARBIER *et al.*, 1961 d). At any particular time the latitudinal extent of the enhancement zones is much smaller than this composite smoothed picture would indicate.

tropical arc appears as a broad subvisual band of enhancement with a latitudinal extent of about 500 km at half intensity, extending across the sky in the east-west direction (Figure 7). The arc's altitude measured by triangulation from two

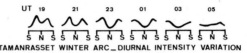

FIGURE 7. The mean nightly intensity of 6300Å on almucantar sweeps at Tamanrasset (BAR-BIER, 1961 d). The southern movement of the arc together with a regular decrease in intensity are noticeable. The predawn enhancement effect is apparent on the 05 hours sweep.

stations can vary between approximately 200 and 400 km. In the early night hours, a smooth intensity variation appears to travel from east to west as if the earth were rotating under a configuration fixed with respect to inertial space. The intensity sometimes appears to be progressively transferred from one fine structure to another (Figure 8).

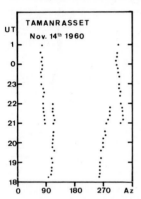

FIGURE 8. An example of a discontinuous equatorward motion of the northern intertropical arc. The points represent relative maxima of intensity of several almucantar sweeps. An arc is visible in the early part of the night until 22 hours, while a second arc appears to the south of it at 21 hours and takes over completely (BARBIER, 1960).

As the night progresses, the arcs slowly move toward the equator. The nocturnal excursion is of the order of 6° (Figure 9). Throughout the night, the arc intensity generally decreases. These variations in intensity and location may produce a confusing picture when a fixed-direction photometer is used.

   4.) Seasonal Variations in the African Sector. Most of the observations

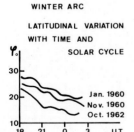

FIGURE 9. The mean nightly movements of the northern arc as seen from Tamanrasset at various phases in the solar cycle.

have been made on the northern arc which is most intense in autumn and early winter. In summer, fixed-direction observations have shown that it practically disappears; the residual 6300 intensity may then be weaker than that observed at middle latitudes. However, every two or three days a strong enhancement occurs, and typical winter intensity levels can be reached for a few hours.

The structure of these enhancements is unknown as yet. Although the southern arc region has been less consistently studied, fixed-direction observations from Lwiro (DELSEMME, A. and D., 1960) have shown strong enhancements almost every night, with a maximum intensity toward the midnight hours. These measurements as well as airborne measurements (BARBIER, 1961 d) indicate simple seasonal variations for both arcs which exhibit yearly intensity maxima during the local autumn and early winter time.

5.) Variations with the Solar Cycle. Marked variations in intensity and appearance occur with solar cycle activity. These variations deduced from several sets of measurements from 1957–62 can be summarized as follows: (a) the global intensity decreased by 2/3 in the period 1960–62; (b) the mean dip latitude of the arcs decreases with solar activity; in the same period, this systematic latitude shift was about 6° (Figure 9); (c) a nightly equatorward shift occurs throughout the solar cycle and, during low activity periods, the arcs should approach the equatorial region in the late night hours; and (d) at low solar activity, the general arc structure is absent and the structure then degenerates into enhancement regions; in winter at Tamanrasset, three main enhancements occur during the night around 19, 22, and 01 hours UT.

In addition, there is an indication that the statistical relation between the 6300 intensity and the ionospheric parameters does vary systematically according to a decrease of scale height in the F 2 region in the quiet sun years. BARBIER (1964 b) found evidence that the scale height of O_2 had decreased from 53–30 km between November, 1960 and November, 1962, indicating a large temperature change at the 270 km level.

A semi-empirical relation between the 6300 intensity and the ionosphere was found by BARBIER (1962 a) and shown to be quite accurate at low latitudes. This relation, further discussed by PETERSON et al. (1966), can be used to infer optical intensity variations from ionosphere scalings for regions where no direct observations are available. Such an analysis shows that, in addition to the variations described above, the intertropical arcs at different longitudes around the globe (Figure 10) behave differently.

To summarize: (a) at the equator, the intensity level during all seasons is much brighter in America than in Africa; (b) in these two sectors, the arc closest to the local summer pole disappears almost completely in January and July, respectively; and (c) there seems to be a systematic variation of the local time of maximum intensity with longitude. Effects (b) and (c) indicate that the variations obey the compound influence of dip latitude and geographic latitude, the latter modulating the 6300 intensity variations.

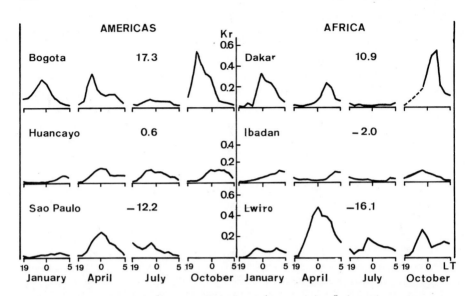

FIGURE 10. The nightly variation of 6300 intensity, at a time of solar maximum activity, for American and African stations located at northern, equatorial and southern dip latitudes. The intensity is deduced from the median $h'F$ and f_0F^2 values by the Barbier formula:

$$Q\ 6300 = 2,95\ f_0F_2{}^2 \exp\left[(h' - 200) / 41.3\right] + 109$$

(BARBIER et al., 1962a)

C. Other Airglow Effects Near the Equator

1.) Predawn Enhancement. The predawn enhancement effect in the European sector can be observed down to tropical latitudes. At Tamanrasset (BARBIER et al., 1961 b,d) it starts at 4.15 UT in the north eastern sector at the end of the winter night when the intertropical arc has died away. Superposed on its general glow, an intense peak then occurs toward the east, about 10° to the south of the solar direction (Figure 11). This "paratwilight" effect increases

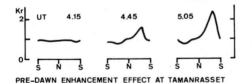

PRE-DAWN ENHANCEMENT EFFECT AT TAMANRASSET

FIGURE 11. The predawn enhancement effect shows a strong latitudinal control in the region of intertropical arcs.

rapidly by as much as 1 kR within 30 min , as though the intertropical arc was locally and suddenly being revived. There is no similar effect in the evening, while the time of onset of the morning effect is generally consistent with the hypothesis of an excitation by photo-detached electrons incoming from the magnetically conjugate area where the sun rises (COLE, 1965). At the very dip equator no such effect should be observable.

2.) Storm effects. At times of intense magnetic storms the intertropical arc system may be severly altered, as can be expected from the analysis of ionospheric storms in those regions. In one case (BARBIER, 1962 b), on November 12 and 13, 1960, unusually low 6300 intensities were observed during parts of the night, and the arc was completely disrupted. At another time during the same night, a very sharp maximum of about 800 R in the red line was recorded toward the northwest. In the same direction, a feeble glow was visible with the naked eye. At the same time, visual observations from western Europe indicate that an aurora could not have been visible from Tamanrasset. It seems likely that in extreme cases, strong airglow enhancements could be seen visually by unwarned observers and mistaken for a polar aurora.

III. Concluding Remarks

This review of existing data and published research results should have shown that the airglow in equatorial regions deserves more attention than it has received so far. The equatorial belt is one of relative and possibly absolute minimal intensities for the F region emissions as well as for those arising in the 100 km region. There is evidence that these emissions are controlled by the compound influence of the magnetic field, of geographic latitude and solar declination or season. Observations near the dip equator should be particularly useful to clarify the distribution of atomic oxygen about the 100 km level. At higher altitudes, strong intensity gradients corresponding to fine spatial structures are observed within a $\pm 15°$ belt; optical observations of the 6300 OI and 5199 NI emissions will be a powerful complement to radio sounding studies of the ionosphere, since they permit good spatial resolution. Such observations may prove decisive in unveiling the ionization transport mechanisms, the ionospheric recombination processes and interactions between the neutral and ionized atmospheric constituents.

References

APPLETON, E. V., 1954, *J. Atmospheric Terrest. Phys.* **5,** 348.
BAPPU, M. K. V., 1950, *Astrophys. J.* **111,** 201–202.
BARBIER, D., 1961a, Année Géophysique Internationale, Série IV, fasc. 1, CNRS.
BARBIER, D., 1961d, *Ann. Géophys.* **17,** 3–15.
BARBIER, D., 1962b, *J. Phys. Soc. Japan* **17,** Supplt. AI.
BARBIER, D., 1963c, *C. R. Acad. Sci.* **257,** 2138–2140.
BARBIER, D., 1963d, *Planetary Space Sci.* **10,** 29–35.
BARBIER, D., 1964a, *Airglow — Research in Geophysics,* vol. 1: *Sun, Upper Atmosphere and Space,* M. I. T. Press, pp. 401–422.
BARBIER, D., 1964b, *Ann. Géophys.* **20,** 22–23.
BARBIER, D., ARGÉMI, L., CAMMAN, G., MARSAN, J., HUILLE, S. and MORGULEFF, N., 1963b, *C. R. Acad. Sci.* **256,** 2215–2216.
BARBIER, D. and GLAUME, J., 1960, *Ann. Géophys.* **16,** 56–76.
BARBIER, D. and GLAUME, J., 1962a, *Planetary Space Sci.* **9,** 133–148.

BARBIER, D., ROACH, F. E., and STEIGER, W. R., 1962c, *J. of Res. Natl. Bur. Std.-D Radio Propagation* **66D**.

BARBIER, D., VOLOT, J., and PELISSIER, J., 1963a, *Ann. Géophys.* **19**, 184–187.

BARBIER, D., WEILL, G., DAGUILLON, J., and MARSAN, J., 1961b, *C. R. Acad. Sci.*, **252**, 304.

BARBIER, D., WEILL, G., and FAFIOTTE, M., 1961c, *C. R. Acad. Sci.* **252**, 3102–3103.

BARBIER, D., WEILL, G., and GLAUME, J., 1961e, *Ann. Géophys.* **17**, 305–318.

BLACKWELL, D. E., INGHAM, M. F., and RUNDLE, H. N., 1960a, *Ann. Géophys.* **16**, 152.

BLACKWELL, D. E , INGHAM, M. F., and RUNDLE, H. N., 1960b, *Astrophys. J.* **131**, 4–24.

CHIPLONKAR, M. W. and AGASHE, V. V., 1961, *Ann. Géophys.* **17**, 231.

CHRISTOPHE-GLAUME, J., 1965, *Ann. Géophys.* **21**, 1–57.

COLE, K. D., 1965, *Ann. Géophys.* **21**, 156–158.

DAVIS, T. N. and SMITH, L. L., 1965, *J. Géophys. Res.* **70**, 1127–1138.

DELSEMME, A. and D., 1960, *Ann. Géophys.* **16**, 507.

HERNANDEZ, G. J. and SILVERMAN, S. M., 1964, *Planetary and Space Sci.* **12**, 97–112.

JENSEN, D. C. and CAIN, J. C., 1962, *J. Geophys. Res.* **67**, 35–69.

MARKHAM, T. P. and ANCTIL, R. E., 1966, *J. Geophys. Res.* **71**, 997.

PETERSON, V. L., VAN ZANDT, T. E., and NORTON, R. B., 1966, *J. Geophys. Res.* **71**, 2255–2265.

ROACH, F. E., 1961, *Ann. Géophys.* **17**, 172.

ROEDERER, J. G., HESS, W. N., and STASSINOPOULOS, E. G., 1965, X-642-65-182 Goddard Space Flight Center, Greenbelt, Maryland.

SILVERMAN, S. M., 1965, AFCRL 65-280.

STEIGER, W. R., BROWN, W. E., and ROACH, F. E., 1966, *J. Geophys. Res.* **71**, 2846.

YAO, I. G., 1962, *Ann. of the Geophys. Year 1957–1958*, vol. XXIV, Pergamon.

LOW LATITUDE OBSERVATIONS OF AIRGLOW*

Walter R. Steiger

University of Hawaii, Honolulu, Hawaii

I. Introduction

The low latitude observations of airglow to be discussed in this paper were made at the Haleakala Observatory of the Hawaii Institute of Geophysics, University of Hawaii, during the period from June, 1961 to December, 1965. Although this is not a survey of low latitude observations in general, we believe that we observed a representative sample of the phenomena found at this latitude.

The Haleakala Observatory is exceedingly well situated for airglow studies because at an elevation of 3080 meters above sea level it is generally above the cumulus clouds suppressed by the trade wind inversion and enjoys an exceptionally transparent atmosphere (STEIGER and LITTLE, 1958), well away from artificial lights. The zenith observations at 300 km correspond to a dip latitude of 19° N and at 80° from the zenith in the south, the photometer reaches about 1000 km towards the equator, or about 10° in latitude.

The photometric equipment includes a scanning, birefringent filter photometer for the emissions of [OI] 5577Å, [OI] 6300Å, and Na I 5890Å–5896Å doublet (ROACH et al., 1958) and a fixed, zenith photometer employing interference filters for the same three emissions as well as a fourth centered near 5300Å to record the background continuum (PURDY et al., 1961).

The scanning photometer covers the sky in a series of almucantar sweeps at zenith angles 80°, 75°, 60°, 40°, and the zenith. Five minutes are required for a complete survey in each of the three colors so that the time interval between successive surveys for a given color is 15 minutes.

The zenith photometer makes a complete series of observations every five minutes. The sky observation through each filter is followed by an observation of a carbon 14-phosphor standard light source. Reduction of the observations by the two-color method (ROACH and MEINEL, 1955) then leads to absolute integrated emission rates in rayleighs. The birefringent photometer observations at the zenith are calibrated by comparison with the zenith photometer. The carbon 14 light source is periodically calibrated against a secondary standard carbon filament lamp. We estimate at most an absolute error of ±20 R in our results.

*Hawaii Institute of Geophysics Contribution No. 169.

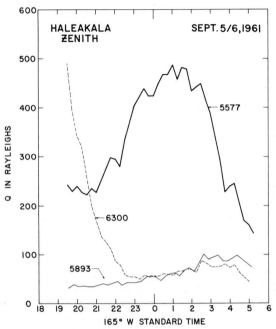

FIGURE 1. Variations of the 5577Å, 6300Å, and 5893Å emissions during the night of September 5/6, 1961.

II. The Nature of the Phenomena

In this section we shall discuss the temporal and spatial variations of the emissions studied.

A. Diurnal Variations

Figure 1 shows an example of the variation of the three emissions during a particular night. This is not necessarily a "typical" night but is a classic example of the completely independent variations among the three lines. The average diurnal variations, presented in Figures 2, 3, and 4 for the years 1962–5, show that, in general terms, the 5577Å emission reaches a maximum during the night, the 6300Å emission is a maximum at the beginning of the night but decreases rapidly and levels off at a fairly low level for the remainder of the night, and the 5893Å emission (as we shall refer to the Na doublet) has no significant diurnal variation. We also note that the 5577Å and 6300Å emissions seem to show a decline toward the minimum of the solar cycle, 1963, and a rise thereafter. The 5893Å emission shows no significant variations from year to year.

Figure 5 illustrates that the diurnal variation can differ dramatically from the "typical" or average behavior. This is a classic example of 6300Å tropical enhancements with covariant 5577Å enhancements. Note that again the 5893Å

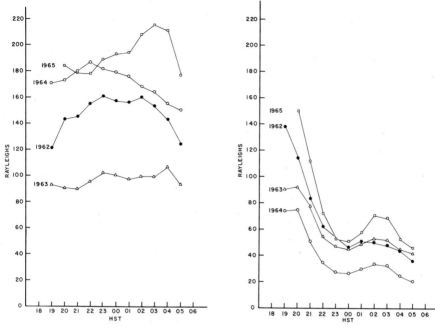

FIGURE 2. Average diurnal variations of 5577Å emission for the years 1962–5.

FIGURE 3. Average diurnal variations of 6300Å emission for the years 1962–5.

emission behaves quite independently of the other two. The temporal and spatial variations of these enhancements and their physical interpretation constitute some of the most fascinating and perplexing problems of the tropical airglow. These shall be discussed at greater length below.

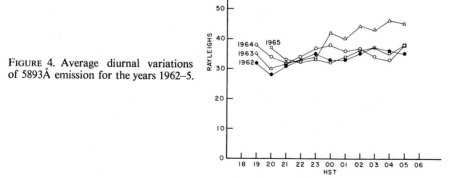

FIGURE 4. Average diurnal variations of 5893Å emission for the years 1962–5.

B. Seasonal Variations

All three of the emissions studied here show distinct seasonal changes in the diurnal variation as well as the monthly average intensity. These changes are

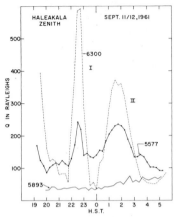

FIGURE 5. Variations of the 5577Å, 6300Å, and 5893Å emissions during the night of September 11/12, 1961.

illustrated in Figures 6, 7, and 8 for 1961–2 and Figures 9, 10, and 11 for 1964–5. The 5577Å emissions do not show a large change between the two periods except for the shift in the spring maximum from early in the night to very late in

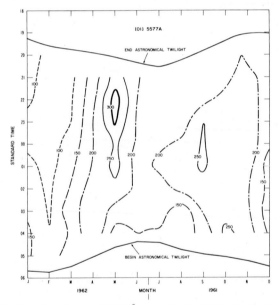

FIGURE 6. Monthly-diurnal variation of 5577Å emission for 1961–2 (after SMITH and OWEN, 1966).

the night. The 6300Å emissions in 1961–2 went through a very strong autumn maximum with a diurnal maximum immediately after twilight. But in 1964–5, this evening maximum in the fall had shifted mainly to the summer, while a weak secondary maximum appears in the early morning hours of spring. The

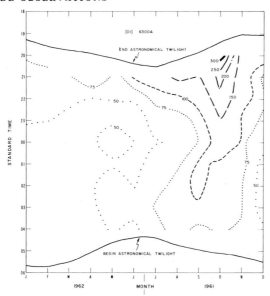

FIGURE 7. Monthly-diurnal variation of 6300Å emission for 1961–2 (after SMITH and OWEN, 1966).

beginning of an autumn maximum appears, but this actually was not present in 1964 and is only a development of late 1965 in an apparent trend to the situa-

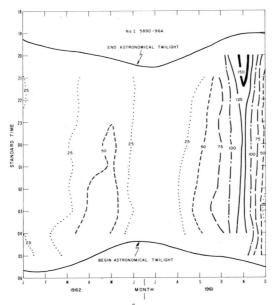

FIGURE 8. Monthly-diurnal variation of 5893Å emission for 1961–2 (after SMITH and OWEN, 1966).

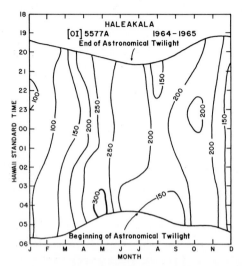

FIGURE 9. Monthly-diurnal variation of 5577Å emission for 1964–5.

tion of 1961–2. The 5893Å emissions also went through a strong autumn maximum in 1961–2 as well as a weaker spring maximum. In 1964–5, the two seasonal maxima still persist, but with the spring maximum slightly higher than the fall.

The differences between the two periods may be associated with the solar cycle, a topic to be discussed later.

C. Spatial Variations

The facts considered thus far have been based entirely on zenith observations, but we now note the nature of the variations over the sky. A simple technique

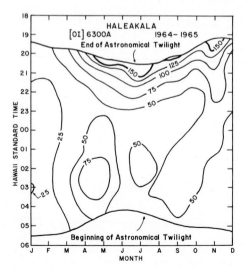

FIGURE 10. Monthly-diurnal variation of 6300Å emission for 1964–5.

of some usefulness is to compare the intensity at some zenith angle south to that at the same zenith angle north. The greater the zenith angle, the greater the latitude difference in the comparison. We have chosen a zenith angle of 75° as

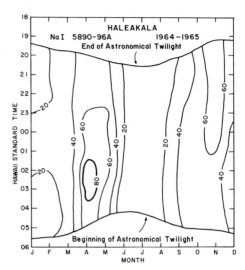

FIGURE 11. Monthly-diurnal variation of 5893Å emission for 1964–5.

the optimum angle in consideration of the possibility that the uncertainty in the extinction at larger zenith angles may introduce unknown errors. Taking the ratio of the south to north intensities at 75° zenith angle, gives us a number which is independent of calibration, scattering, or extinction and assumes only that these factors are identical at the two positions.

The monthly-diurnal variations of the south-to-north ratios of the emissions of the three wavelengths are presented in Figures 12, 13, and 14. In the case of the 5577Å and 5893Å emissions, there seems to be a weak summer maximum in the north, but aside from this effect, it is difficult to describe any systematic pattern to these variations. For this reason only one or two of these plots have been shown. The 6300Å emission, however, shows quite a clear-cut pattern and variation from year to year. A consistent feature is the summertime maximum in the north in the evening hours before midnight. Spring and autumn maxima in the south are features that appear to be altered during the solar cycle, diminishing from 1961–4 and apparently beginning to rise again in 1965. The autumn of 1963 is a notable departure from this pattern. The large ratios observed here may be related to the high level of solar activity and magnetic disturbance that occurred during September and October.

From the observations of the scanning photometer, it is possible to obtain a rather detailed map of the entire sky, down to a zenith angle of 80°, for any one of the three wavelengths. Such a map is available every 15 minutes, as explained earlier. These are normally obtained by reading the records every 22.5° in azimuth at each zenith angle. From the local zenith intensities deduced for each of these 81 points, an isophote map is produced. The maps are plotted to

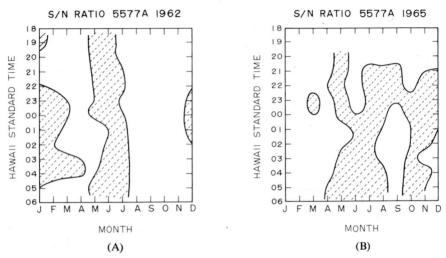

FIGURE 12. Monthly-diurnal variation of 5577Å south-to-north ratio at 75° zenith angle, (A) 1962, (B) 1965.

have a uniform scale of distance along any radius, assuming a height of 300 km for 6300Å, 100 km for 5577Å, and 85 km for 5893Å. These maps are useful for studying the detailed spatial variation of the airglow.

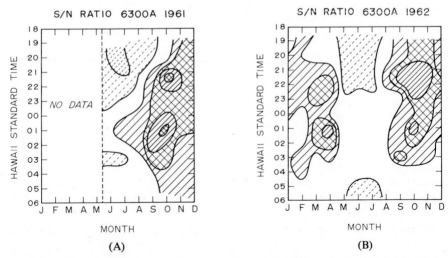

FIGURE 13. Monthly-diurnal variation of 6300Å south-to-north ratio at 75° zenith angle, (A) 1961, (B) 1962, (C) 1963, (D) 1964, (E) 1965.

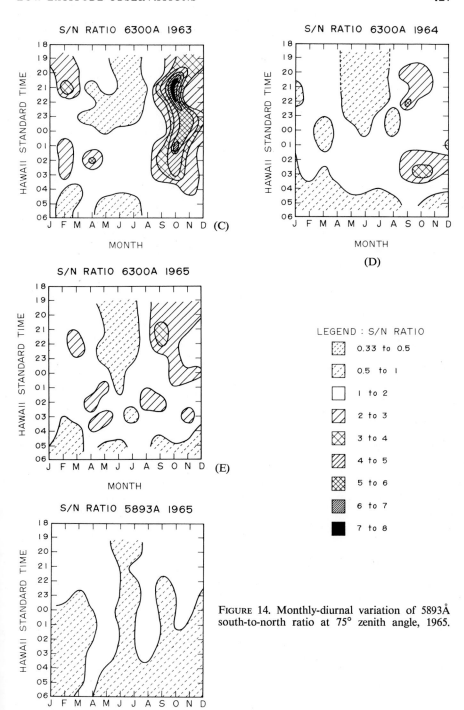

FIGURE 14. Monthly-diurnal variation of 5893Å south-to-north ratio at 75° zenith angle, 1965.

Figure 15(A) is a single map for the night of September 11/12, 1961, as used earlier in Figure 5. A series of such maps for the night of September 11/12 gives a detailed picture of the morphology of the three enhancements which occurred

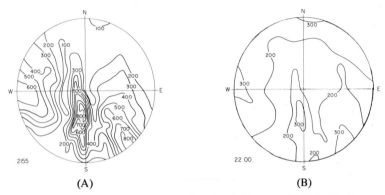

(A)   (B)

FIGURE 15. Isophote maps for the night of September 11/12, 1961: (A) 6300Å, (B) 5577Å.

on this night. We find that these enhancements do not extend over the entire sky, but in fact are rather limited in area, having a diameter of approximately 500 km. Also, they do not necessarily occur at the zenith but generally to the south of Haleakala. This accounts for the peaks in the south-north ratio seen in Figure 13. A careful analysis (PETERSON et al., 1966) of two such nights has shown a gradual motion of the enhancement pattern in a south-easterly direction at a speed of about 200 km/hr.

It was mentioned earlier that the 6300Å tropical enhancements are frequently accompanied by similar variations in the 5577Å emission. This was also seen in the maps of enhancements where the 6300Å structure was quite closely duplicated in the 5577Å structure. An example of such a situation is shown in Figure 15(B) where a map of the 5577Å observed emission is reduced and plotted as though it were entirely at a height of 300 km. Approximately 100 R actually originate from a height of 100 km, with the remainder originating at the same height as the 6300Å emission and hence showing a similar pattern.

There have been a number of occasions when the structure in the 6300Å airglow was so precipitous that much of its detail was lost when reading the records every 22.5° in azimuth, as is customary. On a few of these we have reread the records at smaller intervals to show the photometric peaks and valleys as observed. An example of such structure is shown in Figure 16. Such structure is always associated with a much enhanced emission and is generally in the form of narrow, parallel ridges or fingers running approximately north-south.

The tendency of the fingers to converge towards the meridian, as noted in the figure, is an observational distortion caused by the fact that the bright regions are at a significantly lower altitude than the fainter regions, as we shall discuss later. Hence, they tend to appear further away than in actuality when they are plotted as though they were at 300 km. Since the south ends of the fingers are brighter and hence lower than the north ends, their locations will be more distorted than the north ends, resulting in the converging appearance.

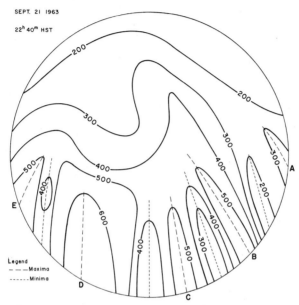

FIGURE 16. 6300Å Isophote map for September 21, 1963, showing highly structured arc.

Actually, the majority of isophote maps do not show any significant structure and, in fact, a great many show a rather uniform emission over the sky, often with a gradual gradient towards the south. These maps have the appearance of approximately straight and parallel isophotes. It has been found (STEIGER et al., 1966) that during the period from 22–03 hr, during which we are free from twilight effects, a large majority of those 6300Å maps on which the isophotes are aligned show a preferred direction of alignment such that the gradient of the radiance is anti-parallel to the horizontal component of the earth's magnetic field. This again suggests some sort of magnetic control in the form of the 6300Å emission.

III. Relationships with the Ionosphere

The relationship of the 6300Å emission to the F-region ionosphere was proposed by Barbier in terms of a semi-empirical formula now known to those in the field as "Barbier's Equation." This relationship is

$$Q = A + B(foF2)^2 e - \frac{h'F - 200}{H}$$

Here Q is the 6300Å integrated emission rate, $foF2$ is the F-region critical frequency in M hertz (the square of this quantity is proportional to the electron number density at the $F2$ peak), the $h'F$ is the virtual height in km of the base of the F-region, and H is the molecular scale height at 200 km (about 40 km). The constants A and B are determined empirically from comparison with observed 6300Å emissions. The significance of B has been interpreted theoretically (PETERSON et al., 1966) in terms of ion exchange-dissociative recombination reactions. But the constant A does not come out of the theory and is not yet fully understood. It has been suggested by PETERSON and STEIGER (1966) that it may

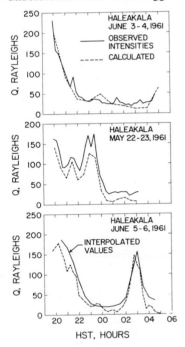

FIGURE 17. 6300Å diurnal variations on three nights, showing the observed intensities and those calculated by the Barbier equation (after BARBIER et al., 1962).

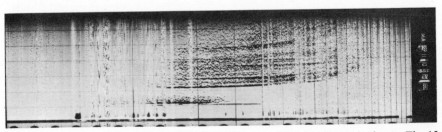

FIGURE 18. Maui ionogram for September 11, 1961, corresponding closely in time to Fig. 15.

be due to contamination by OH emissions entering the optical system. It is also possible that some other mechanism, as yet undiscovered, may be producing a 6300Å emission. For any given night, constants A and B can be found such that this formula gives a surprisingly good fit to the observations, as seen in Figure 17.

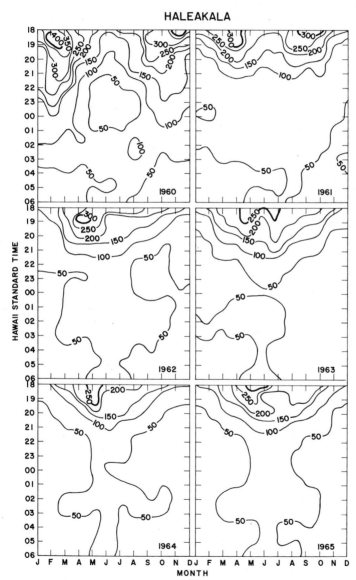

FIGURE 19. Monthly-diurnal variations of 6300Å emission as calculated by the Barbier equation from Maui ionospheric data.

The basis of the earlier statement that the brighter regions are generated at lower altitudes than fainter regions can now be understood in terms of the Barbier equation. Q is related to $h'F$ exponentially but to $foF2$ quadratically. $foF2$ usually varies by a factor of less than 2 during an enhancement, but the height may change by 100 km or more, resulting in a factor of 10 or more change in Q. Thus, Q is more sensitive to $h'F$ than $foF2$ and, as a first approximation, large changes in observed Q can be associated with large changes in the height of the emission. It follows then, that at times when the 6300Å emission is enhanced and highly structured, the F-region ionosphere will present a "corrugated" bottom side. This is borne out in the ionogram for the night of September 11/12, 1961, shown in Figure 18. The oblique and spread reflections from these corrugations make the ionogram extremely difficult to interpret. Indeed, before the establishment of this airglow-ionosphere relationship, the interpretation was impossible in any detailed way.

Earlier we suggested the possibility of a solar cycle variation in the behavior of the 6300Å emission. Unfortunately, our observations started in 1961 when solar activity was rapidly declining towards the minimum, and it will be several years until the next maximum. However, with the aid of Barbier's equation and a catalogue of ionospheric data, it is possible to go back in time and estimate what the 6300Å emission might have been. This has been done by Walter Brown of this observatory, with the results shown in Figure 19. According to these calculations, the general level of 6300Å emissions should reach a very large peak at solar maximum.

Acknowledgments   The author wishes to acknowledge the assistance of Dr. V. L. Peterson, W. E. Brown, and L. L. Smith in the preparation of certain parts of the data presented here. This work was supported in part by NASA grant NsG-135-61 and NASA contract R-18.

References

BARBIER, D., ROACH, F. E., and STEIGER, W. R., 1962, *J. Res. Natl. Bur. Std.* **66D**, 145–152.
PETERSON, V. L. and STEIGER, W. R., 1966, *J. Geophys. Res.* **71**, 2267.
PETERSON, V. L., VAN ZANDT, T. E., and NORTON, R. B., 1966, *J. Geophys. Res.* **71**, 2255.
PETERSON, V. L., VAN ZANDT, T. E., ROACH, F. E., and STEIGER, W. R., (to be submitted to *Ann. Geophys*).
PURDY, E. M., MEGILL, L. R., and ROACH, F. E., 1961, *J. Res. Natl. Bur. Std.* **65C**, 213.
ROACH, F. E., MEGILL, L. R., REES, M. H., and MAROVICH, E., 1958, *J. Atmospheric Terrest. Phys.* **12**, 171.
ROACH, F. E. and MEINEL, A. B., 1955, *Astrophys, J.* **122**, 530–553.
SMITH, L. L. and OWEN, R. W., 1966, *Natl. Bur. Std. Tech. Note* 329, January 10.
STEIGER, W. R., BROWN, W. E., and ROACH, F. E., 1966, *J. Geophys. Res.* **71**, 2846.
STEIGER, W. R. and LITTLE, J. W., 1958, *Publ. Astron. Soc. Pacific* **70**, 556.

Discussion

It was agreed that the spatial plots should show the geomagnetic meridians and L lines. The flat plane presentation should be corrected to account for the 6300Å enhancements, which occur at a much lower altitude than the minima.

Lange-Hesse pointed out that airglow and K_p seemed to be correlated at the antipodal point in Africa.

It was suggested that the Na measurements might well be contaminated by the OH emission at the same wavelengths. Steiger said that they have not studied OH at all, nor made a correction for it.

There was a discussion concerning the relative dimensions of the intertropical red arc and the intensity enhancements observed at 6300Å $\simeq$ the same geographical location. The arcs have a typical width at half-maximum of about 10° of latitude; the arc width varies and shows a general increase towards a magnetic dip of 15°. The arc defines a zone in which the enhancements are observed, but the arc and the enhancements are definitely two separate phenomena. The enhancements are much narrower than the zone, and are very localized events. Then enhancements move with the zone, so during the solar cycle minimum, as the zone moves toward the equator, the enhancements tend to follow, and from Hawaii are, therefore, observed to the south.

There was a question concerning the interpretation of the variable corrrelation between the 5577Å and 6300 Å emission. The 5577Å emission consists of two layers — one at an altitude of about 100 km and the other at 250 km. The latter is correlated with the 6300Å emission, since it is from the same region, and the former is not. Thus observations of the entire 5577Å emission may or may not be correlated with the 6300Å emission, depending on the degree to which emission from the lower level masks that from the upper level.

KINETIC TEMPERATURE MEASUREMENTS OF THE 5577Å [OI] LINE OF THE NIGHT AIRGLOW

G. J. Hernandez

Air Force Cambridge Research Laboratories, Bedford, Massachusetts

J. P. Turtle

Northeastern University, Boston, Massachusetts

Abstract Results of kinetic temperature measurements of the night airglow 5577Å [OI] line at Bedford, Massachusetts with a Fabry-Perot interferometer are presented. Nightly mean temperatures, as well as variations about this mean, are discussed.

A considerable portion of airglow investigations consists of the measurements of the emissions of atomic species which occur as a product of upper atmospheric processes. These investigations can be divided into three broad categories: wavelength measurements, rate of emission studies, and line profile determinations. Wavelength measurements are performed to ascertain the nature of the emitting species, exemplified by BABCOCK's (1923) green nightglow line measurement, which was followed by the laboratory production, wavelength measurement, and identification by McLENNAN and collaborators (1924, 1927). The identification was later confirmed by FRERICHS (1930) from spectral data. Absolute rate of emission measurements have been made since RAYLEIGH's (1930) early investigations in order to determine the number of emitting species, as well as to examine the dynamical processes of the atmosphere at the height of emission. Line profile determinations provide further information about the processes leading to emission as well as, under favorable circumstances, a measure of some of the properties such as temperature of the surrounding medium. Because of the forbidden nature of the transitions which give rise to the more intense visual night airglow emissions, the natural line widths are very small and usually negligible in comparison with the kinetic energy broadening. Also for the same reason there exist negligible radiative transfer effects to interfere with the line profile interpretation. Therefore, if the emitting species is in equilibrium with the surrounding atmosphere, the

435

emission line profile will be a measure of the temperature at the height(s) of emission.

The bulk of the emission of the 5577Å [OI] radiation of the night sky is known to be in a layer located at the 94–99 km height (PACKER, 1961; O'BRIEN et al., 1965; WOLFF, 1966; GULLEDGE et al., 1966). At this level the collision frequency (about 3500 sec⁻¹) (Handbook of Geophysics and Space Environments) is sufficiently large for the thermalization of the emitting oxygen atoms, whose mean lifetime in the upper state has been estimated to be in the order of 0.7 sec (GARSTANG, 1951). From direct measurements (FAIRE and CHAMPION, 1965; SMITH et al., 1964), as well as from atmospheric models (KANTOR and COLE, 1964; COSPAR, 1965), temperatures in the order of 200°K are expected at this height. The narrow Doppler profiles associated with this temperature require high resolution techniques coupled with large luminosity because of the inherent feebleness of the radiation. On the basis of these two requirements, a Fabry-Perot photoelectric spectrometer has been chosen for measurement of line profiles. The basic instrument consists of a 140 mm clear aperture etalon (HERNANDEZ and TURTLE, 1965) operated at a resolving power of about one

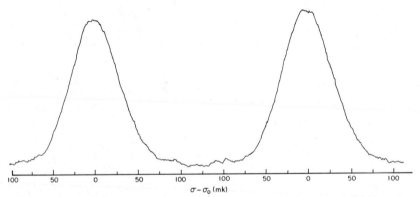

FIGURE 1. Fringe profile obtained with the Fabry-Perot spectrometer. Abscissa units are millikaisers (10^3 mK = 1 cm⁻¹.

million. Under these conditions an observation every 15 minutes is obtained. A typical fringe profile obtained with the instrument is shown in Figure 1. The Doppler width, and hence the temperature, is extracted from the instrumentally-broadened profile either by comparison with computed profiles (HERNANDEZ and TURTLE, 1965; HERNANDEZ, 1966; TURGEON and SHEPHERD, 1962; JARRETT and HOEY, 1966) or by direct deconvolution. A discussion of the uncertainties and deviations in the measurements reported here is found elsewhere (HERNANDEZ and TURTLE, 1965).

Figures 2 and 3 show typical measurements at Bedford, Massachusetts for

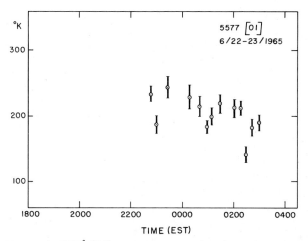

FIGURE 2. 5577Å [OI] temperatures as a function of local time.

which average temperatures of 211°K and 220°K were obtained for June 22–23, 1965 and June 22–23, 1966, respectively. The temperature deviations shown in these figures are 95% confidence limits for the measurements, and for these nights the average deviation is of the order of ±15°K. Within the precision of

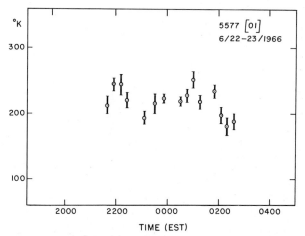

FIGURE 3. 5577Å [OI] temperatures as a function of local time.

our measurements, the two previously quoted average temperatures are not significantly different.

Figure 4 shows a less typical measurement of temperatures in which large variations about a mean of 220°K can be observed. From previous experiments

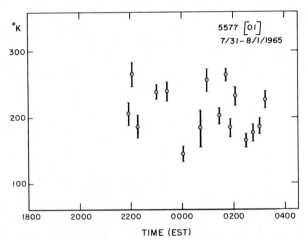

FIGURE 4. 5577Å [OI] temperatures as a function of local time, showing large temperature fluctuations during the observing period.

it was known that the correlation of temperature with rate of emission was negligible for a sample of our measurements; therefore, it is not possible to attribute these variations in Figure 4 (on a statistical basis) to the rate of emission, or to instrumental effects, since the interferometer is independently monitored. Similar temperature excursions can be deduced from the airglow 5577Å [OI] measurements obtained with a modified Michelson interferometer (HILLIARD and SHEPHERD, 1966) at Saskatoon, Saskatchewan. Other evidence of large temperature variations at the 90 km level have been observed with the rocket grenade experiment (SMITH et al., 1964).

Any attempt in the interpretation as well as correlation of temperatures obtained by line profile techniques with other atmospheric processes must take into account both the height and profile of the emitting layer, because of the inherent integration of flux along the line of sight of the instrument. This is particularly true if a height is to be associated with the temperature measurement with the help of a height-temperature model profile (KANTOR and COLE, 1964; COSPAR, 1965), since at the level of the emitting layer the temperature gradient is reasonably large, the green line emission layer width is both large and variable (6–15 km) and the profile is neither symmetrical nor constant from observation to observation (PACKER, 1961; O'BRIEN et al., 1965; GULLEDGE et al., 1966). Also, measurements of temperature as a function of height in the region of interest show considerable variation as can be seen from the results of FAIRE and CHAMPION (1966), SPENCER et al. (1964), and those of SMITH et al. (1964) at slightly lower heights. Therefore, for a specific kinetic temperature measurement made by line profile determination, any height determination is only an approximation. In addition to a variable temperature-height profile it is not known whether the emission profile could move relative to the local temperature profile as a function of time (or its equivalent, a change of the emission profile by a redistribution of the radiating atoms). A displacement of an emission profile such as that of O'BRIEN et al. (1965) by about 5 km relative to a given temperature-height profile (FAIRE and CHAMPION, 1965) could account for temperature changes of the order of 30°K. Another source of temperature excursions can be ascribed to internal gravity waves (HINES, 1963), although estimates of the contributions in temperature changes from this source at the green line emission height are relatively small, possibly 10°K (HINES, 1965). The second 5577Å [OI] emitting layer located at 245 km (GULLEDGE et al., 1966) could give an apparent heating effect in the measurements. If the emitting atoms in this second layer are in equilibrium with the surrounding atmosphere, their line emission profile will be broader and additive to the line profile of the lower layer. Because of the small intensity contribution and much higher temperature of the upper layer, the effect in the present measurements would be either a slight broadening of the observed line profile with a slight loss of the fringe contrast, or a washing-out of the broader profile because of the high resolution used in the experiment. A simultaneous measurement with a lower resolving power could solve this question.

At the time of this writing there is not a sufficient number of temperature

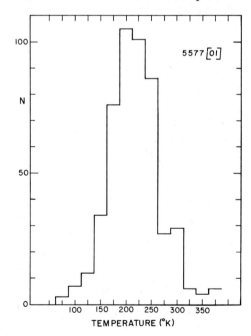

FIGURE 5. Histogram of green line temperatures obtained during 1965 and early 1966, at Bedford, Massachusetts.

measurements to make a statistically significant sample in order to determine the presence of temporal variations. A compilation of Bedford data for part of 1965 and part of 1966 is shown in Figure 5 as a histogram from which an average temperature of 208°K (with 95% confidence limits of about ±20°K) was obtained. This result is in agreement with measurements of other workers (HILLIARD and SHEPHERD, 1966; WARK, 1960; ARMSTRONG, 1959; KARANDIKAR, 1956; PERRIN, 1960; MULYARCHICK, 1960) at different locations.

Acknowledgments   The authors wish to thank Dr. B. S. Dandekar for helpful discussions during the course of this work. This investigation was supported in part by the Air Force In-House Laboratory Independent Research Fund.

References

ARMSTRONG, E. B., 1959, *J. Atmospheric Terrest. Phys.* **13**, 205.
ARMSTRONG, E. B., 1959, *J. Phys. Radium* **19**, 358.
BABCOCK, H. D., 1923, *Astrophys. J.* **57**, 209.
COSPAR *International Reference Atmosphere 1965*, 1965, North-Holland Publishing Co., Amsterdam.
FAIRE, A. C. and CHAMPION, K. S. W., 1965, *Space Res.* **5**, 1039.
FRERICHS, R., 1930, *Phys. Rev.* **36**, 398.
GARSTANG, R. H., 1951, *Monthly Notices Roy. Astron. Soc.* **111**, 115.
GULLEDGE, I. S., PACKER, D. M., and TILFORD, S. G., 1966, *Trans. Am. Geophys. Union* **47**, 74.
Handbook of Geophysics and Space Environments, 1965, McGraw-Hill Book Co., Inc., New York, Chapter 2.
HERNANDEZ, G. J., 1966, *Appl. Opt.* **5**, 1745
HERNANDEZ, G. J. and TURTLE, J. P., 1965, *Planetary Space Sci.* **13**, 901.
HILLIARD, R. L. and SHEPHERD, G. G., 1966, *Planetary Space Sci.* **14**, 383.
HINES, C. O., 1963, *Quart. J. Roy. Meteorol. Soc.* **89**, 1.
HINES, C. O., 1965, *J. Geophys. Res.* **70**, 177.
JARRETT, A. H. and HOEY, M. J., 1966, *J. Atmospheric Terrest. Phys.* **28**, 175.
KANTOR, A. J. and COLE, A. E., 1964, *J. Geophys. Res.* **69**, 5131.
KARANDIKAR, R. V., 1956 "*The Airglow and The Aurora*" (edited by Armstrong, E. B. and Dalgarno, A.) Pergamon Press (London) p. 374.
McLENNAN, J. C., McLEOD, J. H., and McQUARRIE, W. C., 1927, *Proc. Roy. Soc. (London)* **A114**, 1.
McLENNAN, J. C. and SHRUM, G. M., 1924, *Proc. Roy. Soc. (London)* **A106**, 138.
MULYARCHICK, T. M. 1960 *Bull (12v) Acad. Sci.*, USSR, Geophys. Ser **3**, 449.
O'BRIEN, B. J., ALLUM, F. R., and GOLDWIRE, H. C., 1965, *J. Geophys. Res.* **70**, 161.
PACKER, D. M., 1961, *Ann. Geophys.* **17**, 67.
PERRIN, M., 1960 *Compt. Rend.* **250**, 2406.
LORD RAYLEIGH, 1930 *Proc. Roy Soc. (London)* **A129**, 458. (For a complete bibliography of Lord Rayleigh's airglow investigations see: HERNANDEZ, G. J. and SILVERMAN, S. M., 1964, *Planetary Space Sci.* **12**, 97.
SMITH, W., KATCHEN, L., SACHER, P., SWARTZ, P., and THEON, J., 1964, *Temperature, Pressure, Density and Wind Measurements with the Rocket Grenade Experiment 1960–1963*, NASA Technical Report, NASA TR-R-211.
SPENCER, N. W., BOGGESS, R. L. TAEUSCH, D. R., 1964 *J. Geophys. Res.* **69**, 1367.
TURGEON, E. C. and SHEPHERD, G. G., 1962, *Planetary Space Sci.* **9**, 295.
WARK, D. Q., 1960, *Astrophys. J.* **131**, 491.
WOLFF, M. M., 1966, *J. Geophys. Res.* **71**, 2743

LOW LATITUDE AIRGLOW VARIATIONS 1962-1965

Robert D. Sears

Geophysics Division
IIT Research Institute
Chicago, Illinois

Measurements of night airglow intensity at 5577Å and 6300Å were made in 1962 and 1965 in the South Pacific low latitude regions. In 1962 (May and June) measurements were made from the island of Tongatapu. In 1965 identical instrumentation was located at Aitutaki, Cook Islands during May and June. The geomagnetic latitudes were close enough to permit useful comparison of the average diurnal behavior of the airglow intensity and its overall change in the 1962 and 1965 interval.

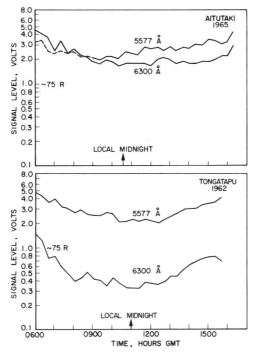

FIGURE 1. Average diurnal variation of low latitude airglow in 1962 and 1965.

An automatic continuum compensating photometer (FILOSOFO, 1965), was run continuously pointed at zenith. During both the 1962 and 1965 periods, about ten days of good data were obtained in moonless or new moon conditions so that the scattered light continuum contamination was negligible. The instruments were internally calibrated each night against a calibrated radioactive light source. The signal levels are given in volts which correspond to the airglow intensity in rayleighs by the formula, 1 volt = 75 rayleighs. Internal calibration keeps the relative accuracy of the data within a few per cent, and the absolute calibration in rayleighs is believed to be within ±10%.

The average diurnal variation of the airglow intensity in the two spectral regions monitored from the island sites in 1962 and 1965 is shown in Figure 1. Several features of the data are notable. The relative level of the 5577Å emission has not appreciably changed during the three year interval, in contrast to the factor of 3–4 increase in 6300Å intensity.

Three possible causes of the observed decrease in red intensity are suggested. The overall intensity of the F region red night glow could have decreased in the Pacific region, the sampling periods could have been too small, or the edge of the maximum could have moved or become more diffuse. The island sites lie near the outside edge of the more enhanced red glow. The 5577Å emissions observed by the instrument are produced both in the F region as well as at 100 km altitude. The lower maximum generally dominates (ROACH, 1967), therefore, the correlation of F region emission at 5577Å with 6300Å could be excellent and yet obscured by the stronger emission at 100 km. In conclusion, a solar cycle variation of the F region red night glow intensity is suggested.

Acknowledgments   The IIT Research Institute expeditions to Tongatapu and Aitutaki were supported by the Defense Atomic Support Agency. Part of the data reduction and analysis was supported by internal research funds of IITRI.

References

FILOSOFO, I., GREENSPAN, J. A., and GROOM, C. M., 1965, *Appl. Opt.* **4**, 215.
ROACH, F., 1967, this volume.

HIGH LATITUDE NIGHT-SKY EMISSIONS

B. P. Sandford

Physics and Engineering Laboratory, DSIR
Private Bag, Lower Hutt, New Zealand

I. Introduction

In the last ten years extensive quantitative measurements of high latitude night-sky emissions have significantly changed our concepts of the auroras. These observations revealed the necessity to consider the auroras as a complex family of phenomena and not as a single geophysical event. Here we review the broad statistical features of those distinct optical phenomena which are recognized. Attention is confined to the [OI] lines at 5577Å and 6300Å, the First Negative band of N_2^+ at 3914Å, and the hydrogen lines in the visible region of the spectrum.

The data are mostly obtained from photographic spectrographs in Antarctica, using 100 minute exposures which do not provide detail of small space and time variations. Information on these variations is obtained from all-sky camera and photometric data, riometer data, and satellite recordings of particle precipitation. The spectrograph observations are confined to periods not influenced by twilight enhancements. The calibration of the Byrd Station spectra for 1963 is based on the assumption that the spectrograph calibration lamp had the same properties as the one used in 1959 (SANFORD, 1964).

The magnitude (e.g., percentage occurrence, intensity, etc.) of an auroral phenomenon can be measured as a function of time, latitude and longitude in a geographic, centered dipole, eccentric dipole, or magnetic dip coordinate system, and also as a function of the level of magnetic disturbance or any other desired variable. Plots of the magnitude against pairs of these coordinates can thus result in different auroral zones, that is, regions in which the magnitude exceeds a given level in the particular coordinate system. One should be very careful not to confuse the different concepts involved in these zones (DAVIS, 1966). The classical auroral zone is the discrete visual auroral occurrence plotted against geographic latitude and longitude.

A system of eccentric dipole latitude and eccentric dipole time (COLE, 1963) is used here because previous work has shown that most of the emissions discussed are generated in regions which are fixed relative to the earth's magnetic field and the earth-sun line. This system is similar to the "auroral latitude" and "auroral time" used by SANDFORD (1964).

II. Classfication of Night-Sky Emissions

We will loosely consider aurora as emission primarily associated with the impact of energetic particles, including the effects of electric fields present at such times (CUMMINGS et al., 1966; MOZER and BRUSTON, 1966), while airglow is emission primarily associated with photochemical processes. In this chapter we will discuss the following groups of night-sky emissions, which are different by virtue of distinctive behavior in their spatial distribution, relationship with magnetic activity, etc.: two groups of aurora excited by energetic electrons, the discrete visual aurora and the mantle aurora; aurora excited by protons, the proton excited aurora; aurora excited by solar cosmic ray proton and alpha particles, the polar glow aurora; 6300Å emission which has distinctive behavior, the red line emission; and emission related to the normal airglow.

III. Discrete Visual Aurora

The discrete visual aurora, the phenomenon known classically as aurora, can be seen with the naked eye in the form of arcs, bands, and rays. As it seems unnecessary to set an arbitrary limit determined by the eye's sensitivity, subvisual discrete aurora are included; however, they seem to generate only a small fraction of the total emission from discrete visual aurora.

The discrete visual aurora are subclassified by their appearance in the sky as arcs, bands, etc., or by their color (IUGG, 1963). On a less subjective basis, AKASOFU (1965) has used a subclassification based on their gross dynamic behavior, where, in calm magnetic conditions, a quiet homogeneous arc is observed, but in association with a magnetic disturbance, an auroral display or auroral substorm develops in a systematic manner on a global scale. Within 10–15° of the pole are found discrete visual aurora, the polar cap auroras (LASSEN, 1966), which behave differently from those in the auroral zone. We are not concerned with these subclasses, but rather with some gross details that can be contrasted with the groups in the previous section.

The statistical position of the southern discrete visual auroral zone, averaged over all levels of magnetic activity, is shown in Figure 1(A) for the solar maximum period 1958-9 (SANDFORD, 1964). The intensity and radius of this zone vary with magnetic activity (AKASOFU, 1965; FELDSTEIN, 1964; SANDFORD, 1964). In 1963, near solar minimum, the mean position of this zone was about 5° nearer the pole in the midnight sector. This change is probably related to the reduction in the average level of planetary magnetic activity (K_P), to be discussed later.

The discrete auroral zone is the zone of occurrence of many other phenome-

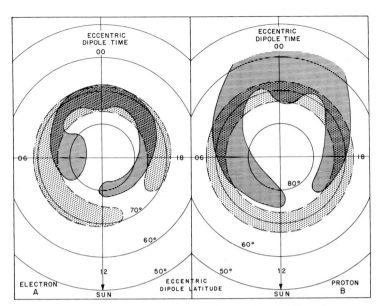

FIGURE 1. (A) The statistical zone of discrete visual auroral probability of occurrence > 0.6 in 1959 (hatched) and the zone of mantle aurora shown by the region in which the 3914Å emission exceeds 0.6 kR in 1959 (dotted).

(B) A zone of hydrogen emission that fits observational data (hatched) and a second tentative zone of proton precipitation (dotted). Both of these proton zones should be considered only as guides to the true situation.

na, as PIDDINGTON (1965) and HARTZ and BRICE (1966) have shown. The latter list these phenomena as:

1) Discrete localized, bright, often rapidly fluctuating auroral forms having characteristic heights >100 km (discrete visual aurora).

2) Abrupt auroral absorption events, seen on a riometer.

3) Rapidly fading, impulsive type VHF signals scattered by field aligned ionization at heights ≈105 km.

4) Intense sporadic-E (auroral sporadic) at indicated heights of 100 km or more.

5) Spread-F echoes on ionograms.

6) Bursts of relatively high frequency (>4 kHz) VLF emissions (auroral hiss).

7) Impulsive (P_i) geomagnetic micropulsations.

8) Bursts of bremsstrahlung x rays of characteristically soft energies.

9) Negative magnetic bays having rapid or abrupt onsets and rather slow recoveries.

10) Relatively short duration bursts of intense fluxes of soft electrons (energies ≈ a few keV).

All these phenomena have a maximum intensity in the midnight sector and a very impulsive character. The precipitating electron energy spectrum has a peak at a few keV and falls very steeply at higher energies. For a more complete discussion, see HARTZ and BRICE (1966).

IV. Mantle Aurora

The intensity of the 3914Å and 5577Å emissions observed in the absence of discrete visual aurora in Antarctica in 1958–9 (SANDFORD, 1964) has a zonal distribution, shown in Figure 1(A), which differs significantly from the discrete visual auroral zone. The maximum intensity occurs in the morning hours and varies with the level of magnetic activity. However, the radius of this zone does not appear to change, unlike that of the discrete auroral zone. This emission differs from the discrete visual aurora in many ways and is an extensive glow covering the sky, hence the name *mantle aurora* (SANDFORD, 1964).

Some features of the mantle aurora are presented in Figure 2(A), where the

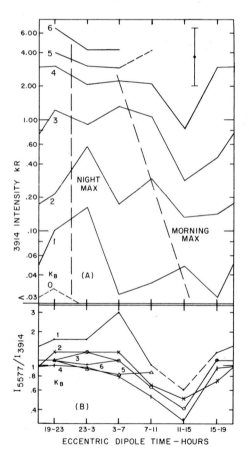

FIGURE 2. (A) The diurnal variation of 3914Å emission for 1963 at Byrd Station for each level of local magnetic K-index.
(B) The diurnal variation of the intensity ratio I_{5577}/I_{3914} for the same period.

diurnal variation of the median intensity of 3914Å, for each level of local magnetic K-index (K_B), is shown from Byrd Station, Antarctica (eccentric dipole latitude 69°) for the four winter months (April 20–August 23) of 1963. The interquartile range of the measurements for each point is approximately constant and is given by the error bar.

The 3914Å intensity increases with K_B at all times of the day, but, the intensity at midnight is always about five times greater than the noon minimum for a given level of K_B. The dotted lines indicate two series of maxima. The night maxima do not shift significantly with time and arise from the discrete visual auroras which have a maximum occurrence at this time. The second morning maximum occurs near noon during quiet magnetic activity and with increasing magnetic activity, shifts back into the morning hours. The morning maxima are caused by the mantle auroras because they remain evident in measurements made when discrete visual auroras are not present.

Another difference between the morning and night emissions is found in the intensity ratio I_{5577}/I_{3914}, in Figure 2(B). This ratio shows a large variation, indicating that emission processes around midnight are different from those around midday.

In their study of the large scale pattern of auroral particle precipitation, PIDDINGTON (1965) and HARTZ and BRICE (1966) show that the mantle zone is a zone common to many geophysical phenomena:

1) Steady, diffuse, mantle aurora.
2) Slowly-varying ionospheric absorption (SVIA).
3) Steady or slowly varying mean signal level for VHF forward scatter echoes from isotropic ionization irregularities at heights ≈ 85 km.
4) Sporadic-E echoes from a height in the range of 80–90 km.
5) Quasiconstant VLF emissions (polar chorus) at frequencies below 2 kc/sec.
6) Continuous (P_c) geomagnetic micropulsations.
7) Long duration, slowly varying, and characteristically hard x ray events.
8) Consistent, moderately intense fluxes of electrons of energies >20 keV.

All these phenomena have a maximum intensity in the morning and are widespread and persistent events. The precipitating particle energy spectrum is much flatter than that associated with the discrete visual auroral zone.

Satellite observations (JOHNSON et al., 1966) and the above discussions indicate, then, that the discrete visual and mantle auroras are caused by two distinct energetic particle populations. The satellite and rocket data (SILVERMAN et al., 1964) indicate that the two particle populations are present in the daylight and at night, implying that the auroral processes are a day and night phenomenon.

The morning mantle aurora intensity, when the local K-index exceeds 3, is high enough to be recorded on an all-sky camera. Almost all visible aurora seen at this time in the mantle auroral zone are of the patch type described by AKASOFU (1965) and AKASOFU et al. (1966). The all-sky camera shows an extensive aurora almost like a cumulus cloud, slowly drifting across the sky, while on other occasions the sky has a blotchy appearance, suggesting a fairly uniform illumination modulated with periods of about one minute. Emission of this type, with periods of a few seconds, is reported by JOHANSEN and OMHOLT (1966). The visible features in the maximum intensity region of the mantle auroral zone have properties which resemble the mantle aurora rather than the discrete visual aurora. Thus, it seems that at least some patch aurora and, particularly, the blotchy looking aurora belong to the mantle auroral group. Further careful study is required to determine the exact relationship between the discrete visual aurora and the mantle aurora.

V. Magnetic Dependence of Discrete Visual and Mantle Aurorae

At Byrd Station, Antarctica, the intensity of the 3914Å and 5577Å emissions shows a closer relationship with local than with planetary magnetic activity. For values of local $K_B \geqslant 3$, the intensity of these emissions (Figure 3) in 1959

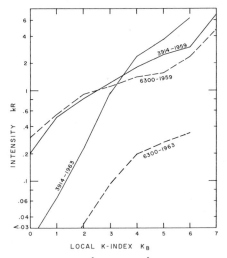

FIGURE 3. The median intensity of 3914Å and 6300Å emission at Byrd Station in 1959 and 1963 as a function of local magnetic K-index.

(solar maximum) was almost identical to that in 1963 (solar minimum). For $K_B < 3$, the emissions were considerably weaker in 1963.

An examination of the behavior of the local and planetary magnetic activity is helpful. The sums of K_P for a particular 3 hour interval in the four austral winter months (Figure 4) were on the average 40% greater in 1959 than in 1963, as might be expected from solar cycle variations. We see in Figure 4, however, that the sums of K_B over the same periods are almost identical around midnight. At midday the higher level of K_B in 1959 is probably only a reflection of the higher K_P sums for that year.

Since both the local K-index and the 3914Å intensity were about the same in 1959 as in 1963, in the nine hours centered on midnight, it is concluded that the 3914Å intensity is related directly to local magnetic activity. The constant level

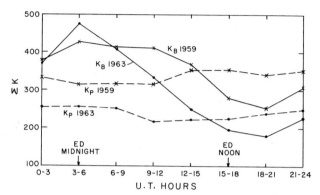

FIGURE 4. Sums of planetary and Byrd Station local magnetic K-indices for each three hour interval in the period April 20–August 16, 1959 and 1963.

of local magnetic activity suggests that the auroral disturbances are a local magnetospheric phenomenon which continue in the absence of solar disturbances. The reason why the 3914Å intensity was much higher in 1959 than in 1963 for $K_B < 3$ is not clear, but as the intensity is better correlated with local than with planetary activity, it seems that magnetospheric or ionospheric processes are connected with this behavior.

It was noted earlier that the average radius of the discrete visual auroral zone was larger in 1959 than in 1963. Since the planetary and not the local magnetic activity decreased over this period, it seems reasonable to relate this change to the change in the position of the trapping region boundary over the solar cycle (FRANK and VAN ALLEN, 1966).

It appears that the position of the discrete visual auroral zone is closely related to planetary magnetic activity and hence solar activity, whereas the intensity of the auroral phenomena is more closely related to the local magnetic activity and hence to magnetospheric behavior.

The 6300Å emission will be discussed in a later section because it behaves differently from the 3914Å and 5577Å emissions.

VI. Proton Excited Aurora

Hydrogen emission is commonly observed as a broad arc about 7° wide lying on the equatorward edge of the discrete visual auroral zone (EATHER and JACKA, 1966b). The protons do not enter the atmosphere in a thin sheet like the electrons sometimes do, because the arc is too wide (EATHER, 1966) to be explained by charge exchange effects (DAVIDSON, 1965). An average zone of emission that fits the observational data is shown in Figure 1(B) (EATHER and SANDFORD, 1966).

EATHER and JACKA (1966a) report that slowly varying ionospheric absorption (SVIA) events show time variations in common with hydrogen emission. Since it has been indicated that SVIA events are associated with the mantle aurora, it is possible that hydrogen emission is also associated with the mantle aurora. Satellite recordings on the noon side, where two zones of proton precipitation have been observed (SHARP *et al.*, 1967; JOHNSON *et al.*, 1966), support this contention. This second tentative zone of proton precipitation is shown in Figure 1(B).

In the midnight sector an enhancement of hydrogen emission is often observed (SWIFT, 1965; EATHER and JACKA, 1966b) in association with an auroral disturbance.

It seems notable that we now have two major zones of proton precipitation analogous to the two zones of electron precipitation; both electron and proton precipitation are enhanced near midnight when an auroral substorm begins.

There is no certain evidence of any relationship between magnetic activity and proton excited aurora, but there is a large variation of hydrogen emission intensity over the solar cycle (EATHER and JACKA, 1966b; EATHER and SANDFORD, 1966).

VII. Polar-Glow Aurora

The name *polar-glow aurora* (SANDFORD, 1966) refers specifically to optical emission generated by solar cosmic rays during polar cap absorption events (PCA). The polar-glow aurora usually begins within a couple of hours of a solar proton flare. In large events roughly equal numbers of proton and alpha particles, in the energy range of 1–100 MeV, arrive in the polar regions. A uniform glow is generated over the whole polar cap down to a latitude of about 60°, where the cosmic-ray cut-off limits penetration. The intensity of this aurora rises steadily for about a day, normally reaching a maximum near the time of the onset of the magnetic storm usually associated with such events. The intensity at 3914Å can reach 10 kR. The glow then decays slowly over the next few days.

The solar cosmic rays penetrate to altitudes between 20–100 km where the optical emission is generated (SANDFORD, 1963; BROWN, 1964). The brightest features are the allowed molecular transitions and the metastable levels, with atomic emissions being less prominent.

The polar-glow aurora is the only major natural process that generates optical emission in the visible region of the spectrum between altitudes of 20–100 km. Height profile measurements of the emissions could be a very valuable aid in understanding atmospheric processes and for measuring the particle energy spectrum of the solar cosmic rays. By mapping the global buildup of the polar-glow aurora, it should be possible to study the arrival of the solar particles.

VIII. Red Line Emission

The emission at 6300Å is not always directly related to the groups already discussed. The 6300Å intensity in 1959 (SANDFORD, 1964), during quiet magnetic activity, had its normal mid-latitude intensity up to about 50°. At higher latitudes the intensity rose steadily, reaching six times the mid-latitude intensity between 80° and 90°. In 1959 at Scott Base, Antarctica, color film observations show that 70% of all discrete visual aurora have extensive red glow above them, but do not always show fluctuations immediately related to the auroral forms below them (SANDFORD, 1961).

In 1962–5 (solar minimum) such red enhancements were very rare at Scott Base. The mean intensity at 6300Å also dropped by more than one order of magnitude between 1959 and 1963 at Byrd Station (Figure 3), although the intensity of the mantle and discrete visual auroras remained virtually unchanged.

This 6300Å emission may arise from thermal excitation when electron temperatures in the F-region exceed 3000°K, perhaps being related to the processes discussed by COLE (1965). BAKER et al. (1966) have shown that in a bright discrete aurora, electron temperatures as high as 2700°K occurred in 1965. If the ambient electron temperature is higher at sunspot maximum, caused by a more continuous level of disturbance, then electron temperatures exceeding 3000°K may be common at solar maximum but not at solar minimum.

A further unexplained aspect of the 6300Å emission is a series of narrow subvisual red arcs reported by WEILL et al. (1965) in the auroral regions.

IX. Airglow

The airglow can be observed only when particle bombardment effects are negligible; such times are generally identified with periods of very quiet magnetic activity. At these times, the 5577Å airglow intensity appears to be of the same order at all latitudes between 50° and 90° as is observed at mid-latitudes and it exhibits a change over the solar cycle similar to that reported by HERNANDEZ and SILVERMAN (1964).

At solar minimum the 6300Å airglow intensity is similar to the mid-latitude airglow, but at solar maximum it is concealed by the red line emission discussed in the previous section.

X. Concluding Remarks

An attempt has been made to discuss some of the major features of the night-sky emissions. Clearly, there are many features and problems yet to be investigated. The emissions discussed in this paper may also be generated by other processes associated with such things as ionospheric electric fields, atmospheric mass transport, etc. The subject of high latitude night-sky emissions is a complex one, the classical auroral phenomenon representing only one aspect on which most work in the past has been concentrated.

References

AKASOFU, S-I., 1965, *Space Science Reviews* **4**, 498.
AKASOFU, S-I., MENG, C-I., and KIMBALL, D. S., 1966, *J. Atmospheric Terrest. Phys.* **28**, 505.
BAKER, K. D., PFISTER, W., and ULWICK, J. C., 1966, Proc. COSPAR *Space Research VII.* (to be published).
BROWN, R. R., 1964, *Planetary Space Sci.* **12**, 665.
COLE, K. D., 1963, *Australian J. Phys.* **16**, 423.
COLE, K. D., 1965, *J. Geophys. Res.* **70**, 1689.
CUMMINGS, W. D., LAQUEY, R. E., O'BRIEN, B. J., and WALT, M., 1966, *J. Geophys. Res.* **71**, 1399.
DAVIDSON, G. T., 1965, *J. Geophys. Res.* **70**, 1061.
DAVIS, T. N., 1967, this volume.
EATHER, R. H., 1966, *J. Geophys. Res.* **71**, 5027.
EATHER, R. H. and JACKA, F., 1966a, *Australian J. Phys.* **19**, 215.
EATHER, R. H. and JACKA, F., 1966b, *Australian J. Phys.* **19**, 241.
EATHER, R. H. and SANDFORD, B. P., 1966, *Australian J. Phys.* **19**, 25.
FELDSTEIN, Y. I., 1964, *Tellus* **16**, 258.
FRANK, L. A. and VAN ALLEN, J. A., 1966, *J. Geophys. Res.* **71**, 2697.
HARTZ, T. R. and BRICE, N. M., 1966, *Planetary Space Sci.* (to be published).
HERNANDEZ, G. J. and SILVERMAN, S. M., 1964, *Planetary Space Sci.* **12**, 97.
IUGG, 1963, *International Auroral Atlas*, Univ. Press, Edinburgh.
JOHANSEN, O. E. and OMHOLT, A., 1966, *Planetary Space Sci.* **14**, 207.
JOHNSON, R. G., SHARP, R. D., SHEA, M. F., and SHOOK, G. B., 1966, *Trans. Amer. Geophys. Union* **47**, 64.
LASSEN, K., 1967, this volume.
MOZER, F. S. and BRUSTON, P., 1966, *J. Geophys. Res.* **71**, 2201.
PIDDINGTON, J. H., 1965, *Planetary Space Sci.* **13**, 565.
SANDFORD, B. P., 1961, *J. Atmospheric Terrest. Phys.* **21**, 177.
SANDFORD, B. P., 1963, *Planetary Space Sci*, **10**, 195.
SANDFORD, B. P., 1964, *J. Atmospheric Terrest. Phys.* **26**, 749.
SANDFORD, B. P., 1966, Proc. COSPAR, *Space Research VII* (to be published).
SHARP, R. D., JOHNSON, R. G., SHEA, M. F., and SHOOK, G. B., 1967, *J. Geophys. Res.* **72**, 227.
SILVERMAN, S. N., LLOYD, J. W., COCHRUN, B. L., and NARDONE, L. J., 1964, *Nature* **204**, 461.
SWIFT, D. W., 1965, Univ. of Alaska Report UAGIR 165.
WEILL, G., DELANNOY, J., FAFIOTTE, M., and HUILLE, S., 1965, *Ann. Geophys.* **21**, 469.

Discussion

The possibility of using polar region observations to resolve whether the field lines are open or closed was discussed. It was concluded that conjugate region measurements are essential to resolving which field lines are open and which are closed.

It was remarked that a diffuse glow is often observed during auroral break-up, and asked if this could be related to the polar phenomena observed by Sandford. He acknowledged this as a possibility that has not yet been studied. The mantle aurora cannot be observed in the presence of the discrete visual aurora, and while the diffuse glow may be related to the mantle aurora, it is difficult to separate the various effects.

POLAR CAP AURORA

Knud Lassen

Danish Meteorological Institute, Geophysical Section

Polar Cap Aurora

If we define the Polar Cap as the area with corrected geomagnetic latitude (MAYAUD, 1960; MCILWAIN, 1961; HAKURA, 1965) greater than some 70°, auroras observed near zenith at polar cap stations may be classified into three main groups, namely auroras which seem to be stationary in high latitude, auroras approaching the station from the auroral zone, and auroras which are observed in connection with world-wide magnetic storms.

1. High-Latitude Auroras

MAWSON (1925) reported that the main feature of the diurnal periodicity of auroras at Cape Denison ($-80°$ corrected geomagnetic latitude, hereafter abbreviated as corr. geom. lat) was the regular appearance in the zenith of quiet auroral forms late in the afternoon and early in the morning until observation became impossible due to twilight. The appearance of many parallel bands in the zenith was characteristic for the morning hours, in all cases early morning auroras were characterized by regularity and the absence of the intense and spectacular element which is a feature of the storm period of evening auroras. The forms assumed were typical pale nebulous bands, often curtained, which on occasions of greater auroral intensity might become brilliant and warm up the reddish tones below, and develop rippling motions of the filaments.

The diurnal periodicity at Cape Denison is typical for stations near 80° corr. geom. lat. At Godhavn (77°.5 corr. geom. lat) quiet rays and rayed bands are observed at zenith and on the northern sky in the early evening hours. At 5–6 hr corr. geom. time (as defined by MAYAUD, 1960), faint auroras suddenly appear in the zenith region, which is soon covered by quiet auroral forms. A maximum seems to be reached at about 9 hr corr. geom. time, just before twilight. Even at the maximum, auroras of this type are seldom observed near the southern horizon.

Both at Cape Denison and at Godhavn it is clear that part of the auroral distribution is hidden by daylight. The Danish station Nord (80°.4 corr. geom.

lat) is situated at 81°.6 geographic latitude. During the midwinter months the sun is therefore so deep below the horizon that auroras may be observed even at noon. Figure 1 shows the daily distribution of auroral frequency at this sta-

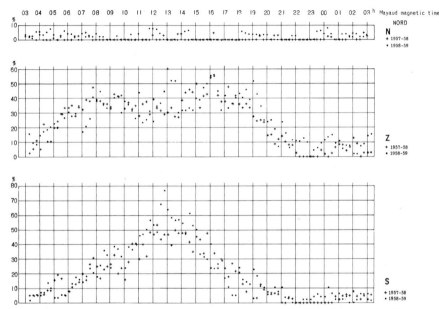

FIGURE 1. Mean daily variation of auroral frequency at Nord 1957–9. N (10°–30° northern elevation), Z (elevation between 30° north and 30° south), and S (10°–30° southern elevation).

tion during 1957–9. In the zenith area two maxima occur, one at 9 hr and one at 16–17 hr corr. geom. time. Auroras are observed all day, but rarely at night. In the southern part of the sky the same distribution may be traced. The main feature is, however, a rather sharp maximum at 13–14 hr corr. geom. time, which seems to be due to auroras approaching the station from the south (cf. next section). The auroral frequency on the northern part of the sky is extremely low.

Nearer to the pole the frequency of zenithal auroras decreases. At Vostok (−85° corr. geom. lat) and Thule (87° corr. geom. lat) the zenith forms are most often fragments of bands, which are very short-lived, sometimes of only a few minutes duration. The majority of the auroras observed from these latitudes are situated in low elevation. At Thule the principal maximum occurs at 6–8 hr corr. geom. time; a second maximum may in some years be observed late in the afternoon. The most common forms are patches which may develop into fragments of arcs or complete diffuse arcs with a relatively short lifetime. In the morning it seems as if the auroral activity starts simultaneously over the whole southeastern sector of the central polar cap at about 2–3 hr corr. geom. time

(cf. Figure 2). The activity starts with short-lived auroras. It increases gradually and reaches a maximum later in the morning. Slowly pulsating patches are
observed 3–6° above the horizon between east and south. Diffuse bands approach the zenith. In the cases where they pass the zenith they are often seen
to be 20–30° broad. They nearly always fade away shortly after the passage of
zenith.

The distribution of high-latitude auroras on quiet days is illustrated in Figure
2. Isoauroral lines have been drawn in a polar graph, in which the polar and

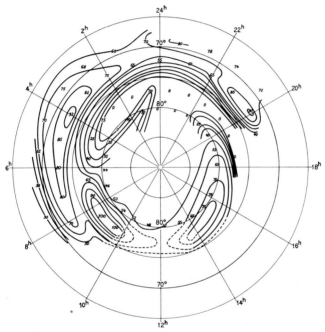

FIGURE 2. Auroral frequency pattern 1957–58, international quiet days. Isoauroral lines drawn
on a polar graph with corr. geom. lat. and time as coordinates. Isoauroral lines are based on
zenithal frequencies and shown for multiples of 10%.

azimuthal angular coordinates indicate geomagnetic latitude and time, respectively. Observations from the near-pole latitudes are not included. By comparison with Figure 8 it is seen, however, that the high-latitude auroras are concentrated in two groups, one in the morning with a maximum at 77–80° about
9 hr, stretching through higher latitudes till the first hours after midnight, the
other in the afternoon with its maximum at 77–80°.

Near the morning maximum, the frequency of occurrence of zenithal auroras at Godhavn has little dependence on planetary magnetic activity. However,
it has been found to decrease a little with increasing magnetic activity. The
decrease is clearly confirmed by FELDSTEIN (1962), who showed that in the

eastern hemisphere at a distance of 8–20° from the auroral zone, auroras appear in the zenith more frequently on magnetically quiet days than on magnetically disturbed days. According to SANDFORD (1964), the dependence on magnetic activity in the Antarctic changes its sign at the corr. geom. lat 78–79°. The change is observable from Scott Base (−81° corr. geom. lat) when different parts of the sky are studied separately.

From Figure 1 it was noted that the two maxima of the high-latitude aurora might be traced in the distribution from the southern part of the sky (auroras overhead at 76–79° corr. geom. lat), although the dominating part of the daily variation was due to a group of auroras invading this area from the south. A more detailed study has shown that the southern group becomes the more important on magnetically disturbed days and nearly disappears on quiet days, whereas the opposite is the case with the high-latitude auroras (LASSEN, 1963).

In general, it is not possible to state that there is a relationship between local magnetic disturbance and the occurrence of auroras in the zenith. Magnetic disturbances occur both when auroras are in the zenith and when they are absent.

The morning auroras at Godhavn are closely related to the occurrence of disturbances in the E- and F-layers of the ionosphere. Auroral Es appears at the same time as the first faint auroras, and the top frequency of the sporadic layer increases with increasing zenithal auroral activity. It was therefore considered appropriate to represent the year-to-year variation of the morning auroras by the variation of the limiting frequency of the simultaneously oc-

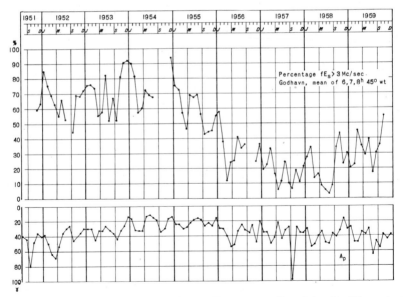

FIGURE 3. Month-to-month variations 1951–9 of percentage of total time for ƒEs greater than 3 Mc/sec (upper curve) and magnetic activity index A_p (lower curve).

curring sporadic E. Figure 3 shows that during the years 1951–59 this variation was nearly opposite in phase to the variation of the sunspot number. It may also be noted that the month-to-month variation is, in general, opposite to the variation of the international magnetic index A_p, often with minima at the equinoxes. For a more direct determination of the sunspot variation, the auroral frequency determined from visual observation at 8 hr local time (9.30 hr corr. geom. time) at Godhavn has been plotted in Figure 4. The auroral fre-

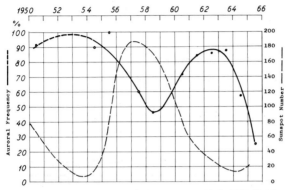

FIGURE 4. Year-to-year variation of auroral frequency at 11 hr UT (9.30 corr. geom. time). Visual observations, Godhavn 1950–66.

quency is here seen to have its maxima about one year before the sunspot minima. The first minimum occurred about one year after the sunspot maximum of 1957–58, whereas the tendency for the next minimum seems to be to occur not later than the corresponding sunspot maximum. Taking the uncertainty of the frequencies in Figure 4 into consideration, the variations in Figures 3 and 4 may be regarded as identical and nearly opposite to the variation of the sunspot number.

Quite a different variation has been found in older observations (LASSEN, 1963). Thus, during the period 1873–1916 the variation of the frequency of morning auroras observed at Jakobshavn near Godhavn showed two maxima, one shortly after the sunspot maximum in 1884, the other shortly after the sunspot maximum in 1906. The existence of the second maximum was confirmed by a study of observations from a group of Antarctic stations all located at about 80°.5 corr. geom. lat between 1902 and 1919 (VESTINE and SNYDER, 1945). Observations from Godhavn 1923–36 seem to speak in favor of a maximum between sunspot maximum and sunspot minimum. In Figure 5 the variation of the frequency of morning auroras is shown together with the variation of the sunspot number. A one-to-one correlation between the two quantities cannot be found. The phase of the auroral variation may have changed in the first part of this century, or the variation may be accidental. More and better observations are needed.

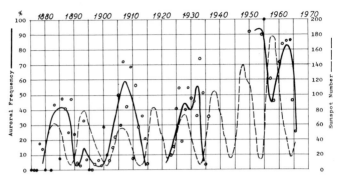

FIGURE 5. Comparison of the variation of auroral frequency with the sunspot cycle 1874–1965. Morning observations, 78° corr. geom. lat.

The frequencies of morning and afternoon auroras seem to vary independently. During the years 1952–6 the frequency just after dusk at Godhavn was gradually increasing, whereas in the morning hours it was decreasing. The independent and possibly irregular variation of the two maxima is illustrated in Figure 6, which shows the daily variation of zenith auroras at Nord during two winters of sunspot maximum and two winters of sunspot minimum. In one of the two minimum winters the afternoon maximum is depressed, in the other, the morning maximum.

Whereas in lower latitudes auroral arcs are directed nearly along the auroral zone, it was found at Cape Denison (MAWSON, 1925) that the azimuth of the arcs near zenith varied through the day in such a way that the arc was always approximately directed towards the sun. The result was confirmed at Dumont d'Urville (WEILL, 1958) and at a number of IGY-stations in Canada and Greenland (DAVIS, 1962). The transition between the two types of direction of arcs seems to take place at 75–80° corr. geom. lat. At Godhavn both types may be found. At Thule, DANIELSEN (1966) noticed that with very few exceptions auroral arcs moving across the sky move towards the left as seen by an observer ⸳ facing the sun. The velocity is 300–400 m/sec if a height of 100 km is assumed. The same type of motion is observed at Godhavn, where a series of parallel arcs is often seen to move from the eastern to western horizon near corr. geom. midnight.

Photographic measurements of the height of the high-latitude auroras have not been published. Photometric measurements (WEILL *et al.*, 1965) give a higher ratio of the intensities of the 6300Å to the 5577Å lines in high-latitude auroras than in usual auroras, thus indicating that the height of the first-mentioned ones is appreciably more than 100 km. The height of the sporadic layers observed at Godhavn simultaneously with the morning auroras is 110 to several hundred kilometers. Some of the greater virtual heights may, however, be oblique or due to reflections from upper parts of the rays, some of which have been estimated from visual observations to reach more than 1000 km altitude.

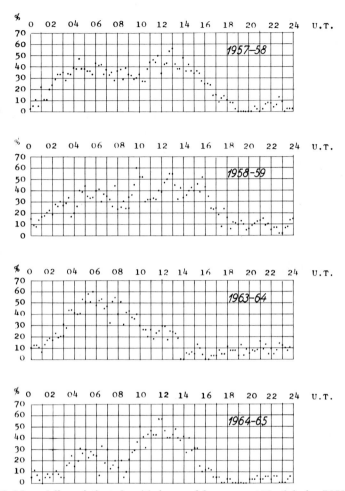

FIGURE 6. Mean daily variation of zenithal auroral frequency at Nord during IGY and IQSY.

2. Auroras Belonging to the Main Auroral Zone

Observations from stations near the classical geographic auroral zone show a daily maximum of auroral occurrence near magnetic midnight. At this time the auroral zone is broadening, auroras approach higher latitudes and may be observed in low elevation even from Thule. Thus, on quiet nights homogeneous arcs and bands are observed near the south-eastern horizon at Godhavn. With increasing disturbance the bands approach the station and a break-up effect is observed, followed by the well-known sequence, where rayed bands cross the zenith in vivid motion with colored rays, which are running rapidly along the bands from the west towards the east, after which the forms become diffuse with very slow intensity-pulsations, until they retreat to lower latitudes. The event seems to follow the description given by AKASOFU (1965) of the auroral substorm. During years with low auroral activity, all of the display is observed a few degrees above the horizon as a closed flat ring of active bands. The variation of the auroral frequency at corr. geom. midnight (01.30 UT), shown in Figure 7 for each of the areas S (10°–30° above the southern horizon), Z

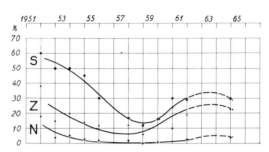

FIGURE 7. Year-to-year variation of auroral frequency at 01.30 hr UT (corr. geom. midnight), Godhavn, 1952–65.

(30° above the southern horizon–30° above the northern horizon), and N (10°–30° above the northern horizon), gives an impression of the varying intrusion of auroras from the main zone on the polar cap around magnetic midnight. The data from 1951–6 were taken from visual observations made by the author. After 1957, an all-sky camera has been used. The observations from the three parts of the sky agree in showing that during the years 1951–65 the polar distance of the inner border of the nighttime auroral zone varies in a smooth way, being greatest near or about one year after sunspot maximum, and least about two years before sunspot minimum. This is in accordance with the variation during the years 1943–56 of the magnetic activity at midnight, which is strongly related to the auroral substorms (LASSEN, 1958).

Several degrees from the auroral zone the midnight maximum becomes less important. More obvious are two maxima, one in the evening and one in the morning hours. With increasing latitude these maxima are gradually displaced towards the day-hours until at 75–78°, they merge into one single maximum near magnetic noon. This may indicate that the zone of maximum auroral precipitation forms an eccentric circle or oval in the corrected geomagnetic system. Figure 8 shows the distribution of frequencies on all days of 1957–8 based on hourly values. It may be concluded from the figure that the maximum zone forms an eccentric oval in the polar graph. However, it is not certain that the groups on the night-side and on the day-side constitute one continuous ring. In a similar diagram for disturbed days of 1957–8 all isoauroras are closed ovals; further, the special high-latitude areas have disappeared. According to KHOROSHEVA (1962) data from all-sky cameras in the Soviet sector covering approximately 180° of longitude have shown that the oval zone is not a purely statistical one. In a number of cases auroral bands could be followed from high latitudes in the morning part of the sector till auroral zone latitude in the night part.

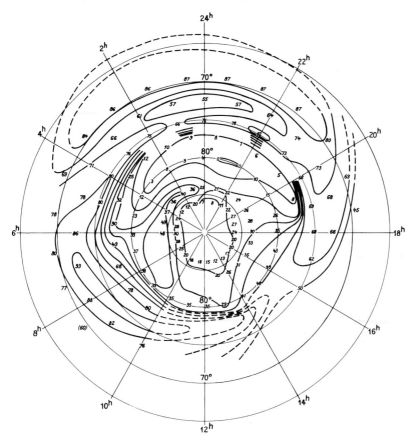

FIGURE 8. Auroral frequency pattern 1957–8, all days. Isoauroral lines drawn on a polar graph with corr. geom. lat and time as coordinates. Isoauroral lines are based on zenithal frequencies and shown for multiples of 10%.

Stations at 75–80° observe an advance from the equatorial horizon of auroras, which are nearest to the station around magnetic noon. This variation was observed from South Pole at 75° corr. geom. lat (GARTLEIN et al., 1960) and from Nord at 80° corr. geom. lat (LASSEN, 1963), cf. Figure 1.

As mentioned in Section 1, observations from Nord 1957–9 have shown that auroras on the southern sky which are believed to constitute the northern part of the eccentric oval, are frequently observed on magnetically disturbed days with a maximum at 13 hr corr. geom. time ($9\frac{1}{2}$hr UT), whereas the frequency is very low on quiet days. The difference between sunspot maximum and minimum years is illustrated by Figure 9, from which it is seen that few auroras from the eccentric oval were observed from Nord during 1964–5. In Figure 10 it is seen that both the night-group and the day-group in the polar graph are in 1964–5 reduced in comparison with 1957–8.

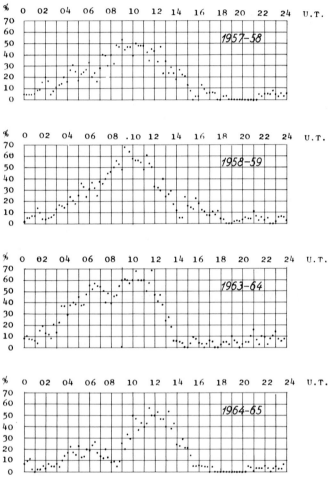

FIGURE 9. Mean daily variation of auroral frequency, 10–30° elevation above southern horizon. Nord, IGY and IQSY.

3. Polar Cap Auroras During Magnetic Storms

During three magnetic storms of July, 1957 auroras of great intensity were observed from Vostok. FELDSTEIN (1959) noticed that the aurora began practically simultaneously with the beginning of the magnetic storm, but ceased as

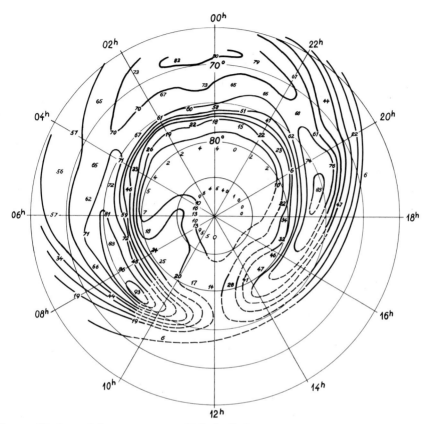

FIGURE 10. Auroral frequency pattern 1964–5, all days. Isoauroral lines drawn on a polar graph with corr. geom. lat and time as coordinates. Isouaroral lines are based on zenithal frequencies and shown for multiples of 10%.

the magnetic storm developed. A comparison with the magnetic records from Kakioka shows that the aurora was present at Vostok during the initial phase of the storm only.

In a study of twenty-six SSC-storms from 1957–61 WEILL (1963) found that the probability of observation of an aurora at Dumont d'Urville in the time interval SSC + 15–SSC + 45 min was 0.8, whereas the mean probability of observation of an aurora during half an hour was 0.2. The auroras were among the most intense observed at the station. They approached the zenith from the auroral zone and withdrew after about an hour.

Very active and brilliant auroral displays were reported by the Fort Conger expedition (87° corr. geom. lat) in connection with the severe magnetic storm of November, 1882. The duration of the display seems to have been greater than the initial phase of the storm. Similarly, bright zenithal auroras were recorded at Thule and Godhavn during the October and December storms of

1961, at the same time as MAEHLUM and O'BRIEN (1963) reported that the northern boundary of precipitating electrons and of auroras was displaced to low latitudes. Obviously, further studies are needed before the appearance of active auroras near the pole during magnetic storms can be understood.

References

AKASOFU, S.-I., 1965, *Space Sc. Rev.* **4**, 498.
DANIELSEN, C., 1966, private communication.
DAVIS, T. N, 1962, *J. Geophys. Res.* **67**, 75.
FELDSTEIN, Y. I., 1959, *Isv. Akad. Nauk USSR. Ser. Geophys.*, **1**.
FELDSTEIN, Y. I., 1962, *Geomagnetism and Aeronomy* **2**, 706.
GARTLEIN, C. W., NACK, B., and SPRAGUE, G., 1960, IGY General Report 12, Nov. 1960.
HAKURA, Y., 1965, *Rep. Ionosphere Space Res. Japan* **19**, 121.
KHOROSHEVA, O. V., 1962, *Geomagnetism and Aeronomy* **2**, 696.
LASSEN, K., 1958, *Det Danske Meteor. Inst., Comm. Magn.* **23**, Copenhagen.
LASSEN, K., 1963, *Det Danske Meteor. Inst., Medd.* **16**, Charlottenlund.
MCILWAIN, C. E., 1961, *J. Geophys. Res.* **66**, 3681.
MAEHLUM, B. and O'BRIEN, B. J., 1963, *J. Geophys. Res.* **68**, 997.
MAWSON, D., 1925, Australasian Antarctic Exp. 1911–14, Sci. Rep., Series B, Vol. II, Part I, Records of the Aurora Polaris, Sydney.
MAYAUD, P. N., 1960, *Ann. Geophys.* **16**, 278.
SANDFORD, B. P., 1964, *J. Atmospheric Terrest. Phys.* **26**, 749.
VESTINE, E. H. and SNYDER, E. J., 1945, *Terr. Magn. Atm. Electr.* **50**, 105.
WEGENER, A., 1930, *Medd. Grønland*, **75**, 662, København.
WEILL, G., 1958, *Compt. Rend. Acad. Sci.* **246**, 2925, Paris.
WEILL, G., 1963, Acad. Sci., Note, Session of January 7, 1963, Paris.
WEILL, G., DELANNOY, J., FAFIOTTE, M., and HUILLE, S., 1965. *Ann. Geophys.* **21**, 469.

AURORAL OBSERVATIONS FROM
WEST CENTRAL CANADA

A. VALLANCE JONES*

Institute of Space and Atmospheric Studies
University of Saskatchewan, Canada

Abstract A summary of some new observations of the position and characteristics of the proton precipitation zone as a function of magnetic activity is presented. A rotational temperature of $2200°$ K for the $\lambda3914$ N_2^+ band is reported for type-A red aurora. Temperatures for the Vegard-Kaplan bands of up to $2200°$ K were measured in other high temperature auroras. High temperature sunlit aurora was relatively common between 1958 and 1960. A method of measuring temperatures from the First Positive N_2 bands is reported.

I. Introduction

Observations from Saskatoon (60°N geomagnetic) to Churchill (69°N geomagnetic) encompass the classical auroral zone and the region into which aurora expands in disturbed conditions. For about the last fifteen years, a program of auroral observations has been based on these stations. This paper covers some recently available results of studies initiated by the University of Saskatchewan. These results concerning the behavior of hydrogen emissions and abnormally high temperatures in auroras are of interest in a theoretical interpretation of bombardment processes in the upper atmosphere.

II. Observations of the Hydrogen Emission Lines

The extreme variability of the ratio in the brightness of the hydrogen lines and the other main features of the auroral spectrum is very well known (CHAMBERLAIN, 1961a). In studying the variations in the brightness of the $H\alpha$ and $H\beta$ lines relative to that of the aurora, a useful ratio is that between the brightness of the $H\beta$ line at 4861Å and the neighboring (0,2) N_2^+ First Negative band at 4709Å. This ratio, hereafter denoted $R(H\beta)$, may be measured easily from photographic spectra with an accuracy sufficient for statistical studies. Earlier theoretical

*The research reported in this paper was partially supported by the Air Force Cambridge Research Center, Office of Aerospace Research, U. S. Air Force, under Contract AF 19 (628)-2829.

work (OMHOLT, 1959) indicates that this ratio should have a value greater than 3.5 for a purely proton excited form at normal auroral heights, while recent calculations by EATHER (1966) employing improved cross sections suggest that the value may be closer to 1.0. Figure 1, taken from a recently completed

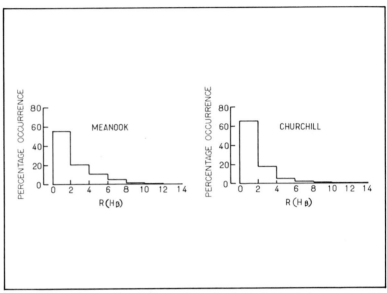

FIGURE 1. Relative frequencies of observation of values of $R(H\beta)$ (see text) at Meanook and Churchill. After Montbriand and Vallance Jones, 1966.

analysis of I.G.Y. data by MONTBRIAND and VALLANCE JONES (1966), shows the frequency of observations of values of $R(H\beta)$ from Meanook (62° N geomagnetic) and Churchill. These frequencies have been corrected by weighting each spectrogram with a weight proportional to the N_2^+ band intensity. Consequently, they correspond to the frequencies with which one would obtain different values of R on spectrograms having the same exposure to the N_2^+ bands. Somewhat different results would be obtained if spectrograms having equal exposure times were analyzed. Figure 1 shows that over 50% of aurora has $R < 0.2$ and 97% has $R < 1.0$. However, in five cases at Churchill from a total of 1858 measured ratios, R exceeded 3.0.

These results confirm quantitatively the relatively small contribution of proton excited luminosity in visual aurora. Nevertheless, the appearance of hydrogen lines is a good indicator of bombardment by protons capable of penetrating to auroral heights. A full knowledge of the variations in location, in time and place of regions of proton bombardment should be extremely significant in formulating theories of aurora and magnetic storms. This requires a full study of the morphology of the hydrogen emissions. Many in-

vestigators have examined the question, including MONTALBETTI and VALLANCE
JONES (1957), REES *et al.* (1961), MONTBRIAND and VALLANCE JONES (1962),
STOFFREGEN and DERBLOM (1962), MONTALBETTI and MCEWEN (1962), GAL-
PERIN (1963 a and b), YURCHENKO (1963), and EATHER and SANDFORD (1966).
Most of this work covers the I.G.Y. period. Over the I.Q.S.Y. period the
University of Saskatchewan, in collaboration with the Defence Research
Northern Laboratory at Churchill, undertook an extensive program of observations along a line of overlapping stations from Saskatoon to Baker Lake
covering a range of geomagnetic latitudes from about 58–74°N. Each station
was equipped with an all-sky camera, a magnetometer, a Perkin-Elmer patrol
spectrograph similar to that described by CLARK and ROMICK (1959). Syn-
chronized exposures were taken by the photographic instruments using accurate timers. The analysis of the data obtained is not yet complete. However,
some preliminary results obtained by Montbriand and Wiens are shown in
Figure 2. Montbriand finds that even under very quiet magnetic conditions,
there exists a region of weak Hα emission in the 70–75° N geomagnetic latitude
region. This emission field shows a systematic diurnal movement, being fur-
thest south near midnight. The position of this emission is indicated in Figure 2

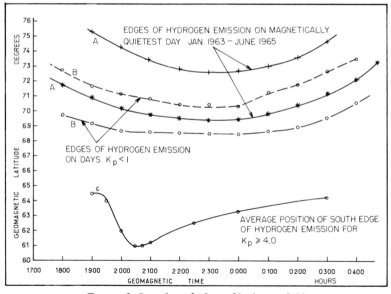

FIGURE 2. Location of edges of hydrogen field.

by the two solid lines in the north which show the location of the zone for the
magnetically most quiet day on which observations were made in the period
January 1963–June, 1965. The dashed line shows the zone location averaged
for all magnetically quiet days. These observations were made from Baker

Lake and Churchill; no emission would be detectable from the southern stations under these conditions. SHARP *et al.* (1966) report satellite observed distributions of proton flux from 70–66° N; this may be compared with the limits from 71–69°N for the curves B of Figure 2. The lowest line on Figure 1 summarizes Wiens' observations of the average position of the southern boundary of the hydrogen emission region under disturbed conditions with $K_p > 4.0$. In this case, there is a pronounced asymmetry with respect to magnetic midnight; the most southerly extent of the hydrogen emission is observed between 2000 and 2100 hr. At this time the variance in the location of the southern boundary is also most pronounced.

As a by-product of this study, Wiens has also determined the space distribution of the Hα emission. From fourteen pairs of Perkin-Elmer spectrograms obtained simultaneously from Flin Flon and Saskatoon, it was possible to draw the following conclusions:

1) A more consistent interpretation of the data is possible if it is assumed that the emission is distributed in the form of a relatively thin horizontal sheet.

2) If 1) is true, then the twenty-eight possible heights measurable from the data (a pair of values from the north and south edges of the sheet) have a mean value of 106 km ± 7 km. The average north-south extent was 194 km. This result applies to occasions when the Hα emission was relatively bright (> 500 R).

This result may be compared with the theoretical prediction of DAVIDSON (1965), who showed that a narrow beam of protons entering the atmosphere would spread out to give a diffuse emission in the form of a thin sheet having an extent of the order of several hundred kilometers.

III. Rotational Temperatures in Auroras Near Sunspot Maximum

A. Theory

The intensity of a rotational line in an allowed electronic vibration rotation band $\sim v^4 S(K') \exp[-F'''(K')hc/KT]$ where $S(K')$ is the line strength factor for the transition from the K' th level of the upper state, F''' is the rotational term value for the initial state from which the excitation occurs and v, n, c, and T have their usual meanings. This involves the assumption that in the excitation process $\Delta K = 0$, i.e., that the population of a given rotational level in the excited state will be proportional to the population of the rotational level in the initial state having the same molecular rotational angular momentum.

This is likely to be true for electron excitation and higher energy proton excitation. STAIR (1967) has shown that changes in K do occur for slow electrons with energies close to the excitation threshold. Since almost all the excitation in aurora must be due to higher energy electrons, the $\Delta K = 0$ approximation should hold good. Excitation by slow protons alone might produce anomalous effects. Such excitation should be indicated by values of $R(H\beta) > 2$ which is most uncommon and does not seem to be characteristic of type-A red displays (Figure 3). REES (1961), however, has argued that the excitation of a high altitude red arc with $R(H\beta) = 1.1$, was by protons of a few keV energy, but it seems doubtful that this need be true in general. Certainly $R(H\beta)$ appears much less than unity in Figure 3.

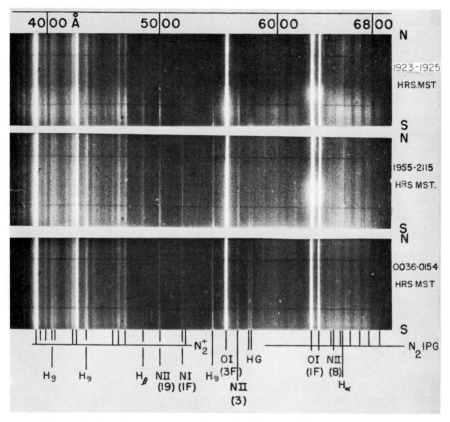

FIGURE 3. Patrol spectrograms of type-A red aurora of February 10/11, 1958.

In the case of the First Negative N_2^+ bands, $F'''(K') \simeq B'''K'(K' + 1)$ and $S(K') \sim K'$ for the R-branch. Consequently, if the intensities of the individual rotational lines can be measured, then a plot of $\log_e \dfrac{I(K')}{\nu^4 K'}$ against $K'(K' + 1)$ gives a straight line of slope $B'''hc/KT$. If the aurora is sunlit, VALLANCE JONES and HUNTEN (1960) showed that the Swings effect is observed. In this case, a high proportion of the emission arises from fluorescence of N_2^+ ions produced initially by particle impact. Even in this process the ground state rotational distribution appears to be preserved; some rotational lines are and others are depressed in intensity because of the presence of Fraunhofer lines in the exciting solar spectrum. VALLANCE JONES and HUNTEN (1960) showed that this effect led to the line intensity becoming $\sim \nu^4 S(K') \exp[-F'''(K')hc/KT]\bar{u}$, where $\bar{u}$ is essentially the average solar intensity contributing to the excitation of a particular upper state rotational level.

B. First Negative Band Rotational Temperature in a Type-A Red Display

Type-A red aurora are characterized by visually bright red patches. Spectroscopically the type-A red displays observed near sunspot maximum showed high brightness ratios of [OI] red line to [OI] green line, abnormally strong forbidden lines of O^+ and N^+, and abnormal N_2^+ vibrational band ratios (BELON and CLARK, 1959; CLARK and BELON, 1959; WALLACE, 1959; VALLANCE JONES, 1960). Doppler temperature measurements of the [OI] red lines of up to 3400° K were reported by MULYARCHIK and SCHEGLOV (1963). It would be of interest to have a high resolution spectrum for the unambiguous determination of the rotational temperatures. WALLACE (1959) obtained a spectrum from the February 10/11, 1957 great red aurora from Yerkes Observatory. He reported

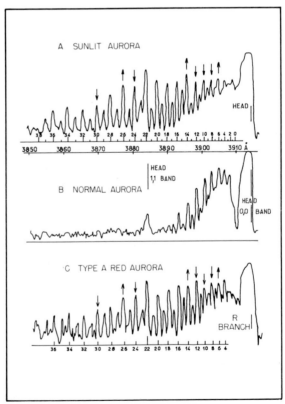

FIGURE 4. Spectra of λ3914 N_2^+ band. Predicted large swings effect perturbations are shown by arrows.

temperatures of 225° K from the R-branch lines of low K and obtained a good fit for the lines $K = 10–20$ with a temperature of 575° K. From low resolution spectra, CLARK and BELON (1959) reported a synthetic spectrum fit for a temperature of 2500° K.

A spectrum of an aurora observed visually to be type-A red was obtained from Saskatoon, on the evening of March 6/7, 1959, with a spectral slit width of about 1Å. The atmosphere was dark in the zenith to 500 km at the beginning of the 53 min exposure. A microphotometer tracing of the $(0, 0)N_2^+$ band is shown in Figure 4. In Figure 4 are shown also the spectra of sunlit rays and normal aurora discussed by VALLANCE JONES and HUNTEN (1960). The lines which show the strongest Swings effect and the changes which the effect produces are shown by arrows on the figure. It is clear that there is no sign in Figure 4 of the Swings effect seen in the sunlit spectrum B. A least squares analysis of this spectrum carried out by AHMED (1966) for the lines $R(14)$–$R(43)$ showed that the sunlit contribution to this spectrum did not exceed 40% and gave a rotation temperature of about 2200° K. The absence of Swings effect

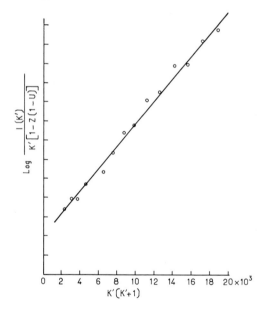

FIGURE 5. Plot of log $I(K')/K'$ [1 − 0.4 (1 − $\bar{u}$)] against K' $(K' + 1)$ for spectrum of Figure 4(C).

for the stronger lines of Figure 4(C) suggests this value of 40% may be a considerable over-estimate arising from the effects of a little solar contamination on the weaker lines. Figure 5 shows the plot of log $I(K')/K'$[1 − 0.4 (1 − $\bar{u}$)] against K' $(K' + 1)$ for this spectrum. The modified denominator reflects the finding that the plot fits best when a 40% contribution from sunlit excitation is assumed. The plot fits a straight line with little sign of any curvature which would indicate a serious mixture of temperatures. The final conclusion is that this type-A red aurora came from a region of the atmosphere in which fluorescent enhancement by solar illumination was of minor importance but in which the ground state temperature of the nitrogen molecules was about 2200° K.

C. First Negative N_2^+ Rotational Temperatures in Sunlit Aurora

Between 1958 and 1960 many displays of aurora similar to that analyzed by VALLANCE JONES and HUNTEN (1960) were observed. These spectra were analyzed by AHMED (1966). The data, summarized in Table I, give some idea of

Table I. High Temperature Mixed Type-A Red and Sunlit Auroral Spectra Observed from Saskatoon 1958–60

Date	Aurora Type	T_R (°K)	Minimum Zenith Shadow Height (km)
August 22/23, and August 23/24, 1958	Bright red aurora at times	1850 ± 200	320
September 3/4, and September 4/5, 1958	Sunlit rays and type-A-red	2100 ± 3	220
March 6/7, 1959	Sunlit rays	2000 ± 200	260
March 27/28, 1959	Sunlit rays	2150 ± 250	90
April 8/9, 1959	Sunlit rays red rays	2300 ± 300	190
October 6/7, 1959	Sunlit aurora	2650 ± 350	68
November 15/16, 1960	Red sunlit aurora	2000 ± 200	120

the frequency of this phenomenon during this period. These spectra show a strong Swings effect.

D. Rotational Temperatures from Vegard-Kaplan Bands

The Vegard-Kaplan bands are quite sensitive to variations in the rotational temperature of the ground state N_2 molecules. PETRIE (1954), WALLACE (1959), and BROADFOOT and HUNTEN (1964) have obtained temperatures by comparing synthetic with observed spectra. This prodecure is necessary since even at 1Å resolution the individual rotational lines are not completely resolved. Petrie and Broadfoot and Hunten obtained temperatures of about 800° K from apparently normal auroral displays, while Wallace obtained a lower limit of 800° K and an upper limit of perhaps 3000–4000° K, from the February 10/11, 1958 type-A red aurora. The main difficulty in using these bands, at least from the ground, is that the strongest and most accessible bands are partially overlapped by Second Positive N_2 bands. Figure 6 illustrates the situation for the 1–11 V-K band. The main part of the rotational structure from 3694–3712Å cannot be used because of the underlying 2P N_2 band of which the synthetic spectrum would be difficult to calculate. However on well-exposed high resolu-

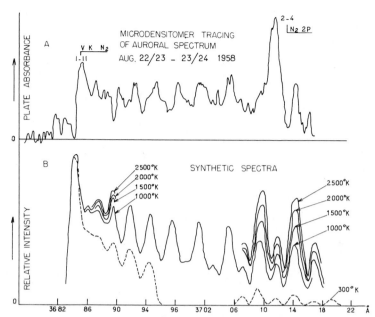

FIGURE 6. A. Observed spectrum of 1–11 V-K N₂ band (August 22/23, 23/24, 1958). B. Synthetic spectra of 1–11 V-K band, for 2500° K, 2000° K, 1500° K, 1000° K, and 300° K. After Ahmed, 1966 .

tion spectra the part of the V-K band at wavelengths greater than 3712Å can be readily detected and measured. AHMED (1966) was successful in discovering the correct way to utilize the line strength factors in calculating the synthetic spectra for the V-K bands. It had apparently been generally overlooked that in applying SCHLAPP's (1937) line strength factors for the $^1\Sigma_g - {^3\Sigma_g}^-$–O₂ system to the ${^3\Sigma_u}^+ - {^1\Sigma_g}^+$ N₂ system that the factors for the P-branches in one case are appropriate to the R-branches in the other and vice versa. This is rather important in reproducing the very pronounced maximum at the band-head which is characteristic of the bands. By comparing the observed and calculated ratios of intensity at 3714Å and 3684Å, it is possible to derive V-K temperatures from well-exposed spectra showing the 1–11 band. Some results are shown in Table II.

Table II. Vegard-Kaplan N₂ Rotational Temperatures from Some Strong Auroras 1955-1959

Date	T N₂⁺	T (Vegard-Kaplan)	Remarks
January 15/16, 1955	450 ± 30°	1200 ± 120°R	
January 16/17	1350 ± 150°		
January 17/18, 1955	1250 ± 100°R	1500 ± 150°R	Very strong
May 25/26, 1955	1300 ± 100°R	1400 ± 150°R	Very strong
August 22/23, 1958	1850 ± 200°R	2200 ± 250°R	Bright red aurora
August 23/24			
September, 1959	1150 ± 100°R	1250 ± 200°R	Weak long rays and pulsating aurora

The apparent agreement between the N_2^+ and V-K rotational temperatures would be expected in normal low-level auroras as was pointed out by BROADFOOT and HUNTEN (1964). Collisional quenching should suppress the V-K system below perhaps 200 km. The near equality shown in Table II is probably the result of the fact that the exposures are very strong, so that the N_2^+ temperatures have been derived from the lines with higher values of K. These come predominantly from the higher temperature, higher altitude regions of the display from which the V-K bands were also presumably being emitted.

However, the conclusion again is that temperatures of 1200–2000° K are found in regions of the atmosphere from which an important amount of auroral light is emitted.

IV. Other Auroral Temperature Measurements

An interesting advance in the technique of determining temperatures from auroral spectra has been made recently by SHEMANSKY (1966). He has been successful in measuring temperatures from the First Positive N_2 bands. The structure of these bands is very complicated since the $^3\Pi_g(a) - {}^3\Sigma_u^+$ transition involved leads to twenty-seven overlapping branches. However, it proved possible using a computer, and assuming excitation from the ground state with $\Delta K = 0$, to prepare synthetic spectra for a range of temperatures. As may

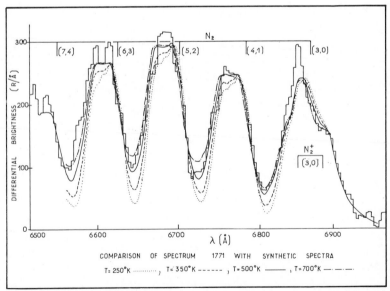

FIGURE 7. Synthetic and observed spectra of $\Delta v = 3$ sequence of IP N_2 bands. The best overall fit was judged to be for 500° K. After Shemansky, 1966.

be seen from Figure 7, quite significant variations with temperature occur in the shape of the bands. The figure also shows the comparison with an observed spectrum recorded with a scanning photoelectric spectrometer equipped with a memory system. With this procedure, Shemansky has derived temperatures which seem reasonable in that they show a high correlation with the brightness ratio of the [OI] red lines and the 4-1 N_2 1P band. The temperatures obtained range from 330° K for $r = \dfrac{I(6300)}{I(\text{4-1 1PN}_2)} = .05$ to 700° K for $r = .95$. Since the lifetime of the $^3\Pi_g$ state is rather long ($\simeq 10^{-5}$ secs), it is possible that at the lowest heights for type-B red aurora that rotational equilibrium in the excited state might be established since the collision rate at 80 km is about 10^5 sec. In this case the temperature would be modified by the ratio of the upper to lower state B-values, so that the lowest temperature should possibly be 250° K rather than 330° K.

Finally, in this review of recent work at Saskatchewan, mention should be made of the very interesting temperature fluctuations observed by HILLIARD and SHEPHERD (1966). They were able to use a specialized wide-angle Michelson interferometer to follow rapid variations in temperature by measuring the modulation of the interference fringes produced by the λ5577 green line. In certain rapid brightness fluctuations, taken in a time of about 5 sec, a clear variation of the temperature in the opposite direction to that of the brightness over a temperature range of 100° K was observed. A further remarkable tendency reported was a persistent tendency for temperatures and brightnesses to maintain a definite inverse relationship over substantial periods of time. This is illustrated in their paper, which sometimes shows the point brightness of λ5577 plotted against the temperature to fall on an almost hyperbolic curve. The most plausible phenomenon is in terms of variations in the average energy of the incoming electrons, leading to variations in the height distribution, and thus, the temperature of the luminosity.

V. Conclusions

This paper has reviewed some observations which are of interest in the theoretical interpretation of aurora. The hydrogen emission zone observations are clearly to be explained by a satisfactory aurora and magnetosphere theory, while the phenomenon of the occurrence near sunspot maximum of type-A red and sunlit aurora indicating rotational temperatures for N_2 of 2000° K is significant in an understanding of the variation of atmospheric structure and particle influx over the sunspot cycle. Finally, the inversely related temperature and brightness fluctuations reported by Hilliard and Shepherd are a phenomenon of fundamental interest in relation to acceleration and precipitation mechanisms for auroral particles.

Acknowledgments   The author is indebted to his students and former students at Saskatoon for access to material from theses and unpublished notes. The work on the synoptic hydrogen observations has been supported by the National Research Council and Defence Research Board of Canada. Almost all the high resolution photographic auroral spectra were obtained by Mr. H. J. Koenig, to whom a warm acknowledgment is due.

References

AHMED, M., 1966, *Ph. D. Thesis*, University of Saskatchewan.

BELON, A. E., and CLARK, K. C., 1959, *J. Atmospheric Terrest. Phys.* **16**, 220–227.

BROADFOOT, A. L. and HUNTEN, D. M., 1964, *Can. J. Phys.* **42**, 1212.

CHAMBERLAIN, J. W., *Physics of Aurora and Airglow*, Academic Press, New York and London, p. 191.

CLARK, K. C. and BELON, A. E., 1959, *J. Atmospheric Terrest. Phys.* **16**, 205–219.

CLARK, K. C. and ROMICK, G. J., 1959, *J. Opt. Soc. Am.* **49**, 141.

DAVIDSON, G. T., 1965, *J. Geophys. Res.* **70**, 1060.

EATHER, R. H., 1966, private communication.

EATHER, R. H. and SANDFORD, B. P., 1966, *Australian J. Phys.* **19**, 25.

GALPERIN, Y. I., 1963, *Planetary Space Sci.* **10**, 187.

GALPERIN, Y. I., 1963, Aurorae and Airglow, IV section of IGY Program, Acad. Sci. U.S.S.R., Moscow, 10, p. 70.

HILLIARD, R. E. and SHEPHERD, G. G., 1966, *Planetary Space Sci.* **14**, 383.

MONTALBETTI, R. and McEWEN, D. J., 1962, *J. Phys. Soc. Japan* **17**, Supplement A-I, 212.

MONTALBETTI, R. and VALLANCE JONES, A., 1957, *J. Atmospheric Terrest. Phys.* **11**, 43.

MONTBRIAND, L_e E. and VALLANCE JONES, A., 1962, *Can. J. Phys.* **40**, 1401.

MONTBRIAND, L. E. and VALLANCE JONES, A., 1966, *Can. J. Phys.* (to be published).

MULYARCHIK, T. M. and SHCHEGLOW, P. V., 1963, *Planetary Space Sci.* **10**, 215.

OMHOLT, A., 1959, *Geophys. Pub.* **20**, 11, 1.

PETRIE, W. J., 1954, *J. Atmospheric Terrest. Phys.* **4**, 6.

REES, M. H., 1961, *Planetary Space Sci.* **8**, 59.

REES, M. H., BELON, A. E., and ROMICK, G. J., 1961, *Planetary Space Sci.* **5**, 87.

SCHLAPP, R., 1937, *Phys. Rev.* **51**, 342.

SHARP, R. D., JOHNSON, R. G., SHEA, H. F., and SHOOK, G. B., 1967, this volume.

SHEMANSKY, D. E., 1966, Ph. D. Thesis, University of Saskatchewan.

STAIR, A. T., JR., 1967, this volume.

STOFFREGEN, W. and DERBLOM, H., 1962, *Planetary Space Sci.* **9**, 711.

VALLANCE JONES, A., 1960, *Can. J. Phys.* **38**, 453–457.

VALLANCE JONES, A. and HUNTEN, D. M., 1960, *Can. J. Phys.* **38**, 458–476.

WALLACE, L., 1959, *J. Atmospheric Terrest. Phys.* **17**, 46–56.

YURCHENKO, O. T., 1963, Aurorae and Airglow, IV section of IGY Program, Acad. Sci. U.S.S.R., Moscow, 10.

Discussion

Meyerott asked if the sunlit aurora was produced where it was observed or if it rose from below. Apparently, the origin cannot be determined at this time.

The proton-alpha particle ratio in aurora has not been measured yet.

A question was raised concerning to which part of the aurora the temperatures are related, and if the temperature is related to altitude. In general, they attempted to view definite auroral forms, and it is apparently well known that one can get low temperatures by viewing the bottom of the form, and higher temperatures by observing above the lower border. It was pointed out that such measurements require a good bit of care.

BALLOON MEASUREMENTS OF AURORAL X RAYS

G. Kremser

Max-Planck-Institut für Aeronomie
Institut für Stratosphären-Physik
Lindau/Harz, Germany

1. Introduction

Electron precipitation in the auroral zone causes a wide range of phenomena, as auroral emissions, enhanced cosmic noise absorption, and bremsstrahlung x rays and plays a role in the development of some types of geomagnetic disturbances. These various effects can be attributed to electrons in different energy regions.

The x rays with which we are mainly concerned in this paper are caused by electrons with energies above approximately 30 keV. Measurements of these x rays indirectly provide information about temporal and spatial changes of the intensity and the energy spectrum of the higher energetic electrons which are precipitated in the auroral zone.

The main purpose of this paper shall be a review and a discussion of x-ray measurements and the relationships between x-ray bursts and other auroral zone phenomena. This main part shall be preceded by some short remarks on the usefulness and limitations of balloon observations and on the x-ray detectors. Those who are interested in a historical summary are referred to the review papers by ANDERSON (1965), BROWN (1966), and PFOTZER (1965).

Usefulness and Limitations of Balloon Measurements

Though the electrons precipitated in the auroral zone can now be directly observed by rocket and satellite instruments, the balloon measurements have revealed several characteristic features mainly concerning their temporal behavior which could not have been obtained by any other method. The satellites and rockets move so fast that it is not always possible to distinguish between temporal and local variations, whereas balloons under favorable conditions stay at practically the same location up to 20 hours or more. Other indirect methods depend strongly upon ionospheric and atmospheric parameters which hide the time variations of the parent electron flux. On the other hand, the information about the energy spectrum is limited, as the balloons only reach heights of about 30–35 km, whereas the x rays are produced at about 100 km. Therefore, the x rays have to traverse a layer of air of about 8–10 g/cm² before reaching the detectors.

The main effects which influence the x-ray flux in this layer are photoelectric absorption and the Compton effect. The photoelectric absorption strongly changes the energy spectrum of the photon flux and is also the main cause for the lower energy limit of about 30 keV for the detection of electrons via x rays at balloon heights. The Compton scattering considerably restricts the significance of directional measurements.

A further limitation of the information obtained by balloon measurements is the rather low production efficiency for the bremsstrahlung process: 10^4–10^5 electrons are needed to produce one photon. Therefore, the x-ray fluxes have to be multiplied by rather high conversion factors to obtain the electron flux, thereby enlarging its uncertainties.

X-Ray Detectors

For the x-ray measurements, Geiger-Müller counters, ionization chambers, and scintillation counters have been employed in different combinations. Because of their high efficiency to photons, the scintillation counters have proved to be the best detectors for x-ray measurements. They consist of a NaI(Tl)-crystal and a photomultiplier. Spectral measurements are obtained by pulse height analysis.

The SPARMO groups (Solar Particles and Radiations Monitoring Organization) use a detector consisting of a scintillation counter and Geiger counters (SAEGER, 1965). Since the combination of a scintillation counter and a telescope of Geiger counters permits one to distinguish between photons and charged particles, this detector discriminates properly between x rays and PCA protons.

2. Spatial and Temporal Variations of the X-Ray Flux and Energy Spectrum

The Geographical Distribution

In the latitudinal direction the x-ray flux is confined to the auroral zone (MEREDITH et al., 1955; VAN ALLEN, 1957; ANDERSON, 1965). In the longitudinal direction simultaneous measurements are mostly restricted to small distances. During such flights x-ray fluxes were observed simultaneously at distances of some hundred kilometers, though often with different time structures. From the few simultaneous measurements at greater distances (up to 180° longitude), together with riometer recordings, it is concluded that in many cases the x-ray precipitation takes place over great parts of the auroral zone, but that there are appreciable differences between the precipitation in the evening and morning sector (BROWN, 1966; BEWERSDORFF et al., 1966b).

Regarding the extension of the x-ray precipitation, simultaneous measurements at conjugate points in the northern and southern auroral zones are also of great interest. From such measurements it can be decided whether the acceleration mechanisms responsible for the precipitated electrons are symmetrical to the geomagnetic equatorial plane. Though such measurements are not yet performed at exactly conjugate points, BROWN *et al.* (1963, 1965a, 1965b) have reported on observations at conjugate areas. These observations showed that more intense, long lasting x-ray events which usually occur over great regions were observed simultaneously in both auroral zones. But the same relationship cannot be confirmed for events on shorter time scales for which the precipitation region is known to be rather small, as the balloon locations were not close enough to conjugacy (< 100 km).

Temporal Variations of the X-Ray Intensity

At a first glance it seems impossible to arrange the complex temporal intensity variations into several distinct groups. However, detailed analyses of the x-ray events on different time scales have shown that one can at least distinguish between long lasting events with smoothly varying intensity, more impulsive, rather featureless bursts usually lasting much less than one hour, and several types of more or less regularly pulsating events which in general are

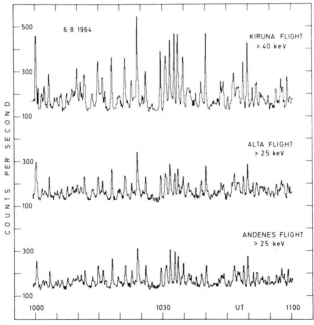

FIGURE 1. Intermediate x-ray pulsations, recorded simultaneously with three balloons at distances of about 300 km from each other. Temporal spacings between 60 and 100 sec (part of a figure by ULLALAND *et al.*, 1967). The cosmic ray background is 130 counts/sec for all three detectors.

superimposed on smooth events (BROWN, 1966; BARCUS and ROSENBERG, 1966a; ULLALAND *et al.*, 1966). Besides the temporal behavior, the events of these groups also differ in their daily occurrences, their spatial distribution, and energy spectrum. The different types of events are summarized in Table I.

In general the following diurnal sequence can be observed; before local midnight, impulsive short time bursts occur, after midnight, more smoothly varying long lasting events, which are often superimposed by fast pulsations in the morning hours, intermediate and slow pulsations during the daytime, and microbursts around noon.

In connection with the pulsations the question arises as to whether these events are really a phenomenon different from the extensive smoothly varying events on which they are superimposed or whether they are only the result of some hydromagnetic modulation of the already existing smooth events. Regarding the energy spectrum of both types of events, BROWN (1966), BARCUS

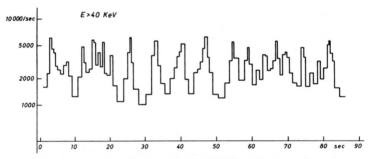

FIGURE 2. Example for fast pulsations (BEWERSDORFF *et al.*, 1966 a).

and ROSENBERG (1965, 1966a), and BARCUS *et al.* (1966) concluded that the slow pulsations are the result of some hydromagnetic modulation, whereas the fast pulsations are caused by processes differing from those responsible for the smooth background events, on which they are superimposed.

The X-Ray Energy Spectrum

As already mentioned in the introduction, all estimates of the x-ray energy spectrum in the source region and of the precipitated electrons are limited through the photoelectric absorption and Compton scattering. Though the absorption and scattering coefficients are well known for air (WHITE, 1952), up to now no unobjectionable reduction of the measured x-ray energy spectrum to the source spectrum and also to the electron spectrum has been performed. This is mainly due to the lack of knowledge about the extension, the location, and the motion of x-ray source regions. Up to now only a few measurements with directional detectors instead of the usually employed omnidirectional ones

Table I. Temporal Structure of X-ray Events

Type of Event	Time of Occurrence	Precipitation Region	Energy Spectrum	References
Long lasting, smoothly varying events	After midnight until noon, sometimes also in the afternoon	Confined to the auroral zone, but 100° in longitude and more	Diurnal variation (see Fig. 5)	BEWERSDORFF et al., 1966
Impulsive bursts	Late evening and night, rarely after midnight			
Slow pulsations (several minutes)	Daytime	Up to more than 1000 km	Relatively flat	ANGER et al., 1963b; BARCUS and ROSENBERG, 1965
Intermediate pulsations (80–100 sec) (Fig. 1)	Daytime	More than 300 km	Relatively flat	EVANS, 1963; BARCUS and CHRISTENSEN, 1965; ULLALAND et al., 1967
Fast pulsations (4–30 sec) (Fig. 2)	Morning	About 100 km	Relatively steep	ANGER et al., 1963a; BEWERSDORFF et al., 1966b; BARCUS et al., 1966
Microbursts (halfwidth below 0.2 sec)	Morning and around noon	About 100 km	Relatively flat	ANDERSON and MILTON, 1964; TREFALL et al., 1966; BARCUS et al., 1966; EHMERT et al., 1966

have been performed at heights where the Compton scattering is still negligible (at atmospheric depths less than 5 g/cm²) (ANDERSON, 1965; KEPPLER, 1965; BROWN, 1966; GOSLING, 1966; HUDSON *et al.*, 1965).

As an example for spectral measurement the results during a part of a balloon flight are shown in Figure 3, during which fast pulsations were superim-

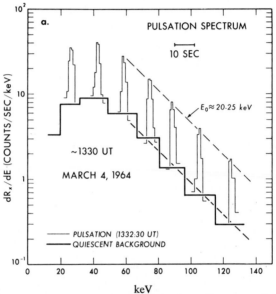

FIGURE 3. Measured x-ray spectrum for fast pulsations (BARCUS and ROSENBERG, 1966).

posed on a smooth background event. The decrease of intensity below 40 keV is mainly due to photoelectric absorption. Also indicated is the range of e-folding energies from 20–25 keV for the usual exponential approximation of the energy spectrum.

But it is not always possible to describe the total energy spectrum with only one value for the e-folding energy. Often for nighttime events two or perhaps even more values are needed. Then for energies below about 50 keV, the e-folding energies range between 5 and 10 keV; for higher energies between 20 and 30 keV (KEPPLER, 1965; KREMSER *et al.*, in preparation). These results are in agreement with rocket measurements by RIEDLER (1966).

As already mentioned in the section on temporal intensity variations, the various types of x-ray events also have different energy spectra. As a result of an extended study of x-ray energy spectra, BARCUS and ROSENBERG (1966) have proposed a diurnal pattern of e-folding energies for these different types, which is shown in Figure 4. It can be seen that the impulsive events before midnight consist of hard x rays with e-folding energies between 25 and 40 keV. The smooth events, which are observed after midnight until the afternoon, are soft around midnight and harden in the course of the day. Fast pulsations are relatively soft, microbursts relatively hard.

The rather sudden softening of smooth events around local midnight and

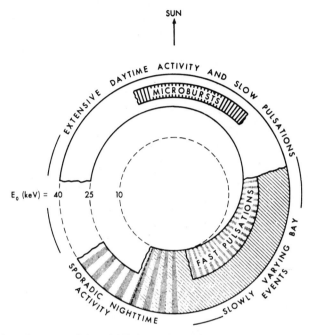

FIGURE 4. Diurnal pattern of the *e*-folding energies E_0 for spectrums of auroral x rays (modified, after BARCUS and ROSENBERG, 1966).

their gradual hardening afterwards was also found by BEWERSDORFF *et al.* (1966a). These authors used Geiger counter data, for which the ratio of the excess counting rates of two different counters can be regarded as a measure for the steepness of the x-ray energy spectrum. They obtained a diurnal pattern of the spectral variations presented as Figure 5. This pattern shows an appreciable softening of the radiation between 20 hr local time and midnight and a subsequent gradual hardening until about 17 hr local time. Due to the lack of measurements, nothing can be said about the spectral changes between 17 and 20 hr local time.

3. Relationships between X-Ray Bursts and Other Auroral Zone Phenomena

Association of X Rays with Aurora

Up to now no conclusive results concerning the association of x rays with aurora have been obtained, as events with close association as well as with no association at all were observed (WINCKLER *et al.*, 1958; ANDERSON and DEWITT, 1963; ANDERSON, 1960, 1962). It was hoped to improve these measurements by employing balloon-borne photometers together with the x-ray detectors. But though such auroral measurements were performed from the near ultraviolet to the infrared, no better correlation could be found than with ground based observations (BARCUS, 1965; ROSENBERG, 1965; WAX, 1966).

The only possible conclusion up to now is that the more energetic electrons which are responsible for the x rays are not to be considered as constituting the high energetic tail of the spectrum of those electrons which cause the visible aurora (HULTQVIST, 1964). Therefore, different precipitation mechanisms must be assumed for the high and low energy parts of the electron spectrum, which may, on the other hand, sometimes be coupled. For further studies of this kind, not only the auroral luminosity, but also the different types of auroral forms should be taken into account.

Association of X Rays with Enhanced Cosmic Noise Absorption (CNA)

In general the association of x rays with CNA is rather close, but the correlation between the x-ray counting rates and the degree of absorption varies greatly. This cannot always be explained by geometrical factors, such as differ-

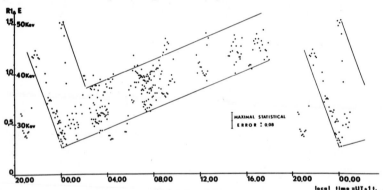

FIGURE 5. Diurnal energy variation of auroral x rays. R_1: ratio of the excess counting rates of two different Geiger counters. E: mean energy of the x rays (BEWERSDORFF *et al.*, 1966a).

ences in the location of the balloon and the riometer antenna pattern, which could be caused by the balloon drift. BARCUS and BROWN (1966) have shown that the energy spectrum of the incident electrons is also of importance. They found no CNA during hard x rays ($E_0 \approx 40$ keV), whereas soft ones ($E_0 \approx 10$–20 keV) were well accompanied by CNA.

Magnetic Storms and Polar Magnetic Substorms

During magnetic storms, x rays are observed throughout great parts of the auroral zone and also at lower latitudes. But great local and temporal intensity variations are observed, which cannot always be related to corresponding magnetic variations. This relationship is not so complicated if one regards the more isolated polar magnetic substorms, which are known as bay-disturbances at middle and low latitudes. But for the occurrence and the development of these disturbances the particle precipitation as well as emf-fields are of importance. Therefore, the accompanying polar magnetic substorm must be investigated on a planetary scale.

Generally these disturbances are represented as the magnetic field of a model ionospheric current system. Figure 6 shows two such systems. In this figure

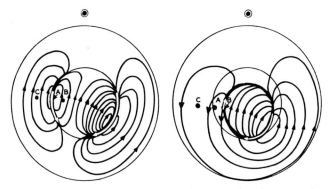

FIGURE 6. Schematic model current system for polar magnetic substorms, after VESTINE and SILSBEE (1942) (to the left) and AKASOFU *et al.* (1965) (to the right). The direction to the sun is indicated by ··· (AKASOFU *et al.*, 1965).

the older configuration obtained by SILSBEE and VESTINE (1942) and a newer one by AKASOFU *et al.* (1965) are presented schematically. The current system of SILSBEE and VESTINE (1942) consists of two strong currents in the auroral zone — the auroral electrojets — which flow in opposite direction on the day and on the nightside, and of their return currents. The current system by AKASOFU *et al.* (1965) has only one — westward — electrojet forming an oval whose center is displaced from the earth's magnetic axis pole. Both model current systems have a fixed orientation with respect to the sun-earth direction. They have gaps before noon where only weak or no currents flow and only weak or no geomagnetic disturbances can be recorded.

If only magnetograms, which were recorded at the balloon launching station, are used for the investigation of the relationships between DP-substorms and x-ray bursts, the result is that x-ray bursts are often accompanied by negative bay-disturbances, but at times, also by positive ones, or by no disturbances at all. In an extended study, the author has shown that these results are only different aspects of the same phenomenon, depending only on what part of the current system was just overhead at the time of the x-ray event (KREMSER, 1964, 1965). He showed for several x-ray events, during which no bay-disturbance was recorded at the balloon launching location, that strong disturbances then were observed at stations on the nightside, where the current systems are strongest. There the bay-disturbance could even be detected at low latitude stations. Two examples are shown in Figure 7. According to these findings,

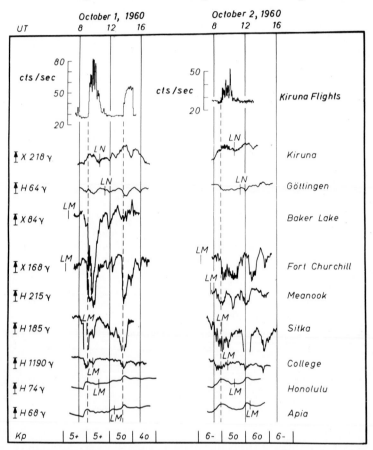

FIGURE 7. Examples for x-ray events, during which only small geomagnetic disturbances were recorded at the balloon launching station, but intense bay-like disturbances on the nightside of the earth (KREMSER, 1964).

it can be assumed that all of the more intense x-ray bursts are accompanied by polar magnetic substorms. But due to the influence of emf-fields on the development of ionospheric current systems, it is not always possible to observe both events at the same location.

X-Ray Events During Storm Sudden Commencements

On three occasions x-ray fluxes coincident with storm sudden commencements were observed by balloon-borne instruments (ANDERSON, 1958; BROWN *et al.*, 1961; HOFFMAN and WINCKLER, 1963; KEPPLER *et al.*, 1962). In all these cases the x-ray flux began to increase just after the ssc, reached its maximum in about 5 min, and then decreased during 1–2 min.

From riometer recordings during ssc's it is known that the electron precipitation takes place over great parts of the auroral zone, depending somewhat on the amplitude of the ssc. The problem about the origin of these electrons is not yet solved.

Acknowledgment The author is grateful to Dr. G. Pfotzer, Prof. A. Ehmert, Dr. E. Keppler, Dr. A. Bewersdorff, and Mr. S. L. Ullaland for helpful support and advice.

References

AKASOFU, S. I., CHAPMAN, S., and MENG, C. J., 1965, *J. Atmospheric Terrest. Phys.* **27**, 1275–1305.
ANDERSON, K. A., 1958, *Phys. Rev.* **111**, 1397–1405.
ANDERSON, K. A., 1960, *J. Geophys. Res.* **65**, 551–564.
ANDERSON, K. A., 1962, *J. Phys. Soc. Japan* **17**, Supp. A-1, 237.
ANDERSON, K. A., 1965, *Auroral Phenomena* (Ed. by M. Walt), Stanford University Press, Chapter 4.
ANDERSON, K. A., 1966, preprint.
ANDERSON, K. A. and DEWITT, R., 1963, *J. Geophys. Res.* **68**, 2669–2676.
ANDERSON, K. A. and MILTON, D. W., 1964, *J. Geophys. Res.* **69**, 4457–4479.
ANGER, C. D., BARCUS, J. R., BROWN, R. R., and EVANS, D. S., 1963a, *J. Geophys. Res.* **68**, 1023–1030.
ANGER, C. D., BARCUS, J. R., BROWN, R. R., and EVANS, D. S., 1963b, *J. Geophys. Res.* **68**, 3306–3310.
BARCUS, J. R., 1965, *J. Geophys. Res.* **70**, 2135–2147.
BARCUS, J. R. and BROWN, R. R., 1966, *J. Geophys. Res.* **71**, 825–834.
BARCUS, J. R., BROWN, R. R., and ROSENBERG, T. J., 1966, *J. Geophys. Res.* **71**, 125–141.
BARCUS, J. R. and CHRISTENSEN, A., 1965, *J. Geophys. Res.* **70**, 5455–5459.
BARCUS, J. R. and ROSENBERG, T. J., 1965, *J. Geophys. Res.* **70**, 1707–1716.
BARCUS, J. R. and ROSENBERG, T. J., 1966, *J. Geophys. Res.* **71**, 803–823.
BEWERSDORFF, A., DION, J., KREMSER, G., KEPPLER, E., LEGRAND, J. P., and RIEDLER, W., 1966 a, *Ann. Géophys.* **22**, 23–30.
BEWERSDORFF, A., KREMSER, G., RIEDLER, W., and LEGRAND, J. P., 1966b, *Arkiv Geofysik* **5**, 115–127.
BROWN, R. R., 1966, *Space Sci. Rev.* **5**, 311–387.
BROWN, R. R., ANDERSON, K. A., ANGER, C. D., and EVANS, D. S., 1963, *J. Geophys. Res.* **68**, 2677–2684.
BROWN, R. R., BARCUS, J. R., and PARSONS, N. R., 1965 a, *J. Geophys. Res.* **70**, 2579–2598.
BROWN, R. R., BARCUS, J. R., and PARSONS, N. R., 1965 b, *J. Geophys. Res.* **70**, 2599–2612.
BROWN, R. R., HARTZ, T. R., LANDMARK, B., LEINBACH, H., and ORTNER, J., 1961, *J. Geophys. Res.* **66**, 1035–1041.
EHMERT, A., KREMSER, G., PFOTZER, G., SAEGER, K. H., WILHELM, K., RIEDLER, W., BEWERS-DORFF, A., LEGRAND, J. P., PALOUS, M., OKSMAN, J., and TANSKANEN, P., 1966, *SPARMO Bulletin*, No. 3.
EVANS, D. S., 1963, *J. Geophys. Res.* **68**, 395–400.
GOSLING, J. T., 1966, *J. Geophys. Res.* **71**, 835–848.
HOFFMAN, D. J. and WINCKLER, J. R., 1963, *J. Geophys. Res.* **68**, 2067–2098.
HUDSON, H. S., PARKS, G. K., MILTON, D. W., and ANDERSON, K. A., 1965, *J. Geophys. Res.* **70**, 4979–4980.
HULTQVIST, B., 1964, Goddard Energetic Particles, Preprint Series X-611-64-97.

KEPPLER, E., 1965, Mitt. a.d. Max-Planck-Institut für Aeronomie, No. 20, Springer-Verlag, Berlin, Heidelberg, New York.

KEPPLER, E., EHMERT, A., PFOTZER, G., and ORTNER, J., 1962, *J. Geophys. Res.* **67**, 5343–5346.

KREMSER, G., 1964, Mitt. a.d. Max-Planck-Institut für Aeronomie, No. 14, Springer-Verlag, Berlin, Heidelberg, New York.

KREMSER, G., 1965, *Introduction to Solar Terrestrial Relations* (Ed. by J. Ortner and H. Maseland), D. Reidel Publ. Comp., Dordrecht, Holland, pp. 415–422.

MEREDITH, L. H., GOTTLIEB, M. B., and VAN ALLEN, J. A., 1955, *Phys. Rev.* **97**, 201–205.

PFOTZER, G., 1965, *Proceedings of a Symposium on High Latitude Particles and the Ionosphere, Alpbach* 1964 (Ed. by B. Maehlum), Logos Press.

RIEDLER, W., 1966, *Arkiv Geofysik* (to be published).

ROSENBERG, T. J., 1965, *J. Atmospheric Terrest. Phys.* **27**, 751–759.

SAEGER, K. H., 1965, *SPARMO Bulletin*, No. 1.

SILSBEE, H. C. and VESTINE, E. H., 1942, *Terr. Magn.* **47**, 195–208.

TREFALL, H., BJORDAL, J., ULLALAND, S. L., and STADSNES, J., 1966, *J. Atmospheric Terrest. Phys.* **28**, 225–233.

ULLALAND, S. L., TREFALL, H., KREMSER, G., and BEWERSDORFF, A., 1967, *J. Atmospheric Terrest. Phys.* (to be published).

VAN ALLEN, J. A., 1957, *Proc. Natl. Acad. Sci. U. S.* **43**, 57.

WAX, R. L., 1966, *J. Atmospheric Terrest. Phys.* **28**, 397–407.

WHITE, G. R., 1952, unpublished Natl. Bur. Std. Report 1003.

WINCKLER, J. R., PETERSON, L., ARNOLDY, R., and HOFFMAN, R., 1958, *Phys. Rev.* **110**, 1221–1223.

Discussion

Rosenberg pointed out that he had flown a 5577Å photometer together with x-ray detectors. The 5577Å correlated with x rays but had a 0.5–0.75 sec time delay for the latter portion of the one hour event and showed no correlation early in the event. Dr. Meyerott pointed out that since x rays are produced with the harder flux it might be expected that the N_2^+ bands, i.e., 3914Å or 4278Å, would be better correlated with the high energy flux, and would also have the advantage of not being quenched at lower altitudes. The OI 5577Å line is presumably excited only by slow electrons, and therefore, the correlation would be an indication of (1) the extent to which the higher energy electrons are related to the low energy electron flux, or (2) the time delay involved in a 10 keV electron producing slower secondary electrons. It was agreed that there probably is some confusion concerning the interpretation of the 5577Å however, the emission from N_2^+ at 4278Å was also measured from the ground, and it varies in the same manner as the 5577Å emission.

It was suggested that the x-ray events might be related to the appearance of Anderson's electron islands. The form of the events, i.e., they start rapidly and decay slowly, suggested this relation.

Session

6

THEORY II

Dr. Franklin Roach

Institute for Telecommunication Sciences and Aeronomy

AURORAL PARTICLES ACCELERATED IN THE GEOMAGNETIC TAIL*

T. W. Speiser

Imperial College, London

Some of the questions that must be answered by any auroral theory are the following. What near-Earth acceleration mechanism accelerates particles to energies of tens of kilovolts? Why does the auroral zone or auroral oval exist, and why does it move to lower latitudes with increasing solar activity? Why are auroral structures so thin? What causes the multiplicity of forms? Why is there a morning/evening asymmetry between precipitating electrons and protons, and a latitudinal separation between proton and electron forms at least before midnight? The purpose of this study is to see if particle trajectories computed in model fields of the geomagnetic tail as suggested by DUNGEY (1961) can explain some of these auroral observations. Dungey originally suggested the "open-model" of the magnetosphere in order to explain the DS current system, the existence of the auroral zones, and particle acceleration at near-Earth associated neutral points. An interplanetary magnetic field added to the Earth's dipole field should create two neutral points at which particle acceleration can occur (DUNGEY, 1953). The topology of the limiting lines of force through the neutral points would intersect the Earth at the auroral zones, and the electric field fitting the flow of field lines at the neutral points could drive the DS current system, assuming the lines of force are equipotentials. The essential part of the open or reconnection model of the geomagnetic field (DUNGEY, 1961; AXFORD *et al.*, 1965) is that the reconnection can occur, and that some field lines beginning on the Earth may eventually be found in interplanetary space, or with one end on the sun. The recent observations by ANDERSON and LIN (reported in these proceedings by ANDERSON) that low rigidity solar electrons are found inside the magnetospheric cavity with little delay seem to imply that there must be reconnection, at least at times.

FAIRFIELD and CAHILL (1965) have made a comparison of high latitude ground magnetometer readings with the direction of the magnetic field in the

---

*This work was done while the author was a National Academy of Science Research Associate at the Goddard Space Flight Center.

magnetosheath region. They find that an exterior magnetic field (interplanetary) with a southward component appears to be a necessary, although perhaps not sufficient, condition for the occurrence of a negative bay.

Is there any evidence of the electric field existing as a result of reconnection? Thus far, experimental observations in space have not been made. BRATENAHL and HIRSCH (1966) have, however, set up an x-type neutral point geometry in the laboratory by discharging capacitor banks through two parallel line currents. The x-type null is set up, this flattens into a sheetlike configuration, and from the measured change in magnetic field, an electric field is inferred while the reconnection process is going on.

If the geomagnetic tail is to be the source of auroral particles, are there any observations of particles coming down magnetic field lines from the tail in the auroral zones? Many recent satellite observations (McDIARMID and BURROWS, 1965; JOHNSON, these proceedings) show that particles are precipitating above the limits of the trapping regions, and these field lines are, therefore, presumably connected to the tail. AXFORD (these proceedings) has shown an

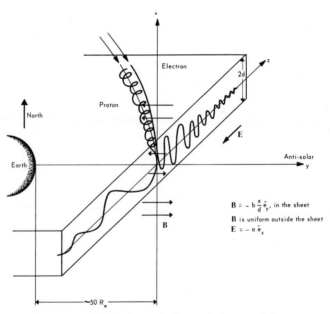

FIGURE 1. Particle trajectories in a strictly neutral sheet.

apparent correlation between auroral absorption events and the "Islands" of energetic electrons seen in the tail. Similar results are reported by REID and PARATHASARATHY (1966), although ROTHWELL (these proceedings) finds no correlation between the energetic electron islands observed by Anderson and high latitude negative magnetic bays.

If the tail is to be the source of auroral particles, are there observations of increased particle fluxes in the tail? ANDERSON and NESS (1966) find the occurrence of the energetic electron islands usually within a broad region of depressed magnetic field in the tail, within which is usually found a neutral sheet crossing. MURAYAMA (1966) has analyzed energetic electron data in the tail from the cosmic ray telescopes on board the IMP-1 satellite in the University of Chicago experiment. He finds a positive correlation between the occurrence of energetic electron events in the tail and the distance from the neutral sheet (larger fluxes close to the sheet) as defined by the magnetic field data on IMP-1 (NESS, 1965). The plasma measurements on the Vela satellite show plasma in a broad region, presumably about the relatively narrow neutral sheet. This broad region may be defined as the plasma sheet, in agreement with the broad region of depressed magnetic field found in the tail where Anderson's "Islands" of energetic electrons are observed. (Bame, *et al.*, 1967).

For a simple model of fields in the magnetospheric tail, assume that the magnetic field is in the solar direction above the neutral sheet, antisolar direction below it, goes linearly to zero within the sheet, and the electric field is across the tail from the dawn to the dusk side (see Figure 1). Using the coordinate system and fields of Figure 1, the Lorentz force equations become:

$$\ddot{x} = x\dot{z}$$

$$\ddot{y} = 0$$

$$\ddot{z} = -1 -x\dot{x}$$

where the constants have been normalized to unity for simplicity. (For a more complete mathematical treatment of this and the following section, see SPEISER, 1965.)

From the first equation, we see that as long as $\dot{z}$ is negative (for a proton), the x coordinate of the particle will execute some type of oscillatory motion, so that from the last equation we see that $\dot{z}$ grows essentially as $-t$. A proton, therefore, is trapped in the sheet, accelerated by the electric field, and shot out the dusk side of the sheet. (An electron moves in the opposite direction; see Figure 1.) Qualitatively we can see that the particle is trapped in the sheet because of the motion with the electric field and the reversal of the magnetic field above and below the sheet, keeping the Lorentz force always directed toward the center of the sheet. This example was for a strictly neutral sheet, that is, for a model where the magnetic field goes to zero at the center of the sheet and no field lines cross the sheet.

What happens now if the neutral sheet is not strictly neutral, but some field lines cross the sheet in the dipole sense? If the small component of magnetic field normal to the sheet is η in the $\hat{e}_x$ direction, (see Figure 2) the normalized equations become:

$$\ddot{x} = x\dot{z}$$

$$\ddot{y} = \eta\dot{z}$$

$$\ddot{z} = -1 - x\dot{x} - \dot{y}\eta$$

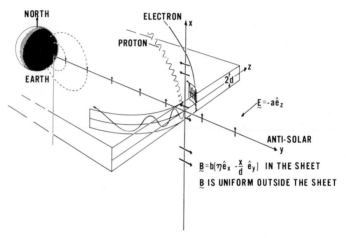

FIGURE 2. Particle trajectories in a simple neutral sheet with small perpendicular field.

From the last equation, we see that again, initially $\dot{z}$ goes like $-t$, thus x again executes a type of oscillatory motion, but now $\dot{y}$ goes like $-t^2$. Thus in the last equation $\dot{z}$ will grow negatively with time until the term $(-\eta\dot{y})$ overwhelms the constant term, after which $\dot{z}$ will diminish, eventually going to zero and becoming slightly positive. When that happens we see that the first of the three equations no longer implies oscillatory motion, but rather, some type of exponential increase. When that happens, the particle is no longer trapped, but is ejected from the sheet.

To repeat this result again from a qualitative viewpoint: a particle incident on the sheet is initially trapped in the sheet by the magnetic field reversal and is accelerated by the electric field within the sheet. Now, however, since there is a normal component of magnetic field within the sheet, the particle is turned by this $\mathbf{E} \times \mathbf{B}_\perp$ drift toward the Earth. (The particle would be turned away from the Earth — down the tail — if the normal component were reversed, as would happen, for example, after crossing an x-type neutral point.) Both electrons and protons, while being accelerated initially in opposite directions by the electric field, are turned toward the Earth (see Figure 2). When the particles are turned enough by this normal component, so that their velocity vector changes sign, the Lorentz force changes sign and the particles are no longer trapped in the sheet, but are ejected from the sheet. Thus this model provides the seemingly magic result that protons and electrons are accelerated in opposite directions, gaining energy, and are both turned toward the Earth and ejected from the sheet just as they are turned toward the Earth. Since all of the energy gained is now directed essentially along magnetic field lines, the particles come out or are ejected with small pitch angles.

As a specific example, for a tail field of 20 gammas away from the neutral sheet, a normal component of $\frac{1}{4}$ gamma, an electric field of strength 3×10^{-4} V/m, a proton travels about 16 R_e (Earth-radii) across the tail, gaining about 30 keV, while an electron travels only about 50 km across the tail and gains only about 16 eV energy. Thus for this model, in the region where a proton would gain an energy essentially like auroral energies, an electron would gain only a few volts of energy. For this example the particles would all be ejected within a cone about a line of force of approximately 1°. In order to enable electrons to gain kilovolts of energy, the normal component must be considerably smaller, allowing the electrons to drift a large distance with the electric field before being turned toward the Earth and ejected. As a further example, if the normal component is reduced to 0.01 gamma, then an electron will drift about 6 R_e across the tail and gain an energy of about 12 keV before being ejected. The ejection cone is smaller than for protons, less than 0.1°, assuming both are incident on the sheet initially with about the same bulk flow velocity. (For more details of the mathematics and applications, see SPEISER, 1965, 1967.)

As of this writing, little is known about the variation of the normal component beyond about 30 R_e, although the tail presumably extends far beyond the moon's orbit. DUNGEY (1965) has estimated a tail length of about 1000 R_e while reconnection is going on, which might put the backside neutral point somewhere around 500 R_e. For such a model, protons of about 30 keV energy would come from about 400 R_e, and electrons of about 12 keV would come from about 500 R_e, very close to the neutral point. Since the electrons are ejected farther back in the tail, they would be attached to a field line at a higher latitude than for protons. For this example, the latitude difference at the Earth is about $\frac{1}{2}$°.

For a given energy input distribution and for a given field topology as in the preceding example, the particles are turned and all are ejected from the sheet in a small region of space. This thinness, coupled with the focusing effect of the increased magnetic field near the Earth, can produce extremely thin beams of auroral particles at the Earth. For the preceding neutral point model, electrons in the range of 1–10 keV would be found within a beam of about 0.8 km thickness at the Earth. Protons would also be found in thin beams, although not so thin as electrons.

Awaiting further in situ observations of electric and magnetic fields in the magnetospheric tail, other models of the fields, normal components, etc., might be used. Indeed, this mechanism may be applied to any model with a "neutral sheet," electric field directed generally from the dawn to dusk side across the tail, and with a normal component which decreases with distance and reaches small values.

As another model, consider a three-dimensional dipole field, representing the Earth's magnetic field, added to a tail field which is uniform in the solar direction above a "neutral sheet," in the antisolar direction below the sheet and goes linearly to zero within the sheet. For this model, the normal component at the center of the sheet is furnished by the Earth's dipole field and falls off as the inverse cube of the distance, although no neutral point is reached. The preceding nonadiabatic analytic treatment is difficult to apply for such complicated fields. Many particle trajectories have, therefore, been computed for this model. The results show that protons with energies of tens of kilovolts will come from about 25–50 R_e in the tail, and electrons with an energy of the order of 10 kV will come from about 150 R_e. Particles are given initial conditions of zero output pitch angle along a magnetic line of force at some point on an output plane, and the trajectories are then computed backwards in time to see where the particles come from. On the input side, the value of the distribution function can be determined for a particular trajectory assuming that particles are incident on the neutral sheet with some thermal distribution about the bulk flow velocity. Liouville's theorem, which states that the distribution function is constant along a trajectory, can then be used. The particle density can then be found as a function of position on the output plane. Using this technique, it is found that the greatest intensity of output protons occurs in an output sheet of about 100 km thickness at the position of the output plane in the tail, which is at about 25 R_e. The same computation has not been made for electrons because of the inordinate amount of computer time required.

Figure 3 shows the mapping of this output sheet of protons onto the Earth

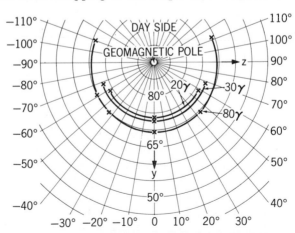

FIGURE 3. Mapping of output sheets onto the earth.

for three possible tail fields: 20, 30, and 80 gammas. These mappings have the character of the auroral oval, as described by AKASOFU (these proceedings). The mappings also move to lower latitudes (or the oval expands) as the tail field is increased. For a 20 gamma field, the mapping is approximately 74° at midnight, which is too high for the auroral zone. However, this model was very simple, consisting of just a tail field added to a dipole field. If a more realistic current sheet field were used (WILLIAMS and MEAD, 1965), the mapping for 20 gammas would move down to between 65° and 70°, with the 30 and 80 gamma mappings at lower latitudes.

Summary

These results are based on individual particle trajectories using model fields based on the "open" or reconnection model of the magnetosphere. The "neutral sheet" type magnetic field has been observed to distances of about 30 R_e, but electric field measurements have yet to be made. There may be times when the tail is long and the merging of field lines is negligible, as suggested by DESSLER (1965). At those times this acceleration process will not be effective. The self-consistency of these solutions and the effects of various instabilities should be investigated, but as yet have not been examined.

Professor Axford argues that noise or turbulence in the sheet should disrupt these particle trajectories. Noise may certainly be the limiting factor but until measurements are made, I will assume that noise will not completely disrupt this process. (See Dungey and Speiser, 1967.)

A neutral point model and a dipole-plus-tail model are used to apply the results of the nonadiabatic analytic theory. In both cases, electrons and protons incident on the neutral sheet are trapped, accelerated, turned toward the Earth, and ejected from the neutral sheet with small pitch angles to a magnetic line of force. The main difference between the two models is the ejection point back in the tail. For the two models, electrons of the order of 10 keV are ejected at about 500 R_e and 150 R_e, respectively, and for protons of about 30 keV, the ejection distances are about 400 R_e and 30 R_e, respectively. The model produces extremely thin beams of incoming particles at the Earth, about 1 km for electrons between 1 and 10 keV. Proton auroras are produced at latitudes about $\frac{1}{2}°$ lower than electrons.

Many trajectories of about 12 keV protons have been computed for a three-dimensional dipole-plus-tail model in order to see how the fluxes map onto the Earth. Using Liouville's theorem, regions of large intensity are found which are like the auroral oval when mapped onto the Earth. The "oval" expands to lower latitudes with an increase of the tail field.

These features generally agree with some auroral observations, namely: the location and shape of the auroral oval; the energies of auroral protons and electrons; the fluxes of auroral protons and electrons; the appearance of proton auroras at lower latitudes than electron auroras, at least in afternoon and evening; a dawn/dusk asymmetry for electron/proton auroras; the expansion of the auroral oval to lower latitudes with an increasing tail field (hence solar wind pressure); the thinness of auroral forms; and the gross conjugacy of auroral events.

EGELAND (these proceedings), using Störmer's data, reports that the heights of the lower borders of auroral rays and draperies are lower toward morning than near evening or midnight. The models presented here would predict the most energetic electrons to be found toward morning. (Similarly, the most energetic protons would be found toward evening and afternoon.)

CHAPMAN (these proceedings) has suggested multiple neutral lines in the tail for the production of multiple arcs. The acceleration mechanism reported here would be effective for accelerating particles at each neutral line, producing multiple arcs. However, that is rather speculative and it is not necessary for this mechanism to have multiple neutral points or lines, but merely a change in the current density supporting the sheet so that the normal field component becomes alternately stronger and weaker. The question of multiple arcs may also involve a self-consistent analysis of a thin sheet of output particles.

These trajectory calculations may be applicable to other situations where neutral points or sheets are thought to exist, as the day-side magnetospheric current sheet, neutral points in the interplanetary field, and solar flares.

Acknowledgment   The preparation of this paper has been sponsored in part by the Air Force Cambridge Research Laboratories under Contract AF (052)-927 through the European Office of Aerospace Research (OAR), U.S. Air Force.

References

ANDERSON, K. A. and NESS, N. F., 1966, *J. Geophys. Res.* **71**, 3705.

AXFORD, W. I., PETSCHEK, H. F., and SISCOE, G. L., 1965, *J. Geophys. Res.* **70**, 1231.

BAME, S. J., ASBRIDGE, J. R., FELTHAUSER, H. E., HONES, E. W., STRONG, I. B., 1967, *J. Geophys. Res.* **72**, 113.

BRATENAHL, A. and HIRSCH, 1966, *AIAA* Plasmad. Conf., 66–162, March.

DESSLER, A., 1964, *J. Geophys. Res.* **69**, 3913.

DUNGEY, J. W., 1953, *Phil. Mag.*, **44**, 725.

DUNGEY, J. W., 1961, *Phys. Rev. Letters* **6**, 47.

DUNGEY, J. W. and SPEISER, T. W., 1967, *J. Geophys, Res.* (submitted).

FAIRFIELD, D. and CAHILL, 1966, *J. Geophys. Res.* **71**, 155.

McDIARMID, I. B. and BURROWS, J. R., 1965, *J. Geophys. Res.* **70**, 3031.

MURAYAMA, 1966, *J. Geophys. Res.* **71**, 5547.

NESS, N. F., 1965, *J. Geophys. Res.* **70**, 2989.

REID, G. C., and PARATHASARATHY, R., 1966, *J. Geophys. Res.* **71**, 3267.

SPEISER, T. W., 1965, *J. Geophys. Res.* **70**, 4219.

SPEISER, T. W., 1967, *J. Geophys. Res.* (to be published).

WILLIAMS, D. J. and MEAD, G. D., 1965, *J. Geophys. Res.* **70**, 3017.

Discussion

Axford is in favor of field line reconnection as a means of trapping and accelerating particles, but does not like to see too much weight placed on the neutral sheet. He does not see how the neutral sheet can explain daytime auroras or low latitude auroras.

THE INTERACTION BETWEEN THE SOLAR WIND
AND THE MAGNETOSPHERE*

W. I. Axford

Cornell Sydney University Astronomy Center
Astronomy Department
Cornell University
Ithaca, New York

I. Introduction

The gross features of the interaction between the solar wind and the Earth's magnetosphere are essentially what one would expect for a magnetic dipole immersed in a hypersonic stream of highly conducting plasma; that is, the interaction is hydromagnetic to a first approximation (AXFORD, 1964, 1965, 1967). A shock is formed on the upstream side of the magnetosphere, causing the flow to become locally subsonic so that it can be diverted around the magnetosphere. The standoff distance to the shock should be about 20% of the radius of curvature of the magnetosphere at the forward stagnation point, provided the interplanetary magnetic field does not distort the flow too greatly. Since the shock in this case is "collision-free," it must depend on particle-wave and wave-wave interactions, rather than particle-particle interactions, to produce the necessary dissipation; hence one expects to see the appearance of suprathermal particles and a random wave field which can be described as a sort of turbulence.

The shape of the magnetosphere is determined by the condition that the normal and transverse stresses exerted at the boundary should be continuous. On the upstream side, the normal stresses predominate and the shape can be calculated with fair accuracy using the Newtonian approximation for the pressure on the upstream side of a blunt body; it must be remembered, however, that this is an approximation only, and the extent to which it is good determines the usefulness of the calculations. On the downstream side of the magnetosphere, the transverse stresses become important and these cause the formation of a pronounced "tail" within which the geomagnetic field lines

*This work was supported under the National Aeronautics and Space Administration Grant No. NsG-382

extend to great distances from the Earth, so that the whole configuration is reminiscent of a comet. A cross section of the tail can be described as forming a θ, with the magnetic field roughly uniform and directed away from the Earth in the southern half and toward the Earth in the northern half; the bar of the θ is a current sheet, which we will call the "neutral sheet," and within which the field is very weak and connects from south to north.

II. The Quiet Magnetosphere

It is believed that solar wind plasma is accelerated and injected via the neutral sheet into the inner magnetosphere, so producing the aurora and the radiation belts (AXFORD, 1965; DUNGEY, 1961, 1965; LEVY, 1964; AXFORD et al., 1965). This process takes place largely in sporadic, intense bursts, called auroral or polar substorms (AKASOFU, 1966), which occur mainly during geomagnetic storms. Most of our subsequent discussion is, therefore, involved with considerations of the stability and dynamics of the tail of the magnetosphere, but before passing on to this topic it is convenient to examine some aspects of the quiet (metastable) magnetosphere.

In magnetically quiet periods, the magnetosphere has a configuration such that the geomagnetic field lines can be divided into two categories, "closed" and "open." In magnetically quiet periods the closed field lines form a doughnut-shaped region, and include the field lines which meet the Earth at geomagnetic latitudes less than $\lambda_c \approx 72$–$75°$; this region of the magnetosphere rotates more or less rigidly with the Earth, although the field lines must undergo changes of shape during the day, especially in the outer parts. The open field lines, which meet the Earth at latitudes higher than λ_c, extend out into the tail of the magnetosphere and evenutally join with the interplanetary field. The approximate value of λ_c quoted here has been calculated using flux conservation and observations of the field in the tail of the magnetosphere (AXFORD, 1965); it agrees reasonably well with the observations of the boundary of trapping (McDIARMID and BURROWS, 1964) and the termination of the low energy cosmic ray cutoff (Fan et al., 1964). Obviously phenomena such as the aurora, auroral absorption, magnetic bays, and so on, which at low latitudes usually show detailed correlation between conjugate points, should be expected to be at best only statistically correlated at latitudes greater than λ_c.

It has been suggested by DESSLER and JUDAY (1965) that the boundary of trapping is coincident with the boundary separating open and closed field lines in the magnetosphere. The colatitude of the trapping boundary is observed to vary between $\sim 18°$ on the day side of the magnetosphere and $\sim 25°$ on the night side (McDIARMID and BURROWS, 1964). Also the magnetosphere must be rotating with the Earth since the field lines are rather firmly held by the upper atmosphere (AXFORD, 1966). Clearly these two requirements cannot easily be met if the suggestion of Dessler and Juday is correct. In fact, there is no observational or theoretical reason why the boundary of trapping should coincide with the boundary between closed and open field lines. We believe that it is more likely that the boundary of trapping is determined simply by the trajectories of those high energy particles which can make a complete orbit of the Earth, and that the asymmetry of the boundary with respect to the geomagnetic poles is due to the asymmetric form of the magnetosphere, and possibly, to some extent, to electric field effects.

The boundary between open and closed field lines must be at a latitude of roughly λ_c at all longitudes, but its actual form depends very much on the electric fields which exist at any time. This boundary, which is defined by the outermost closed field lines, must merge with the neutral sheet on the night side of the Earth. Hence the field lines in the region between this and the trapping boundary must be substantially disturbed from a dipole form, as found by CAHILL (1965), and indeed the outermost field lines on the night side must be cusp-shaped during quiet periods when the neutral sheet is expected to be thin. It is tempting to identify this region with the "skirt" and "cusp" regions found by ANDERSON (1965) from his observations of $\sim$40 keV electron fluxes. There must, of course, be a plasma in the region in order to maintain equilibrium, but the particle energies are expected to be rather lower than 40 keV (perhaps 1–10 keV) since the more energetic particles tend to be lost by longitudinal drifts; this plasma is probably the so-called "third radiation belt" discovered during the flight of Lunik II (GRINGAUZ et al., 1962).

It is still suggested occasionally (COPPI et al., 1966) that auroral arcs must be directly connected to a well-defined neutral sheet in order that the thinness of the arcs should be explainable, as well as allowing for the possibility of an accelerating mechanism. This is hardly reasonable, however, as it is quite commonly observed that two or more arcs can lie parallel to each other and separated by distances of the order of 100 km (AKASOFU, 1966; AKASOFU and CHAPMAN, 1961). On the other hand, it seems more reasonable to identify the entire band of auroral zone precipitation (as distinct from the polar cap aurora) with the region between the trapping boundary (approximately) and the boundary of closed field lines. In this case it is necessary to look for some mechanism which can produce auroral arcs on closed field lines, but since the bulk of the particle precipitation takes place over a wide area, the problem of arc formation should be considered a secondary one.

III. Auroral and Polar Substorms

It is our contention that auroral and polar magnetic substorms are directly caused by the sudden reconnection of magnetic field lines in the tail of the magnetosphere. The process of reconnection causes the boundary separating open and closed geomagnetic field lines to move to higher latitudes on the night side, in agreement with observations of the behavior of the high latitude edge of the auroral zone during substorms (AKASOFU, 1966). The region of distended but closed field lines beyond the trapping boundary on the night side of the magnetosphere is enlarged at such times, and the newly closed field lines become populated with energetic particles (see Figure 1).

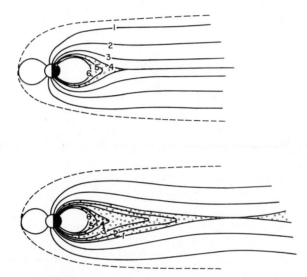

FIGURE 1. Schematic diagram illustrating the reconnection of field lines in the tail of the magnetosphere that might take place during a substorm.

One can explain the appearance of "islands" of energetic electrons and proton fluxes in the tail very easily on this basis if the sudden appearances and disappearances of the flux are interpreted as the passage of the various boundaries of the region of newly connected field lines over the point of observation; the slow decay of flux often observed within the islands is presumably due to precipitation of the particles into the Earth's atmosphere (thus producing auroral absorption events) and also to longitudinal drift toward the dawn side of the magnetosphere (in the case of electrons). It is, of course, implicit in this discussion that: (a) the islands are not local, but exist transiently throughout a large volume; (b) the occurrence of islands is associated with auroral substorms, magnetic bays, and, especially, auroral zone absorption events (SERLEMITSOS, 1965; REID and PARTHASARATHY, 1966; ANDERSON, 1965; ROTHWELL, 1965) and (c) the islands occur in the vicinity of the neutral sheet in regions of closed magnetic field (ROTHWELL, 1965).

Newly reconnected field lines tend to contract violently, implying that the initiation of reconnection should be observable as a hydromagnetic impulse which propagates toward the Earth; as pointed out by DUNGEY (1965), this can be identified with the P_i's which occur at the beginning of magnetic bays. Furthermore, the wave concerned tends to compress the plasma on previously existing closed field lines as they are overrun; the consequent betatron acceleration of the particles produces a large pitch angle anisotropy and subsequently enhanced precipitation of electrons due to the resultant growth of whistler mode (or other) turbulence (KENNEL and PETSCHEK, 1966). The brightening of the low latitude aurora at the beginning of a substorm can readily be understood on this basis. (Note also that a similar explanation can be given for sudden commencement absorption, where the betatron acceleration is presumably due to compression of the outer parts of the magnetosphere at the beginning of a geomagnetic storm.) On newly connected field lines it is likely that Fermi acceleration of electrons due to the approach of mirror points as the field lines contract, might well predominate over betatron acceleration, thus producing a steep pitch angle distribution (SERLEMITSOS, 1965).

The acceleration mechanisms we have discussed can be described simply as adiabatic compression. The energy given to the particles is derived from a large-scale electric field, part of which is associated with the change in configuration of the magnetic field (i.e., $\partial \mathbf{B}/\partial t = c$ curl $\mathbf{E} \neq 0$), and part with magnetospheric interchange motions which are such that curl $\mathbf{E} = 0$ (Axford, 1964, 1966). A few particles are accelerated nonadiabatically in the small region where reconnection takes place, since in a collision-free plasma processes, such as resonant particle-wave interactions, (turbulence) must be relied upon to produce dissipation. In this connection it should be noted that there can be no steady electric field at a neutral sheet unless there is dissipation, and no dissipation without turbulence; hence, it appears that calculations of particle trajectories in model configurations with nonturbulent fields are unrealistic. Note also that whatever process dominates, electrons tend to drift and gain energy by moving toward the dawn side of the magnetosphere, while protons do the opposite; one should, therefore, expect to see equivalent asymmetries in the distribution of particle fluxes (MONTGOMERY et al., 1965; SINGER, 1965).

The electric field associated with interchange motions is especially significant since this can be observed at ground level through the ionospheric currents it generates. These currents produce the large magnetic variations observed at high latitudes during substorms, and, in heating the ionosphere, dissipate a significant part ($10^{17}-10^{18}$ ergs/sec) of the energy made available by reconnection of the magnetic field in the tail. The interchange motions carry what was formerly solar wind plasma deep into the inner magnetosphere, causing it to become inflated, at first mainly on the night side, but later, more or less uniformly as the freshly injected particles drift around the magnetosphere as a result of the combined effects of the electric field and magnetic field gradients. The process of injection has recently been observed directly by the satellite Explorer 26 (CAHILL, 1966; DAVIS, 1966; BROWN and ROBERTS, 1966). The pattern of recovery of an auroral substorm (AKASOFU, 1966) suggests that the electron component of the injected plasma drifts towards the sun around the dawn side of the magnetosphere, and this is consistent with observed patterns of various ionospheric phenomena associated with particle precipitation (AXFORD, 1966; HARTZ and BRICE, 1966), which show a pronounced dawn-dusk asymmetry. This is, of course, essentially the behavior predicted by AXFORD and HINES (1961).

It appears from a variety of observations that the injected plasma (especially the proton component) penetrates quite deeply into the magnetosphere (e.g., direct satellite observations in the magnetosphere, the position of the plasma-pause (CARPENTER, 1966; CARPENTER and ANGERAMI, 1966), and the F-region troughs (MULDREW, 1965) etc. It is not clear at present how this happens in detail, but there is no doubt that protons of 100–300 keV, for example, can appear at much lower latitude regions than the usually assumed electric fields and magnetic field gradients would allow. If the process is purely an injection, we venture to suggest that it might be quite effective even for protons with energies of the order of 10 MeV, and that this is the cause of the sudden lowering of cutoffs which permits PCA events to occur at latitudes as low as that of Ottawa. We emphasize that the cause is probably not simply the large symmetrical inflation of the magnetosphere (ring current) which is observed at such times, but rather the process of injection which precedes the formation of the complete ring current.

An estimate of the rate at which energy must be converted in the tail of the magnetosphere can be made by combining the rate of energy dissipation in auroral and polar substorms (about 10^{18} ergs/sec) (AXFORD, 1964, 1965, 1966) with the rate at which energy is supplied to fill the radiation belts and inflate the magnetosphere (about 10^{18}–10^{19} ergs/sec). [The last figure is obtained by noting that the internal energy of the particles concerned must be comparable to the strain energy in the magnetic field which contains them (about 10^{22}–10^{23} ergs (CHAPMAN and BARTELS, 1940), and that the process of injection takes place over a period of about 10^4 sec.] The electric field associated with interchange motions has been estimated to have a total potential variation of about 30 kV (AXFORD, 1964, 1966). These figures can readily be shown to be consistent with the process of field reconnection in the tail of the magnetosphere if one uses Petschek's result that the merging velocity is of the order of one-tenth the Alfven speed* together with observations (NESS, 1965) of the magnetic field strength and dimensions of the tail (AXFORD, 1965). Furthermore, if one assumes that field line reconnection at the front of the magnetosphere is the dominant process for producing transverse stresses at the magnetosphere's boundary, then it can be shown that the rate at which work is done by the solar wind can comfortably exceed the rate of injection of energy into the

---

*It is appropriate to use this result although it refers to a steady state since merging continues for much longer than the time it takes a signal to cross the system at the Alfven speed.

magnetosphere. This is a necessary result since much of the work done must go into heating the wake of the magnetosphere (AXFORD, 1965).

We emphasize that the discussion of substorms must be first made on a macroscopic basis since microscopic processes are largely of secondary importance. Even the question of the stability of the neutral sheet, we will argue, is determined by conditions on a large rather than small scale, despite the fact that the dissipation which permits reconnection of field lines is essentially of a microscopic nature. Nevertheless, the most striking features of the aurora, visually at least, are the discrete forms such as arcs, bands, and rays, which do seem to require some microscopic process for their explanation. Since the precipitation of particles probably results from pitch angle diffusion due to nonlinear interaction with a wave field, one possible explanation for discrete forms would be that pitch angle diffusion is more rapid in restricted regions (ducts) where the wave intensity can build up to a higher than normal level. An explanation of this sort does have the advantage that the requirements are not too severe, since efficient ducting of whistler mode waves, for example, can be produced with quite small density gradients.

It is implicit in the reconnection model that substorms should coincide with the relaxation of the magnetic field in the tail and with the injection of plasma into the inner magnetosphere to produce a ring current. These effects have been reasonably well established by satellite observations; the correlation of tail field relaxation with magnetic bays was observed by IMP A and OGO A (HEPPNER, 1965; BEHANNON and Ness, 1966), and the injection of plasma and subsequent inflation of the inner magnetosphere following a bay was observed by Explorer 26 (CAHILL, 1966; DAVIS, 1966; BROWN and ROBERTS, 1965). The latter effect has also been established on a statistical basis by SUGIURA and CHAPMAN (1960), who showed that the maximum DS magnetic variations during a storm coincide roughly with the maximum of $|d(D_{st})/dt|$, and precede the maximum of $|D_{st}|$.

IV. The Merging of Magnetic Field Lines

In the above discussion it has been assumed that the magnetosphere is normally in a metastable, quiet state, but is subject to a gross resistive instability which leads to a rearrangement of the plasma and field configuration and to the conversion of magnetic energy to particle energy. During periods of relative stability, the amount of emerging of oppositely directed field lines in the tail of the magnetosphere is presumed to be slight, and the neutral sheet is correspondingly thin. When the instability occurs, field lines are reconnected rapidly and the "neutral sheet" becomes very thick, except in the small region around a neutral line where the merging actually occurs. The phenomenon is essentially the same as a solar flare (AXFORD, 1965).

We consider that the reconnection model is in good agreement with observations and is probably correct. There are, however, other models which can be made to seem convincing. We will discuss two such models: the first, which has been promoted by DESSLER and his colleagues (DESSLER and JUDAY, 1965; DESSLER, 1964; DESSLER and MICHEL, 1966), is based on the premise that no significant merging of field lines can take place in the magnetosphere; the second, which has been discussed by a number of workers (PIDDINGTON, 1966; COPPI et al., 1966), places great emphasis on the instability of neutral sheets on a microscopic scale and entirely ignores the influence of external conditions on the rate of conversion of magnetic energy to particle energy.

There has been no serious attempt to apply the no-reconnection model of DESSLER and JUDAY (1965) to the problem of auroral and polar substorms other than to assert that the trapping boundary, the boundary separating open and closed field lines, and the auroral zone should all coincide. The difficulty that such a model gets into when one tries to take into account the rotation of the magnetosphere with the Earth has already been pointed out. Dessler and Juday have also suggested that during magnetic storms closed field lines are dragged into the tail and stretched out indefinitely so that the boundary between open and closed field lines moves equatorward, which is more or less consistent with observations of the occurrence of aurora at lower latitudes at such times and with the behavior of the trapping boundary. Since, however, these authors do not permit any reconnection of field lines to occur, it is not clear how the boundary of trapping and of closed field lines can ever recover to their normal position.

MICHEL and DESSLER (1965) have argued that observations of the development of PCA events favor the Dessler-Juday model, rather than models in which connection between the interplanetary and geomagnetic fields is permitted. This is not the case, however, since most PCA events seem to begin first near the geomagnetic poles and spread towards the auroral zone (HAKURA, 1966). Furthermore, their discussion fails to take into account the broad spectrum of solar protons that contribute to PCA, the long-lasting anisotropy of the flux, and the possibility of particle drifts due to field gradients in the tail region near the Earth.

The elementary theory of merging of oppositely-directed magnetic field lines has been reviewed elsewhere (AXFORD, 1965), only the conclusions will be quoted here. The simplest approach to the problem suggests that the field lines can reconnect at any speed, ranging anywhere from zero to the Alfven speed, depending on boundary conditions. Effectively, the rate of merging in any given situation is determined largely by the rate at which the newly reconnected field lines can get away from the region where merging occurs. Merging will be most rapid if the reconnected lines can contract perfectly freely, but it can be reduced to any lower rate by suitably throttling the flow. PETSCHEK's (1964) contribution to this discussion has been to show that the maximum possible rate of merging is somewhat less than the Alfven speed due to choking of the flow by nonlinear effects; this result is, therefore, not to be considered as providing an anomalous "fast merging" mechanism.

Our conclusion is that any initial configuration of magnetic field and plasma containing a neutral sheet can undergo a rapid change by field line reconnection, provided this leads to a state of lower energy; if there is no neighboring lower energy state, the neutral sheet will exist quite stably except for slow diffusion due to purely ohmic dissipation. It should be no surprise then to see thin and apparently perfectly stable neutral sheets in the interplanetary medium and in the tail of the magnetosphere, and their existence should certainly not be taken as evidence that rapid reconnection of field lines cannot occur, as DESSLER and MICHEL (1966) have argued.

Even if a given configuration of magnetic field and plasma is initially stable against field line reconnection, it is possible for subsequent changes in the configuration (induced say, at the boundaries) to lead towards instability, in which case the original system is better described as being metastable. The changes can take place either slowly or in jumps, with the latter producing a "triggered" instability as is often observed in solar flares. The auroral and polar substorms are presumably further examples of this type of instability. It is important to note that during periods of rapid reconnection of field lines, the neutral sheet must expand in the manner described by PETSCHEK (1964); the fact that the magnetic field in the tail of the magnetosphere undergoes substantial changes in direction whenever electron "islands" are observed (ROTHWELL, 1965) is strong evidence that reconnection has taken place in the manner described.

DESSLER (1964) has asserted that magnetic fields "cannot be merged in a time shorter than several times the ion-ion or ion-atom collision period." If this were true, there could be no significant reconnection of magnetic field lines in the tail of the magnetosphere since the plasma is effectively collision-free. However, there is no reason why dissipation in a plasma should depend on such collisions, and it is quite consistent to rely on "collision-free" processes in this case having already done so in discussing the formation of the shock wave on the upstream side of the magnetosphere. DESSLER and MICHEL (1965) have further commented that in discussions of the merging process, such as Petschek's, "near the neutral line diffusion is allowed to proceed further than wave motion"; since the relevant wave speed for the magnetic field where it is not frozen to the fluid is the speed of light, this comment seems to have little significance.

At almost the opposite extreme to the point of view taken by Dessler and his colleagues, there is a school of thought which contends that a neutral sheet is violently unstable even without reference to external conditions. That is, it is claimed that the dynamics of the tail of the magnetosphere (and of a solar flare) is controlled entirely by resistive instability on a microscopic scale (COPPI *et al.*, 1966; PIDDINGTON, 1966; JAGGI, 1964), which is fundamentally different from our contention that the instability, although resistive, depends on the configuration of the magnetosphere as a whole. It is of course useful to have it demonstrated that microscopic instabilities exist in a collision-free plasma which could be adequate to produce the dissipation required for field line reconnection. However, it must be remembered that such calculations merely show that some particular highly idealized situations are linearly unstable, and it is not clear that these are relevant to what is essentially a nonlinear problem. One can justifiably make use of the argument of Dessler and Michel at this point, and note that very thin neutral sheets are commonly observed in the interplanetary medium and in the tail of the magnetosphere and there is no indication whatever that anything violent is happening; indeed, in the case of the magnetosphere, it seems that when violent substorms do occur the "neutral sheet" is not thin at all, but has an open structure similar to that described by Petschek in his discussion of steady nonlinear merging. It is, of course, entirely possible that the thin neutral sheets observed during quiet periods do suffer from a microscopic instability, but this can produce only the effect of a finite resistivity which is not normally adequate to permit rapid reconnection of the magnetic field without the additional factor of gross instability of the whole configuration to reconnection.

References

AKASOFU, S. I., 1966, *U. of Iowa Report* **66-19**.
AKASOFU, S. I. and CHAPMAN, S., 1961, *Phil. Trans. Roy. Soc.* A253, 359.
ANDERSON, K. A., 1965, *J. Geophys. Res.* **70**, 4741.
AXFORD, W. I., 1964, *The Solar Wind* (Ed. by Mackin and Neugebauer), Pergamon Press, Ch. 16.
AXFORD, W. I., 1965, Proceedings of ESRO Conference on the Magnetosphere, Stockholm, 1965, *Space Science Reviews* (to be published).
AXFORD, W. I., 1966, in "Physics of Geomagnetic Phenomena" (to be published).
AXFORD, W. I. and HINES, C. O., 1961, *Can. J. Phys.* **39**, 1433.
AXFORD, W. I., PETSCHEK, H. E., and SISCOE, G. L., 1965, *J. Geophys. Res.* **70**, 1231.
BEHANNON, K. W. and NESS, N. F., 1966, *J. Geophys. Res.* **71**, 2327.
BROWN, W. L. and ROBERTS, C. S., 1966, *Trans. A.G.U.* **47**, 135.
CAHILL, L. J., 1965, *Space Research VI*, COSPAR.
CAHILL, L. J., 1966, *J. Geophys. Res.* (to be published).
CARPENTER, D. L., 1966, *J. Geophys. Res.* **71**, 693.
CARPENTER, D. L. and ANGERAMI, J. J., 1966, *J. Geophys. Res.* **71**, 711.
CHAPMAN, S. and BARTELS, J., 1940, *Geomagnetism*, Oxford University Press.
COPPI, B., LAVAL, G., and PELLAT, R., 1966, *Phys. Rev. Letters* **16**, 1207.
DAVIS, L. R., 1966, *Trans. A.G.U.*, **47**, 426.
DESSLER, A. J., 1964, *J. Geophys. Res.* **69**, 3913.
DESSLER, A. J. and JUDAY, R. D., 1965, *Planetary Space Sci.* **13**, 63.
DESSLER, A. J. and MICHEL, F. C., 1966, *Radiation Trapped in the Earth's Magnetic Field* (Ed. by B. M. McCormac), Reidel Publishing Company, Dordrecht, Holland.
DUNGEY, J. W., 1961, *Phys. Rev. Letters* **6**, 47.
DUNGEY, J. W., 1965, Proceedings of ESRO Conference on the Magnetosphere, Stockholm, *Space Science Reviews* (to be published).
FAN, C. Y., SIMPSON, J. A., and STONE, E. C., 1964, *Phys. Rev. Letters* **12**, 269.

GRINGAUZ, K. I., KURT, V. G., MOROZ, V. I., and SHKLOVSKII, I. S., 1962, *Planetary Space Sci.* **9**, 21.
HAKURA, V., 1966, *G.S.F.C.* preprint, X-641-66-278.
HARTZ, T. R. and BRICE, N. M., 1966, preprint.
HEPPNER, J. P., 1965, Proceedings of ESRO Conference on the Magnetosphere, Stockholm, *Space Science Reviews* (to be published).
JAGGI, R. K., 1964, AAS-NASA Symposium on the Physics of Solar Flares (Ed. by W. N. Hess), NASA SP-50.
KENNEL, C. F. and PETSCHEK, H. E., 1966, *J. Geophys. Res.* **71**, 1.
LEVY, R. H., PETSCHEK, H. E., and SISCOE, G. L., 1964, *AIAA Journal* **2**, 2065.
MCDIARMID, I. B. and BURROWS, J. R., 1964, *Can. J. Phys.* **42**, 616.
MICHEL, F. C. and DESSLER, A. J., 1965, *J. Geophys. Res.* **70**, 4305.
MONTGOMERY, M. D., SINGER, S., CONNER, J. P., and STOGSDILL, E. E., 1965, *Phys. Rev. Letters* **14**, 209.
MULDREW, D. B., 1965, *J. Geophys. Res.* **70**, 2685.
NESS, N. F., 1965, *J. Geophys. Res.* **70**, 2989.
PETSCHEK, H. E., 1964, AAS-NASA Symposium on the Physics of Solar Flares (Ed. by W. N. Hess), NASA SP-50.
PIDDINGTON, J. H., 1966, preprint.
REID, G. C. and PARTHASARATHY, R., 1966, *J. Geophys. Res.* **71**, 3207.
ROTHWELL, P., 1965, Proceedings of ESRO Conference on the Magnetosphere, Stockholm, *Space Science Reviews* (to be published).
SERLEMITSOS, P., 1965, *G.S.F.C.* preprint, X-611-65-378.
SINGER, S., 1965, *Proc. I.E.E.E.* **53**, 1935.
SUGIURA, M. and CHAPMAN, S., 1960, Akad. Wiss. Gottingen.

Discussion

The macroscopic picture gives particles of about 10 keV energy; however, certain microscopic processes can give much higher energies.

F REGION PHOTOCHEMICAL
NIGHTGLOW EMISSIONS

Vern L. Peterson

Institute for Telecommunication Sciences and Aeronomy
Environmental Science Services Administration
Boulder, Colorado

Introduction

In contrast to most other, if not all other emissions in the aurora and airglow, the 6300/6364Å and 5577Å airglow emissions of atomic oxygen from the nighttime F region can be said to be fairly well understood, at least between magnetic latitudes $\pm 45°$. Twenty years ago BATES (1946) suggested that atomic oxygen in the upper atmosphere could be excited by the dissociative recombination of ions and electrons. This suggestion has been developed and successively refined by several authors (NICOLET, 1954; CHAMBERLAIN, 1958; BARBIER, 1959; LAGOS et al., 1963; KAMIYAMA, 1962; NAGATA and OGAWA, 1964; and PETERSON, VANZANDT, and NORTON, 1966). The present paper is intended to review this theory, to discuss evidence for its essential validity, and to discuss a few uses of the theory.

Theory

Because the theory has been recently discussed in detail by PETERSON, VANZANDT, and NORTON (1966), only the salient features of the theory will be given here. For defense of many of the statements made here, and for explicit equations, the reader is referred to that paper.

The emissions considered originate from the first two excited levels of atomic oxygen. The appropriate portion of the oxygen energy level diagram is shown in Figure 1. The designation of each term, its energy above ground state, the mean lifetime of the two excited states, and the wavelengths (in Å) of the four principal emissions are indicated. Also shown with the wavelengths are the percentages of the times that radiative transitions from the given level yield the indicated emission.

The emission rate (photons cm^{-3} sec^{-1}) of a spectral line of a given wavelength is simply the product of the Einstein transition coefficient for that line and the number density of atoms in the given level. Therefore, the theory must provide an expression of this number density in terms of parameters that can either be measured or inferred. To check the theory, either the computed emis-

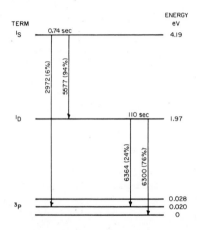

FIGURE 1. The low-energy portion of the atomic energy level diagram. The wavelengths of the four principal emissions and the percentages of the times that these radiative transitions occur from the given level are shown on the arrows. The term designation, lifetimes of the two upper levels, and the energies above ground are also shown.

sion profile must be compared with rocket observations of the emission profile, or the integrated emission rate must be compared with ground based observations.

Expressions for the number densities of the oxygen atoms excited to a given level can be derived by solving their continuity equations, in which the time rates of change of the number densities are set to equal the rates at which the excited atoms are produced, minus the rates at which they are lost, minus the net rates at which motions carry them out of the volume considered. Normally, throughout the major portion of the emitting layer (in the lower F region), both the time derivative and motion terms are small compared with the production and loss rates, and thus may be ignored.

Considering the several mechanisms which can be conceived to produce excited oxygen atoms, the only one of importance at night between geomagnetic latitudes $\pm 45°$ also happens to be the principal mechanism for the loss of electrons in the F region. For this reason, the intensities of these emissions correlate well with the electron loss rate. This mechanism is the dissociative recombination of the ions O_2^+ and NO^+ with electrons

$$O_2^+ + e \rightarrow O + O + 6.96 \text{ eV} \tag{1a}$$

$$NO^+ + e \rightarrow N + O + 2.76 \text{ eV}. \tag{1b}$$

Referring to the excitation energies shown in Figure 1, we see that reaction (1a) is energetically capable of producing atomic oxygen in the following pairs of terms: $(^3P, ^3P)$, $(^3P, ^1D)$, $(^3P, ^1S)$, $(^1D, ^1D)$, or $(^1D, ^1S)$. Similarly, (1b) is energetically capable of producing $N(^2D)$ and $O(^3P)$, or $N(^4S)$ and $O(^1D)$. The latter possibility does not conserve spin (DALGARNO and WALKER, 1964), yet (1b) cannot be ignored as a source of $O(^1D)$ because the $N(^2D)$ produced by (1b) can be quenched by collisions with $O(^3P)$, thus producing $O(^1D)$ (MEGILL, 1965):

$$N(^2D) + O(^3P) \rightarrow N(^4S) + O(^1D). \tag{2}$$

The importance of this reaction depends on its reaction rate. If the reaction rate is fast, the $O(^1D)$ produced acts as the direct product of (1b). If (2) proceeds slowly, $N(^2D)$ will be quenched primarily by collisions with electrons and (2) may be ignored. With an intermediate reaction rate for (2), some $O(^1D)$ will be produced but diffusion of $N(^2D)$ will be important, so that the resulting density of $O(^1D)$ will have little correlation with the local electron loss rate. This point is referred to again in the next section.

The detailed calculation of this contribution to $O(^1D)$ has not been made. In the following discussion any effect (2) may have is treated as if its reaction rate is so fast that the $O(^1D)$ may be considered to be coming directly from (1b), or as if the reaction rate is so slow that (2) may be ignored. Therefore, the production rate of $O(^1S)$ is the rate at which (1a) proceeds, multiplied by the probability that the recombination will produce $O(^1S)$. Similarly, the production rate of $O(^1D)$ is the rate at which (1a) proceeds, times the probability that it will give an $O(^1D)$, plus the reaction rate of (1b), multiplied by the probability it will produce $O(^1D)$, plus the rate of 5577Å emission, since this is produced by the $^1S \rightarrow {}^1D$ transition.

The ^1S level is depopulated only by radiative transitions, making the loss rate the product of the $O(^1S)$ density and the Einstein transition coefficient for this level. The ^1D level is depopulated not only by radiative transitions, but by collisional transitions (quenching) as well. Therefore, the loss rate of $O(^1D)$ is the product of the $O(^1D)$ density and the sum of the radiative (Einstein) and collisional transition coefficients. The latter coefficient is proportional to the density of the quenching constituent, which is probably either O_2 or N_2, and therefore, decreases rapidly with increasing height.

The $O(^1S)$ and $O(^1D)$ concentrations are found by equating the production and loss rates. The resulting expressions, however, are in terms of the O_2^+ and NO^+ concentrations. Such expressions would be ideal for checking the theory if simultaneous measurements could be made of the emission profiles and the O_2^+ and NO^+ concentrations. Because such observations have not yet been made, the O_2^+ and NO^+ densities have to be expressed in terms of quantities whose height variations can either be observed or inferred. Such quantities are the electron, O_2 and N_2 concentrations.

The molecular ions O_2^+ and NO^+ in the nighttime F region are formed almost entirely from the predominant O^+ ion by the reactions

$$O^+ + O_2 \rightarrow O_2^+ + O + 1.53 \text{ eV} \tag{3a}$$

$$O^+ + N_2 \rightarrow NO^+ + N + 1.09 \text{ eV}. \tag{3b}$$

The O_2^+ and NO^+ concentrations are found by solving their continuity equations in conjunction with the expression for charge neutrality. As with the continuity equations for $O(^1S)$ and $O(^1D)$, it is usually valid to ignore the motion and time derivative terms over most of the emitting region. (YOSHISAKI (1965), however, concludes that vertical motions of ions and electrons are important at the magnetic equator.) The production rates of O_2^+ and NO^+, as deduced from (3), are then equated to their loss rates, as deduced from (1). The $O(^1S)$ and $O(^1D)$ concentrations can then be put in terms of the electron, O_2 and N_2 concentrations, the reaction coefficients of (1) and (3), the excitation probabilities, and the radiative and collisional transition coefficients. The electron density profile can be computed from an ionogram; the O_2 and N_2 are in diffusive equilibrium, since the chemical reactions involve only a small portion of them, and their concentrations decrease rapidly with increasing height in a known way.

The resulting height profile of the $O(^1S)$ concentration shows a maximum value always below the F layer electron density peak and a width between half-maximum points of 1–1.5 scale heights of atomic oxygen, depending upon the ionospheric conditions and rate coefficients. If the F layer has an α-Chapman layer shape, and if the so-called "linear" electron loss rate dominates the whole emitting layer, the $O(^1S)$ layer peak is 1.6 scale heights of atomic oxygen below the F layer peak (cf. LAGOS et al., 1963). The shape of the $O(^1D)$ layer differs from that for $O(^1S)$ only in that quenching of the ^1D state becomes important at the lower heights, so that the concentration of $O(^1D)$ approaches zero more rapidly with decreasing height than does the concentration of $O(^1S)$.

Barbier's formula, relating the ionospheric parameters $h'F$ and f_0F2 with the integrated 6300Å intensity, follows naturally from this theory (BARBIER, 1959; PETERSON, 1967). By using the same approximations as mentioned above and assuming an isothermal atmosphere and no quenching of $O(^1D)$, the equation

$$Q_{6300} = BH_{32}(f_0F2)^2 e^{-h_{max}/H_{32}} \tag{4}$$

results from the integration of the emission profile. In (4), h_{max} is the height of the F layer maximum electron density, H_{32} is the molecular oxygen scale height, and the dissociative recombination rate coefficient is contained in the factor B. The height h_{max} is not directly scaled from an ionogram. The approximation implicit in Barbier's formula is that h_{max} is a constant but unknown height above $h'F$, the minimum virtual height of the F layer; there are better ways of estimating h_{max} from an ionogram but the $h'F$ method is usually quite satisfactory. Barbier's formula also contains an additive "constant." This "constant" does not follow from the theory as discussed above, and will be discussed again in the next section.

Comparison of Theory and Observations

A good correlation between theory and observations has been found by many authors by using the Barbier formula (e.g., BARBIER, 1959; DELSEMME and DELSEMME, 1960; BARBIER, ROACH, and STEIGER, 1962; CARMEN and KILFOYLE,

1963). By using electron density profiles calculated from ionograms, examples of good agreement between the detailed theory and observation have also been found by PETERSON and STEIGER (1966). Figure 2 illustrates some comparisons from this paper.

Whether one uses the Barbier formula or the more exact equations, a background component unrelated to the ionospheric parameters is nearly always-found. This is represented in Figure 2 by the intercept on the Q(obs) axis at

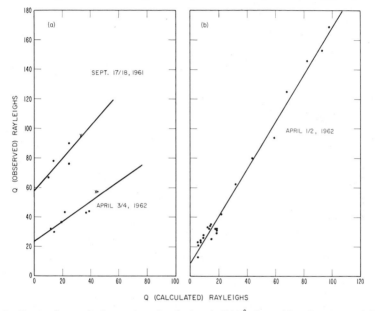

FIGURE 2. Comparison of observed and calculated 6300Å intensities for three nights of Maui data. The intercepts at Q(calc) ≈ 0 represent a background component that is not explained by the theory. The lines are least square fits to the data. The product of certain atomic parameters can be evaluated by normalizing these lines to a slope of 45°.

Q(calc) $= 0$. PETERSON and STEIGER (1966) have shown that this background component is not the result of inaccuracies in choosing the rate coefficients, the quenching coefficient, or the temperatures which are used in the calculations. Before the comparison with theory was undertaken, an attempt was made to correct the observed 6300Å intensities for extraneous light; even so part of the background component is probably contamination. However, part of this background radiation may be the truly atmospheric 6300Å emission. A likely source of such radiation is reaction (2); as discussed in the previous section, if (2) proceeds at an appropriate rate, the N(^2D) will diffuse to distances sufficiently far from where it was formed so that the O(^1D) produced by (2) has little correlation with ionospheric parameters.

The theory is also in agreement with rocket observations. GULLIDGE, PACKER, and TILFORD (1966) report that both 6300Å and 5577Å had emission maxima at about 250 km during a rocket flight from White Sands, New Mexico. This height agrees with that predicted from the electron density profile that was deduced from an ionogram taken just before that flight.

This theory of F region atomic oxygen nightglow seems to explain the observations of 6300Å over a wide latitude range. Ionospheric and 6300Å data were gathered from the research ship, Croatan, as it cruised along the 75° W meridian between geomagnetic latitudes 45°N and 50°S. By using the Barbier formula GREENSPAN and PETERSON (1966) found good agreement between theory and observation throughout the trip. It must be pointed out, however, that examples have been found, for example, in the Maui, Hawaii data, where the agreement is hardly perfect. In these cases it seems possible to explain the discrepancies as time variations in the O_2 and N_2 densities at the emission peak.

Applications

The agreement between observation and theory inspires the use of observations to evaluate certain atomic parameters. For example, by using O_2 and N_2 densities taken from model atmospheres and the laboratory measured rates for reactions (1) and (3), PETERSON and STEIGER (1966) find that approximately one dissociative recombination in ten yields an $O(^1D)$ atom.

The $O(^1D)$ to $O(^1S)$ excitation ratio and the quenching rate of $O(^1D)$ may also be evaluated from the nightglow data. The data from Maui, Hawaii give definite evidence that the ^1S state, as well as the ^1D state, is excited by reaction (1a). Figure 3 is a sample of this evidence; four almucantar sweeps, two each in 6300Å and 5577Å, are shown here. It is obvious that the two emissions are coming from the same height, the source being the lower F region. The 5577Å emission, of course, also has a component coming from the 100 km altitude level. The 6300–5577Å emission ratio (not counting the 100 km level 5577Å emission) is about 4 to 1, but because of quenching of the ^1D level, the excitation ratio may be a great deal higher than this. By using data as shown in Figure 3, VANZANDT and PETERSON (1967) have argued that the quenching of $O(^1D)$ is not severe at 250 km, a typical height for the emission peak, and thus the excitation ratio is approximately the same as the observed emission ratio. This evaluation of the quenching rate contradicts the evaluation by WALLACE and MCELROY (1966) using 6300Å dayglow data.

Perhaps the most important use of the theory-observation agreement is in making inferences about the F region of the ionosphere in locations where no ionospheric measurements are available (PETERSON, VANZANDT, ROACH, and STEIGER, 1967). The large enhancements of the 6300Å nightglow provide a dramatic illustration of this. Such enhancements can be seen in Figure 15 of Steiger's contribution to this volume, in which very bright elongated features are separated by valleys of low intensity. The central enhancement shown is about 200 km wide and 1000 km long. During the passage of this enhancement

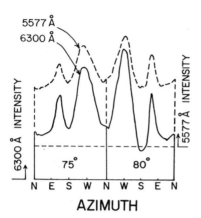

FIGURE 3. Almucantor sweeps in 5577Å and 6300Å at zenith angles of 75° and 80° from Maui, October 10, 1961, 150° W time = 1910/1915. The enhancements in green and red are obviously coming from the same heights, which theory tells us is in the lower F region.

through Maui's zenith (center of the circle), the electron density increased somewhat, and the F layer dropped in height quite dramatically. As the next enhancement passed overhead this recurred. We infer that these elongated north-south enhancements primarily represent height depressions of the F layer, although they may be accompanied by an increased electron density of perhaps a factor of 2. The maps suggest, in fact, that the so-called ionospheric equatorial anomaly seen in meridian slices through the ionosphere may not be as uniform a structure at night as commonly thought; if a meridian slice is made along such an elongated bright feature, the anomaly might be seen, but if another slice is made just 100 km east or west of the first one, the anomaly might not be seen. If this inference is correct, theories that have been proposed to explain the anomaly may have to be drastically revised.

The slopes in the ionosphere suggested by such 6300Å isophote maps are quite steep. Taking the maps at face value and interpreting the enhancements as due entirely to height differences, F layer tilts as high as 45° are found. However, the maps are not to be taken at face value, since the 5° field of view of the photometer smooths the real structure; the true slopes may be as great as 70° or 80°. Such structure not only has profound implications in ionospheric physics, but must also play an important role in radio communication.

Acknowledgment I acknowledge the partial support of NASA Grant R-18 in the preparation of this report.

References

BARBIER, D., 1959, *Ann. Geophys.* **15**, 179–217.
BARBIER, D., ROACH, F. E., and STEIGER, W. R., 1962, *J. Res. Natl. Bur. Std.* **66D**, 145–152.
BATES, D. R., 1946, *Monthly Notices Roy. Astron. Soc.* **106**, 509–514.
CARMEN, E. H. and KILFOYLE, B., 1963, *J. Geophys. Res.* **68**, 5605–5607.
CHAMBERLAIN, J. W., 1958, *Astrophys. J.* **127**, 54–66.
DALGARNO, A. and WALKER, J. C. G., 1964, *J. Atmospheric Sci.* **21**, 463–474.
DELSEMME, A. and DELSEMME, D., 1960, *Ann. Geophys.* **16**, 507–524.
GREENSPAN, J. and PETERSON, V. L., 1967, in preparation.
GULLIDGE, I. S., PACKER, D. M., and TILFORD, S. G., 1966, *Trans. American Geophys. Union* **47**, 74–75.
KAMIYAMA, H., 1962, *J. Geomag. Geoelec.* **14**, 58–65.
LAGOS, P., BELLEW, W., and SILVERMAN, S. M., 1963, *J. Atmospheric Terrest. Phys.* **25**, 581–587.
MEGILL, L. R., 1965, private communication.
NAGATA, T. and OGAWA, 1964, T., *Rept. Iono. Space Res. Japan* **18**, 394–409.
NICOLET, M, 1954, *Phys. Rev.* **93**, 633.
PETERSON, V. L., 1967, *Planetary Space Sci.* (to be published).
PETERSON, V. L. and STEIGER, W. R., 1966, *J. Geophys. Res.* **71**, 2267–2277.
PETERSON, V. L., VANZANDT, T. E., and NORTON, R. B., 1966, *J. Geophys. Res.* **71**, 2255–2265.
PETERSON, V. L., VANZANDT, T. E., ROACH, F. E., and STEIGER, W. R., 1967, *Ann. Geophys.* (to be published).
VANZANDT, T. E. and PETERSON, V. L., 1967, in preparation.
WALLACE, L. and MCELROY, M. B., 1966, *Planetary Space Sci.* **14**, 677–708.
YOSHISAKE, W., 1965, *Rept. Iono. Space Res. Japan* **19**, 299–310.

Discussion

During a discussion of the two types of motion — wave and drift — it was suggested that an attempt be made in the data analysis to separate them.

RADIO AURORA

I. Observations

II. Comparison of the Observations with a Theoretical Model

Günther Lange-Hesse

Max-Planck-Institute for Aeronomy
Lindau/Harz, West Germany

Dedicated to Professor Dr. W. Dieminger
for his 60th birthday.

I. OBSERVATIONS

1. Historical Review

The influence of the aurora on radio wave propagation has been recognized for some time. Reflections of radio waves from ionization associated with aurora — called radio aurora — were first investigated in 1938 by HARANG and STOFF-REGEN (1940) in the VHF range. At about the same time amateur radio operators in the USA had discovered that VHF radio wave propagation via auroral ionization was possible (MOORE, 1951). Ionosonde echoes in the HF range associated with aurora were reported at Tromsö, Norway in 1933 by APPLETON *et al.* (1937). After World War II and particularly during the last twelve years, radio aurora has been studied by a number of researchers in North America, Britain, Norway, Sweden, Finland, Germany, Russia, New Zealand, and the Antarctic.

Most studies of radio aurora[1] have been made by means of radar, i. e., with the transmitter and receiver at the same place. Radar echoes from the aurora

---

[1] In this paper the following expressions are mostly used as synonyms without alluding to different physical mechanisms: radio aurora, auroral echoes, auroral reflections.

can be obtained at frequencies in the HF, VHF, and UHF band. The lowest frequencies used are about 6 Mc/sec (LEADABRAND and PETERSON, 1958, and the highest are 3000 Mc/sec (GROTH et al., 1964). Most of the studies have been made in either the VHF or the lower UHF range, i.e., the 400–800-Mc/sec range. Several summaries of the results of these radar auroral experiments have been published by LITTLE et al. (1956), LANGE-HESSE (1956), BIRFELD (1960), PETERSON (1960), BAGARYATSKY (1960), BOOKER (1960), CHAMBERLAIN (1961), HULTQVIST and EGELAND (1964), and LEADABRAND (1965).

Other studies of radio aurora have been made by investigating oblique — or bistatic — auroral reflections, i.e., with transmitter and receiver at different places. Observations of this kind were carried out in northern Scandinavia by recording the transmissions from several FM broadcast stations between 87 and 100 Mc/sec at one place in case of aurora reflections (EGELAND et al., 1961a; EGELAND, 1962a, b; OKSMAN, 1964, 1966a, b). Observations of bistatic radio reflections in the lower VHF range were carried out e.g., in Canada (COLLINS et al., 1959; GREEN, 1961) and in the USA (DYCE, 1955b).

Investigations of bistatic auroral reflections have also been made by means of a geographically extended net of amateur radio stations. Observations of this kind were first carried out in North America during the years before the IGY (MOORE, 1951; DYCE, 1955a; GERSON, 1955a, b). During the IGY and later years similar observations were carried out in Europe, especially in Britain (e.g., STONE, 1960, 1965; SMITH-ROSE, 1960; NEWTON, 1966) and Germany (LANGE-HESSE, 1962, 1963a, b, 1964a, b; LANGE-HESSE et al., 1965, 1966).

2. Aspect Sensitivity Control by the Geomagnetic Field

The reduction of VHF radar echoes from aurora has shown that these echoes can only be obtained from a very restricted strip of sky corresponding to the region where the line of sight from the radar location to the aurora intersects the local geomagnetic field lines at right angles (see e.g., DYCE, 1955c; UNWIN, 1958; and WATKINS, 1960). There is a fundamental difference between the visual and the radio echo observations in that visual forms can be observed if they occur anywhere above the horizon whereas radio echoes are detected only if the ionization within the region of the auroras is located within the specular reflecting region. Figure 1 shows the geometry of the VHF auroral backscatter problem. On the condition that perpendicularity is necessary, aurora displays at points A and B in Figure 1 used to give backscatter echoes, but not at points C and D. Perfect 90° intersection, however, is not required, because of the finite length of auroral scatters. Depending upon the frequency, peak power, and sensitivity of the radar, echoes can be obtained at intersection angles that differ from 90° by as much as 10°. The deviation of the intersection angle from 90° is called the off-perpendicular angle.

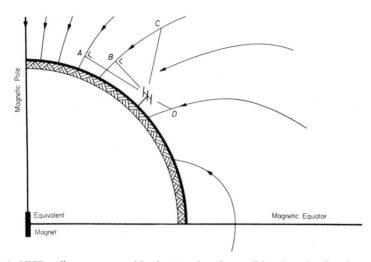

FIGURE 1. VHF radio wave auroral backscatter is only possible when the direction of radio wave propagation and the direction of the lines of force of the earth's magnetic field are perpendicular at the reflection point. Under this assumption auroral displays at the points *A* and *B* used to give backscatter echoes, but not displays at the points *C* and *D*.

In many of the cases the observed off-perpendicular angle is not a true off-perpendicular angle because the geomagnetic field lines can change their orientation during a magnetic storm which accompanies aurora displays, especially at lower latitudes. STÖRMER (1926) describes an analysis of the movement of the radiant point of coronal forms. This point was traced through a movement of as much as 3–4° in inclination during the course of the great auroral display of March 22–23, 1920. The auroral rays forming the corona are aligned with the geomagnetic field, and their motion reflects a similar distortion of the local magnetic field, probably at 200–300 km heights. As the disturbance current system during a geomagnetic storm is usually considered to flow in the E-layer, one would expect any field distortions to be as great or greater there than those occurring at more considerable heights. This means that in many of the cases the true off-perpendicular angle is not the observed one for an undistorted geomagnetic field especially during severe geomagnetic storms ($K_p = 8$ and 9). In Part II of this paper the influence of geomagnetic dip variations on bistatic auroral backscatter is described in detail.

The influence of the magnetic field geometry on the radar echoes (perpendicular intersection) had been proposed by MOORE (1951), and in the investigations conducted at locations to the south of the auroral zone, the majority of the echoes came from azimuths centered about magnetic north. Although this result agreed with the requirement for orthogonal or nearly orthogonal intersection, the evidence was not conclusive until DYCE (1955c) carried out a similar experiment from Point Barrow, Alaska, which is north of the auroral zone. Even at such a magnetic northern location the radar ray intersects the magnetic field lines at angles closest to 90° in the magnetic north direction from Point Barrow, while the maximum occurrence of visual aurora is to the south. The distribution of the observed echoes should indicate whether the reflection is influenced more by the magnetic field geometry or by the maximum of the auroral occurrence. The results obtained by DYCE (1955c) indicate that the magnetic field orthogonality is an overruling criterion because the majority of the echoes were seen in the region north of Point Barrow and not to the south where the occurrence of aurora is a maximum (Figure 2).

3. Reflection Mechanism

The first proposals for the reflection mechanism were very simple ones. LOWELL et al. (1947) first suggested that the radio waves at 46 Mc/sec may be reflected from auroral ionization in the same way that HF waves are reflected by the ordinary ionospheric layers, i.e., by critical reflection. The value for critical densities N_e is in the first approximation expressed by

$$N_e = \frac{\pi m f_c^2}{e^2} = 1.24 \cdot 10^4 f_c^2$$

f_c is the frequency in Mc/sec. That radio aurora may be due to subcritical reflections from strong gradients in fairly weak ionization (partial reflections) was proposed by HERLOFSON (1947).

Both mentioned mechanisms were based on the simplest possible assumption that the critical and partial reflections, respectively, arise from ionization configurations similar to the configuration of the auroral form, i.e., a large vertical plane surface of ionization. The later observations of the fading and the angular distribution of the auroral echoes made it evident that specular reflection, either critical or partial, from large surfaces could not be the relevant process. Several workers have therefore suggested that critical reflections from ionization blobs with dimensions which are large compared to the wavelength are responsible for auroral echoes, at least on frequencies in the lower VHF range and HF range (see e.g., FORSYTH, 1953; BOLLOUGH et al., 1954; KAISER, 1956; FORSYTH et al., 1957; COLLINS et al., 1959). Other workers have modified the partial reflection mechanism proposed by HERLOFSON (1947) by introducing smaller irregularities of low electron density in the normal ionosphere (see e.g., BOOKER et al., 1955; BOOKER, 1956, 1960; PRESNELL et al., 1959; FLOOD, 1960).

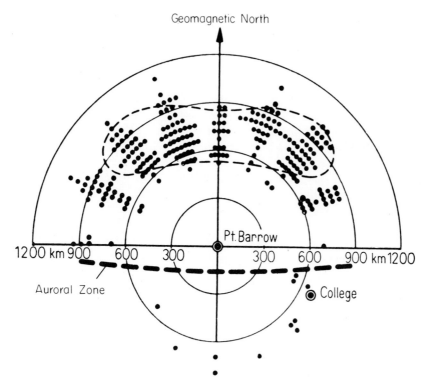

FIGURE 2. Centers of radar auroral echoes observed from Point Barrow, Alaska, north of the main auroral zone in November, 1954. Each dot represents the occurrence of an echo as a function of slant range and bearing. Off-perpendicular angle is between 6° and 7° within the dashed line at a height of 80 km. After DYCE (1955c).

From the numerous reflection models which have been proposed, the theory of auroral radar scattering as developed by BOOKER (1956, 1960), based upon the observed wavelength dependence and aspect sensitivity (controlled by the geomagnetic field geometry), appears most nearly to explain the observations, except for occasions in the HF and lower VHF range when auroral ionization becomes overdense. The Booker theory involves the concept of scattering by nonisotropic irregularities in electron densities. These irregularities provide discontinuities in the dielectric constant which are short compared to the radar wavelength and which scatter only a small fraction of the incident energy back toward the radar (reflection coefficient $\sim 10^{-6}$).

To produce the observed aspect sensitivity, these irregularities must be in the form of columns of ionization with their long axes parallel to the earth's magnetic field. The length of the irregularities then determines the scattering aspect sensitivity of auroral reflections. The discontinuity of electron density and the dimension of the irregularity transverse to the earth's magnetic field determine the wavelength dependence of the auroral reflections.

The wavelength dependence of the auroral echoes is well pronounced. The echo power decreases strongly with increasing frequency. Wavelength dependence, together with aspect sensitivity, have been measured by a number of workers, e.g., PRESNELL et al. (1959), BLEVIS et al. (1963), FLOOD (1960), STONE et al. (1959). The results obtained by LEADABRAND (1962) and LEADABRAND et al. (1965) with elaborate auroral equipment located at Fraserburgh, Scotland, however, could be interpreted most easily, primarily because of the narrow beam involved. The radar was specifically designed for this purpose, having identical beamwidths (1.2°) at 400 and 800 Mc/sec. Thus the identical volume of aurora was illuminated simultaneously at both frequencies. Wavelength dependence observations carried out with this equipment resulted in a power law dependence of λ^7 and aspect sensitivity observations in energy decrease of 10 dB/degree of off-perpendicular. The interpretation of these results according to the Booker scattering theory indicates that the size of the backscattering irregularities is 45–90 m along the magnetic field lines and 0.7 m across the field lines.

4. Bistatic Aurora Backscatter Propagation

The Booker scattering theory has been worked out in considerable detail for the radar backscatter case. This theory has been extended to oblique — or bistatic — auroral reflections by EGELAND (1962b). Figure 3 shows a representation of the geometry of the propagation path in the vertical direction in case of bistatic auroral backscatter communication between the points S_0 and S_1. The z-axis of a three-dimensional xyz-coordinate system in Figure 3 is tangent to the geomagnetic line of force at the point of the backscattering center or irregularity. The xy-plane is perpendicular to the geomagnetic line of force; k_0 and k_1 is the vector of the wave normal of the incident and backscattered wave, respectively; Ω_0 and Ω_1 is the propagation angle = the angle between the direction of radio wave propagation and the magnetic lines of force; ϵ_0 and ϵ_1 is the angle between k_0 and k_1, respectively, and the xy-plane. According to the theory (EGELAND, 1962b), optimum conditions are given for the possibility of VHF aurora backscatter propagation, if the relation $\cos \Omega_0 + \cos \Omega_1 = 0$ is fulfilled at the point of the backscattering center (Figure 3). This means that the vectors k_0 and k_1 describe the same angle with the xy-plane, in this case $\epsilon_0 = \epsilon_1$ and the vector $(k_0 - k_1)$ is perpendicular to the xy-plane. Optimum conditions of that kind will be referred to as "ideal backscatter conditions."

If the angles ϵ_0, ϵ_1 or Ω_0, Ω_1 deviate from the ideal backscatter conditions by only a few degrees (similar to the radar off-perpendicular backscatter case) bistatic backscatter propagation in principle is possible according to the theory. The backscattered power, however, decreases very rapidly with increasing angle deviation from the ideal conditions. Therefore, one needs very strong

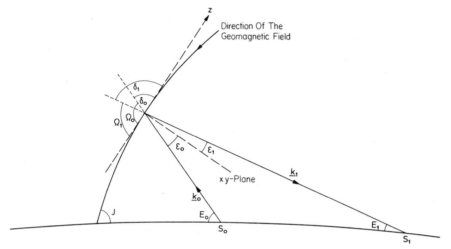

FIGURE 3. Cross-sectional view of the earth with the geometry of the propagation path in the vertical direction for VHF bistatic auroral backscatter propagation between the two points S_0 and S_1; k_0, k_1, vector of the wave normal of the incident and backscattered wave, respectively; δ_0, ϵ_1, angle between k_0 and k_1, respectively, and the xy-plane; J, magnetic dip angle; Ω_1, Ω_0, propagation angle = angle between the direction of radio wave propagation and the magnetic lines of force; E_0, E_1, elevation angle above the horizontal.

transmitters and antennas with high gain in order to establish communications if the angles mentioned before deviate by only a few degrees from the ideal backscatter conditions, especially in the UHF and higher VHF range. For particulars see the curves in the publications by CZECHOWSKY (1966), Figure 14 and Figure 11A and EGELAND (1962b), pp. 198–201. Figure 4 shows the geometry of the propagation path in the horizontal direction in case of bistatic aurora backscatter communication.

Azimuth, range, and intensity of the aurora backscattered radiation can be recorded by the pulse radar methods. The limitations are that scattering in other directions than directly backwards to the radar location cannot be studied and that the pulse signal is not suitable for investigating the changes of fine structure in the reflection process. This, however, is possible by investigating oblique — or bistatic — auroral backscatter signals transmitted from FM broadcast stations or beacon transmitters.

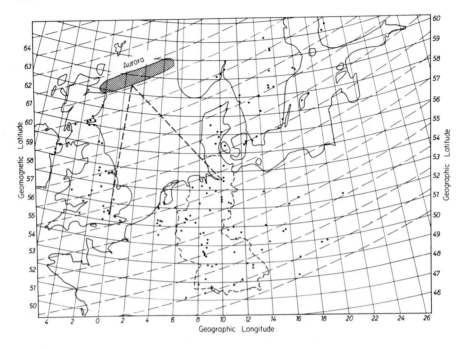

Geographic Longitude

Figure 4. Map of Middle Europe with a) the net of VHF amateur radio stations observing and reporting bistatic auroral backscatter communications (auroral contacts) on about 145 Mc/sec during the years from 1957–64, and b) a representation of the geometry of the propagation path in the horizontal direction. The dashed lines are the geomagnetic parallels of latitude.

5. Bistatic Auroral Backscatter Observations by a Net of Amateur Radio Stations

The observation of the VHF aurora backscatter phenomenon by a net of amateur radio stations is a relatively simple method. But if this net of stations has a big geographical extension and if the observations are dense in time, this method provides the possibility to observe the variations and characteristics of the aurora backscatter radiation phenomenon over a large geographical region which would be very expensive and difficult to do by means of a great number of radar sets.

Radio amateurs use the backscatter features of the aurora in order to carry out "VHF bistatic auroral backscatter communications" between two stations (Figures 3 and 4) using CW-transmitters of about 50–100 W and, in general, low gain directional antennas. An aurorally-propagated VHF signal has a characteristic growl or hiss due to a fast fading that is at an audio rate up to several hundred cycles per second (BOWLES, 1952). As the carrier frequency is increased to higher VHF frequencies, the growl increases in pitch. Amplitude modulated phone signals are badly garbled, although relatively slow CW-telegraphy can get through without difficulty (for particulars see, e.g., MOORE, 1951; DYCE, 1955a; or LANGE-HESSE, 1962). Unlike E- or F-layer propagation, strongest signals are usually obtained when both stations point their directional antennas northward towards the aurora, regardless of the actual great-circle bearing between the stations. The geometry of the propagation path is shown in Figure 4. During especially strong auroras the signals may appear to come from a variety of directions spread about north. As already mentioned, communications of the kind shown in Figure 4 are called "bistatic auroral backscatter communications" or single "auroral contacts."

A reported VHF bistatic auroral backscatter telegraphy communication contains the following details:

a) The clear existence of such a kind of communication recognizable with great certainty by the typical rough tone of the telegraphy signals.
b) The exact beeline distance between the two stations getting in contact by such a kind of communication.
c) Date and time of day of the communication, as well as the simultaneously occurring geophysical events, e. g. degree of geomagnetic activity, location of the visual aurora display, etc.

The reported communication, however, contains no information about the traveling time of the waves (as given by a radar) and no information about the exact value of the field strength at the receiver, as well as the directions of the sky from where the signals arrived. The first results of the reduction of this kind of communication, especially of statistical character and about correlations with other geophysical phenomena, have been reported by MOORE (1951), DYCE (1955a), GERSON (1955a, b), STONE (1960), and LANGE-HESSE (1962, 1963a, b; 1964a, b).

The results of the studies of radio aurora by means of radar are described in numerous summaries which were mentioned previously. In Part I of this present paper mainly the results of the investigations by means of a net of amateur radio stations are reviewed. Some of these results are compared with the results of the radar studies in order to show that the amateur observation method is reliable and that it is possible to study a number of characteristics of the VHF auroral backscatter phenomena using this method. In Part II of this paper the results from amateur observations are compared with those computed according to a theoretical model for the auroral backscatter phenomena.

6. Time Variations of the Characteristics of Auroral Backscatter

A. Diurnal Variation

Figure 5 shows the diurnal variation of the frequency of occurrence of VHF auroral backscatter in median latitudes given by the number of bistatic auroral

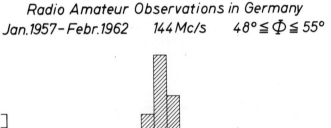

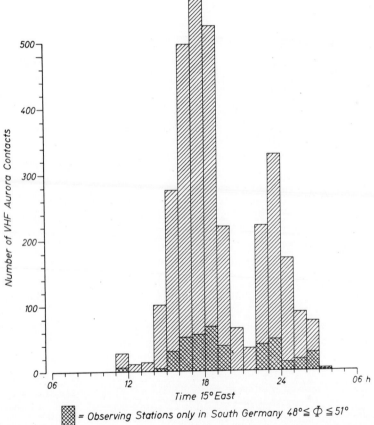

FIGURE 5. Frequency of VHF auroral backscatter communications (auroral contacts) as a function of local time in $48° \leqq \Phi \leqq 55°$ geomagnetic latitude according to amateur observations on 144–146 Mc/sec. January, 1957 to February, 1962. After LANGE-HESSE (1963a).

backscatter communications (auroral contacts) observed and reported by a net of amateur radio stations during the time from January, 1957 to February, 1962. Two strong maxima occur, the first at about 1700–1800 hr and the second around midnight local time. One sharp minimum occurs at about 2100 hr, a second broad one extends from early morning until about noon.

A comparison of the diurnal variation according to amateur observations and to radar observations (at about the same geomagnetic latitude) is shown in Figure 6. The diurnal variation is about the same in both cases. Contrary to Figure 5, the number of days with the occurrence of bistatic auroral backscatter communications and auroral radar echoes, respectively, is shown in Figure 6 for hourly intervals.

The maxima in Figures 5 and 6 show a strong dependence on the geomagnetic latitude of the observations. The approximate times of peak backscatter activity for observations taken at various geomagnetic latitudes have been investigated by EGELAND et al. (1961). Their results are summarized in Figure 7. They studied the times of occurrence of the maxima because these seem to depend only very slightly on the observation and reduction method (see e.g. Figures 5 and 6). The pattern which emerges on the polar diagram shows a fairly wide scatter but may be schematically represented by the three spiral curves shown in Figure 7. The spirals represent the various echo maxima. As may be seen in Figure 7, the times of peak auroral echo activity are latitude dependent.

a) The evening maximum occurs between 1800 and 2400 hr geomagnetic time. In latitudes close to or in the auroral zone this maximum is most pronounced in the winter and is rarely observed during the summer months. In median latitudes, however, this maximum shows only a slight seasonal variation (see Figure 12).

b) The early morning maximum occurs between 2400 and 0700 hr. This spiral closely approximates that derived by LEONARD (1961) from recent radar observations of aurora over Alaska. This maximum has been reported by virtually all observers irrespective of latitude. In middle European latitudes ($\Phi \approx 50$–$55°$) the difference between geomagnetic and local time is small and not more than one hour. Therefore the results from Figures 5 and 6 coincide with those given in Figure 7.

c) The early afternoon maximum has been noted only by observers working close to or in the auroral zone. Recently, UNWIN (1966) has made extended investigations similar to those of Egeland by taking into account more observational data from the southern hemisphere and from Antarctica. According to Unwin's investigations, the maximum radio aurora occurrence can also be associated with three separate spirals similar to those shown in Figure 7, but with some other position. In addition to this, the position and relative prominence of the spirals is sensitive to the

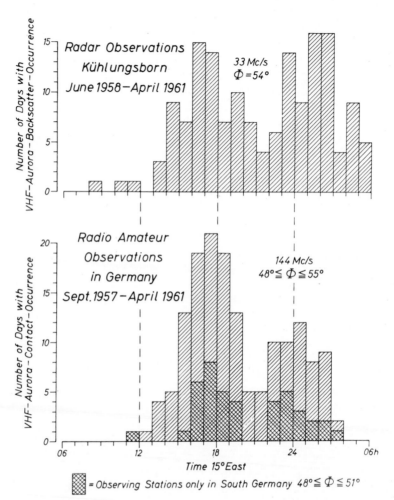

FIGURE 6. Comparison of the diurnal variation of the frequency of auroral backscatter echoes according to amateur observations (low figure) and to radar observations at about the same geomagnetic latitudes but on different frequencies. Contrary to Figure 5, the number of days with the occurrence of bistatic auroral backscatter communications and auroral radar echoes, respectively, is shown in this figure for hourly intervals. After LANGE-HESSE (1962).

level of magnetic disturbance. They are similar to the spirals of maximum magnetic activity derived by FELDSTEIN (1963).

B. Control of the Diurnal Variation of the Echo Characteristics by the Geomagnetic Field's Disturbed Daily Variation

Figure 8 illustrates the mean daily magnetic departures from the basic for the horizontal (H) and the vertical (V) component on disturbed days for the

MAXIMUM AURORAL ECHO OBSERVATIONS
AT VARIOUS LATITUDES

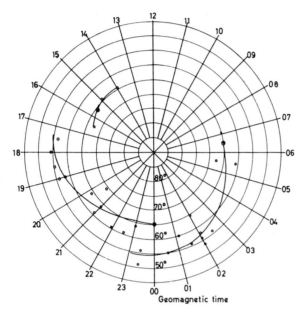

FIGURE 7. Times of peak auroral echo activity as observed at various geomagnetic latitudes. The spirals represent the various echo maxima. After EGELAND et al. (1961).

year 1959 at Eskadalemuir. The departures in Figure 8 are caused by a current system (S_D-current system, after CHAPMAN and BARTELS, 1940) which flows during disturbed conditions along the maximum auroral zone in the ionosphere at about the same height as the E-layer. The maximum of the positive departure of H occurs between 1700 and 1800 hr local time. This is exactly the time of maximum backscatter occurrence in Figures 5 and 6. The change from positive to negative departures occurs at about 2200 hr. This is the time of the frequency minimum. The maximum around and after midnight (Figures 5 and 6) occurs during the negative departure of V in Figure 8. According to the investigations of UNWIN (1966), the similarity between the times of peak backscatter occurrence and the times of maximum geomagnetic activity can be observed in all latitudes.

The extended radar studies of the aurora have shown that two types of radar auroral echoes exist. These types were labeled discrete and diffuse owing to their appearance on the radar A-scope display (see e.g. CURRIE et al., 1953; BULLOUGH et al., 1955; PRESNELL et al., 1959). The discrete type of echo resembles the shape of the transmitted pulse; the diffuse type of echo is spread in range and has a triangular shape. The diffuse type used to occur during the

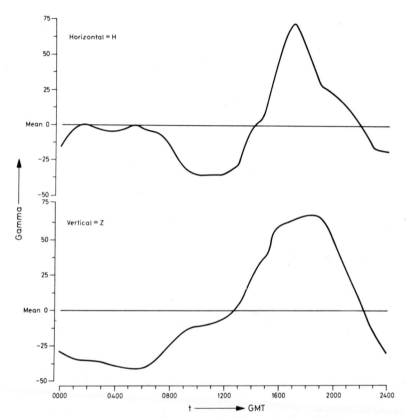

FIGURE 8. Daily mean magnetic departures from the basic of the H- and V-component on disturbed days for the year 1959 at Eskdalemuir (Scotland). Geomagnetic latitude $\Phi \approx 59°$. Note that it is the extent of change which varies with disturbed conditions, and not so much the general character of the curves.

positive departure of the geomagnetic H-component (mainly daytime) and the discrete type after the change from positive to negative departures of the V-component (mainly nighttime), see Figure 8. Figure 9 shows, for a single occasion, the complete daily trend in magnetic disturbance and radar aurora echo characteristics observed with 72 Mc/sec radar equipment at Jordell Bank Experimental Station (geomagnetic latitude $\Phi \approx 57°$N). The echo observations commenced at 1550 hr; echoes were recorded until 1845 hr and were mainly diffuse during this daytime interval (see lowest diagram in Figure 9). The echoes faded out from 1845 till 2200 hr while the departure of the magnetic disturbance reversed in sign. After 2200 hr the echoes occurred again and lasted until the end of the geomagnetic disturbance at about 0430 hr. During this

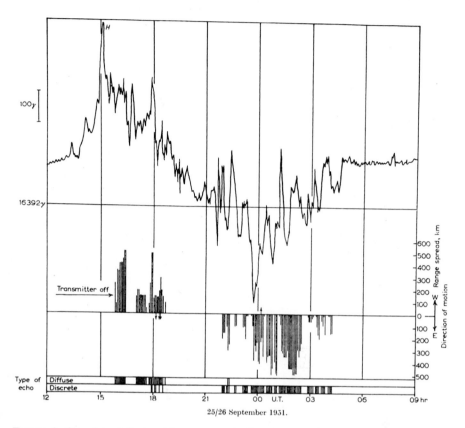

FIGURE 9. Complete daily trend in geomagnetic disturbance and radar auroral echo characteristics observed with 72 Mc/sec radar equipment at Jodrell Bank Experimental Station.
After BULLOUGH *et al.* (1957). Note that the magnetic record of the H-component has a fine
structure unlike the the curves in Figure 8 which are yearly means. The general character and
directions of the departures of the magnetic record, however, are similar to the curve in
Figure 8.

nighttime interval the echoes were mainly discrete. According to the middle
diagram in Figure 9, the echoes show a motion to the west during the positive
(up) departures of the H-component and a motion to the east during the negative (down) departures of the H-component. The general order of the drift
motion is about 600 m/sec but individual velocities in excess of 1000 m/sec
were reported (BULLOUGH *et al.*, 1955).

The directions of motion of the echoes as shown in Figure 9 were confirmed
by investigations of HARANG and TRÖIM (1961) using a 40 Mc/sec radar with

two fixed aerials pointing in different directions at Kjeller (southern Norway). They found for Kjeller (geomagnetic latitude $\Phi \approx 60°N$) a good correlation between the diurnal variation of the drift motion direction for the echoes and the corresponding diurnal curves of the H and V departures (Figure 8). They also found that the drift motion directions of the visual aurora forms determined from all-sky camera photos (STOFFREGEN, 1961) are closely correlated with the directions of the echoes. Measurements made at Tromsö (northern Norway) close to the auroral zone (identical to those made at Kjeller) did not show a systematic behavior as shown in Figure 9. The lack of a systematic diurnal variation for the drift direction of auroral ionization close to the auroral zone was also confirmed by observations of EGELAND (1961) at Kiruna on 92.8 Mc/sec, and by observations at College (Alaska) by LEADABRAND et al. (1959), working at a frequency of 398 Mc/sec and using the Doppler method for drift studies. They could not find any significant dependence of the drift velocity on the time of day, the range and the type of echo (discrete or diffuse). The east-west velocity was normally found to vary between 0.5 and 1 km/sec, but sometimes amounted to several km/sec. North-south drift velocity comparable with the east-west one has only been observed occasionally.

Besides the measurement of the drift motion of the auroral ionization with the pulse-radar method, the motion can also be determined by Doppler shift measurements. Investigations using methods of this kind have been employed by BOWLES (1952, 1954), McNAMARA (1955), NICHOLS (1957), BLEVIS (1958), LEADABRAND et al. (1959), and PRESNELL et al. (1959). BOWLES (1954) found that the drift motions obtained with the Doppler method were only slightly correlated with the velocity measured with the pulse-radar method at the same moment. That means that the scattering centers affecting the Doppler shift have a different velocity from that of the bulk of the ionization. The motion of the latter one is probably dependent on the motion of the ionizing beam. It is, however, not clear why the same motion is not measured by the Doppler method.

The drift velocities mentioned above — amounting to several km/sec in the auroral latitudes — cannot possibly be a real mass velocity (wind). The close correlation between auroral ionization motion and geomagnetic disturbances in subauroral latitudes, as shown in Figure 9 and also confirmed by observations in North America (LYON et al., 1958; NICHOLS, 1959) and New Zealand (UNWIN 1959a, b), points to the fact that the motion is obviously due to electric fields which drive currents in the ionosphere.

As already mentioned, two types of auroral radar echoes were found to exist: discrete and diffuse. The discrete type of echo resembles the shape of the transmitted pulse. The diffuse type of echo is spread in range and has a triangular shape. The discrete echoes do not change in range as a function of elevation angle of the radar beam. The reason for this is the fact that they obviously arise from ionization aligned along the magnetic field but limited in latitude, or transverse to the field as shown in Figure 10. The diffuse echoes, however, give a changing range as a function of elevation angle of the radar beam. These echoes are, therefore, interpreted as arising from field-aligned scatter regions,

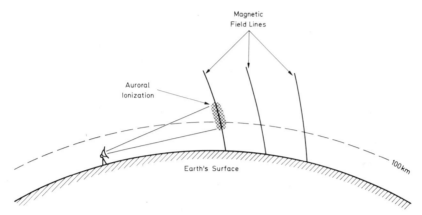

FIGURE 10. Shape of auroral ionization resulting in a discrete auroral echo. After LEADA-BRAND (1965a).

but from ionization which was quite extensive in a latitude-like layer as shown in Figure 11. The aspect sensitivity of the two types appears to be quite similar. The plane-view configuration of the discrete echo would resemble an auroral

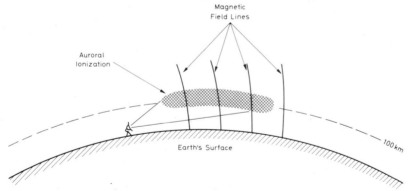

FIGURE 11. Shape of auroral ionization resulting in a diffuse auroral echo. After LEADABRAND (1965a).

arc. The diffuse echo would resemble a layer of auroral ionization. As already mentioned the discrete echo appears to be predominantly a nighttime phenomenon and the diffuse echo a daytime phenomenon. That is, the diffuse echo seems to occur when the reflection region is sunlit.

C. Seasonal Variations

The seasonal influence on the diurnal frequency variation is shown in Figure 12. As may be seen from this figure the afternoon maximum is later in winter than in summer in subauroral latitudes, and the early evening minimum is later and less pronounced in winter than in summer. The results shown in Figure 12, reduced from amateur radio observations, were confirmed by radar in-

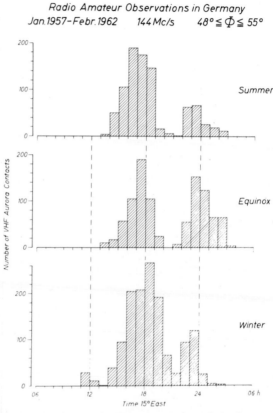

FIGURE 12. Seasonal influence on the diurnal variation of the frequency of VHF bistatic auroral backscatter communications (auroral contacts). Same observational data as in Figure 5. After LANGE-HESSE (1963a).

vestigations in New Zealand (UNWIN, 1966), Germany (SPRENGER, 1961; SPRENGER *et al.*, 1964), and Russia (YARIN, 1960, 1961) at subauroral latitudes. For seasonal influence on the diurnal frequency variation in auroral latitudes see Section 6A.

The seasonal variation of the frequency of occurrence of VHF bistatic aurora backscatter communications is shown in Figure 13. The echo occurrence is greatest during equinox and the autumn maximum is higher than the spring maximum. The variation in Figure 13 has close similarity with the monthly frequency distribution for visual aurora in subauroral regions given by MEINEL *et al.* (1954). The seasonal variation of the radio echo occurrence with peaks

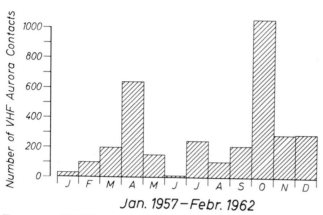

FIGURE 13. Frequency of VHF bistatic auroral backscatter communications (auroral contacts) during the months of the year. Same observational data as in Figure 5. After LANGE-HESSE (1963a).

during the equinoctial months has also been reported by CURRIE *et al.* (1953), BOOKER *et al.* (1955), BULLOUGH *et al.* (1955), DYCE (1955b), FRICKER *et al.* (1957), COLLINS *et al.* (1959), HARANG *et al.* (1961), WATKINS (1961), SPRENGER *et al.* (1964), and UNWIN (1966).

7. Influence of Geomagnetic Activity Degree on the Probability of Occurrence

A. Influence on the Diurnal Variation

The diurnal variation of the echo frequency in subauroral latitudes shows two maxima, one before and one around or after midnight (Figure 5). This result has been confirmed by all investigations at geomagnetic latitudes Φ < 58° (Fig. 7), POGORELOV (1958), GARTLEIN *et al.* (1960), BHATTACHARYYA (1960), YARIN (1960, 1961), WATKINS (1961), SPRENGER *et al.* (1964), UNWIN (1966). The observational data used for Figure 5 includes all observations without consideration of the simultaneous level of geomagnetic activity. For the diurnal variation curves in Figure 14, however, the observational data are arranged according to the simultaneous planetary geomagnetic indices K_p (for details about the K_p-indices see BARTELS, 1957). If one excludes the curve for $K_p = 7$ in Figure 14, it can be seen that the later maximum around midnight increases as K_p increases, and for strong disturbances ($K_p = 9$) it approaches

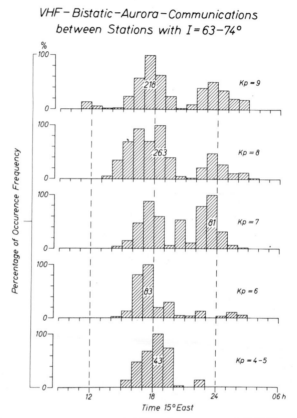

FIGURE 14. Diurnal variation of the probability of occurrence of VHF bistatic auroral back-scatter communications for different degrees of planetary geomagnetic activity K_p. The number in the 100% column of each diagram gives the number of auroral communications which corresponds to 100%.

the amplitude of the late afternoon maximum. This result is in complete agreement with radar results from New Zealand (UNWIN, 1966). The curve for $K_p = 7$ in Figure 14 was strongly influenced by a very large number of auroral backscatter communications during the magnetic storm of October 28/29, 1961 when there was a radio amateur contest in Europe, which means that on these days the number of observing amateur radio stations was very high (LANGE-HESSE, 1963 b). This curve therefore is not representative for the average diurnal variation for $K_p = 7$.

B. Influence of Geomagnetic Latitude

The influence of K_p on the frequency of occurrence of VHF bistatic auroral backscatter communications is shown in Figure 15 for subauroral latitudes. The highest probability is during $K_p = 8$ and 9; it decreases remarkably with decreasing K_p degree. During $K_p = 0$–3, no backscatter communications were observed. Note that the number of observed K_p indices increases with decreasing K_p. By taking account of this fact, the probability of occurrence of back-

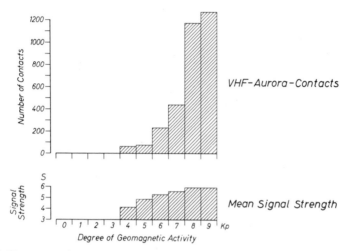

Radio Amateur Observations in Germany
Jan. 1957 – Febr. 1962   144 Mc/s $48° \leqq \Phi \leqq 55°$

FIGURE 15. Frequency of VHF bistatic auroral communications (auroral contacts) as well as variation of mean signal strength S of the auroral-backscattered signals as a function of the degree of the planetary geomagnetic activity K_p. Same observational data as in Figure 5. After LANGE-HESSE (1963a).

scatter communications decreases very strongly with decreasing K_p. The results shown in Figure 15 are confirmed by radar observations at about the same geomagnetic latitude (SPRENGER *et al.*, 1964).

The observational data used for Figure 15 (published in detail by LANGE-HESSE, 1963 b) are not arranged according to the geomagnetic latitude Φ nor magnetic dip I of the stations getting in contact via auroral backscatter. In order to investigate the latitude influence, the net of observing stations in Figure 4 was divided into five zones, A, B, C, D, E (Figure 16, right), according to the dip angle I of the observing stations. Zone A is the most southern one with dip angles I ranging from 63–66°. It covers the region of northern France, southern Germany, Austria, and Czechoslovakia. Zone E is the most northern one with dip angles ranging from 72–74°. It covers the region from southern

Finland via southern Norway to the region north of Scotland. The division
into zones of equal dip angle was made since the reduction of the IGY visual
auroral observations has shown that the lines of equal auroral frequency
(isochasm) follow closer to the lines of equal dip angle (isoclines) than to the
parallels of geomagnetic latitudes (GARTLEIN et al., 1959).

The left part of Figure 16 shows the influence of the K_p-index on the probability of occurrence of VHF bistatic auroral backscatter communications for
communications from stations in zone B (dark zone in the figure) to stations
in zones A, B, C, D, and E. The upper diagram in Figure 16, left, shows the
K_p influence on the communication frequency from stations in zone B to E

VHF – Bistatic – Aurora – Communications
from Stations with I = 66 – 69° to:

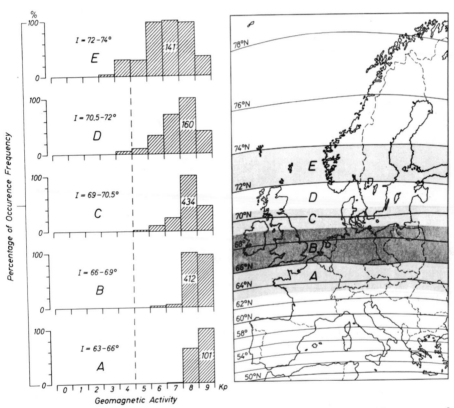

FIGURE 16. Influence of planetary geomagnetic activity K_p on the probability of occurrence of
VHF bistatic auroral backscatter communications for communications from stations in
zone B (dark zone in the Figure, dip angle I = 66–69°) to stations in zones A, B, C, D, and E
according to amateur observations on 144–146 Mc/sec from 1957 to the beginning of 1963;
after LANGE-HESSE (1964 a). The number in the 100% column of each diagram (A–E) gives the
number of auroral communication which corresponds to 100%.

(the most northern one) and the lowest diagram A the K_p influence on the communication frequency from stations in zone B to A (the most southern one). The highest occurrence freqency of auroral communication has been made to 100% in every diagram of Figure 16. In the upper diagram E the highest frequency of 100% (which occurs at $K_p = 7$) corresponds to 141 auroral contacts. In the lower diagram A the highest frequency of 100% (which occurs at $K_p = 9$) corresponds to 101 auroral communications. 100% does not mean in these cases that auroral communication is possible during 24 hr of the day, but only the highest probability of occurrence. This type of standardization makes it easier to compare the different diagrams in Figure 16.

According to the upper diagram E in Figure 16, the highest communication probability occurs at $K_p = 6$–8 with the maximum at $K_p = 7$. At $K_p = 4$ and 5, auroral contacts are possible with about 30% of the maximum occurrence frequency. During geomagnetic quiet conditions, $K_p = 0$–2, no communications are possible. The maximum frequency of aurora communications shifts from $K_p = 7$ in diagram E to higher K_p values as one moves to the more southern zones D, C, B, and A. The highest frequency of auroral communications from zone B to A (the most southern one) occurs at $K_p = 9$. Auroral communications between stations within zone B and from stations in zone B to stations in zone A are nearly impossible during $K_p = 6$ and 7, contrary to contacts from stations in zone B to stations in zone E, which are possible with maximal probability during these two K_p degrees. The results shown in Figure 16 can be interpreted as a shift of the backscattering centers to southern latitudes with increasing K_p degree similar to the southward movement of visual auroral displays and of the S_D-current system (CHAPMAN et al., 1940) with increasing geomagnetic activity. For details about the southward movement of the visual aurora see, e.g., LANGE-HESSE (1960) and AKASOFU (1964).

The correlation between the probability of auroral echo occurrence on 92.8 Mc/sec and polar geomagnetic activity degree Q at Kiruna (Sweden) close to the auroral zone is shown in Figure 17. The method of representation in this figure is similar to that in Figure 16. In Figure 17, however, the activity degree Q (after BARTEL et al., 1956) is used. The Q index is defined only for the H-component at observatories near the auroral zone down to $\Phi \approx 58°$. The scale for Q is the same as for $K(0, 1, 2, \ldots, 9)$, but Q is defined for a 15 min–interval, and K and K_p are defined for a 3 hr–interval (BARTELS, 1957). Starting from $Q = 6$ in Figure 17, the probability of echo occurrence decreases with declining magnetic activity. At $Q = 6$, the maximum of echo occurrence is observed (in Figure 16E at $K_p = 7$). Auroral echoes were recorded more than 96% of the time at this Q value. When the Q index increases to more than 7, the auroral echoes almost invariably disappeared. If this is interpreted as the cause of the southward shift of the backscatting centers, the results from Figure 17 coincide well with those from Figure 16. During strong polar cap absorption events the disappearance of auroral echoes can also be caused by absorp-

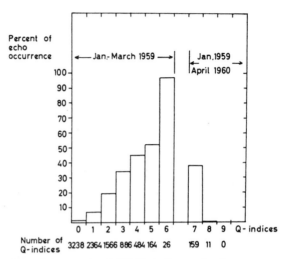

FIGURE 17. Correlation between the probability of auroral echo occurrence and polar geo-magnetic activity degree Q at Kiruna (Sweden) close to the auroral zone; after EGELAND *et al.* (1961).

tion in the D-region. The southward shift of the auroral ionization during increased magnetic activity and a lessening of the backscatter activity well north of the auroral zone are also confirmed by radar investigations by LEONARD (1961) in Alaska.

II. COMPARISON OF THE OBSERVATIONS WITH A THEORETICAL MODEL

1. Introduction

In this section the observations of VHF bistatic auroral backscatter communications described in Part I are compared with those computed according to a special theoretical model. First the geometry of the propagation paths for that kind of communication as well as the geographical location of the back-scattering centers are computed for fixed pairs of stations. Then comparisons with experimental results are carried out in order to see whether the computed geographical location of the backscattering centers coincides with the observed visual aurora. In addition to this the maximum beeline distances which can be contacted by this kind of communication are computed for selected stations and represented by curves. The computed maximum-possible-distances are compared with experimental observations. Finally the influences of special geophysical phenomena on the variation of these maximum-distance-curves are investigated. Geophysical phenomena of this kind are a) radio meteorological influences on the geometry of the propagation path or b) variations of the magnetic dip angle in connection with strong geomagnetic storms, and c) variations of the height (above the ground) of the backscattering centers. The computed distance variations are compared in some cases with experimental observations.

The geometry of the propagation path for VHF bistatic auroral backscatter communications is shown for the vertical direction in Figure 3 and for the horizontal direction in Figure 4. Compared with these figures the following Figure 18 gives a more detailed representation of the propagation path. As already mentioned in Section I, optimum conditions are given for the possibility of VHF auroral backscatter communications according to the theory (BOOKER, 1956, extended to bistatic backscatter echoes by EGELAND, 1962b) if the relation $\cos \Omega_0 + \cos \Omega_1 = 0$ is fulfilled at the point of the backscattering center (labeled P_h in Figure 18).

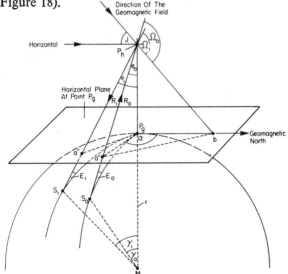

FIGURE 18. Geometry of the propagation path for bistatic VHF auroral backscatter communication between the two points S_0 and S_1; P_h, backscattering center; P_g, projection of P_h on the ground; R_0, R_1, distance between transmitter s_0 and receiver s_1, respectively, and the backscattering center P_h; E_0, E_1, elevation angle above the horizontal, e_0, e_1, angle between the vector of the wave-normal k_0 and k_1, respectively, and the projetction line from P_h to the ground; J, magnetic dip angle; T Ω_0, Ω_1, propagation angle = angle between the direction of radio wave propagation and the magnetic lines of force; α, angle between geomagnic north and the projection of the direction of radio wave propagation on the tangent plane in P_g; r, earth radius.

2. Computation of the Location of the Backscattering Centers

On the map of Europe (Figure 19) the solid curves at the left represent the location where the line of sight from London in different directions intersects the geomagnetic lines of force at constant angles at the height of 110 km. This is about the mean observed height of the backscattering centers (see e.g. UNWIN *et al.*, 1957; UNWIN, 1959a; BARBER *et al.*, 1962; LEADABRAND *et al.*, 1965). In Figure 19 the curves are shown for an angle of intersection of 88°, 90°, and 92°. The curves were computed with the help of an electronic computer using magnetic dip angle and declination from the ground (description of the method in MILLMAN, 1959 and EGELAND, 1962b). The calculation of the curves was restricted to elevation angles E_0, E_1 (Figure 18) greater than or equal to zero for the line of sight to 110 km height. The dotted curves to the right in Figure 19 show the same as the solid curves to the left but referred to Wolszyn (Poland). It can be seen in the figure that the curves intersect each other. For the two locations, London and Wolszyn, the ideal backscatter condition cos Ω_0 + cos Ω_1 = 0 or ϵ_0 = ϵ_1 (Figures 3 and 18) is fulfilled along the dashed line in Figure 19 for elevation angles E_0, E_1 (Figures 3 and 18) of the wave-normal with the ground greater than or equal to zero. As one can see in Figure 19, the dashed line connects the points of intersection of a) the 88°–London curve with the 92°–Wolszyn curve, b) the 92°–London curve with the 88°–Wolszyn curve, and c) the 90°–London and –Wolszyn curves.

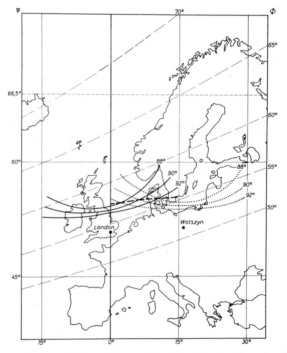

FIGURE 19. Curves of constant intersection angle between the direction of radio wave propagation and the magnetic lines of force at the 110 km height level for the two points London (————) and Wolszyn (Poland) (· · · · ·). The dashed line represents the location at the 110 km height level where the "ideal backscatter conditions" cos Ω_0 + cos Ω_1 = O, or ϵ_0 = ϵ_1 (Figures 3 and 18) are fulfilled for bistatic auroral backscatter communications from London to Wolszyn; φ = geographic latitude, Φ = geomagnetic latitude. After LANGE-HESSE *et al.* (1965).

The locations where the ideal backscatter conditions (as shown in Figure 19) are fulfilled at 110 km height is shown in Figure 20 for the two points Oslo and Aberdeen. If auroral communication occurs between these points, an aurora

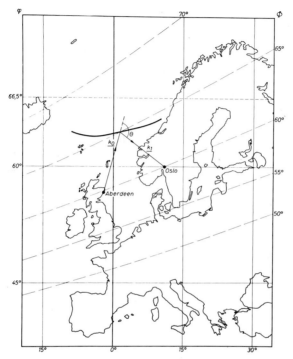

FIGURE 20. Geometry in the horizontal direction for VHF bistatic auroral backscatter communications between the two points, Aberdeen and Oslo. The solid curve at about $\Phi \approx 65°$ (called "backscatter curve") represents the location at the 110 km height level where the ideal backscatter conditions (Figure 19) are fulfilled, this means where aurora (and simultaneously, auroral ionization) must be located in case of the occurrence of auroral backscatter communication between Aberdeen and Oslo; θ angle between the wave normals of the incident and reflected wave, φ geographic latitude, Φ geomagnetic latitude. After LANGE-HESSE et al. (1965).

(and simultaneously, auroral ionization) must occur at the same time at one point along the solid curve in the figure. The solid curve in Figure 20 leads from the geomagnetic latitude $\Phi \approx 68°$ in the west to $\Phi \approx 64°$ in the east.

The backscattered power also depends on the angle $\ominus$ between the two wave-normals k_0, k_1 of the incident and reflected wave (Figure 20). $\ominus$ can vary between $\ominus = 180°$ (radar case, the two points fit together, Figure 1) and small values of $\ominus$ (forward-scatter case). The backscattered power varies in these extreme cases according to the theory in a ratio of about one to two.

The map of Europe in Figure 21 represents three different curves. The ideal backscatter conditions as described before are fulfilled along these curves for the pairs of stations specified in the figure text. These curves are referred to as "backscatter curves" in the following. The most northern solid backscatter curve refers to communications from Hamburg to Oslo and the most southern dotted backscatter curve refers to communications from Hamburg to London. Figure 22 represents similar backscatter curves as shown in Figure 21 but for

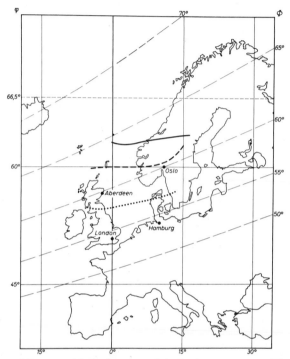

FIGURE 21. Map of Europe with the location of the backscatter curves (Figure 20) for VHF bistatic auroral backscatter communication between the pairs of stations specified below. Height level = 110 km. a) solid curve: Hamburg-Oslo; b) dashed curve: Hamburg-Aberdeen; c) dotted curve: Hamburg-London; φ geographic latitude, Φ geomagnetic latitude. After LANGE-HESSE et al. (1965).

other pairs of stations specified in the figure text. The most northern solid back-scatter curve in Figure 22 refers to communications from Hamburg to Oslo, and the most southern dotted backscatter curve refers to communications from Munich to Mannheim (southwest Germany).

3. Relation to the Location of the Visual Aurora Display

From the observed data reported by radio amateurs (LANGE-HESSE, 1963b), it follows that, e.g., on October 28, 1961 at about 2200 UT, VHF bistatic auroral backscatter communications were possible from Hamburg to Oslo, Stockholm, Aberdeen (Scotland), and Vaernamo (southern Sweden) as well as

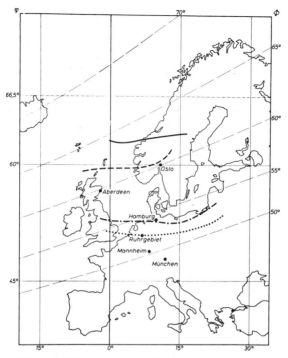

FIGURE 22. Map of Europe with the location of the backscatter curves (Figure 20) for VHF bistatic auroral backscatter communications between the pairs of stations specified below. Height level = 110 km. ——— Hamburg-Oslo; – – – – – – – Ruhr District-Aberdeen; – · – · – Munich-Ruhr District; · · · · · · Munich-Mannheim; φ, geographic latitude; Φ, geomagnetic latitude. After LANGE-HESSE et al. (1966).

from the Ruhr District to Aberdeen. The computed backscatter curves for the pairs of stations mentioned by name before are represented in Figure 23. The location of the auroral display observed simultaneously is also represented in Figure 23 in a manner of representation explained in the figure. It can be seen that at least one part of the backscatter curves shown in the figure coincides with the visual aurora display. The backscattering centers at these parts of the backscatter curves (coinciding with the aurora) have caused the communications between the pairs of stations specified in the text of Figure 23. According to this the backscattering centers which caused the communication from Hamburg to Vaernamo (dotted backscatter curve in Figure 23) were located halfway between north Scotland and southern Norway. At the time of day given in Figure 23, radio amateurs in southern Germany (e.g. in Munich) tried to get VHF communications via auroral backscatters but without success. It follows from Figure 22, however, that the backscatter curves for communications from Munich to Mannheim and to the Ruhr District are located much more to the south than the auroral display in Figure 23. These two curves, therefore, did not coincide with the aurora so that it was impossible to get VHF contacts from Munich via auroral backscatter to Mannheim and to the Ruhr District.

An example similar to that in Figure 23 is shown in Figure 24 for September 4, 1958 at about 2300 UT. The backscatter curves for all auroral backscatter communications observed during that time between pairs of stations specified in the figure text are represented on the map together with the visual auroral display observed simultaneously. It can be seen (as in Figure 23) that at least

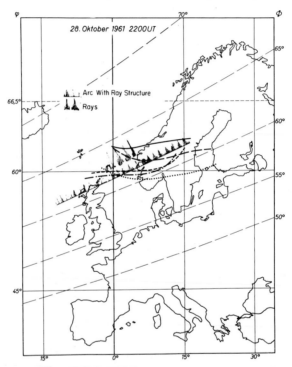

FIGURE 23. Location of the visual auroral display on October 28, 1961 at about 2200 UT ($K_p = 7 +$) and the location of the backscatter curves for the VHF bistatic auroral backscatter communications carried out simultaneously between the following pairs of stations: ———— Hamburg-Oslo; ——— —— Hamburg-Stockholm; — — — — Hamburg-Aberdeen; — · —— Ruhr-District-Aberdeen; · · · · · · Hamburg-Vaernamo; φ, Φ see text Figure 22. After LANGE-HESSE et al. (1966).

one part of the backscatter curves coincides with the visual aurora. In the majority of the cases more than one part of the backscatter curves coincides with the aurora. This is the reason that the backscattered signals come from a variety of directions spread about north during strong auroral activity like that in Figure 24. At the time given in Figure 24 it was impossible to get auroral backscatter communications from Hamburg to Oslo and Stockholm. The reason for this is the fact that the relevant backscatter curves (Figures 21 and 22) are located more to the north than the visual aurora (Figure 24) so that it was not possible for the aurora and the backscatter curves to intersect.

The geophysical events described in Figure 23 were accompanied by a degree of geomagnetic activity of $K_p = 7+$, the events described in Figure 24 by $K_p = 8+$, and the visual auroral displays are located at lower latitudes than the displays in Figure 23. This southward shift of the visual aurora with increasing

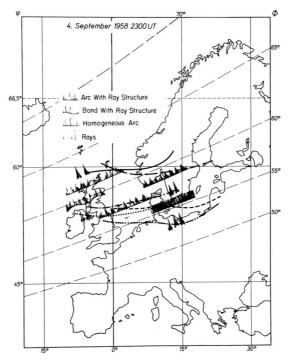

FIGURE 24. Location of the visual aurora display on September 4, 1958 at about 2300 UT ($K_p = 8+$) and the location of the backscatter curves for the VHF bistatic aurora backscatter communications carried out simultaneously between the following pairs of stations: ——— Ruhr District-Aberdeen; —— —— Hamburg-Vaernamo; — — — Hamburg-Munich; — · — Hamburg-London; — · · —München-Ruhr District; · · · · · · Ruhr District-London; φ, Φ see text Figure 22. After LANGE-HESSE et al. (1966).

K_p-degree is known (see, e.g., LANGE-HESSE, 1960; AKASOFU, 1964). The simultaneous shift of the backscattering centers to the south can also be seen from the results shown in Figures 16 and 17. Additional examples as shown in Figures 23 and 24 had been compiled by CZECHOWSKY (1966), but because of limited space it is not possible to publish them here.

Figure 22 shows the most northern (solid) and the most southern (dotted) possible backscatter curve for the net of amateur stations which contributed to the observations (published by LANGE-HESSE, 1963b). The most northern curve (Hamburg-Oslo) has a latitude extension up to $\Phi \approx 64°$ geomagnetic latitude and the most southern curve (Munich-Mannheim) an extension down to $\Phi \approx 51°$. According to the results shown in Figures 23 and 24, it is possible later to reconstruct from the observations mentioned before the location of the visual auroral displays to a first approximation for overcast and foggy days in a region which is covered by the backscatter curves belonging to the net of observing stations. Maps with more backscatter curves (additional to those shown in Figures 21 and 22) are given by CzECHOWSKY (1966) for Middle European, British, and southern Scandinavian regions.

4. Maximum Distance for Bistatic Auroral Backscatter Communications

The three curves shown in Figure 25 represent the computed maximum distances which can be contacted by VHF bistatic auroral backscatter communications from Hamburg (dotted curve), Stockholm (dashed curve), and Oslo (solid curve). The curves are valid for a height of the backscattering centers of 110 km above the ground. The following assumptions are made for the computation of the curves:

a) At the place of the receiver and the transmitter, it must be possible to receive and to radiate the waves in the critical case with an elevation angle $E_0 = E_1 = 0$ (Figures 3 and 18).
b) Only those directions of propagation of the backscattered waves are taken into consideration which fulfill the ideal backscatter condition. That means

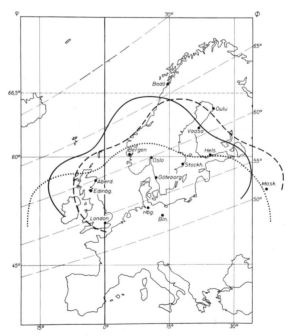

FIGURE 25. Computed maximum-distance-curves for VHF bistatic auroral backscatter communications from Oslo (————), Stockholm (— — —), and Hamburg ($\cdot \cdot \cdot \cdot \cdot$). Adopted height above the ground of the backscattering center $h = 110$ km. φ, Φ, see text Figure 22. After LANGE-HESSE et al. (1966).

$\cos \Omega_0 + \cos \Omega_1 = 0$ or $\epsilon_0 = \epsilon_1$ (Figures 3 and 18). According to the theoretical estimations mentioned in Section I, the ideal backscatter conditions must be fulfilled for communications with low power transmitters (the power used by radio amateurs is of the order of 50–100 W) in order to have sufficient signal strength at the receiving point.

c) The maximum backscattered energy propagates from the backscattering center (labeled P_h in Figure 18) along the (convex) surface of a cone with an (opening) angle of $90° - \epsilon$ (Figure 3). The axis of the cone is the z-axis in Figure 3, which is the tangent to the magnetic field line at P_h.

If the surface of the cone intersects the earth, this intersection curve then defines on the ground the maximum distance in case of a radiation of the waves from the transmitter with an elevation angle $E_0 = 0$. If one computes these intersection curves for nearly all the backscattering centers then the envelope of these curves describes the maximum-distance-curve shown in Figure 25 (for three different stations).

In supplement to Figure 25, the curves shown in Figure 26 represent the computed maximum-distance-curves for Munich for the two heights of the backscattering centers of 110 and 200 km. The dots in Figure 26 represent stations

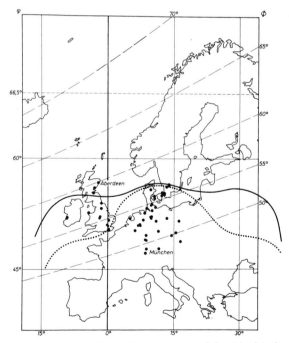

FIGURE 26. Similar curves as in Figure 25 but computed for Munich for the two adopted heights $h = 110$ km (————) and $h = 200$ km ($\cdot\;\cdot\;\cdot\;\cdot\;\cdot$) of the backscattering center. The dots represent stations which could be contacted from Munich via VHF auroral backscatter communications. φ, Φ, see text Figure 22. After LANGE-HESSE et al. (1966).

which could be contacted from Munich via VHF auroral backscatter communication. A few of these stations were contacted from Munich more than once. If these recurring contacts are taken into consideration by corresponding (statistical) weights, only 5% of the total number of contacts were carried out with stations located outside the maximum-distance-curve for 110 km height, but 30% of the contacts were carried out with stations located outside the 200 km curve (dotted curve in Figure 26). It follows from the results represented in Figure 26 that the computed maximum distances for a height of the backscattering centers at 110 km coincide to a first approximation with the observations.

LEADABRAND and YABROFF (1958) have computed similar curves as shown in Figures 25 and 26 for some points in North America but using the basic magnetic elements from the geomagnetic dipole field which is only a first approximation to the true geomagnetic field. The curves in Figures 25 and 26, however, are computed using the observed magnetic dip angle and the declination from the ground. LEADABRAND and YABROFF (1958) have also computed for each maximum-distance-curve the appertaining "region of useful

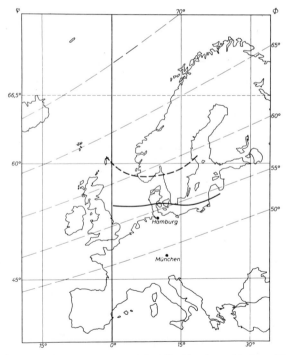

FIGURE 27. Location of the backscatter curves (described in Figure 21) for VHF bistatic auroral backscatter communications from Munich to Hamburg for the two adopted heights $h = 110$ km (————) and $h = 200$ km ($\cdot\ \cdot\ \cdot\ \cdot\ \cdot$) of the backscattering centers. φ, Φ see text Figure 22. After LANGE-HESSE et al. (1966).

ionization," a region of approximate semicircular shape which must be covered by auroral ionization in order to get communication to every point within the maximum-distance-curve.

5. Probable Reasons for the Maximum Distance Variations

A. Influence of Height Variations of the Backscattering Centers

Backscatter curves for communications from Munich to Hamburg for the two heights, 110 km (solid curve) and 200 km (dashed curve), of the back-scattering centers are shown in Figure 27. The backscatter curve for 200 km is located more to the north than the 110 km curve. The maximum-distance-curve (Figure 26), however, shows smaller distances for the 200 km than for the 110 km scatter height. The reason for this is that the propagation angle (Figures 3 and 18) increases with increasing height (Figure 28). Therefore, it becomes

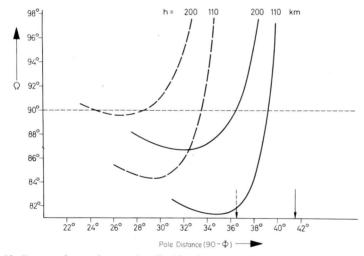

FIGURE 28. Propagation angle Ω (as described in Figures 3 and 18) as a function of the magnetic pole distance angle $(90° - \Phi)$, Φ geomagnetic latitude, for two different heights $h = 110$ km and $h = 200$ km referred to München (———) and Hamburg (— — —). The location of these towns is indicated by arrows on the horizontal scale; dashed arrow refers to Hamburg. After LANGE-HESSE et al. (1966).

more difficult to fulfill the ideal backscatter condition $\cos \Omega_0 + \cos \Omega_1 = 0$ with increasing height for definite regions. This causes the reduction of the maximum distance with increasing height of the backscattering centers. The observed increase of the maximum distance for 5% of the observations carried out at Munich (Figure 26), therefore, cannot be caused by an increase of the height of the scatter centers.

It is known that in middle latitudes the frequency of occurrence of aurora in-

creases with increasing geomagnetic latitude. If one considers aurora backscatter communications between two fixed stations (e.g. Hamburg and Munich
in Figure 27), the backscatter curve shifts to the north with increasing height of
the scatter centers (Figure 27). Because of this, the curves move into a region of
higher aurora probability which in turn causes a higher probability of the occurrence of aurora backscatter communications. The conclusion from this behavior is that an increase of the height of the backscattering centers causes a
reduction of the maximum distance and, indeed, an increase of the probability
of occurrence of bistatic auroral backscatter communications.

B. Influence of Magnetic Dip Angle Variations

All of the propagation angles, backscatter, and maximum-distance-curves
shown in the figures of this paper are computed using the assumption of an undisturbed geomagnetic field or for the "static situation." It is well known that
during geomagnetic storms the components of the geomagnetic field, H and Z,
as well as the declination D can deviate very much from their normal values on
geomagnetic quiet days. The H-component usually shows the largest deviations;
they are known to exceed 1000 γ near the auroral zone. The deviations are
caused by the superposition of an additional magnetic field which results from
an electric current system in the ionospheric E-layer along the auroral zone.
The above mentioned deviations also cause a variation of the magnetic dip
angle J. The geometrical situation corresponding to this dip variation is represented in detail in Figure 29. In this figure the z-axis is tangent to the geomag-

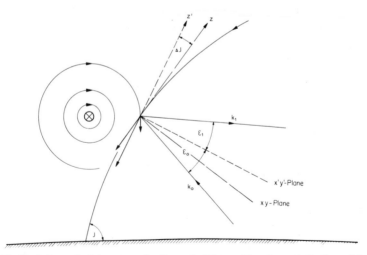

FIGURE 29. Variation ΔJ of the magnetic dip angle J (caused by the perturbation of the magnetic field of an electric current in the ionosphere) and the simultaneous variation of the backscatter conditions (determined by the angle of incidence and backscatter ϵ_0 and ϵ_1 referred to
the xy-and $x'y'$-plane, respectively) for the propagation path given by the wave-normal vectors
k_0 and k_1. See also Figure 3. After LANGE-HESSE et al. (1966).

netic field at the point of the backscattering center (labeled P_h in Figure 18), and the xy-plane is perpendicular to the z-axis. If a pair of stations (with low power transmitters) get in contact with each other, the ideal backscatter condition $\epsilon_0 = \epsilon_1$ (Figures 29 and 3) must be fulfilled for the propagation path with the wave normal vectors k_0 and k_1. If the geometry of a propagation path deviates from this condition no communication will be possible along this path (in case of a low power transmitter). In connection with a variation ΔJ of the dip angle J^* and the simultaneous variation of the direction of the z-axis and the xy-plane (caused by the perturbation-magnetic field of a current system, Figure 29) the ideal backscatter condition may be fulfilled for propagation paths which do not normally fulfill this condition under undisturbed geomagnetic conditions (Figure 29). The propagation path for the communication Munich-Aberdeen deviates from the ideal backscatter condition by 1.3°. For this special case it is computed, that a ΔJ of 1° will result in the exact fulfillment of the ideal backscatter condition $\epsilon_0 = \epsilon_1$ (Figure 29) for this pair of stations. It follows from a simple consideration, that dip variations of this order can occur. From

$$\text{Tan } J' = \frac{Z_0 + 3\Delta Z}{H_0 + \frac{2}{3}\Delta H}$$

it follows that the perturbation vector components $\Delta Z = \pm 350 \, \gamma$ and $\Delta H = \pm 750 \, \gamma$ are sufficient to give a variation ΔJ of the order of 1°. In the above mentioned formula the factors 3 and 2/3 have to be included because of the induction field in the ground (according to AKASOFU, 1960). Therefore, two thirds of the horizontal and the threefold of the vertical perturbation vector component must be added to the normal static field in order to obtain the true varied dip angle. The factor 3 and 2/3 are effective under the condition that the S_D-current system has a height above the ground between 100 and 160 km. Variations of the dip angle of 3–4° were observed by STÖRMER (1926) during strong geomagnetic storms as has already been mentioned in Section I of this paper. The auroral backscatter communications from Munich to stations beyond the maximum-distance-curve in Figure 26 (110 km) were carried out during times when the magnetic perturbation components ΔZ and ΔH showed values which caused dip angle variations of 1° or more according to the above formula. The dip angle variation, therefore, provides a possible explanation of the communications beyond the computed maximum distances.

C. Radio Meteorological Influences

The computation of the propagation paths for bistatic aurora backscatter communications in the preceding figures was carried out using the assumption of straight line propagation in the atmosphere. For frequencies above 30 Mc/sec it is, however, necessary to take into consideration the refracting influence of the lower atmosphere (troposphere) in cases of low elevation angles E (Figures

*The letters I and J are used for the magnetic dip angle in this paper.

3 and 18). Low elevation angles $0° \leqq E \leqq 3°$ are necessary in order to carry out long distance auroral backscatter communications. The special atmospheric data in those days when the long distance communications exceeding the maximum-distance-curve (110 km) in Figure 26 were carried out result in a maximal-distance-extension of $F_{ges} = 140$ km (Figure 30). The shift of the

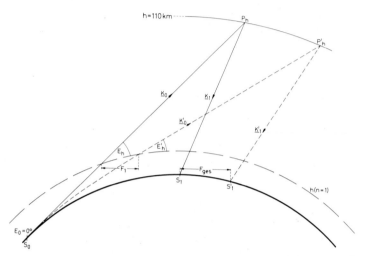

FIGURE 30. Cross-sectional view of the earth with the geometry of the propagation path in vertical direction for VHF bistatic aurora backscatter communication from S_0 via P_h to S_1 in the case of straight line propagation and from S_0 via P'_h to S'_1 in case of deviation by radio meteorological influences in the lower atmosphere (troposphere). F_{ges}: extension of communication distance by radio meteorological influences. For the significance of the other abbreviations, see text of Figures 3 and 18. After LANGE-HESSE et al. (1966).

110 km-maximum-distance-curve for 140 km to the north does not include all of the stations in Figure 26 which could be contacted from Munich, since e.g., Aberdeen is located about 250 km north of the curve. This fact leads to the conclusion that the largest maximum-distance-extensions can only be caused by magnetic dip angle variations.

6. Relation to the S_D-Current System, Plasma Acoustic Wave Theory

The occurrence of auroral displays is accompanied by an auroral current system (S_D-current system) which flows simultaneously along the maximum auroral zone in the ionosphere at about the same height as the E-layer. The magnetic field of this current system is superposed on the normal magnetic field of the earth and causes geomagnetic disturbances (Figure 9) and variations of the dip angle (Figure 29). Several investigations have led to the suggestion that the center of the current system (region of maximum current density) coincides in space with a visual auroral arc (see e.g. HEPPNER, 1958; WEAVER *et al.*, 1960). If this proves to be correct, the backscattering centers also must coincide in space with the center of the current system to a first approximation according to the results shown in Figure 23. This idea was proved by reducing only the amateur observations of VHF bistatic auroral backscatter communications in a manner shown in this paper (LANGE-HESSE *et al.*, 1966).

By comparing the time of the beginning of the auroral backscatter phenomenon with the magnetogram of the horizontal component it can be recognized that the backscattering of the radio waves takes place only when the departures in the magnetograms exceed a fixed value of about 200 γ (Figure 31 and 32), that means that the S_D-current must exceed some threshold value

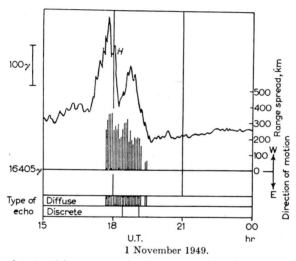

FIGURE 31. Complete trend in geomagnetic disturbance and radar auroral echo characteristics observed with 72 Mc/sec radar equipment at Jodrell Bank Experimental Station. After BULLOUGH *et al.* (1957). Note that the backscattering of radio waves begins only when the departure of the geomagnetic H-component exceeds some threshold value (about 200 γ).

before the field aligned backscattering centers occur. BOWLES *et al.* (1963) have found similar results by comparing the scattered power at 50 Mc/sec from E-region field-aligned equatorial irregularities (seen by EGAN, 1960 and others) with the magnetogram of the horizontal component. The backscattering of the radio waves at the equator also takes place only when the electrojet current along the geomagnetic equator exceeds some threshold value.

Some years ago BUNEMAN (1963) and FARLEY (1963a, b) pointed out independently the possibilities that an ionospheric current system represents a "two-stream" instability described in modern plasma theory. BOWLES *et al.* (1963) applied this concept to explain the existence of field-aligned E-region irregularities at the magnetic equator. BUNEMAN (1963) and BOWLES *et al.*

(1963) have suggested that this theory can also be used to explain the field-aligned auroral ionization irregularities. Buneman has proposed an instability model, in which the instability resulting from the current flow is assumed to

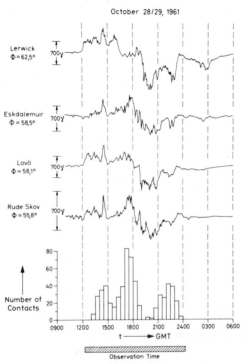

FIGURE 32. Complete daily trend in geomagnetic disturbance characteristics (H-component) at four European Observatories: Lerwick (Shetland Islands), Eskdalemuir (Scotland), Lovö (Sweden), and Rude Skov (Denmark). The lower diagram shows the simultaneous frequency of occurrence of VHF bistatic auroral backscatter communications (auroral contacts) in Middle Europe. Note that (as also shown in Figure 31) the backscattering of radio waves begins at about 1300 UT only when the departure of the geomagnetic H-component exceeds some threshold value. The peaks in geomagnetic departures are accompanied by an simultaneous increase in the occurrence frequency of aurora backscatter communications. Observational data taken from LANGE-HESSE (1963b).

produce "plasma acoustic waves" which are thought to be the immediate cause of the electron density irregularities.

If one again examines Figure 9, it can be seen there that during the reversal of the current system, i.e. when the departure of the H-component is zero (related to the undisturbed H-value) at about 2000 hr and roughly one hour before and later, no backscatter echoes occur. During this time the departure of the H-component is below the threshold value mentioned before which means that the current strength in the ionosphere is too low to produce the field-aligned backscatter electron density irregularities according to the plasma acoustic wave theory. The early evening minimum in the diurnal variation of the occurrence frequency of auroral echoes in subauroral latitudes (shown in Figure 5) might be explained by this theory.

Recently LEADABRAND (1965) has made a comparison between 400 and 800 Mc/sec radar auroral backscatter data. This comparison indicates that although many of the key features of the plasma acoustic wave concept can be found in the radar auroral data, the spectral characteristics of the auroral echoes are much too complicated to be simply understood in their present form. This new plasma acoustic wave theory, therefore, offers much incentive to the radio auroral researcher for further work.

Acknowledgments   The author wishes to express his thanks to Dr. J. Paton of the World Data Centre C (visual aurora), Edinburgh, for the copies from the synoptic aurora maps, European sector, further to many European Magnetic Observatories for copies from the magnetograms, and to the Institute for Radio Meteorology and Marine Meteorology at the University of Hamburg for the radio meteorological data. Finally, the author wishes to express his thanks to many European radio amateurs for the careful and extended observations of VHF bistatic aurora backscatter communications and to the RSGB (Radio Society of Great Britain) and the DARC (German Amateur Radio Club) for collecting the comprehensive observation data. Here again is a good example of amateur radio supplying research information which is difficult and more expensive to obtain in any other way.

Discussion

D region refraction should not be significant for frequencies above 150 mHz but especially at hf such refraction may be important.

Gadsden pointed out that radar backscatter measurements from Boston were compared to airglow observations of the same aurora and no correlation could be found with 3914, 5577, and 6300Å.

References

AKASOFU, S-I. 1960, *J. Atmospheric Terrest. Phys.* **19**, 10–25.
AKASOFU, S.-I., 1964, *J. Atmospheric Terrest. Phys.* **26**, 1167–1174.
APPLETON, E. V., NAISMITH, R., and INGRAM, L. J., 1937, *Phil. Trans. Roy. Soc.* A236, 191–259.
BAGARYATSKY, B. A., 1960, *Spectral Electro-Photometrical and Radar Researches of Aurora and Airglow*, No. 2–3, Pub. House of Acad. of Science of USSR, Moscow, pp. 7–14.
BARBER, D., SCITCLIFFE, H. K., and WATKINS, C. D., 1962, *J. Atmospheric Terrest. Phys* **24**, 599–609.
BARTELS, J., 1938, *Z. Geophys.* **14**, 297–313.
BARTELS, J., 1957, *IGY Annals*, Vol. 4, Pergamon Press, London, 227–236.
BARTELS, J. and FUKUSHIMA, N., 1956, *Abhandlungen Akad. Wiss. Göttingen*, Math. -Phys. Klasse, Sonderheft, No. 3, Verlag Vandenhoek and Ruprecht, Göttingen, Germany. For a review about *Q*, see Bartels (1957).
BHATTACHARYYA, B. K., 1960, *Can. J. Phys.* **38**, 624–637.
BIRFELD, J. G., 1960, Bull (Izvestia) Acad. Sci. USSR, Geophys. Ser., No. 12, 1248–57.
BLEVIS, B. C., 1958, *J. Geophys. Res.* **63**, 867–868.
BLEVIS, B. C., DAY, J. W. B., and ROSCOE, O. S., 1963, *Can. J. Phys.* **41**, 1359–1380.
BOOKER, H. G., 1956, *J. Atmospheric Terrest. Phys.* **8**, 204–221.

BOOKER, H. G., 1960, *Physics of the Upper Atmosphere* (Ed. by J. A. Ratcliffe), Academic Press, New York, 355–375.
BOOKER, H. G., GARTLEIN, C. W., and NICHOLS, B., 1955, *J. Geophys. Res.* **60**, 1–22.
BOWLES, K. L., 1952, *J. Geophys. Res.* **57**, 191–196.
BOWLES, K. L., 1954, *J. Geophys. Res.* **59**, 553–555.
BOWLES, K. L., BALSLEY, B. B., and COHEN, R., 1963, *J. Geophys. Res.* **68**, 2485–2501.
BULLOUGH, K., DAVIDSON, T. W., KAISER, T. R., and WATKINS, C. D., 1957, *J. Atmospheric Terrest. Phys.* **11**, 237–254.
BULLOUGH, K. and KAISER, T. R., 1954, *J. Atmospheric Terrest. Phys.* **5**, 189–200.
BULLOUGH, K. and KAISER, T. R., 1955, *J. Atmospheric Terrest. Phys.* **6**, 198–214.
BUNEMAN, O., 1963, *Phys. Rev. Letters* **10**, 285–287.
BURROWS, C. R. and ATTWOOD, S. S., 1949, *Radio wave propagation*, Academic Press, New York.
CHAMBERLAIN, J. W., 1961, *Physics of the Aurora and Airglow*, Academic Press, New York.
CHAPMAN, S. and BARTELS, J., 1940, *Geomagnetism*, Clarendon Press, Oxford, reprinted. 1951 and 1962.
COLLINS, C. and FORSYTH, P. A., 1959, *J. Atmospheric Terrest. Phys.* **13**, 315–345.
CURRIE, B. W., FORSYTH, P. A., and VAWTER, F. E., 1953, *J. Geophys. Res.* **58**, 179–200.
CZECHOWSKY, P., 1966, Master's Thesis, University of Gottingen, Germany.
DYCE, R., 1955 a, *QST* **39**, (Jan. 1955) 11–15.
DYCE, R., 1955 b, *Trans. Inst. Radio Engrs.*, **AP-3**, 76–80.
DYCE, R., 1955 c, *J. Geophys. Res.* **60**, 317–323.
EGAN, R. D., 1960, *J. Geophys. Res.* **65**, 2343–2358.
EGELAND, A., 1961, Scientific Report No. 7, Kiruna Geophysical Observatory, Kiruna C, Sweden.
EGELAND, A., 1962 a, *Arkiv Geofysik* **4**, 6, 103–169.
EGELAND, A., 1962 b, *Arkiv Geofysik* **4**, 7, 171–209.
EGELAND, A., ORTNER, J., and HULTQVIST, B., 1961, Scientific Report No. 7, Kiruna Geophysical Observatory, Kiruna C. Sweden.
FARLEY, JR., D. T., 1963 a, *Phys. Rev. Letters* **10**, 279–82.
FARLEY, JR., D. T., 1963 b, *J. Geophys. Res.* **68**, 6083–6097.
FELDSTEIN, Y. I., 1963, SBORNIK III, No. 5. "Sbornik" refers to the USSR results of the IGY, published by Akademii Nauk SSSR. Section III deals with Geomagnetism, Section IV, with Aurorae and Airglow.
FLOOD, W. A., 1960, *J. Geophys. Res.* **65**, 2261–2268.
FORSYTH, P. A., 1953, *J. Geophys. Res.* **58**, 53–66.
FORSYTH, P. A. and VOGAN, E. L., 1957, *J. Atmospheric Terrest. Phys.* **10**, 215–228.
FRÄNZ, K. and LASSEN, H., 1956, Antennen und Ausbreitung, 2nd Edition, Springer-Verlag, Berlin.
FRICKER, S. J., INGALLS, R. P., STONE, M. L., and WANG, S. S., 1957, *J. Geophys. Res.* **62**, 527–546.
GARTLEIN, C. W., GARTLEIN, H. E., and SPRAGUE, G., 1959, Report of the IGY World Data Centre IV (a), Cornell University, Ithaca, N. Y.
GARTLEIN, C. W., SPRAGUE, G., and WAAG, R. C., 1960, *J. Geophys. Res.* **65**, 2255–2259.
GERSON, N. C., 1955 a, *Proc. Phys. Soc.* **68**, 408–414.
GERSON, N. C., 1955 b, *J. Atmospheric Terrest. Phys.* **6**, 263–267.
GREEN, F. D., 1961, Radio Studies, Report No. RS-9, Institute of Upper Atmospheric Physics, Univ. of Saskatchewan, Saskatoon, Canada.
GROTH, L. H., ANDERSON, L. J., EASTERBROOK, C. C., and BURDETTE, L. R., 1964, *J. Geophys. Res.* **69**, 194–196.
HARANG, L. and STOFFREGEN, W., 1940, *Hochfreq. u. Elektroak.* **55**, 105–108.
HARANG, L. and STOFFREGEN, W., 1940, *Nature* **142**, 832–833.
HARANG, L. and TRÖIM, J., 1961, *Planetary Space Sci.* **5**, 33–45.
HEPPNER, J. P., 1958, Report No. DR 135 Defence Res. Board, Ottawa, Ontario.
HERLOFSON, N., 1947, *Nature* **160**, 867–868.
HULTQVIST, B., and EGELAND, A., 1964, *Space Science Review* **3**, 27–78.

KAISER, T. R., 1956, *The Airglow and the Aurora* (Ed. by E. B. Armstrong and Dalgarno), Pergamon Press, London.

LANGE-HESSE, G., 1957, *Archiv d. elektr. Übertragung (AEÜ)* 11, 253–261, 283–288.

LANGE-HESSE, G., 1960, *Naturwissenschaften* 47, 423–424.

LANGE-HESSE, G., 1962, *Archiv d. elektr. Übertragung (AEÜ)* 16, 251–261.

LANGE-HESSE, G., 1963 a, *Z. Geophys.* 29, 35–44.

LANGE-HESSE, G., 1963 b, *Abhandlungen der Akademie der Wissenschagten in Gëttingen*, math. -phys. Klasse, Beitrage zum Internationalen Geophysikalischen Jahr, Heft 10, Verlag Vandenhoek and Ruprecht, Göttingen, Germany.

LANGE-HESSE, G., 1964 a, *Archiv d. elektr. Übertragung (AEÜ)* 18, 430–438.

LANGE-HESSE, G., 1964 b, AGARDograph 78 (Ed. by B. Landmark), Pergamon Press, Oxford, pp. 253–262.

LANGE-HESSE, G. and CZECHOWSKY, P., 1965, *Archiv d. elektr. Übertragung (AEÜ)* 19, 511–514.

LANGE-HESSE, G. and CZECHOWSKY, P., 1966, *Archiv d. elekt. Übertragung (AEÜ)* 20, 365–373.

LEADABRAND, R. L., 1962, *J. Phys. Soc. Japan*, 17 (Supp. A-1), 218–222.

LEADABRAND, R. L., 1965, *Auroral Phenomena* (Ed. by M. Walt), Stanford Univ. Press; Oxford Univ. Press, London, pp. 99–129.

LEADABRAND, R. L., DOLPHIN, L. T., and PETERSON, A. M., 1959, *IRE Trans. Antennas Propagation* AP-7, 127–136.

LEADABRAND, R. L. and PETERSON, A. M., 1958, *IRE Trans. Antennas Propagation*, AP-6, 65–79.

LEADABRAND, R. L., SCHLOBOHM, J. C., and BARON, M. J., 1965, *J. Geophys. Res.* 70, 4235–4284.

LEADABRAND, R. L., and YABROFF, I., 1958, *IRE Trans. Antennas Propagation*, January 1958, 80–87.

LEONARD, R. S., 1961, Sci. Rep. No. 9, UAG-R116, University of Alaska, College, Alaska.

LITTLE, C. G., RAYTON, W. M., and ROOF, R. B., 1956, *Proc. I.R.E.* 44, 992.

LOVELL, A. C. B., CLEGG, J. A., and ELLYETT, C. D., 1947, *Nature* 160, 372–373.

LYON, G. F. and KAVADAS, A., 1958, *Can. J. Phys.* 36, 1661–1671.

MCNAMARA, A. G., 1955, *J. Geophys. Res.* 60, 257–269.

MEINEL, A. B., NEGAARD, B. J., and CHAMBERLAIN, B. J., 1954, *J. Geophys. Res.* 59, 407–413.

MILLMAN, G. H., 1959, *J. Geophys. Res.* 64, 717–726.

MOORE, R. K., 1951, *J. Geophys. Res.* 56, 97–106, *QST 35*, 14 (June 1951); and *QST 23*, 78 (May 1939), author unknown.

NEWTON, C., 1966, part I, *RSGB-Bulletin* (Journal of the Radio Society of Great Britain) 42, 289–294, 785–790.

NICHOLS, B., 1957, *J. Atmospheric Terrest. Phys.* 11, 292–293.

NICHOLS, B., 1959, *Proc. I.R.E.*, 47, 245–254.

OKSMAN, J., 1964, *Ann. Acad. Sci. Fennicae* A VI. Physica 169, 1–16 (Helsinki).

OKSMAN, J., 1966 a, *Geophysia* (Helsinki) 9, 3, 235–250.

OKSMAN, J., 1966 b, *Kleinheubacher Berichte*, Fernmeldetechnisches Zentralamt, F. Gr. Vc, Darmstdat, Germany, 10

PETERSON, A. M., 1960, *The Radio Noise Spectrum* (Ed. by Donald H. Menzel), Harvard Univ. Press, Cambridge, Mass.

Pogorelov, V. I., 1958, Bull. (IZV.) Ser, Geofiz, No. 8, 1048, Akad. Nauk, SSSR.

PRESNELL, R. I., LEADABRAND, A. M., PETERSON, A. M., DYCE, R. B., SCHLOBOHM, J. C., and BERG, M. R., 1959, *J. Geophys. Res.* 64, 1179–1190.

SMITH-ROSE, R. L., 1960, *RSGB-Bulletin* (Journal of the Radio Society of Great Britain) 35, 392–394.

SPRENGER, K., 1961, *Forsch. Fortsch.* 35, 161 (Akademie-Verlag, Berlin).

SPRENGER, K. and GLÖDE, P., 1964, *J. Atmospheric Terrest. Phys.* 26, 193–198.

STÖRMER, C., 1926, *Geofys. Publikasjoner* 4, No. 7, Oslo.

STOFFREGEN, W., 1961, *J. Atmospheric Terrest. Phys.* 21, 257–259.

STONE, G. M. C., 1960, *RSGB-Bulletin* (Journal of the Radio Society of Great Britain) 35, 395–397.

STONE, G. M. C., 1965, *Interradio—The International Radio Journal*, ITU Centenary Edition Geneva 20, 24–27.

STONE, M. L., INGALLS, R. P., DUGAN, C. H., RAINVILLE, L. P., 1959, paper presented at URSI meeting, Washington, D. C.

UNWIN, R. S., 1958, *J. Géophys. Res.* **63**, 501–506.

UNWIN, R. S., 1959 a, *Ann. Geophys.* **15**, 377–394.

UNWIN, R. S., 1959b *Nature* **183**, 1044–1045.

UNWIN, R. S., 1966, *J. Atmospheric Terrest. Phys.* **25**, 1167–1194.

WATKINS, C. D., 1960, *J. Atmospheric Terrest. Phys.* **19**, 1–9.

WATKINS, C. D., 1961, *J. Atmospheric Terrest. Phys.* **20**, 140–149.

WEAVER, J. T. and SKINNER, R., 1960, *Can. J. Phys.* **38**, 1089–1103 1104–1113.

YARIN, V. I., 1960, *Sbornik* IV, Nos. 2–3, 37.

YARIN, V. I., 1961, *Sbornik* IV, No. 5, 56.

A BRIEF REVIEW OF AURORAL
BACKSCATTER THEORY

Walter A. Flood

Cornell Aeronautical Laboratory, Inc.
Buffalo, New York

Other papers in this volume have discussed the salient facts of radio-radar backscatter and forward scatter. We have also heard discussions of Booker's (1956) theory of auroral backscatter irregularities in the electron density distribution and the streaming instability of Farley (1963) which would explain how electron density irregularities are generated. I propose to review the basic ideas of auroral backscatter theory, to point out the limitations of any single scatter theory, and to show the relationship between auroral scatter theory and instability concepts. In order to clarify just what an auroral radar sees, I shall sketch the derivation of the fundamental backscatter equation and show the relationship of this equation to the often quoted Booker "formula."

Studies of auroral radar echoes have shown that the echo amplitude statistics obey the Rayleigh distribution of amplitudes, implying that the time varying amplitude of an auroral echo is the result of many independent scatterers. Since the signal amplitudes are best described statistically, we shall use a statistical model to describe auroral backscatter.

It appears that the source of the backscattered fields lies in the fluctuation of dielectric constant in auroral regions. We shall assume that the fluctuation statistics are uniform throughout the auroral scattering region and that the dielectric constant is a random function of position given by

$$\epsilon(\mathbf{r},t) = \bar{\epsilon} + \Delta\epsilon(\mathbf{r},t) \tag{1}$$

where $\bar{\epsilon}$ = mean dielectric constant and $\Delta\epsilon(\mathbf{r},t)$ = fluctuation from the mean of the dielectric constant as a function of position and time.

With the assumption that the dielectric fluctuations are weak enough so that the total electric field in the presence of the dielectric fluctuations is nearly equal to the electric field intensity which would have existed in the absence of the dielectric fluctuations, it can be shown that the field scattered by dielectric fluctuations $\Delta\epsilon(\mathbf{r},t)$ is given by (see Figure 1):

$$E_s = \frac{\mu_0 \omega^2 |E_0| \sin\chi}{4\pi R} \int_V \Delta\epsilon(\mathbf{r},t) e^{i\mathbf{q}\cdot\mathbf{r}} dV \tag{2}$$

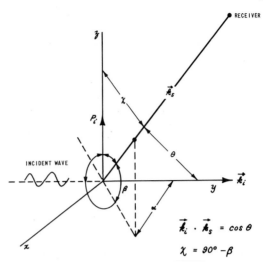

$$\vec{k_i} \cdot \vec{k_s} = \cos\theta$$

$$\chi = 90° - \beta$$

$\vec{k_i}$ = PROPAGATION VECTOR INCIDENT WAVE

$\vec{k_s}$ = PROPAGATION VECTOR OF SCATTERED WAVE

$\dfrac{\vec{k_i}}{|\vec{k_i}|}$ = DIRECTION OF INCIDENT WAVE PROPAGATION (TOWARDS $+y$ IN THIS SKETCH)

χ = ANGLE BETWEEN POLARIZATION VECTOR OF INCIDENT WAVE AND PROPAGATION VECTOR OF SCATTERED WAVE

FIGURE 1. Scatter geometry.

where μ_0 = permeability of free space

ω = angular frequency of the radar

$|E_0|$ = magnitude of the electric field intensity incident upon the scattering volume

R = distance from scattering volume to the radio/radar receiver

$\mathbf{q}$ = difference of the propagation vectors of the incident and scattered fields.

$$|\mathbf{q}| = \frac{4\pi}{\lambda} \sin \theta/2$$

λ = operating wavelength of the radar

θ = scattering angle = angle between incident and scattered waves

χ = angle between the electric polarization vector of the incident wave and the propagation vector of scattered wave.

The scattered field given by Equation 2 is a fluctuating quantity since $\Delta\epsilon(\mathbf{r},t)$ is a random fluctuating quantity. In order to obtain a readily measured quantity, we compute the mean squared field intensity scattered in the direction $\mathbf{k}_s$ by multiplying Equation 2 by its complex conjugate and taking an ensemble average to obtain:

$$\overline{|E_s|^2} = \overline{E_s E_s^*} = \left\{ \frac{\mu_0 \omega^2 |E_0| \sin\chi}{4\pi R} \right\}^2 \int_V \int_{V'} \overline{\Delta\epsilon(\mathbf{r})\Delta\epsilon^*(\mathbf{r}')} e^{i\mathbf{q}\cdot(\mathbf{r}-\mathbf{r}')} dV dV' \quad (3)$$

The quantity $\overline{\Delta\epsilon(\mathbf{r})\Delta\epsilon^*(\mathbf{r}')}$ can be recognized as the spatial correlation function of the fluctuation of dielectric constant. Assuming only that the statistics of the fluctuating quantities are homogeneous throughout the auroral scattering volume, the correlation function will be dependent only upon the vector difference of the two points $\mathbf{r}$ and $\mathbf{r}'$ and not the absolute points $\mathbf{r}$ and $\mathbf{r}'$. Define $\mathbf{R} = \mathbf{r} - \mathbf{r}'$

$$\overline{\Delta\epsilon(\mathbf{r})\Delta\epsilon(\mathbf{r}')} \equiv C(\mathbf{R}) \tag{4}$$

Under these circumstances, a change to relative coordinates in the first or inner integration results in:

$$\overline{|E_s|^2} = \left\{\frac{\mu_0\omega^2\,|E_0|\,\sin\chi}{4\pi R}\right\}^2 \int_V dV \int_{V\text{relative}} C(\mathbf{R})e^{i\mathbf{q}\cdot\mathbf{R}}dV_{\text{relative}} \tag{5}$$

If the correlation function $C(\mathbf{R})$ decreases rapidly enough, the limits on the relative volume integration can be extended to all space without incurring appreciable error.

$$\int C(\mathbf{R})e^{i\mathbf{q}\cdot\mathbf{R}}dV \equiv \overline{|\Delta\epsilon(\mathbf{q})|^2} \tag{6}$$

The Fourier transform of the spatial correlation function is defined to be the spatial power spectrum of the fluctuations.

$$\overline{|E_s|^2} = \left\{\frac{\mu_0\omega^2\,|E_0|\,\sin\chi}{4\pi R}\right\}^2 \overline{|\Delta\epsilon(\mathbf{q})|^2} \times \text{Volume} \tag{7}$$

The scattering cross section per unit volume per unit solid angle is σ.

$$\sigma = \frac{1}{V}\frac{R^2\,|E_s|^2}{|E_0|^2} = \left[\frac{\mu_0\omega^2}{4\pi}\right]^2 = \overline{|\Delta\epsilon(\mathbf{q})|^2} \tag{8}$$

At sufficiently high frequencies, the dielectric constant of an ionized gas is a pure real quantity (absorption is negligible) and fluctuations in dielectric constant are related to fluctuations in electron density through the equation:

$$\epsilon(\mathbf{r},t) = \epsilon_0 - \frac{N(\mathbf{r},t)e^2}{m\omega^2} \tag{9}$$

where ϵ_0 = dielectric constant of free space = 8.854 $\mu\mu$F/m
e = charge on an electron = 1.602×10^{-19} C
m = mass of an electron = 9×10^{-31} kg
$N(\mathbf{r},t)$ = number density of electrons/m³.

$$\sigma = \left[\frac{\mu_0 e^2}{4\pi m}\right]^2 \times \overline{|\Delta N(\mathbf{q})|^2} \equiv r_e^2\,\overline{|\Delta N(\mathbf{q})|^2} \tag{10}$$

where r_e^2 is the classical Thompson cross section of an electron. The radio-radar scattering cross section is therefore seen to be proportional to the power spectrum of the electron density fluctuation, $\overline{|\Delta N(\mathbf{q})|^2}$, evaluated at the vector wave number $\mathbf{q}$. If the spectrum of the fluctuations of electron density is strongly anisotropic, there will be a particular direction of the wave number $\mathbf{q}$ for which the scattering cross section will maximize. Preferential directions for backscatter are a characteristic of auroral radar echoes. In the case of auroral backscatter, the cross section maximizes very sharply when the $\mathbf{q}$ vector is perpendicular to the direction of the earth's magnetic field.

BOOKER (1956) was the first to present the theory of backscattering from anisotropic fluctuations of electron density. In this paper, Booker chose, for mathematical convenience as much as any other reason, to assume that the correlation function $C(R)$ was a cylindrical Gaussian function so that the shape of the fluctuation spectrum was fully determined by two parameters: the correlation distance L measured along the direction of the earth's magnetic field and the correlation distance T measured in a direction perpendicular to the direction of the earth's magnetic field. Experiments have shown that the fluctuation spectrum of the auroral ionosphere is not the simple two parameter Gaussian spectrum used in Booker's 1956 paper, but nevertheless, the basic concept of the anisotropic correlation function (and the resulting anisotropic fluctuation spectrum) is due to Booker.

A group of scaled radars (having the same antenna polar diagram and pulse lengths) will therefore observe auroral radar cross sections which are a direct measure of the electron density fluctuations evaluated at the specific $\mathbf{q}$ numbers of the radars. If all radars view the auroral volume perpendicular to the earth's magnetic field,

$$|\mathbf{q}| = \frac{4\pi}{\lambda}\sin\frac{\theta}{2} = \frac{4\pi}{\lambda} \text{ for backscatter.} \tag{11}$$

If we were to Fourier analyze the fluctuations of electron density in the $\mathbf{q}$ direction, we would arrive at a description of the electron density fluctuations in terms of wave numbers

$$|\mathbf{q}| = \frac{2\pi}{L} = \frac{4\pi}{\lambda} \tag{12}$$

It is clear then that radars observing auroral backscatter pick out those fluctuation components of the spectrum with spatial periodicity of one half wavelength. If the radar wavelength is much less than the smallest scale irregularity in the fluctuation spectrum, the radar cross section per unit volume will be vanishingly small. It should be noted that auroral radar backscatter has been observed at a wavelength of 10 cm, implying that the fluctuation spectrum has strong components with spatial dimensions of 5 cm.

The Relationship Between Auroral Backscatter and Auroral Forward Scatter

We have seen that the scattering cross section of auroral electron density fluctuations is proportional to the "power" in the fluctuation spectrum at the wave number $\mathbf{q}$. If we deal only with the magnitude of q, then because of the relationship

$$|\mathbf{q}| = \frac{4\pi}{\lambda} \sin \frac{\theta}{2}$$

forward scattering at 50 Mc/sec (6 m wavelength), reported by Canadian researchers and AXFORD (1967), corresponds to backscattering at a frequency of 5 Mc/sec (60 m wavelength) when the scattering angle is as small as 12°. The relationship $|q| = \frac{4\pi}{\lambda} \sin \frac{\theta}{2}$ enables one to compare, quantitatively, forward scatter and backscatter results at vastly differing frequencies. The only real point to be made at this time is that 50 Mc/sec forward scatter results correspond to quite large-scale electron density fluctuations and should not be compared with VHF backscatter results.

The Relationship Between the Backscatter and the Instability Theories

The backscatter equation (Equation (12)) relates the measured radar cross section to the intensity of the electron density fluctuation spectrum as a function of wave number. There is nothing in this development which would enable one to predict, a priori, the shape of the fluctuation spectrum or the physical mechanisms which would produce the spectrum. Nevertheless, it offers the experimenter the opportunity to measure the shape of the spectrum if sufficient scaled radar equipment is used simultaneously.

The various instability theories which have been proposed have, as their main point, the explanation of *why* one might expect particular forms of electron density fluctuations. When dispersion relations are sought, the equations are linearized and nonlinear effects are neglected; therefore, although dispersion theory can predict the conditions under which instabilities can grow, it cannot predict the final intensity of the particular instability or the shape of the resultant fluctuation spectrum. The backscatter theory and plasma instability theories naturally complement one another. Backscatter theory enables one, through measurements, to determine the shape of the fluctuation spectrum; instability theory may explain the origin of the fluctuations.

Comparison of Backscatter Theory with Experimental Results

Backscatter theory coupled with the expected anisotropy of the fluctuation spectrum would lead one to expect that whenever auroral echoes can be obtained at a higher frequency, the same volume should give rise to auroral echoes

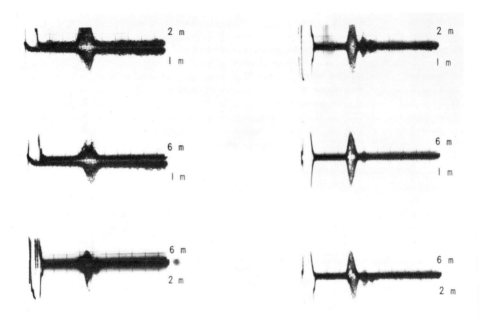

FEBRUARY 20, 1964   FEBRUARY 20, 1964

Figure 2. 6 meter, 2 meter and 1 meter echoes at same ranges.

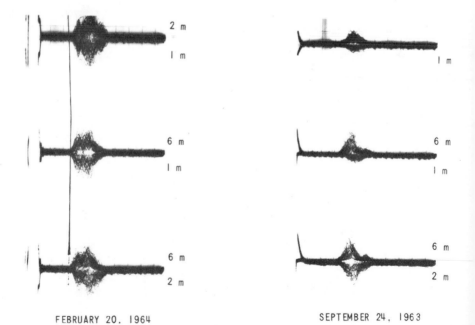

FEBRUARY 20, 1964   SEPTEMBER 24, 1963

Figure 3. 6 meter, 2 meter and 1 meter echoes at same ranges.

at lower frequencies. A series of scaled radar experiments has been completed by Cornell Aeronautical Laboratory in which radars operating at 49.7, 143.5, and 226 Mc/sec employed 5° azimuthal beamwidths. The vertical polar diagrams of all radars were also identical.

Figures 2 and 3 are illustrations of simultaneous echoes at 49.7, 143.5 and 226 Mc/sec (hereafter referred to as 6, 2, and 1 m wavelengths). The presentation is of echo amplitude versus range of echo. The range markers are 150 km apart for a total range of 1500 km. Figure 2 shows what have been called discrete auroral echoes; i.e., the auroral echo is only as wide as the transmitted pulse. Figure 3 shows diffuse auroral echoes where the echoes are spread over 300 km in range. The results of Figures 2 and 3 are in full agreement with predictions made on the basis of backscatter theory or the dispersion theory. It should be noted that over the full 5° azimuthal beamwidth, the "perpendicularity" requirement can be met exactly at heights ranging from 95–110 km.

Figures 4 and 5 present only 6 m and 2 m data. In each frame, the 6 m echo

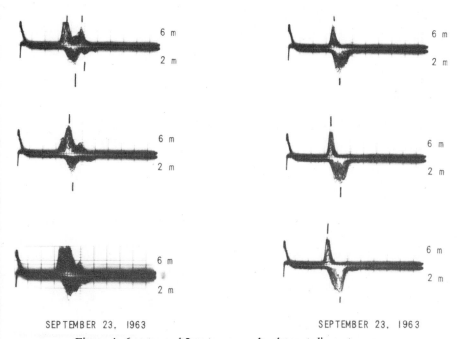

SEPTEMBER 23, 1963   SEPTEMBER 23, 1963

Figure 4. 6 meter and 2 meter auroral echoes at disparate ranges.

amplitude is upwards and the 2 m echo amplitude is downwards. Figure 4 shows cases when the echoes at each frequency have overlapping ranges, but in each case 6 m returns are present where there are little 2 m echoes and vice versa. Figure 5 shows an extreme instance wherein the 6 m and 2 m returns come from totally different ranges. This last result is not expected from considerations of either the backscatter theory presented here or the streaming instability of FARLEY (1963). Note also that in Figure 4, a discrete 6 m echo is observed while at the same time a diffuse 2 m echo is present.

The occurrence of disparate ranges for 6 and 2 m echoes is not uncommon, but whenever 2 m and 1 m echoes have been observed, they are always ob-

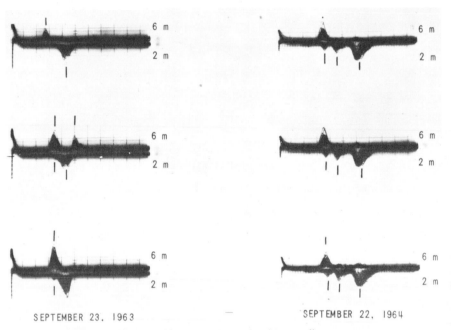

SEPTEMBER 23. 1963   —   SEPTEMBER 22, 1964

Figure 5. 6 meter and 2 meter auroral echoes at disparate ranges.

served at the same ranges. This suggests that some of the assumptions used in the development of the backscatter theory are not fulfilled at wavelengths as long as 6 m. If the mean electron density at auroral E region heights can be as high as 10^6 electrons/cm^3, E region refraction and E and D region absorption may modify the apparent radar cross section of frequencies as low as 50 Mc/sec. We would therefore suggest that when multiple frequency auroral radar experiments are planned to investigate aspects of plasma instability theories, frequencies greater than 100 Mc/sec be used so that the measurements of intensity and Doppler frequency shift pertain to the same auroral scattering volume.

The auroral radar technique is a useful, sensitive, ground-based tool for the investigation of the presence and intensity of aurora. The radar technique is not limited to observations through the dark hours, although the echo intensity is a function of the strength of the irregularities of electron density and not a simple

function of mean electron density. While our knowledge of the auroral ionosphere has greatly increased in the postwar years, there are more than sufficient
problems in auroral-radio physics to make it a promising field for future
research.

References

AXFORD, W., 1967, this volume.
BOOKER, H. G., 1956, *J. Atmospheric Terrest. Phys.* **8,** 204.
FARLEY, D., 1963, *J. Geophys. Res.* **68,** 6083.

Session

7

OBSERVATIONS III

Dr. Gilbert Weill

Institut d'Astrophysique de Paris

AURORAL ABSORPTION OF RADIO WAVES

C. Gordon Little

Institute for Telecommunication Sciences and Aeronomy
Environmental Science Services Administration
Boulder, Colorado

I. Introduction

The purpose of this chapter is to summarize the observations of radio wave absorption associated with auroras. The chapter concludes by outlining a proposed new radio technique, based on the emission of thermal radio noise, for the measurement of the temperature and spatial distribution of the electrons forming the absorbing region.

II. Theory

The Appleton-Hartree magneto-ionic theory shows that a radio wave traversing an ionized medium will experience attenuation if the free electrons undergo collisions. Basically, the concept is very simple; the free electrons oscillate under the influence of the electric component of the electromagnetic field and transfer a small fraction of their oscillatory energy when they collide with other particles. In effect, part of the coherent electromagnetic energy of the radio wave is transformed via these collisions into the random kinetic energy of the gas.

A plane wave of angular frequency w undergoes an exponential attenuation of the form

$$E = E_0^{-ks}$$

where E_0 is the incident field strength and E is the field strength after passing a distance s through the medium. The exponential attenuation factor k is given, for frequencies high compared with the local plasma and gyro-frequencies, by

$$k = C \cdot \frac{N\nu}{\nu^2 + w^2}$$

Here C is a constant, N is the number density of free electrons, and ν is the collision frequency of the electrons. This formula assumes that ν is independent of electron energy; the atmospheric D region case where ν is proportional to energy has been worked out by SEN and WYLLER (1960) and others and results in a slightly modified form. For simplicity, we present here the Appleton-Hartree case, although for accurate work the Sen-Wyller formulation is required.

To compute the absorption in a given electron density profile it is of course necessary to integrate through that profile, so that the absorption A, in decibels, is given by

$$A = 20 \log_{10} \frac{E}{E_0} = D \cdot \int \frac{N(h)\,\nu(h)}{[\nu(h)]^2 + w^2} \cdot dh,$$

where D is a numerical constant and $N(h)$ and $\nu(h)$ are the height profiles of the electron density and collision frequency, respectively.

If the absorption is occurring only in a region where $\nu \ll w$, then ν^2 can be ignored in the denominator and

$$A \sim \frac{\int N(h)\,\nu(h)\,dh}{w^2},$$

and the absorption is inversely proportional to the square of the observing radio frequency. On the other hand, if the absorption is occurring at extremely low heights such that $\nu \gg w$,

$$A \sim \int \frac{N(h)}{\nu(h)} \cdot dh,$$

and the absorption is independent of the observing radio frequency. Studies of the variation of the absorption with frequency have been used by several authors (see, for example, PARTHASARATHY et al., 1963; LERFALD et al., 1964) to determine the effective value of $\frac{\nu}{w}$ during absorption events, and, assuming an electron collision frequency profile $\nu(h)$, to derive the electron density profile $N(h)$ responsible for the absorption.

The above simplified treatment has ignored the effect of the earth's magnetic field. The presence of this field changes the refractive index of the medium in a sense determined by whether the electromagnetic field is rotating in the same direction as the gyro-rotation of the electron, or in the opposite direction; i. e., the medium becomes birefringent. For the auroral absorption case this complication is handled quite simply by replacing w by $w + w_L$ or by $w - w_L$, depending upon whether one is dealing with the ordinary or the extraordinary polarization, respectively. Here w_L is the electron gyro-frequency in radians per second corresponding to the longitudinal component of the magnetic field. Since w_L is of the order 10^7 rad/sec, this magneto-ionic splitting is not of major significance at the frequencies normally used by riometers, although it can be of considerable importance at the lower HF ionospheric communication frequencies.

III. Methods of Measuring Auroral Radio Wave Absorption

Two main methods of studying ionospheric absorption have been developed using man-made and celestial radio waves. In the former category, two main subclasses exist. The first of these involves measurement, either at oblique or vertical incidence, of the intensity of *fixed-frequency* radio signals that have been reflected by the ionospheric E or F region. During auroral absorption the received signal is attenuated by the double passage through the underlying absorbing region — to the extent that the signal may disappear rendering further quantitative measurements impossible. The second subclass of studies of auroral absorption utilizing man-made transmitters has involved the use of *sweep-frequency* ionosondes. These are pulsed HF radars routinely used at vertical incidence to determine the heights and penetration frequencies of the various ionospheric layers. In this case, increasing absorption leads to disappearance of the ionospheric echoes at successively higher and higher frequencies, until eventually, the echo totally disappears and the so-called "blackout" condition prevails. The second main method makes use of celestial radio waves at frequencies *above* (rather than below) the ionospheric penetration frequency. The equipment measures the ionospheric opacity relative to quiet conditions — hence the term riometer, for relative ionospheric opacity meter.

The HF field intensity and ionosonde methods have the important advantage of high sensitivity, both because of the lower operating frequency and the double passage through the layer. However, the simplicity of the riometer and the excellent continuity and quantitative nature of resultant absorption data have made the riometer the preferred method for auroral absorption measurements. This technique has now essentially replaced the former techniques at least for high latitude work, and so most of this review relates to observations made using it.

IV. Field Intensity and Ionosonde Measurements of Auroral Absorption

Anomalous absorption of radio waves occurring at high latitudes was discovered during the International Polar Year 1932–3, and several studies were made prior to about 1955 using HF field intensity measurements or ionosondes. The most important of these studies was by AGY (1954), who analyzed polar blackouts as registered by 18 ionosondes in the American and European longitudes. Five years of data were used for each station, and the average diurnal variations of the occurrence of blackouts was determined for magnetically quiet and disturbed periods, and also for the different seasons of the year. This study showed that the occurrence of blackouts was most frequent in a latitudinal belt lying somewhat south of the auroral zone. This region also showed the greatest diurnal variation in probability of occurrence of blackouts. Essentially all stations showed maximum frequency of blackouts in the morning hours, and a minimum in the afternoon or evening hours. The time of the diurnal maximum was found to be later at the higher latitudes. This point was well brought out by Cox and DAVIES (1954), who used data from five ionosondes in the North American Zone to show an approximately linear delay in the time of the diurnal maximum of occurrence of blackouts with latitude.

As recognized by the above authors, analyses of ionosonde blackout occurrence are subject to a number of uncertainties. Ionosonde performance is likely to differ at different stations and is likely to vary appreciably at a given station as a function of time. Also the amount of underlying absorption required to produce a blackout is a function of ionospheric critical frequency, which typically has important diurnal, seasonal, and latitudinal variations of its own. For these and other reasons, this type of analysis is not favored, and with the advent of the cosmic noise technique in 1954, almost all later high latitude absorption work has been performed using riometers.

V. Riometer Observations of Auroral Absorption

A. Temporal Variations

Several workers have reported the broad temporal behavior of auroral absorption as recorded by riometers. The most complete analyses are those of BASLER (1963), based on analysis of five years of data obtained with the Alaskan chain of riometers, and of HARTZ et al. (1963), based on almost two years of Canadian data.

1. Diurnal Variation. Averaged over the five-year period, the auroral absorption at College (located just south of the optical auroral zone) was found to show a broad maximum centered at about 0900 hr, with a well defined minimum at about 2100 hr. The amplitude of this diurnal variation in the average absorption was three or four to one during winter and equinoctial periods, but almost disappeared during the summer months when the ionosphere over College is illuminated essentially twenty-four hours per day. If one subtracts, for each season, the diurnal variations of absorption observed on the five magnetically quiet days of each month from that observed on the five most disturbed days (this quiet day absorption might be thought to be largely due to the normal D and F regions), one obtains a clearer representation of the diurnal variation of auroral absorption. In this case the diurnal ratio is increased to roughly ten to one between 0900 hr and 2100 hr for winter and equinoctial months, and about three to one for the summer months.

2. Seasonal Variation. The absorption was found to show a marked annual cycle, maximizing in the winter months. It is interesting to note that the approximately twofold ratio between the mean winter absorption and the mean summer absorption is independent of whether the analysis is limited to magnetically quiet or magnetically disturbed days. This suggests that there is a residual anomalous absorption during winter days, even on magnetically quiet days.

3. Sunspot Cycle Variation. During the period 1957–62 the Zurich provisional sunspot number fell from about 240 to 25. It is therefore noteworthy that the average monthly absorption at College, when smoothed in a three-month running average, showed essentially no decrease during the five-year period. The same result is also true when the analysis is limited to the five quietest days per month and the five most disturbed days per month. Apparently, the precipitation of the energetic electrons responsible for the auroral absorption is largely insensitive to the sunspot number.

4. Autocorrelation Time. The above discussion has dealt with the broad diurnal, seasonal, and sunspot cycle variations of absorption at an auroral zone station. Figure 1, from HOLT *et al.* (1961), gives the median autocorrelation function for auroral absorption events observed in Norway. Note that the autocorrelation function falls to about 0.65 at about 10 min, indicating that auroral absorption values taken much more than 20 min apart are largely uncorrelated. This analysis does not, however, discuss possible diurnal variations in the autocorrelation time.

FIGURE 1. Median autocorrelation function for auroral absorption (Holt et al., 1961).

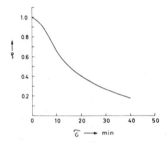

B. Spatial Variations

1. Latitudinal Dependence. Studies of the latitudinal dependence of the auroral absorption by Alaskan, Canadian, and Norwegian workers have all shown that the auroral absorption zone maximizes roughly 2° south of the auroral zone. It must be emphasized, however, that the auroral absorption is primarily a daytime phenomenon and that it occurs slightly south of the position of the *nighttime* (luminous) auroral zone and, therefore, roughly 10° south of the position of the daytime position of the "auroral oval." During magnetically disturbed conditions the auroral absorption zone intensifies and moves equatorward by up to a few degrees (see, for example, BASLER, 1963).

2. Correlation Distance. Figure 2, from LITTLE *et al.* (1965), shows the decay of correlation of auroral absorption events with distance in both north-south and east-west directions. In each diagram the median value of the correlation coefficient for a given spacing is marked with an *X*; the quartile ranges of the correlation coefficients for each distance are also shown. It is noteworthy that the median behavior is such that the correlation falls to 0.65 at about 450 km separation in both the north-south and east-west directions. A similar result was obtained by HOLT *et al.* (1961), who obtained an essentially isotropic 0.65 correlation distance of about 300 km at a somewhat higher geomagnetic latitude. Again, diurnal variations of the correlation pattern were not discussed.

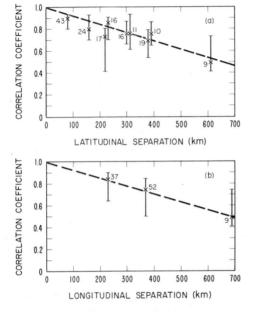

FIGURE 2. Cross-correlation coefficients as a function of riometer spacing. The crosses denote the median values and the lines, the quartile ranges of the correlation coefficients. The number adjacent to each median value is the number of cross-correlation coefficients computed for that pair of stations.

Narrow-beam antennas have been used by several authors to seek small-scale structure in the auroral absorption. The most careful study is that of ANSARI (1964), who concluded that genuine differences of as much as 2.5 dB were occasionally noticed between narrow-beam antennas pointed 12°N and 12°S of the zenith. The combination of the temporal and spatial correlation functions (0.65 autocorrelation times of 10 min, 0.65 cross-correlation distances of about 400 km) together with spaced station data make it plain that the auroral absorption variations seen at a single station are to be thought of as predominantly a temporal variation rather than as the result of a systematic motion past the station of an otherwise stable precipitation. (If motion of the precipitation zone was the predominant cause for the temporal variations, time delays of the order of 10 min would be expected between stations 400 km apart; such time delays are rarely, if ever, seen.) We are, therefore, to think of the impact zone as roughly circular in cross section, approximately stationary, and waxing and waning with a total period of the order of several times the 0.65 autocorrelation time of 10 min.

3. Conjugate Point Observations. The above studies of the spatial distribution of auroral absorption relate to measurements taken simultaneously in neighboring locations in the northern hemisphere. It is also of interest to ask about the relationships between auroral absorption events occurring simultaneously in magnetically conjugate areas, i.e., at the two ends of a computed tube of magnetic force. A number of such studies have been published, notably by the CRPL-ITSA group (HARGREAVES and CHIVERS, 1965; LITTLE et al., 1965) who have concentrated primarily on three pairs of magnetically conjugate riometers at L values of about 4, 7, and 15.

These conjugate observations have shown:

(i) auroral absorption usually occurs simultaneously in conjugate areas;

(ii) the moment-to-moment correlation is often good at $L = 4.0$, but is less marked, though still highly significant, at the larger L values;

(iii) differences in mirror heights as large as 200 km do *not* significantly affect the intensity of absorption occurring at the two ends of a field line;

(iv) instead, and particularly at high latitudes, the ratio of absorption between the northern and the southern conjugate area shows an annual cycle, in that the winter end of the field line shows the stronger absorption;

(v) on occasions, the absorption is detected at only one end of the computed field line; no pattern of behavior identifying which end of the field line will receive the precipitation in single-ended events has been identified;

(vi) the absence of any clear effect of different mirror heights in the two hemispheres indicates that the electrons causing auroral absorption (even at L values as low as 4.0) are perturbed catastrophically in time scales which are short compared with the bounce period.

A detailed example of conjugacy is given in Figure 3, which presents scatter plots of absorption data on two riometers at Eights, Antarctica and at three locations in the northern conjugate area. Note that the correlation between Eights and the Quebec South Station, connected by a field line approximately 55,000 km long, was better for this eight-hour period than that between Quebec South and Quebec North, two stations only 160 km apart in the northern hemisphere (see the top right and bottom right diagrams, respectively).

C. Dipole Time and Latitude Dependence of Auroral Absorption

The temporal and spatial behavior of the occurrence of auroral absorption of a given magnitude may be well summarized in the form of contours on a geomagnetic time latitude diagram. Figure 4 is such a plot and is taken from the analysis by HARTZ et al. (1963) of data from the Canadian chain of riometers. The contours are plots of the percentage of occurrence of auroral absorption greater than 1.0 dB at 30 MHz on riometers directed toward the celestial pole. The main features of the diagram are the strong peak in absorption occurrence at about 64° geomagnetic latitude at 0800 hr magnetic time, with a deep minimum at about 2000 hr. The percentage occurrence falls by a

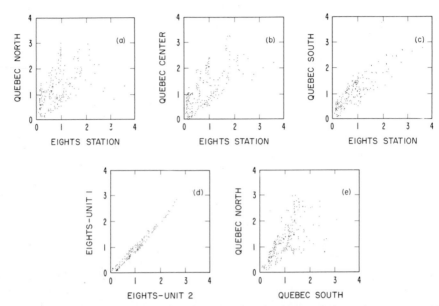

FIGURE 3. Scatter diagrams of absorption occurring simultaneously in conjugate areas: (a) Quebec North vs. Eights, Antarctica; (b) Quebec Center vs. Eights; (c) Quebec South vs. Eights; (d) Eights-Unit 1 vs. Eights-Unit 2; (e) Quebec North vs. Quebec South; 1230–2130 UT January 10, 1962.

factor of 2 at magnetic latitudes of about 58 and 68°, and at about 0400 hr and 1200 hr magnetic time. These authors also showed that similar results were obtained using Norwegian riometer data, except that the peak occurred at a higher magnetic latitude (about 68°), though still south of the auroral zone. These results are also consistent with those of BASLER (1963), discussed earlier in this chapter.

D. Multi-frequency Riometer Data and the Height of the Absorbing Layer

As discussed at the beginning of this chapter, multi-frequency data permit estimates of the height of the absorbing layer if one is willing to assume that the absorption is uniform across the antenna beam and that the collision frequencies of the electrons are unaffected by the aurora. Making these assumptions, LERFALD et al. (1964) obtained the following distribution of heights of the *absorbing* layer (*not* the height of the electron density maximum, because of the exponentially increasing collision frequency with decreasing height).

Median exponents in the range 1.4–1.5 have also been observed by PARTHASARATHY and BERKEY (1965a, 1965b) for their Type F and Type S auroral absorption events, implying heights for these breakup absorption events of the order of 62 km.

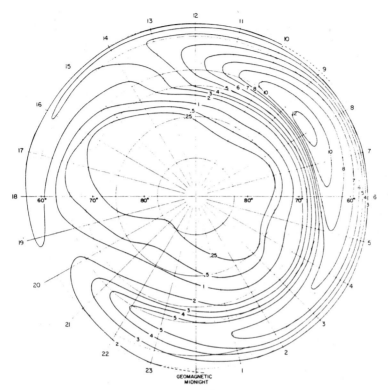

FIGURE 4. Contour diagram showing the time percentage occurrence of auroral absorption of 1.0 dB or more as a function of geomagnetic latitude and mean geomagnetic time (Hartz et al., 1963).

Table I. Multi-frequency Riometer Estimates of the Height of the Absorbing Layer (after LERFALD et al., 1964)

Frequency Exponent n ($A = C \cdot f^{-n}$)	Percentage of Auroral Absorption Events	Height of Peak of Absorbing Layer
>1.9	36	>78 km
1.7–1.9	42	69–78 km
1.5–1.7	12	64–69 km
1.3–1.5	8	59–64 km
<1.3	2	<59 km

Median Exponent ~ 1.83
Median height $\quad \sim 75$ km

These deduced heights are sufficiently low as to create a major problem of interpretation. The experimental observations are such that the error in the interpretation (if any) must be attributed primarily to the assumptions implicit in the analysis rather than to the experimental determination of the frequency exponent. The most likely source of error is nonuniformity of absorption across the antenna beam, though an additional factor not considered in the analysis, namely the nonuniform distribution of radio noise across the celestial sky, could also introduce an error in the interpretation. (This fact arises because the correction of the observed absorption values to zenithal pencil-beam values assumes uniform flux above the ionosphere.)   However, this latter point could not explain the observed variations of the exponent within periods of a few minutes.

In addition, REID (1964) has indicated that auroral electrons in the E region may well be considerably hotter than the ambient medium, and that this would very significantly modify their collision frequency. However, the application of such a correction would tend to *increase* the deduced height of the absorbing region.

E. The Role of Bremsstrahlung in Auroral Absorption

Several authors have estimated the contribution of bremsstrahlung x rays to the auroral absorption problem. For a uniform flux of incident energetic electrons, of typical energy spectrum, the bremsstrahlung contribute only in a very minor way to the production of auroral absorption. However, it should be pointed out that a broad-beam riometer, which integrates over a relatively large area, is particularly sensitive to the presence of bremsstrahlung, which are radiated in all directions from the point of impact of the electron beam and tend to create low-lying ionization over the full beamwidth of the antenna. Thus, a given *total* flux of energetic electrons will produce an approximately constant amount of low-lying absorption due to bremsstrahlung, whereas the focusing of the primary incident beam to a small area will greatly reduce the absorption due to the primary ionization. In this way, the effectiveness of bremsstrahlung in producing auroral absorption on a broad-beam antenna can be enhanced relative to the effect of the intense but more localized primary ionization. It is probable that this feature of bremsstrahlung is at least a partial explanation of the unexpectedly low heights deduced for some auroral absorption events.

F. Auroral Absorption and Auroral Luminosity

The relationships between auroral luminosity and auroral absorption are obviously of potential scientific interest, although it must be recognized that detailed correlations should not necessarily be expected. The auroral absorption tends to occur at appreciably lower heights than the auroral luminosity and is much more sensitive than the auroral luminosity to the number of high energy electrons in the incident precipitation.

Studies of the relationships between auroral luminosity and auroral absorption have been made by several authors (see, for example, CAMPBELL and LEIN-BACH, 1961; ANSARI, 1964; JOHANSEN, 1965, 1966). Ansari found that auroral luminosity during the prebreakup and midnight breakup phases correlated well with auroral absorption, but that the slowly varying ionospheric absorption (SVIA), often occurring for some hours after the breakup, showed poor correlation with auroral luminosity. A 10–100-fold increase in the ratio of absorption to 5577Å luminosity was found to occur during SVIA relative to the prebreakup auroral forms.

CAMPBELL and LEINBACH (1961) and JOHANSEN (1965, 1966) compared absorption data with the intensity of rapid fluctuations in auroral luminosity at 3914Å and 5577Å, respectively. Campbell and Leinbach found a linear correlation between the absorption and the intensity of the 3914Å coruscations; Johansen reports that the absorption is proportional to the square root of the 5577Å coruscations, and that the ratio of absorption to 5577Å fluctuations increased at the higher coruscation frequencies, implying a harder electron energy spectrum. These results support quantitatively the statements of many authors that pulsating and flaming aurora are associated with strong absorption, and that quiescent, nonpulsating forms show much less absorption.

G. Auroral Absorption and Geomagnetic Activity

Since geomagnetic activity is found to occur at high latitudes associated with aurora, it is also of interest to inquire as to the relationships between auroral absorption and geomagnetic activity. Again, however, it is important to note that perfect correlation need not be expected, since the electric currents responsible for the geomagnetic perturbations are believed to flow at heights of the order of 120 km, and, therefore, appreciably above the region believed responsible for the auroral absorption. On a broad time scale, auroral absorption has been found to show good correlation with geomagnetic data — provided that the correlation study is on the basis of a given local time (LITTLE and LEINBACH, 1958). The daytime peak in the absorption, as opposed to the nighttime peak of magnetic activity, indicates a changing ratio in the amount of absorption per unit change in magnetic field strength. An unpublished analysis by the author showed a tenfold increase in the amount of absorption produced by a given magnetic field change if it occurred in daylight; this result is consistent with the suggestion that the daytime peak in the absorption is to be attributed to a hardening of the energy spectrum of the incident electron beam during the morning hours.

CAMPBELL and LEINBACH (1961) have compared micropulsations of period 4–26 sec and auroral absorption and found a high correlation (0.81) between the intensities of the two phenomena. This again is consistent with the suggestion that pulsations are associated with intense absorption.

VI. A Proposed Method for the Measurement of Electron Temperatures in the Auroral Absorption Region

As indicated earlier, two problems plague the interpretation of the auroral absorption data. One of these relates to the question as to whether or not the absorption is uniform across the antenna beam; the second, to the question as to whether the temperature (and hence the collision frequency) of the electrons is enhanced during aurora. Such enhancement could occur because of electric fields, or, as suggested by REID (1964), could result from the fact that the electrons take appreciable time to cool down after initial production in the ionization process.

A possible method for determining the temperature of the absorption region and also obtaining increased angular resolution would be to study the *emission* of radio noise by the absorbing region at a frequency such as 200 MHz. At such frequencies the effective antenna noise temperature due to celestial radio noise is of the order 120 °K, and, therefore, appreciably below that which would be expected in an absorbing D or E region (200–300° K). The appearance of the relatively hot absorbing region along the line of sight would, therefore, lead to an *increase* in received signal strength. By operating simultaneously on two or more frequencies straddling the range of expected temperatures of the electrons responsible for the absorption, it should be possible to deduce the temperature of the electrons. Moreover, because of the higher frequencies required, it should be possible to obtain higher angular resolution at these frequencies than at the normal riometer frequencies of about 30 MHz. Table II shows the effect of a 300° K absorbing region, assumed to completely fill the polar diagram of six scaled systems operating at 30, 50, 100, 150, 200, and 300 MHz, with an absorption of 10 dB at 30 MHz which is proportional to f^{-2}. These computations are idealized and would of course require correction for any losses in the antenna, and for any sidelobes which were not directed toward the absorbing region.

Table II. Effect of a 10 dB (at 30 MHz), 300 °K Absorbing Region at Various Operating Frequencies in the Range 30–300 MHz

$$\Delta T = \alpha \left(T_{\text{absorbing region}} - T_{\text{sky}} \right)$$

$$\alpha = \text{absorption coefficient} = \frac{\% \text{ absorbed}}{100}$$

Frequency MHz	30	50	100	150	200	300
α	0.90	0.564	0.187	0.087	0.05	0.02
$T_{\text{absorbing region}}$ °K	300	300	300	300	300	300
T_{sky} °K	2×10^4	5060	780	260	120	40
ΔT °K	−17,730	−2681	−90	+3.5	+9	+5
dB change	−9.44	−3.28	−0.62	+0.05	+0.32	+0.52

This table shows that small (of the order 9° K) *increases* in antenna temperature would be expected to occur in an idealized system operating at about 200 MHz. After allowing for realistic antenna losses and side-lobes, the increase would probably be about 5° K. Such changes in antenna signal, though small, should be readily detectable using a version of the riometer comparison technique, in which noise power is continuously supplied from a local noise diode in a servo-controlled manner to keep the total noise power (antenna plus noise diode) equal to that from a fixed resistor.

It should be noted that the above estimates of increased antenna temperatures at 200 MHz may prove to be unduly conservative for the following reasons:

A. The electrons may be appreciably hotter than 300° K. Thus electric fields of as low as 0.1 mV/m along the magnetic field lines, or 30 mV/m transverse to the field lines, would heat the electrons very appreciably.

B. The electrons have been assumed to radiate incoherent (thermal) radio noise. Any coherent oscillation could greatly increase the received noise power.

C. An obliquity factor of up to about 5 could be used to increase the absorption, and hence the emission.

D. The 10 dB absorption at 30 MHz is representative of a strong auroral absorption event as registered on a broad-beam riometer. It is possible that over localized areas the absorption is very much greater, perhaps by a whole order of magnitude.

E. It has been assumed that the absorption decreases as f^{-2}. A lower exponent would increase the absorption, and hence the emission at 200 MHz.

In view of the conservative nature of the above calculations, and the obvious importance of determining the temperature of the absorbing region and of obtaining absorption measurements with improved angular resolution, it would seem desirable that radio groups having access to suitable receiving facilities at high latitudes conduct experimental studies of this radio emission phenomenon as soon as possible. It is conceivable, for example, that such studies may provide a method of locating and measuring the increase of temperature of electrons in the auroral ionosphere resulting from electric fields, or the existence of a significant high-energy tail in the distribution of electrons attributable to a slow cooling down of the electrons after initial production.

References

AGY, V., 1954, *J. Geophys. Res.* **59**, 499.
ANSARI, Z. A., 1964, *J. Geophys. Res.* **69**, 4493.
BASLER, R. P., 1963, *J. Geophys. Res.* **68**, 4665.
CAMPBELL, W. H. and LEINBACH, H., 1961, *J. Geophys. Res.* **66**, 25
COX, J. W. and DAVIES, K., 1954, *Can. J. Phys.* **32**, 743.
HARGREAVES, J. K. and CHIVERS, H. J. A., 1965, *J. Geophys. Res.* **70**, 1093.
HARTZ, T. R., MONTBRIAND, L. E., and VOGAN, E. L., 1963, *Can. J. Phys.* **41**, 581.
HOLT, C., LANDMARK, B., and LIED, F., 1961, *J. Atmospheric Terrest. Phys.* **23**, 229.
JOHANSEN, O. E., 1965, *Planetary Space Sci.* **13**, 225.
JOHANSEN, O. E., 1966, *Planetary Space Sci.* **14**, 217.
LERFALD, G. M., LITTLE, C. G., and PARTHASARATHY, R., 1964, *J. Geophys. Res.* **69**, 2857.
LITTLE, C. G. and LEINBACH, H., 1958, *Proc. I.R.E.* **46**, 334.

LITTLE, C. G., SCHIFFMACHER, E. R., CHIVERS, H. J. A., and SULLIVAN, K. W., 1965, *J. Geophys. Res.* **70**, 639.
PARTHASARATHY, R. and BERKEY, F. T. 1965 a, *J. Geophys. Res.* **70**, 89.
PARTHASARATHY, R. and BERKEY, F. T., 1965 b, *Radio Sci.* **69D**, 415.
PARTHASARATHY, R., LERFALD, G. M., and LITTLE, C. G., 1963, *J. Geophys. Res.* **68**, 3581.
REID, G. C., 1964, *J. Geophys. Res.* **69**, 3296.
SEN, H. K. and WYLLER, A. A., 1960, *J. Geophys. Res.* **65**, 3931.

Discussion

It was asked if the monitoring of satellite transmissions, possibly using multiple phase locked frequencies, could provide better techniques for measuring absorption. Little stated that even to frequencies as high as 500 MHz scintillation would significantly obscure absorption.

IONOSPHERIC OBSERVATIONS
OF AURORAL ACTIVITY

G. A. M. King

Geophysical Observatory, D.S.I.R., New Zealand

Abstract After discussing the techniques of ionogram interpretation, the paper considers the thick layer structure which accompanies auroral activity. This structure can be used to give the global distribution of activity, the profiles of ionization in height, and some information on electric fields in the aurora. It occurs over the height range from the D region to the F region and can be found at quite low latitudes during major disturbances. The paper emphasizes that the magnetosphere has an inner as well as an outer boundary and that the auroral activity extends the pattern of transverse conductivities on the inner boundary. It seems likely that the aurora results from the local acceleration of charged particles.

I. Introduction

Some primary agent excites and ionizes the atmospheric gas at auroral heights, and we see the light given out as the gas relaxes. We may learn much from studying the ionization as well as the emitted light. The densities of ionization fall within the range covered by conventional ionosondes so that there is a large body of experimental data going back over many years and hundreds of disturbances. However, very little has been done with these data.

As Figure 1 shows, disturbed ionograms can be a discouraging sight. But, by considering carefully just how ionosonde echoes are obtained, we can gain useful information from this record, and the majority of disturbed ionograms are quite tractable. With experience, we can develop a tool which will carry the study of disturbances through all weather, moonlight, and even daylight. Moreover, the distribution of ionization in height can often be deduced in order to help understand the primary agent.

The next section concerns the interpretation of ionograms from the physical point of view. One particular classification proves most useful — that which divides layer-like structure from the rest. This leads to the study of the night-E layer, considered in the third section. Section four shows some extreme forms of the night-E layer. The final section discusses the implications of the ionospheric observations for the formulation of auroral theories.

589

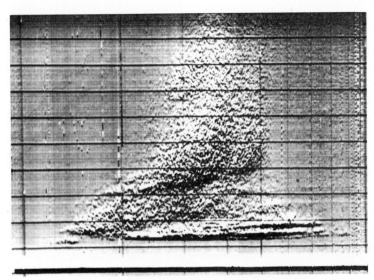

FIGURE 1. Ionogram 0401, May 16, 1958, Hallett.

II. Interpreting Disturbed Ionograms

The ionosonde sends a pulse upwards and gets back echoes. In the daytime under quiet conditions one can usually assume that the ionization lies in roughly horizontal layers, with the echoes coming from overhead. However, consider the possible distribution of ionization on a disturbed night when there might be several rayed auroral arcs in the sky. A contour of constant ion density will certainly not be a horizontal plane; it will have corrugations and bumps, many of them capable of sending back echoes. The ionosonde records most of the echoes in spite of a certain amount of vertical directivity in its antenna. Even a relatively uncomplicated distribution of ionization can produce a complex ionogram. For example, the ionogram in Figure 1 was recorded at the same time as the all-sky camera record in Figure 2.

For further inquiry into the pattern of ionospheric echoes, we must know the smallest size of structure which can give reflection and whether the reflection process is partial or total. Some idea of the least size for a reflecting surface can be gained from the radius of the first Fresnel zone. For example, at 3 Mc/sec the free space wavelength is 100 m, and the Fresnel radius for this wavelength at 100 km is 3 km. Therefore, under these conditions the ionosonde would be observing patches no smaller than 6 km across. Finer structure, which is no doubt present, is just averaged out. If appreciable refraction occurs before reflection, the patches must be larger, as the effective wavelength is longer in a refracting medium.

There is a lot of confusion in the literature on the nature of the reflection process, largely because the word "scattering" is used in several senses. While

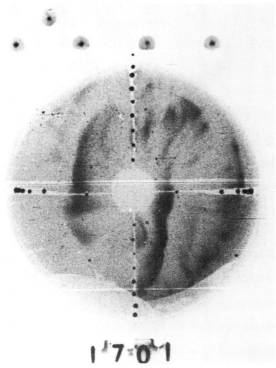

FIGURE 2. Auroral all-sky camera record 1701 UT May 15, 1958, Hallett.

the echoes may appear "scattered" over the ionogram, the reflection process is nearly always total, simply because the normal ionosonde system has insufficient gain to record partial reflections. Exceptions do occur, as shown in Figures 3

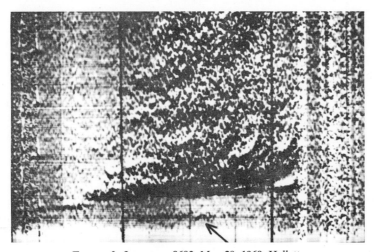

FIGURE 3. Ionogram 0602, May 29, 1960, Hallett.

and 4. Figure 3 shows partial reflections (indicated by the arrow), brought about by the presence of ionization at a level of extreme atmospheric turbulence. This record was taken at the maximum sensitivity of the equipment, and the height marks were suppressed in case they hide weak echoes. Figure 4 is the familiar

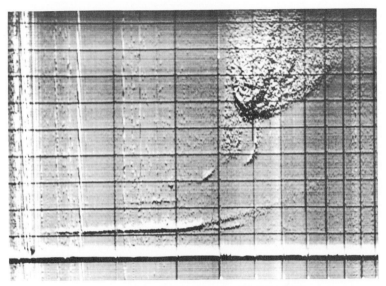

FIGURE 4. Ionogram 0901, October 24, 1958, Hallett.

slant sporadic E, also recorded at the maximum sensitivity of the ionosonde. I believe that it arises from partial reflection but that the signal strength is raised by a measure of coherence between the individual scattering centers. Apart from such easily recognized cases, we can assume that the reflection process is total, and that consequently, the electron density can be deduced from the transmitted frequency in the usual way. Furthermore, it is not possible to get reflections at two different ranges in the same direction on the same frequency; if different ranges are recorded, they are from different directions.

It is now possible to predict, in a general way, what sort of ionogram would be associated with a particular all-sky camera record. The prediction is general only because of the following unknown factors:

1. Intensity of the aurora (apart from rough estimate).

2. Relation between intensity and degree of ionization; this will vary with height since most of the luminosity is caused by collisional excitation, a function of particle energy.

3. Interpretation of the all-sky camera record in terms of horizontal and vertical structure; rays are very useful here.

4. Allowance for refraction of the exploring waves from the ionosonde. This

causes various focusing and defocusing effects; further, the ionization between E and F may be quite dense, yet may not give out much light, making its role hard to assess.

Many papers in the literature indicate that the relationship between the aurora and the ionograms is poor. Because of this, it is surprising and gratifying to find that the principles outlined above allow one to achieve a very good semi-quantitative relationship.

From the ionospheric point of view the comparison between all-sky camera records and ionograms helps to resolve the question as to which echoes are from overhead and which are oblique. Usually, this question is answered from inspection of sequences of ionograms. However, under disturbed conditions one may lack confidence in the conclusions reached. The auroral photographs, especially if taken at one minute intervals, show how much the changes are horizontal movement and how much formation and dispersal in situ. They also make the ionogram reader more ready to accept high rates of change.

The comparison also helps the auroral worker. When the ionization is overhead or nearly so, it is most often seen as a thick layer exhibiting group retardation — the night-E or enhanced-E layer (BEYNON and BROWN, 1959; BULLEN, 1966). Not only do the overhead thick layers give a distribution in height but, more simply, they often point to the presence of a general auroral glow which may be missed on the all-sky camera record — the eye is much more responsive to auroral "forms." Moreover, the ionosonde can record levels of activity below the threshold of the all-sky camera, and there is a surprising amount of it (KING, 1965).

To complete the picture, it is worthwhile to describe the appearance of echoes received obliquely as the ionosonde sweeps in frequency. The ray paths for these echoes nearly always suffer bending by refraction before reflection. With increasing frequency the refraction changes so that the echo is received from a lesser zenith distance, thereby lessening its virtual range. But this is compensated by greater penetration into the ionization with the net result that the range may stay almost constant. Group retardation near the critical frequency is missing because of defocusing. When a number of these echoes are overlapped, we get the familiar "brush" of auroral sporadic E. It is possible, in a small fraction of cases, for the ray paths to become trapped in an almost fixed direction by a concave pattern of isoionic contours. Then, group retardation is seen on oblique echoes — type r sporadic E. However, type r is easily distinguished from the thick layers overhead by its nonblanketing character and the absence of multiples.

III. The Night-E or Enhanced-E Layer

Generally speaking, it is not profitable to study the oblique echoes on ionograms, although at times they can be made to yield horizontal velocities. This means that work based on the most commonly tabulated E parameter, f Es, is unsatisfactory, since the sporadic E echoes are nearly always oblique.

By contrast, the thick overhead layers are very useful. For example, BULLEN (1966) has used enhanced-E to get the occurrence of disturbance in both summer and winter, solar maximum and minimum, at a polar cap and a high-midlatitude station. It is quite impossible to do this from auroral observations because it is daylight half the time, and activity is not confined to the night hours. Recently, BULLEN (private communication) has been working with the distribution of ionization in height, getting the thickness of the layer and relating it to the peak density and its height. Figures 5 and 6 illustrate the general results without the need for conversion to real heights. In Figure 5 the electron density is high

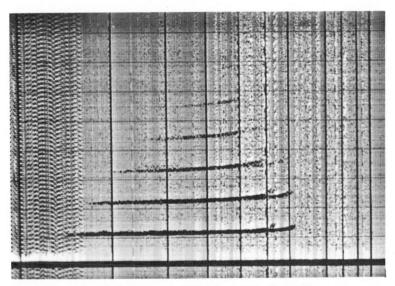

FIGURE 5. Ionogram 1930, July 5, 1961, Campbell.

(high enough to obscure the F region), and at the same time the night-E layer is low and thin. In Figure 6, on the other hand, the electron density is much lower, while the layer is higher and thicker. The change in thickness seems to reflect the change in atmospheric scale height with height; the half-thickness is about one scale height at all heights. The electron density depends to some extent on the number of incident primary particles but their energy is a factor showing greater variability and the energy also determines the height of the layer; thus, the electron density and the height are related.

Bullen has also used magnetic observations with the night-E layer to deduce features of the height profile of conductivity, and estimate electric fields. This work makes severe demands on our ability to interpret ionograms in order that the magnetic effects be attributed correctly to the ionization.

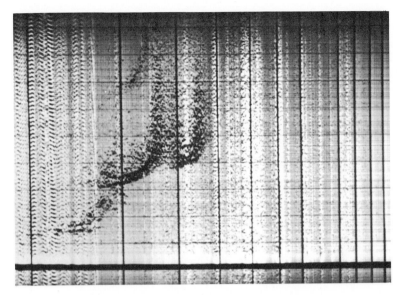

FIGURE 6. Ionogram 0015, May 27, 1961, Campbell.

IV. Extreme Forms of Night-E Behavior

When the night-E layer is formed very low in the ionosphere some of the ionization is in the D region where it can cause absorption of radio waves. On the ionogram this shows as raised values of f-min, even to blackout. As LIND-QUIST (1951) pointed out, the difference between auroral absorption and the night-E layer (his NI) is merely one of height. Figure 7 shows the high absorp-

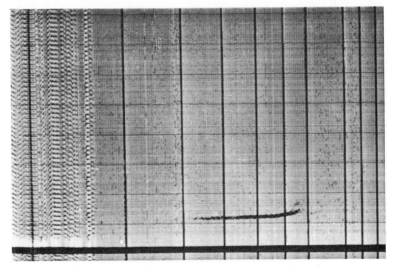

FIGURE 7. Ionogram 2115, July 14, 1961, Campbell.

tion and the night-E together. However, we should not exclude the possibility that at some times of auroral absorption there are overlapping layers of ionization, the upper formed by electrons and the lower, perhaps by energetic protons. At the other end of the height scale is "high-E" (see Figure 8).

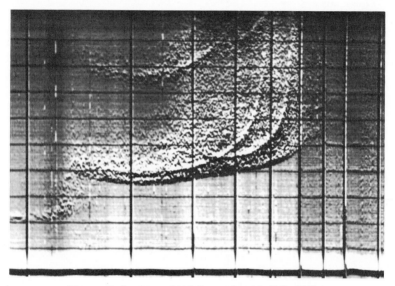

FIGURE 8. Ionogram 0414, September 16, 1959, Hallett.

As far as we have been able to tell, high-E and night-E are merely different levels of intensity in the same phenomenon. A reservation is implied because it has proved very difficult to follow the activity as its intensity changes because of confusion by oblique propagation. If we accept this conclusion, the most interesting property of high-E is its continuity with F. As the high-E and F layers move up and down together, this does not appear to be the result of the overlapping of two electron distributions with different origins. I believe that the

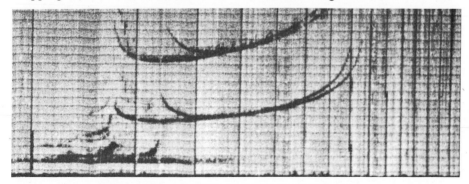

FIGURE 9. Ionogram 2250, September 12, 1957, Rarotonga.

two layers are related. Support for this idea comes from French's (private communication) observation that when high-E forms at the bottom of **F**, the f_0F2 decreases; if the high-E disappears, the f_0F2 recovers its former value.

Times of great activity allow us to study another extreme form of night-E,

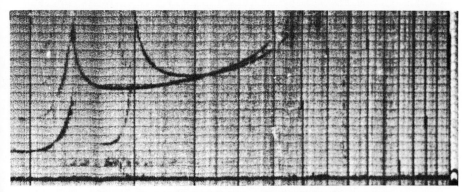

FIGURE 10. Ionogram 0040, September 13, 1957, Rarotonga.

when it appears at low latitudes. When the magnetic K index is 6 or 7, night-E forms at 45° latitude; when K is 9 it is found at 20°, in the equatorial belt. Figures 9 and 10 give two stages of development at Rarotonga on the night of September 12–13, 1957. At 2250 (Figure 9), although the E layer is confused by sporadic E, its least height is not greater than 125 km. By 0040 (Figure 10), the E layer is at 195 km and we would refer to it as a high-E. It can be said, after studying the ionograms between these two, that they are members of a continuous series, each differing only slightly from the preceding one. The suggestion is strongly made that the E regions on both have the same origin.

The F region has also risen over this period from a virtual height of 355 at 2250 to 570 at 0040. In fact, the true height at a plasma frequency of 2 Mc/sec is between 400 and 420 km, much above normal. Also the gradients $\dfrac{dh}{d\log fN}$ are greater than normal by a factor of 2–3 early in the evening and by 10 at 0040. The $n(h)$ analysis also showed that at 0040, the valley between E and F must be almost full — there is continuous dense ionization from the bottom of E right through the F region. It is tempting to conclude that the force which "stretched" the F region, causing the large values of $\dfrac{dh}{d\log fN}$, also drove some of the F region ionization down to form the high-E at 0040 and indeed the night-E at 2250.

V. Discussion

Ionospheric studies have not as yet gone very far, but we do know some of the information they will give.

1. Geographical and temporal distributions of activity.
2. Profiles of ionization in height.
3. Electric fields in active regions.

In active regions the transverse conductivities in the ionosphere are increased. Over the daylight hemisphere, transverse conductivities are high, so that the auroral contribution extends and augments the daytime area. In this way it modifies the motions of the magnetosphere.

The magnetosphere has two boundaries. The outer boundary is formed with the solar plasma and may be regarded as the source of energy for the magnetospheric engine. The inner boundary is the ionosphere which acts as a sink. Over a great volume of the magnetosphere the ratio of longitudinal to transverse conductivities is so large that there is very little change of process occurring. The magnetosphere is little more than a coupling device, and the interesting regions are its boundaries.

The aurora occurs on the inner boundary. It seems to me that the acceleration of the auroral particles must also occur here — a machinery of local acceleration. The present tentative results from ionospheric studies are compatible with this idea. They can show activity at latitudes so low that there is very little magnetosphere above it. They also suggest relations between the F region and the auroral E region which would be inevitable with local acceleration.

For extending the present work two courses are naturally open. First, observations of enhanced-E can be used to map regions of augmented conductivity. Secondly, the motions of the F region should be studied, for they are magnetospheric motions.

In conclusion, it is worthwhile to mention an implication for geomagnetism. The wide-spread zones of augmented conductivity in the night hemisphere permit currents to flow which may be hard to distinguish from the classical ring current.

Acknowledgments: This work is part of the research program of the Geophysical Observatory, D.S.I.R., New Zealand—Superintendent, Mr. J. W. Beagley. I wish to thank J. M. Bullen for providing details of her work.

References

BEYNON, W. J. G. and BROWN, G. M. (Editors), 1959, *Annals of the I.G.Y.* III, Pt. I, p. 106.
BULLEN, J. M., 1966, *J. Atmospheric Terrest. Phys.* **28**, 879.
KING, G. A. M., 1965, *J. Atmospheric Terrest. Phys.* **27**, 426.
LINDQUIST, R., 1951, *Transactions of the Chalmers University of Technology, Sweden.* No. 103.

VERY LOW FREQUENCY EMISSION ASSOCIATED WITH AURORA AND PARTICLE PRECIPITATION

Eigil Ungstrup

Ionosphere Laboratory, Technical University of Denmark, Lyngby, Denmark

Since the IGY the interest in VLF radio emissions has increased considerably and the relationship between VLF emissions and other ionospheric and magnetospheric phenomena has been studied extensively. As the VLF emissions are believed to originate in collective interactions between energetic particles in the earth's magnetic field, the study of these phenomena may be of considerable importance in attempts to learn about the dynamical processes in the upper atmosphere.

It is the purpose of this paper to review the observational evidence for correlations between the different types of VLF emissions and aurora and to show the occurrence patterns for the emissions in such a way that they can be directly compared to similar occurrence patterns for aurora and particle precipitation.

Methods of Observation

The receiving equipment used to detect VLF radio emissions consists of an antenna connected to an audio amplifier, followed by some output device. By using a loudspeaker or a set of headphones as an output device, the radio waves are transformed from electromagnetic waves to audio frequency sound waves of the same frequency as the electromagnetic waves and it becomes possible to hear the different types of VLF emission.

The present use of sophisticated detection and recording devices makes possible a much more detailed study of the emissions. It is now common to connect a tape recorder to the output of the amplifier and record the VLF signals at regular intervals. These records can be analyzed on a sound spectrograph that displays the spectrum of the emissions as a function of frequency and time. In another important type of recording the amplifier is followed by a narrow band filter, a detector with a minimum reading circuit, and a chart recorder. The minimum reading circuit makes it possible to distinguish VLF emissions from impulsive interference from lightning flashes, and with such equipment one obtains a recording of the power flux at the observing frequency as a function of time.

Types of VLF Emissions

VLF emissions were first classified according to the impression they gave by listening to them on a loudspeaker, and it is interesting that the first classification is still in use with small modifications. In connection with auroras, the following three types of emissions are of special interest:

a. *Chorus* consists of a multitude of overlapping, rising tones. It usually occurs in the frequency band of 2–4 kHz and it peaks in the morning hours. Its name results from sounds like those of a distant bird colony.

b. *Hiss* usually appears like band limited thermal noise. It is identified aurally by a hissing sound. Hiss usually shows no substantial change in spectrum for periods of minutes or longer, but there can be marked changes in amplitude over periods of the order of a second. It occurs over a wide frequency band with a possible peak in intensity around 8–10 kHz. The diurnal variation shows peak occurrence shortly before magnetic midnight.

c. *Polar Chorus* or polar hiss often sounds almost like chorus but the structure is not nearly as well developed and may be completely missing. It is confined to the frequency range of 500–2000 Hz and it has a seasonal occurrence very different from chorus. It is usually observed in and inside the auroral zone shortly before magnetic noon, but it may appear at night during aurora.

Observations of Correlation between Aurora and VLF Emission

The first direct observation of VLF emission associated with aurora was made in 1932 in New Hampshire by BURTON and BOARDMAN (1933) while they were listening to atmospherics. In the following two decades the interest in VLF phenomena was small and the next observation of VLF emission associated with aurora was not made until 1959 (MARTIN *et al.*, 1960). Since then observations showed that all common types of emissions are at times correlated with aurora. It is convenient to divide the newer observations according to the type of VLF emission involved.

Statistical correlation between visual aurora and hiss has been established by MARTIN *et al.* (1960), JØRGENSEN and UNGSTRUP (1962), and MOROZUMI (1963, 1965). Hiss associated with visual aurora usually appears above 4 kHz but the lower frequency limit may fall below 1 kHz. The upper frequency limit of the observed hiss is often limited by the equipment and it is known at times to exceed 30 kHz.

MARTIN *et al.* (1960) state that the center frequency of the hiss band usually is around 8 kHz and that intensity and band width vary with ionospheric absorption and may vary with the intensity of aurora. During strong absorption the intensity of the hiss drops to an undetectable level even in the presence of intense and active aurora. They also find indications that the center frequency of the hiss may be related to the type of aurora with a center frequency of 9.6 kHz associated with red aurora. They find strong correlation between aurora and hiss on a statistical basis. Their observations were made at Byrd Station, Antarctica, in the southern auroral zone (geomagnetic latitude 70.5° S).

Simultaneous observations of 8 kHz hiss and visual aurora were carried out by JØRGENSEN and UNGSTRUP (1962) at Godhavn, Greenland (geomagnetic latitude 79.9° N), well inside the northern auroral zone. They found a clear correlation between the two phenomena, and furthermore, the intensity variations of the hiss and the aurora were similar.

MOROZUMI (1963) studied the auroral occurrence at the South Pole (geomagnetic latitude 78.0° S) in relation to VLF emission. The auroral occurrence exhibits two diurnal peaks, one near midnight UT and one near noon UT. The midnight peak was related to VLF hiss and the auroras were of the band type. During the noon peak the auroras were of the rayed types with ionospheric absorption and no hiss. There was a chorus maximum at UT noon but no statistical correlation was found between aurora and chorus.

Later studies by MOROZUMI (1965) at Byrd Station confirm the conclusion about two diurnal maxima in activity, one shortly before magnetic midnight and the other in the morning hours magnetic time. During the evening maximum there is a typical sequence of events which Morozumi divides into three phases. The first phase is the prebreakup phase, characterized by VLF hiss, weak aurora, ionospheric absorption and micropulsations, the hiss being the most prominent feature. The second phase is the breakup where there is a sudden onset of strong aurora, micropulsations, and absorption. During this phase large amplitude variations of the hiss occur. In the third or after breakup phase the aurora and the micropulsations get weaker, the hiss disappears but the absorption continues and the VLF emission is of the chorus type.

HARANG *et al.* (1965) studied hiss at Tromsø, Norway (geomagnetic latitude 67.1° N) and found strong positive correlation between aurora and hiss and between hiss and weak auroral absorption events with absorption less than 1 dB at 30 MHz. During strong absorption events, there was a negative correlation between hiss and absorption, possibly because the hiss was absorbed.

BURTON and BOARDMAN (1933) were the first to recognize a correlation between VLF emissions and aurora. Their observations were made in New Hampshire (about 57° geomagnetic latitude) during flaming or flashing aurora and they found "that nearly every flash coincided with a static crash possessing a prominent frying sound. These crashes were in most cases followed by swishes, usually of the descending variety, although occasionally a short ascending whistle occurred simultaneously with the start of the descending swish." This description seems to indicate that they have observed chorus emissions from aurora.

Later RENARD (1961), working at Kerguelen (geomagnetic latitude 57.2° S), observed chorus during flaming aurora. He reports that occasionally chorus is observed in the evening (around 19 LMT) or during the night (around 02–03 LMT). In these cases the reception of chorus is perfectly synchronous with the appearance of flaming aurora near the zenith of the station. The recordings of the 3914Å photometer show a series of peaks at the same time. Renard notes that these temporary increases in the intensity of chorus during evening and night do not show up in the statistical diurnal variation of chorus occurrence.

During a VLF experiment at Fairbanks, Alaska (geomagnetic latitude 65°N) the author (UNGSTRUP, 1966) observed chorus with a warbling or fluttering sound during flaming aurora. In this case short bursts of emission in the 1000–1800 Hz range lasting about 0.1 sec were synchronous with flashes in a patchy glow type of aurora covering the whole sky. Bursts of emission also occurred when fast movements of rays or kinks along a rayed band took place. The VLF emission in this case appeared in the polar chorus band of frequencies but the sounds gave a more fluttering impression than the usual daytime polar chorus. MOROZUMI (1965) observed chorus during aurora at Byrd Station in the southern auroral zone and found that the emission was characteristic of the after breakup phase of the aurora. This agrees well with the author's observations from Alaska.

Only one report of VLF emission during airglow is known to the author. DUNCAN and ELLIS (1959) report on a strong positive correlation between noise bursts on 4.6 kHz and 6300Å airglow recorded at Camden near Sydney (geomagnetic latitude 42° S). The noise bursts usually lasted a few hours. Both phenomena are related to magnetic disturbance and tend to occur when the K-index reaches or exceeds 5.

In summary, hiss in the frequency band of 4–30 kHz is observed to correlate with auroral arcs and bands. In the auroral zone, hiss is a prominent feature of the prebreakup and breakup phases of the aurora. The hiss is steady in intensity during the prebreakup phase, fluctuating in intensity during the breakup, and usually disappearing thereafter. Inside the auroral zone, hiss is associated with auroral arcs and bands. At medium latitudes, chorus appears with flaming or pulsating auroras. The frequency band of this chorus is not known. In the auroral zone polar chorus in the frequency band of 0.5–2.0 kHz is associated with the past breakup phase of the auroras. The association between hiss and airglow is not well established yet, and further investigations are needed. Hiss bursts, associated with airglow, are known to occur rather frequently in medium-high geomagnetic latitudes.

The Morphology of VLF Emissions

Now that we have established the association between the VLF emission and auroral phenomena, let us study the incidence of the different phenomena on a global scale so that they may be compared to similar incidence patterns for aurora and other related phenomena. For this presentation we have chosen the magnetic latitude system defined by MAYAUD (1960). In this coordinate system, latitudes are determined by projecting a ring in the geomagnetic equator along field lines in an expansion of the geomagnetic field upon the surface of the earth. The differences between latitudes in this system and the invariant latitudes of McIlwain are unimportant in connection with the present study. The data are presented in a Mayaud latitude, local geomagnetic time coordinate system.

In Figure 1 a contour map of the percentage of hiss occurrence on moderately disturbed days in 1964 is shown. This map was obtained by removing the 5 quiet and the 5 disturbed days from each month's data and averaging the rest. The contours surround regions in which the hiss bursts with spectral densities above 10^{-15} W·m^{-2}·(Hz)$^{-1}$ occur in a given percentage of hourly intervals. From Figure 1 it appears that in the auroral zone the hiss occurrence is peaked

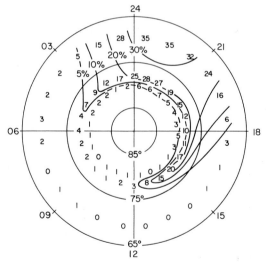

FIGURE 1. Contour map of hiss occurrence on moderately disturbed days in 1964 in magnetic latitude-local magnetic time coordinates. The contours surround regions in which hiss bursts with spectral densities above 10^{-15}W-m^{-2}-(Hz)$^{-1}$ occur in a given percentage of the hourly intervals.

about one hour before magnetic midnight. This is consistent with the occurrence pattern of auroral arcs and bands at that latitude. Between 75° and 80° geomagnetic latitude the percentage occurrence of hiss bursts in the evening hours is smaller, and the bursts are more evenly distributed from the afternoon to the early morning hours. It has been proposed (JØRGENSEN, 1966) that hiss bursts in this latitude range are associated with high intensity electron fluxes observed in the same latitude range by the Alouette I (McDIARMID and BURROWS, 1965) and Injun III satellites (FRITZ and GURNETT, 1965). These intense electron fluxes occur during the same period of the day as the hiss bursts.

The occurrence pattern for chorus is shown in Figure 2, based on observa-

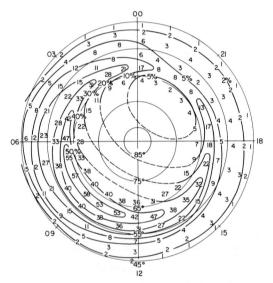

FIGURE 2. Contour map of chorus occurrence in 1957–62 shown in a magnetic latitude-local magnetic time coordinate system. The contours surround regions in which chorus is observed in a given percentage of the hourly recordings.

tions from the period 1957–62. The contours surround regions in which the chorus is observed in a given percentage of the hourly recordings. It appears that the chorus occurrence peaks in the latitude range 60°–63° between 0600 and 1200 local geomagnetic time. The field lines in this latitude range connect to the outer part of the outer radiation belt, and it is likely that the VLF radio waves may be active in determining the decay rate of energetic electrons in the radiation belt (DUNGEY, 1963; CORNWALL, 1964).

The occurrence pattern for polar chorus is shown in Figure 3, based on observations from 1963. The maximum occurrence is found shortly before magnetic noon in the latitude range of 70°–78°. This maximum occurs at the same time as FRANK *et al.* (1964) find the highest median intensity of precipitated electrons of energy greater than 40 keV. The latitude ranges of the electron precipitation and of the polar chorus occurrence also agree.

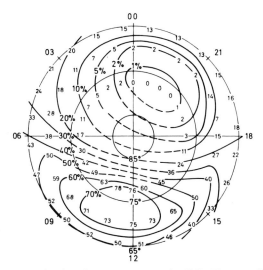

FIGURE 3. Contour map of polar chorus occurrence in 1963. The coordinates are magnetic latitude-local magnetic time and the contours surround regions in which polar chorus is observed in a given percentage of the hourly recordings.

References

BURTON, E. T. and BOARDMAN, E. M., 1933, *Proc. I.R.E.* **21**, 1476.
CORNWALL, J. M., 1964, *J. Geophys. Res.* **69**, 1251.
DUNCAN, R. A. and ELLIS, G. R., 1959, *Nature* **183**, 1618.
DUNGEY, J. W., 1963, *Planetary Space Sci.* **11**, 591.
FRANK, L. A., VAN ALLEN, J. A., and CRAVEN, J. D., 1964, *J. Geophys. Res.* **69**, 3155.
FRITZ, T. A. and GURNETT, D. A., 1965, *J. Geophys. Res.* **70**, 2485.
HARANG, L., LARSEN, R., and SKOGTVEDT, J., 1965 *J. Atmo. Terr. Phys.*, **27**, 1147.
JØRGENSEN, T. S., 1966, *J. Geophys. Res.* **71**, 1367.
JØRGENSEN, T. S. and UNGSTRUP, E., 1962, *Nature* **194**, 462.
MCDIARMID, I. B. and BURROWS, J. R., 1965, *J. Geophys. Res.* **70**, 3031.
MARTIN, L. H., HELLIWELL, R. A., and MARKS, K. R., 1960, *Nature* **187**, 751.
MAYAUD, P. N., 1960, *Ann. Geophys.* **16**, 278.
MOROZUMI, H. M., 1963, *Natl. Acad. Sci., IG Bull.* **73**, 16.
MOROZUMI, H. M., 1965, *Rep. Ionosphere and Space Res. Japan* **19**, 286.
RENARD, C., 1961, *C. R. Acad. Sci., Paris* **252**, 1365.
UNGSTRUP, E., 1966, *J. Geophys. Res.* **71**, 2395.

Discussion

Although VLF emissions have been systematically collected for a long time, the data is just now being put into various formats for comparison with other types of data. Lack of a suitable coordinate system makes correlation difficult.

VLF EMISSIONS OBSERVED NEAR AND SOUTH
OF THE AURORAL ZONE

L. Harang

Norwegian Defence Research Establishment
Kjeller, Norway

Abstract Very low frequency emissions in the 2–14 kHz band have been studied at the Auroral Observatory, Tromsø, during a three year period. Continuous recordings on enhanced emissions at 8 kHz have been compared with geomagnetic activity, riometer absorption, and appearance of aurora. It is shown that bursts of enhanced emissions at 8 kHz regularly appear close to the auroral zone during disturbed conditions with an energy of the order of 10^{-15} -10^{-16} W/m^{2}Hz.

Along with the recordings at Tromsø, simultaneous recordings have been made during February–April, 1966, along a north-south chain of stations: Lycksele, Oslo, and Chambon la Forêt. The recordings from this chain show that two types of enhanced VLF emissions at 8 kHz appear: a *polar* type appearing close to the auroral zone at Tromsø and a *low-latitude* type appearing at the stations of Lycksele and Oslo (these lying 4–10° to the south of Tromsø).

The polar type shows a characteristic annual and diurnal variation. The frequency of appearance is high in the winter months. In October–February the emissions are likely to appear daily for a period of more than one hour. During the summer months, June–July, almost no emissions are recorded. The diurnal curve shows that the emissions are limited to appear within the six hour interval 18–24 MET, with a single maximum at 20.8 hr (which is somewhat before magnetic midnight). The polar type of VLF is thus a night phenomenon. The character of the annual curve is due to absorption in the lower part of the ionosphere. The diurnal curve can be explained as the sum effect of the diurnal curve of primary emissions and the diurnal curve of ionospheric absorption due to geomagnetic and auroral disturbances.

It is shown that the polar emissions recorded close to the auroral zone at Tromsø and which appear only at nighttime can also be traced on the records at Oslo, 10° to the south of the auroral zone, with intensities of about 1/100–1/500 of the Tromsø values.

The polar VLF emissions show a complicated dependence on geomagnetic disturbances and absorption within the ionosphere. Small or moderate geomagnetic disturbances in H appearing early in the night (which often are followed by quiet auroral forms, arcs, and bands on the northern sky) are very frequently accompanied by strong VLF emissions. Sudden and strong commencement in H is usually followed by a strong peak of VLF emission, but when the disturbance develops with strong peaks in H the VLF emissions are completely absorbed. It is pointed out that the close connection between the polar VLF emissions and geomagnetic disturbances is limited to the time interval 18–24 MET. Outside this 6 hr interval VLF emissions do not appear and are independent of the degree of geomagnetic disturbance, auroral activity, and ionospheric absorption.

The riometer absorption (28 MHz) shows the following effects. Small dips of absorption of

0.3–0.7 dB may be accompanied by VLF emissions, and thus there is a positive correlation. When great values of absorption of the order of 1–4 dB are accompanied by a complete cessation of VLF, there is a negative correlation. These two effects indicate conclusively that the VLF emissions are strongly absorbed in a disturbed ionosphere.

The physical properties of the polar VLF emissions have been studied. There seems to be no directional effect of the incoming radiations, these being received simultaneously on two crossed frames. Also the low-latitude VLF do not seem to exhibit directional effects. It is concluded that Tromsø, close to the auroral zone, is lying within an area of arrival of the VLF emissions, and the energies in a burst are coming in from all directions. This point of view is confirmed by polarization studies. The VLF emissions were picked up on two crossed frames, each of which was connected to identical amplifiers and displayed on the pairs of X, Y-plates on an oscillograph. Ordinary broad and irregular VLF bursts showed an irregular oscillograph pattern (of the "snow-ball" type) with changing amplitudes and irregularly appearing reversals of the sense of rotation. The oscillographic pattern is to be explained by the simultaneous arrival of VLF noise trains which are uncorrelated. The frequency spectrum of the polar VLF in the range 2–14 kHz has been studied. It is shown that a sudden burst initially has a high intensity at the higher frequency, while at the end of the burst the relative intensity of the low frequency range has increased. Simultaneous recordings on calibrated 5 channel equipment show the following features. On the lowest frequency, 2.3 kHz, only faint traces could be stated. In the 4–7 kHz band the power spectral densities in strong bursts were of the order of 10–20×10^{-16} W/m²Hz. The intensity increases strongly with increasing frequency, up to 60–70×10^{-16} W/m²Hz at 15 kHz. Thus there is an increase in intensity of 3–5 times.

The low-latitude emissions, recorded 5–10° to the south of the auroral zone, appear only during strong geomagnetic disturbances and appear only on the dayside. These emissions do not appear at the polar station of Tromsø and thus, there seems to be a latitude cutoff effect. There is a time difference of about 12 hr in the diurnal appearance of the polar and low- latitude emissions. Further the low-latitude emissions seem to appear as a post-effect of a great geomagnetic disturbance. In the seven cases when low-latitude emissions have been recorded, the geomagnetic disturbances seem to have been similar to a PCA disturbance. It is pointed out that whereas the polar VLF emissions apparently are produced by the interaction of auroral electrons (in the 10–15 keV range) with the ionosphere or exosphere on the night side, the low-latitude emissions may be produced by the interaction of protons coming in on the day side.

I. Introduction

In this paper the occurrence and physical properties of broad band VLF emissions during disturbed conditions will be discussed. The enhanced emissions of VLF events recorded at Tromsø, lying about 200 km south of the "normal" auroral zone, is a regularly occurring night phenomenon with a characteristic annual and diurnal variation and is closely connected with disturbances within the ionosphere. Those emissions appearing close to the auroral zone are designated as polar VLF emissions, as shown below. Observations at stations lying 5–10° to the south of the auroral zone have revealed other types of VLF emissions which will be designated as low-latitude VLF emissions. These only appear during and after strong geomagnetic disturbances and mainly on the day side. The low-latitude emissions do not appear at Tromsø, a station close to the auroral zone. The analysis of the polar and low-latitude emissions is based on records from a north-south net of stations: Tromsø (70°), Lycksele (64.6°), Oslo (60°), and Chambon la Forêt (48°).

II. Polar VLF Observed at Tromsø

A. Appearance of the Emissions

During midwinter, VLF bursts are likely to occur on most evenings. Figure 1 shows two curves which demonstrate the conditions for appearance of polar VLF at a station close to the auroral zone. During a small geomagnetic dis-

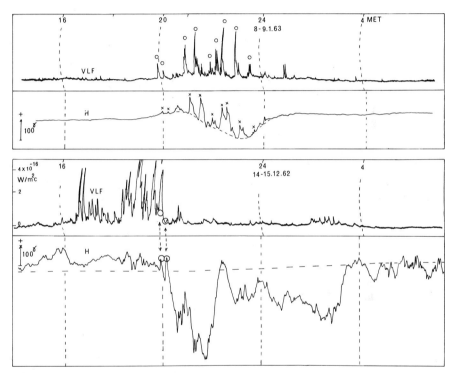

FIGURE 1. Upper Curve: Polar VLF emissions (on 8 kHz) during a small geomagnetic disturbance. The emissions appear at all the small maxima in the disturbance in *H*. Lower Curve: Polar VLF emissions during a strong geomagnetic disturbance. The emissions appear during the first and moderate phase of the storm. During the strong negative phase no emissions are appearing.

turbance a series of VLF bursts may appear which are closely connected with the maxima in the geomagnetic *H*-component. During strong geomagnetic disturbances, emissions are appearing during the first and moderate phase of disturbance, but at the moment when a strong negative amplitude in H develops, no VLF emissions are recorded. It is obvious that at the polar station the amplitude of VLF recorded on the ground is determined by the amount of absorption overhead. This mechanism of absorption of the VLF emissions is more clearly demonstrated from simultaneous riometer records (on 28 mHz), as shown in Figure 2.

The negative correlation between absorption and cessation of VLF always appears for values of absorption above 1–2 dB. For small absorption dips of

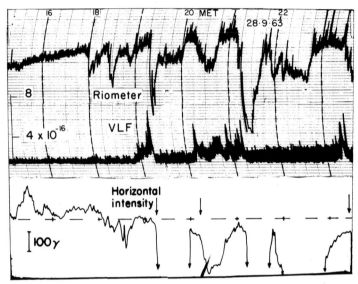

FIGURE 2. Riometer record (on 28 mHz) and polar VLF (on 8 kHz). Strong emissions appear before the absorption dip on the riometer. At the moment when a sudden absorption develops the VLF emission drops to zero.

0.2–0.6 dB, a VLF emission is often observed to coincide with these low absorption dips. There may be a positive correlation. The same complex correlation is also observed with the auroras. One often observes a close correlation between emissions and the formation of faint and medium auroras on the low, northern sky. At a sudden outbreak overhead one usually observes a sudden and sharp VLF amplitude, which, however, rapidly diminishes to zero when auroras develop with great intensity in zenith and over a great part of the sky.

Figure 3 shows the appearance of the polar VLF presented from a period of two years of recordings at Tromsø. The annual variation expressed by the monthly means M (minutes/day) is given in Figure 4. It is evident that during wintertime, emissions appear daily over a time interval of more than one hour. The diurnal variation is presented in Figure 5, which shows the mean hourly numbers, N, of emissions recorded during the two year period.

The annual and diurnal variations of the VLF emissions are compared with the variations of different types of transmissions, the variations of which are fairly well understood. In Figure 6 (left) is the annual variation of the VLF emissions compared with the variation of the monthly means of the noon-

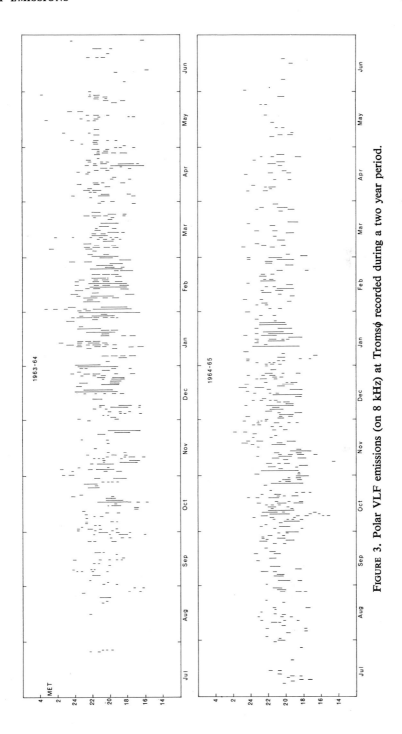

FIGURE 3. Polar VLF emissions (on 8 kHz) at Tromsø recorded during a two year period.

values of the reflection coefficient ρ of 4 mHz echoes from the F-layer measured at Cambridge in 1935. There is a close similarity between these two curves, which indicates that the amount of absorption within the ionosphere is of

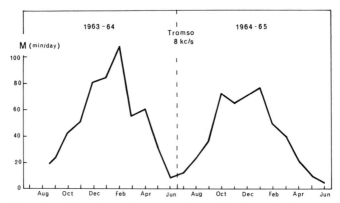

FIGURE 4. Annual variation. Monthly means of the daily burst activity, M, expressed in minutes/day, recorded at Tromsø.

decisive importance for explanation of the annual variation of the polar VLF. The diurnal variation in Figure 5 shows a pronounced maximum at 20.8 hr MET, which is somewhat before magnetic midnight. As previously stated, the occurrence of the VLF emissions will be strongly influenced by

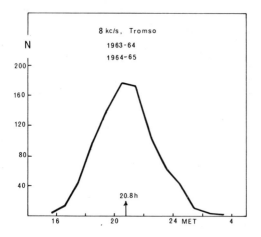

FIGURE 5. Diurnal variation. Hourly means, N, of burst events recorded during a two year period.

the diurnal variation of the absorption. The diurnal variation of the generation of VLF and the absorption will thus counteract, and the diurnal variation of VLF observed on the ground will, therefore, not represent the true diurnal variation of generation of the polar VLF. In Figure 6 (right) the diurnal variation of VLF is compared with the absorption measured by riometer on 28 mHz at Kiruna, which is located about 220 km from Tromsø.

It will be of interest to discuss the numerical estimates of absorption of VLF within the ionosphere. From magnetoionic theory it is possible to calculate numerically the absorption of the VLF waves when passing through a model ionosphere (ALTMAN and CORY, 1963; ONDOH, 1963). Assuming that the ab-

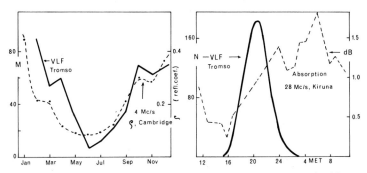

FIGURE 6. Left: Annual variation of the polar VLF at Tromsø compared with noon values of the reflection coefficient, ρ, of 4 mHz s-echoes at Cambridge (APPLETON, 1937). Right: Diurnal variation of polar VLF at Tromsø compared with absorption of 28 mHz radiation (riometer) measured at Kiruna (EGELAND and RIEDLER, 1964).

sorption takes place within the ionosphere at heights 50–170 km, the total amount of absorption of four ionospheric models has been calculated as shown in Table I.

Table I. VLF Absorption

The total ionospheric absorption of VLF waves for various ionospheres from 50–170 km along the geomagnetic line of force (ONDOH, 1963).

Conditions of Ionosphere	4 kHz	10 kHz
Ionosphere during polar blackout near noon	33.1 dB	52.8 dB
Quiet ionosphere near noon	15.4	24.1
Ionosphere during diffuse aurora	16.9	25.3
Quiet ionosphere at midnight in winter	2.2	2.9

Concerning the annual variation, it is of interest to study Figure 6, which shows the annual variation of the reflection coefficient ρ of the F-region echoes at noon, which is similar to the annual variation of the VLF burst activity at Tromsø. The annual variation in ρ is considered to be due to the variations in the amount of absorption in the lower part of the E-layer, and the annual variation of the VLF burst activity must be due to the same effect.

There are no transmissions which exhibit a diurnal variation of the character of the VLF bursts given in Figure 5. We must, however, assume that the primary diurnal curve of VLF burst production above the absorbing layer in the ionosphere is greatly modified by the diurnal curve of absorption, and that the diurnal curve observed on the ground must represent the sum effect of both the diurnal production rate and the cutoff due to absorption. This point of view is supported by the diurnal curve given in Figure 6 (right). The sudden start of the diurnal VLF curve appears at a time of low absorption, and one must assume that the start of the diurnal production rate of VLF bursts at about 16 hr coincide with the start of the diurnal production rate of VLF emissions within the ionosphere. After 23–24 hr, the absorption increases and the sharp decline in the VLF burst rate received on the ground may be due to increased absorption.

From the numerical values of absorption given in Table I, we may draw the following conclusion. The time interval during which VLF bursts are received at Tromsφ, 18–24 MET, should most likely correspond to an ionosphere of the type which is a "quiet ionosphere at midnight in winter," during which the absorption should be of the order of 3 dB. During the sunlit day and, especially, during summer months with midnight sun, it is likely that the absorption must increase 5–10 times in dB.

Several attempts to record VLF emissions within and above the ionosphere via satellites are now being planned. It is thus obvious that a correlation between the appearance of VLF bursts recorded on the ground and within a satel-

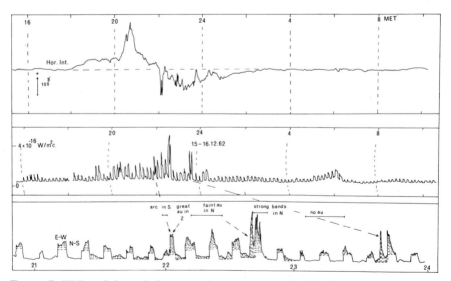

FIGURE 7. VLF emissions during a moderate geomagnetic disturbance accompanied by auroras. Two frames in east-west and north-south are switched alternatively at 5 min intervals. The lower part of the curves are taken with expanded time scale. (The atmospherics noise level is higher in east-west than in north-south.)

lite is only expected to occur during the period of low absorption, 18–24 MET. In the morning period — 2–10 MET — it will, however, be of great interest to investigate if polar VLF emissions can be recorded in satellites. These do not seem to be detectable with the net of ground stations.

B. Physical Properties of the Emissions

By alternative switching between the east-west and north-south frames it is possible to state if a directional effect appears. Figure 7 shows the effect of switching antennas on a series of VLF emissions appearing during a moderate disturbance accompanied by aurora. Records of this type indicate that the emissions do not appear with azimuthal preference. The same nondirectional effect has been stated from observations in Antarctica (MOROZUMI, 1962).

When listening to tapes of VLF emissions and comparing these with tapes of white noise within the same frequency band, there is a striking difference — the VLF emissions are often intermingled with sudden cracks. The start of VLF emissions could also be different. Very often a sharp VLF burst starts with trains of sudden discrete cracks and short, strong trains of bursts, which gradually merge together into continuous emissions. Figure 8 shows how a strong emission is being built up by sudden discrete trains which merge together and finally constitute a continuous emission.

If one assumes that one is observing within an area of VLF precipitation with the waves coming in from overhead as circularly polarized radiation, it should be possible to state a polarization effect. A polarimeter was built consisting of two crossed frames, each connected to amplifiers and the amplitudes displayed on the pairs of X, Y-plates. In Figure 9, atmospherics on the upper part and on the lower part of a VLF burst are shown. The atmospherics exhibit the usual directional effect, the VLF burst shows amplitudes of noise character, and the sense of rotation changes irregularly. The oscillograph pattern of the VLF emission, of a "snow-ball" type, is to be explained by simultaneous arrivals of series of noise trains which are uncorrelated. Patterns of this type are known in acoustics in the study of simultaneous arrivals of uncorrelated white noise trains.

In some cases, however, when observing with the polarimeter on very sharp and sudden bursts, the trace appeared almost circular and exhibited the same sense of rotation. In these cases, apparently only one single train of energy is received and one may assume that it was coming from overhead and was to be circularly polarized.

Wide band records covering the frequency range 2–15 kHz have been performed. From the narrow band records on 8 kHz it is evident that the mean amplitudes are changing rapidly. During a burst event which could last for hours the maximum time for holding constant amplitudes was only some few minutes. In Figure 10 is presented the spectral analysis of a part of a strong VLF

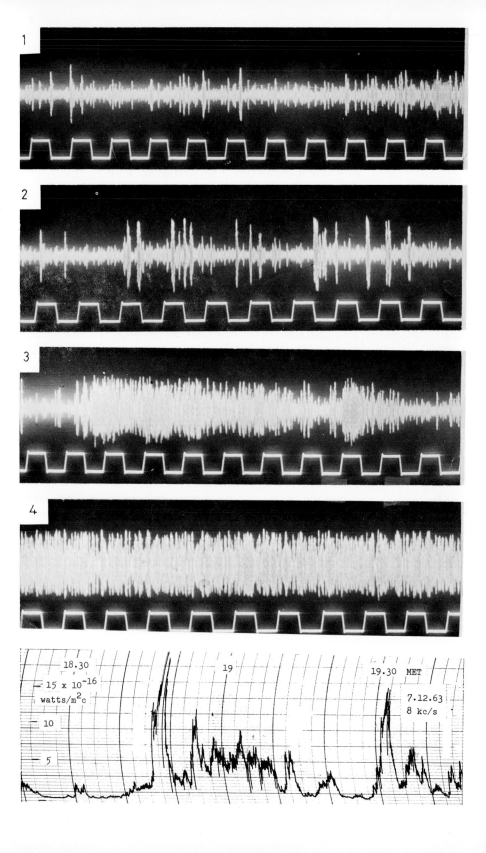

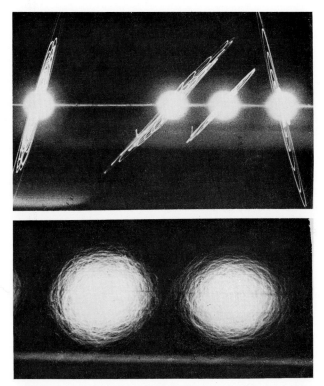

FIGURE 9. Observations with polarimeter. Upper part: Atmospherics coming in from various azimuthal directions, Lower Part: Burst of VLF emission. The direction of rotation is changing irregularly. The "snow-ball" character indicated simultaneous reception of series of nois trains which are uncorrelated.

emission. The amplitude-frequency change with time demonstrated in Figure 10 has been stated in a number of cases. Quantitative measurements show further that the intensity increases with frequency and that the maximum intensity must lie above 15 kHz. Observations at the Antarctica station by MOROZUMI (1965) indicate the same effect. He points out that the hiss center seems to lie higher than 20 kHz.

During the winter of 1965–6 the records at the lower latitude stations of Lycksele and Oslo showed indications of VLF emissions which are simultaneous with the polar emissions appearing in Tromsø. At Tromsø the mean amplitude of the background noise is only a fraction of the polar VLF emissions. This means that the polar bursts appear as well developed amplitudes above a zero

FIGURE 8. The start of a strong VLF emission on 8 kHz displayed on an oscillograph: 1) shows the noise level with atmospherics, 2) separate, short VLF trains appear, which in 3) and 4) merge together into a continuous emission. At the bottom the curve showing the complete burst event is given.

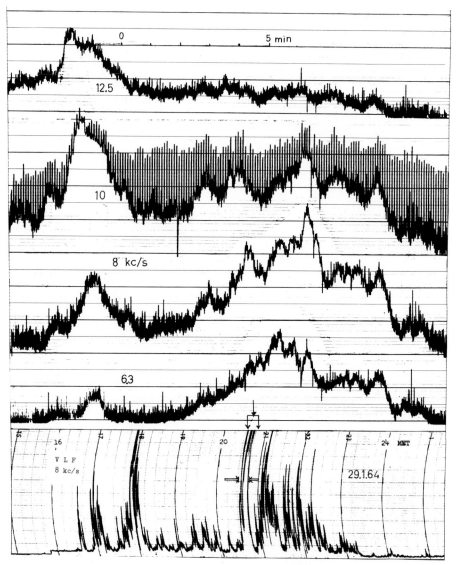

FIGURE 10. Frequency analysis of a short section of a burst (indicated by arrows) which lasted for several hours. The high frequency range, 12–10 kHz, exhibits large amplitudes at the start of the burst. At the end, the energy is strongest on the lower frequency at 6 kHz.

plateau. At the stations of Lycksele and Oslo, however, the gain of the amplifier had to be increased several orders of magnitude in order to trace the faint VLF emissions. This means that on these records the polar emissions are "riding" on a high level of terrestrial noise, and in most cases the faint VLF emissions can only be traced as small secondary maxima and identified only through comparison with the Troms\phi records. Figure 11 shows simultaneous records of polar VLF emissions over a north-south chain of stations covering a latitude decrease of 10°. The intensity of the VLF burst at Oslo is about 1/300 of the

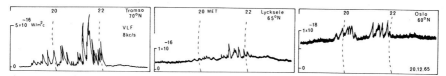

FIGURE 11. Polar VLF emissions (on 8 kHz) observed along a north-south chain of stations.

intensity at Troms\phi. Series of observations indicate that the decrease is of the order 1/100–1/500.

III. Low-Latitude VLF Emissions Observed at Stations South of the Auroral Zone

In the preceding chapters it has been shown that polar VLF emissions recorded close to the auroral zone can be traced on the records at Oslo, lying 10° to the south, with an intensity of 1/100–1/500 of the intensity at Troms\phi. During the months February–April, 1966, however, seven cases of strong VLF emissions have been recorded at the southern stations of Lycksele and Oslo, which were not accompanied by any noticeable emissions at Troms\phi. The appearance of these emissions is different in character from the polar emissions, and will in the following be designated as low-latitude emissions. Figure 12 shows an example of emissions during which strong absorption and geomagnetic disturbances were also recorded at Troms\phi.

The appearance of the low-latitude emissions is illustrated in Figures 13 and 14. In previous sections it has been shown that the appearance of the polar VLF emissions is limited to the hours 21 ± 4 hr; these emissions have not been recorded at daytime. The low-latitude emissions, however, appear almost only during daylight. In some cases the emission started just before sunrise but continued apparently unchanged during daylight. In Figure 13 the diurnal appearance of the low-latitude emissions has been compared with the polar emissions at Troms\phi. There is a time difference of about 12 hr in the mean appearance.

The difference both in time and latitude of the polar and the low-latitude emissions indicates that the process of excitation may be different. This should mean that the frequency spectrum and other characteristics of these two types of radiations may be different. In the analysis of the polar VLF, it was shown that the strongest VLF emissions appeared during weak and moderate geomagnetic storms. The low-latitude emissions, however, appear only during very strong geomagnetic disturbances. Further, there is a tendency for these

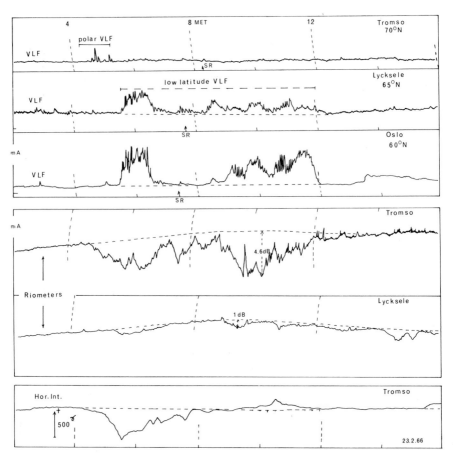

FIGURE 12. Low-latitude VLF emissions appearing at Lycksele-Oslo at daytime, no simultaneous emissions appear at Tromsø. At Tromsø, polar VLF emissions appear at nighttime.

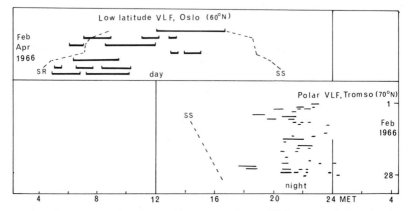

FIGURE 13. The low-latitude VLF emissions at Oslo at 60°N appear during the day, the polar VLF at Tromsø at 70°N only at night. (All observations at 8 kHz.)

emissions to appear not at the beginning or during the most intense phase of the disturbance, but during the last phase or even at the end of a disturbance. Figure 14 shows the appearance of low-latitude VLF in three cases appearing

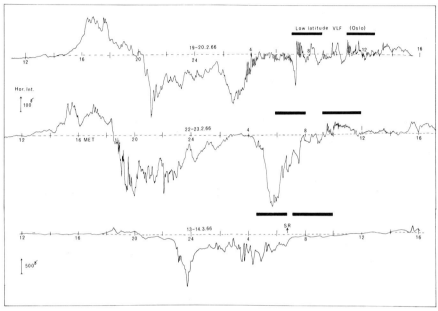

FIGURE 14. Low-latitude VLF emissions (on 8 kHz) during strong geomagnetic disturbances. The VLF appears at the end of the storm, 10–16 hr after the start.

at the end of a strong geomagnetic disturbance (10–16 hr after the start). ELLIS (1960) has pointed out that the VLF emissions recorded by him in Australia showed the same effect.

In one case a VLF emission has been recorded on 8 kHz which only occurred at Oslo (see Figure 15). During this burst the east-west and north-south frames were switched alternatively and it is apparent that no directional effect on the development of the burst amplitude seems to appear. The burst started about 2 hr after a strong riometer absorption was recorded at Tromsø.

It is commonly assumed that the VLF emissions are generated through the interaction of charged particles with the ionosphere or exosphere. For polar VLF emissions it is assumed that the primary particles are 10–50 keV electrons which are like those producing the auroras. For the low-latitude emissions, which occur on the day side and which also seem to exhibit a latitude cutoff effect, it is more probable that the primary charged particles may be protons of the same kind which produce PCA events. The geomagnetic disturbance visible in Figure 12 resembles a PCA disturbance.

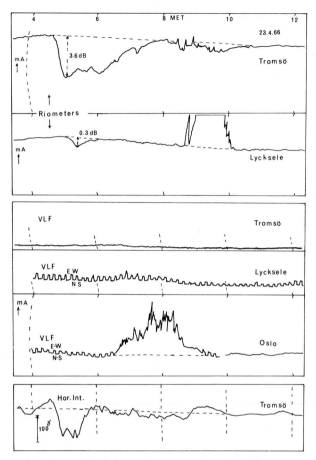

FIGURE 15. Low-latitude emission that only appeared at Oslo. East-west and north-south frames were switched alternatively, and it is apparent that no directional effect on the development of the burst amplitude seems to appear.

References

ALTMAN, C. and CORY, H., 1962, *J. Geophys. Res.* **67**, 4086.
ELLIS, G. R., 1957, *J. Atmospheric Terrest. Phys.* **10**, 302.
ELLIS, G. R., 1959, *Planetary Space Sci.* **1**, 253.
ELLIS, G. R., 1960, *J. Geophys. Res.* **65**, 839.
HARANG, L., 1958, *Geophys. Publ.* **20**, 5.
HARANG *et al.*, Scientific Report No. 5, Contract No. AF 61(052)-811, June 15, 1966.
HARANG, L. and HAUGE, K. N., 1965, *J. Atmospheric Terrest. Phys.* **27**, 499.
HARANG, L. and LARSEN, R., 1965, *J. Atmospheric Terrest. Phys.* **27**, 481.
HARANG, L., LARSEN, R., and SKOGTVEDT, J., 1965, *J. Atmospheric Terrest. Phys.* **27**, 1147.
MOROZUMI, H., 1962, Thesis, Dept. of Physics and Astronomy, State University of Iowa.
MOROZUMI, H., 1965, private communication.
ONDOH, T., 1963, *J. Geomag. Geol.* **15**, 90.

SATELLITE OBSERVATIONS OF PARTICLE
FLUXES AND ATMOSPHERIC EMISSIONS*

Brian J. O'Brien

Department of Space Science
Rice University
Houston, Texas

*Research supported in part by the National Aeronautics and Space Administration under Contract NAS6-1061 and the Department of the Navy, Office of Naval Research under Contract Nonr-4964(1).

Abstract A survey is given of satellite-borne measurements of precipitated particles (in Part I) and of atmospheric emissions of light (in Part II). In Part I the survey shows that while there are increasingly comprehensive measurements of particle precipitation, the basic dynamical causes are still unknown and indeed it is difficult to formulate a definitive experiment in this regard. It is known, however, that there is "always" finite precipitation in the auroral zone (just as Part II shows that there is "always" some emission of auroral light) so that the unknown source must be continuously active. The latitude and diurnal variations of electron and proton precipitation are discussed in detail. Part II summarizes the satellite-borne photometric studies, which have been thwarted by vehicle failures in eight out of twelve studies. Preliminary results of airglow studies (all as yet unpublished) are presented. Principal results have been obtained to date in auroral studies rather than in airglow. Simultaneous measurements of auroral light and the particles exciting it are discussed. Technical advantages and disadvantages of satellite-borne photometry are listed, together with promising lines of future research.

Part I: Summary of Relevant Particle
Measurements Made from Satellites

I. Introduction

In this Symposium on Aurora and Airglow (so often linked like "Tweedledum and Tweedledee"), it is well to begin by distinguishing one phenomenon from the other. To quote CHAMBERLAIN (1961), "The most frustrating aspect of defining the airglow lies in distinguishing it from the aurora." One might adopt the simple approach that "If you can see it, it's an aurora; if you can't see it, it's airglow." But clearly this distinction fails, for example, with bright mid-latitude red arcs, with mantle auroras, and with daytime auroras. Therefore, here I adopt a different distinction, and state that if the atmospheric excitation is due to direct bombardment of atmospheric constituents by nonthermal ("energetic") charged particles we should call it an aurora (e.g., O'BRIEN *et al.*, 1965). Thus, in this first part, discussions of satellite observations of particle fluxes lead to a concentration of attention on the relation of those particle fluxes to auroras. An historical review of the interrelation of particle fluxes and auroras has been given elsewhere (O'BRIEN, 1964a) and only a summary is presented here.

The first direct observation of "auroral particles" (i.e. the energetic particles that bombard the atmosphere to cause auroras) was made with rockoons by a group from the State University of Iowa (VAN ALLEN, 1957). The latitude distribution of counting rate of a geiger tube at an altitude of ≈ 100 km was found to have an "anomalous" increase around magnetic latitude $\lambda \approx 67°$, i.e. in the auroral zone. This increase can now be understood as a statistically prevalent zone of maximum intensity of "precipitated" electrons, i.e. those that plunge into the atmosphere from high altitudes.

During the same period, ground-based studies of Doppler-shifted Balmer emissions showed that although protons with energies up to ≈ 100 keV bombarded the atmosphere during some auroras, they did not carry sufficient energy flux to sustain the auroral luminosity (OMHOLT, 1963). MCILWAIN (1960) fired rockets into auroras, and showed that the brighter auroral displays are excited by bombardment by electrons with energy of ≈ 1–10 keV. The dominant problem then became — where do these electrons come from and how do they acquire their energy and other spatial and temporal characteristics?

With the discovery of the geomagnetically trapped radiation with Explorer I (VAN ALLEN *et al.*, 1958), auroral studies became intimately interwoven with satellite studies of energetic charged particles in the magnetosphere. The several historical developments in this relation have been discussed in detail elsewhere (O'BRIEN, 1964a) and they may be summarized as:

(a) discovery and study of particles in the "loss cone," i.e., precipitated particles (KRASSOVSKY *et al.*, 1962; O'BRIEN, 1962);

(b) discovery that the flux of outer-zone trapped electrons was one thousand times smaller than some previous estimates (GRINGAUZ *et al.*, 1962; O'BRIEN *et al.*, 1962) and hence, that the Van Allen zone was an inadequate reservoir or "leaky bucket" for auroral electrons, with later validation that if Van Allen and auroral particles were related at all, it was in the nature of a "splash-catcher" relation (O'BRIEN, 1964b);

(c) discovery of the high-latitude boundary of trapping, its local time dependence, and its crude correspondence to the auroral zone (O'BRIEN, 1964b) and the discovery of the magnetopause in the equatorial plane (FREEMAN *et al.*, 1963);

(d) discovery of the "neutral sheet" in the extended magnetospheric tail (NESS *et al.*, 1964);

(e) experimental verification of the existence of the collisionless shock front in the equatorial plane (NESS *et al.*, 1964).

The charged particle environment of the earth is now known to be as it is sketched in Figure 1, although very little exploration has been carried out at the higher latitudes between altitudes of some 3000 km (O'BRIEN, 1964b) and 17 R_e

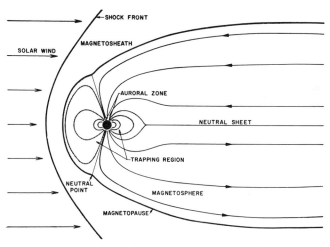

FIGURE 1. Sketch of particle-environment domains in the vicinity of the earth.

(BAME *et al.*, 1966). Here I will not embark on the important but very complicated problems posed by these particle distributions at high altitudes, nor deal with the problem of actually tracing auroral-zone field lines back into the equatorial plane to determine if they are "open" or "closed" (NESS *et al.*, 1964; TAYLOR and HONES, 1964; DESSLER and JUDAY, 1965). Instead, I will concentrate on satellite measurements made near the "feet" of the magnetic field lines at altitudes between about 200 km and 3000 km. Thus, I will concentrate on the relation of these measurements to auroras on an "input-output" basis, and will only summarize some of the broader questions on the origins and causes of particle precipitation.

II. Particle Dynamics

An energetic charged particle must hit the atmosphere in order to produce auroral luminosity. Since most auroras are brightest at an altitude of about 100 km, this altitude is usually chosen to define (somewhat artificially) a distinction between "trapped" and "precipitated" particles. Thus, trapped particles are those whose high-altitude trajectories are such that, without perturbation by atmospheric scattering but with conservation of their magnetic-moment invariant (μ) they would mirror (i.e., have pitch angle $\alpha = 90°$) at an altitude above 100 km. It is then assumed that they would thus have an appreciable probability of mirroring without any collisions, so that they would bounce back to the other hemisphere, i.e. be trapped. Precipitated particles are those that, with the above assumptions, would tend to mirror at altitudes below 100 km.

One can thus define a pitch angle (α_D) at any altitude on a given line of magnetic force, such that particles with $0 \leq \alpha \leq \alpha_D$ are deemed to be precipitated, and those with $\alpha_D < \alpha \leq 90°$ are trapped. One can calculate α_D at any point where the local field strength is B by making use of the magnetic-moment invariant which may be written (see review by VAN ALLEN, 1963):

$$\frac{\sin^2 \alpha}{B} = \frac{1}{B_m}$$

where B_m is the field strength at which the chosen particle trajectory would mirror. Then clearly

$$\frac{\sin^2 \alpha_D}{B} = \frac{1}{B_{100 \text{ km}}}.$$

Thus, for example, on the field line above the rocket range at Fort Churchill, $\alpha_D = 55°$ at 1000 km altitude, while at 10,000 km it is about 14°, and in the equatorial plane it would be only about 2° if one assumed that the geomagnetic field was undistorted.

It is necessary to add words of caution on the artificiality of this loss cone, historically defined for electrons with about 100 keV energy. First, for precipitated electrons, there is a 10–20% probability of Coulomb backscattering from the atmosphere. Also, for low-energy (e.g. 1–10 keV) electrons the altitude of 100 km is actually below the altitude at which they are completely absorbed. The loss cone is therefore energy dependent. Furthermore, for energetic ions subject to temporary and repeated neutralization by charge exchange, the trajectories need to be calculated carefully to allow for the time spent as neutral atoms traveling unaffected by the Lorentz force and hence disobeying the magnetic-moment invariant (e.g. see DAVIDSON, 1965). This effect leads to additional complications for alpha particles since they can become He^+ as well as neutral He. For example, for 100 keV alphas even at the relatively high altitude of 250 km, only a few per cent still retain two positive charges, with the remainder about an equal proportion of He^+ and He. Consequently, if one wishes to detect primary He^{++} energetic ions above an aurora with electrostatic deflection devices, one must fire rockets or satellites to a far higher altitude than the nominal 100 km. Alternatively phrased, the loss cones for electrons and for such ions are not identical.

Another and particularly troublesome amendment to the above definition of a loss cone must be made in order to allow for localized magnetic (CUMMINGS et al., 1966) or electrostatic or other (MOZER and BRUSTON, 1966) effects. For example (CUMMINGS et al., 1966) the localized distortion of the geomagnetic field near an auroral electrojet can lead to a localized "magnetic bottle" and other effects not treated in the above definition of a loss cone. Nevertheless, this simplifying approach does permit quantitative intercomparisons of satellite, rocket, and ground-based data, and we continue to follow it generally here.

III. Electron and Proton Precipitation

I will continue to concentrate here on satellite observations of particle precipitation, even though ground-based balloon or rocket-borne instrumentation have in many cases made vital data impractical to attain with satellites that move across auroral structures with velocities of some 7 km/sec. Reviews of balloon-borne measurements have been given recently by ANDERSON and MILTON (1964) while rocket studies have been summarized by CUMMINGS et al. (1966), and MOZER and BRUSTON (1966), and in several papers in this volume. A general related review has been given by HULTQVIST (1964), who tabulated experimental studies.

The early satellite measurements of precipitated electrons were somewhat hindered by relatively primitive instrumentation in the most important electron energy range, viz $1 \lesssim E_e \lesssim 10$ keV (McILWAIN, 1960). Consequently, the early ($\approx$1962–4) studies were most concentrated on electrons with energy $E_e \gtrsim 40$ keV, as detected by thin-windowed (1.2 mg cm^{-2}) geiger tubes (see, for example, O'BRIEN, 1964a; McDIARMID and BURROWS, 1965; also MANN et al., 1964).

An extensive summary of these studies was given by O'BRIEN (1964b) and Figures 2 and 3 are taken from that summary. In general, that survey showed, for electrons with $E_e \gtrsim 40$ keV at $\approx$1000 km altitudes, that:

(1) The flux of locally trapped or quasi-trapped particles *increased* above auroras so as to maintain approximate isotropy over the upper hemisphere (see Part II, O'BRIEN, 1967). (Whether such isotropy persists for all energies and at higher altitudes is one of the presently unsolved major problems.)

(2) The average world-wide energy dissipation by particle precipitation in the auroral zones is $\approx 4 \times 10^{17}$ ergs sec^{-1} or about 1% of the average energy brought by the solar wind to the front of the magnetosphere, with an average auroral-zone deposition of a few ergs cm^{-2} sec^{-1}.

(3) The precipitated flux varied by a factor of more than 10^6 in time and space near the auroral zone (see Figure 3), although no property of the solar wind is known to vary by this amount.

(4) There is "always" precipitation and "always" an aurora (see Part II, O'BRIEN, 1967) near the auroral zone, so that the unknown source must be

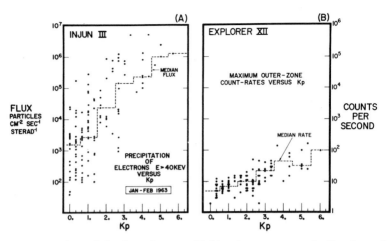

FIGURE 2. Comparison of the dependence on K_p (the planetary magnetic disturbance index) of the maximum flux of precipitated electrons and the maximum flux of trapped electrons with $E_e > 40$ keV, where "maximum" pertains to a survey over all L values at $L > 3$ (O'BRIEN, 1964 b).

continually active. (Early theories were concerned mainly with the "great" auroras that follow large solar disturbances whereas recent theories have treated the continuous aurora, being encouraged since the solar wind and magnetosphere rotation are also continuously present.)

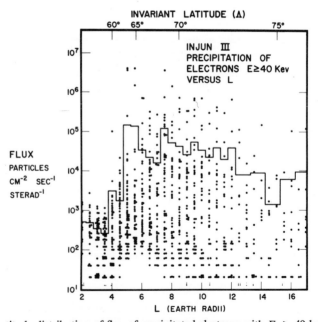

FIGURE 3. Latitude distribution of flux of precipitated electrons with $E_e > 40$ keV (O'BRIEN, 1964 b). Note that the variations at a given latitude are real variations in time, since the statistical or sampling errors are negligible.

(5) The nighttime auroral zone as found by photometers lies near the high-latitude boundary of trapping, although whether it is inside or outside or straddling the boundary is presently unknown (simply because particles with $\alpha \approx 90°$ above auroras may not be truly trapped in the stable magnetosphere, but one cannot examine this problem satisfactorily with a single satellite). McDiarmid and Burrows (1965) have drawn attention to the fact (not evident here in Figure 3) that occasionally there are extremely intense "spikes" in space of electrons with $E_e \gtrsim 40$ keV inside the polar cap, i.e. at latitudes higher than the so-called boundary of trapping.

Other early satellite studies include the detection with Injun 1 of the most intense natural flux yet found by a satellite, viz, some 2000 ergs cm^{-2} sec^{-1} of electrons with energy $E_e \gtrsim 1$ keV (O'Brien and Laughlin, 1962). It is interesting to note that in spite of many years of high-altitude measurements, no comparably intense fluxes have been found near the equatorial plane. Since these fluxes, if isotropic in the equatorial plane, could not be contained or guided by the ambient magnetic field of some tens of gammas (cf. McIlwain, 1960) it is possible that if they occur in the equatorial plane at all (a point not yet proven) it may be that they occupy such a small solid angle (say around **B**) that spinning satellites with directional detectors would sample them inefficiently, if at all.

McIlwain (1960) drew attention to the fact that the energy spectra of auroral electrons were much softer than those of electrons then observed in the near-equatorial plane. This experimental difference has now largely disappeared as probes have reached out with refined instrumentation to some 12–30 R$_e$. Studies such as those by Konradi (1966) and by Bame et al. (1966) (see Figure 4) in these regions find electron spectra not clearly distinguishable from some of those found in auroras. Thus, although the *intensities* found to date in the equatorial plane are not as large as found in auroras, this may be largely due to experimental limitations mentioned above rather than to the lack of an inter-relation.

The most definitive satellite studies of both electron and proton precipitation have been carried out in several short-duration (few days') flights by the Lockheed group. Their "Input-Output" studies have been presented at this Sympo-

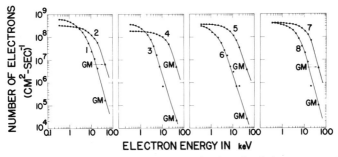

Figure 4. Electron energy spectra found at 17 R$_e$ in the tail of the magnetosphere (Bame et al., 1966).

sium already by Johnson and Meyerott, and I concentrate here more on their particle measurements alone.

One of the most dramatic findings is that of two separate zones of electron precipitation on the dayside (Figure 5). Lower-energy electrons ($0.08 \leq E_e \leq 21$

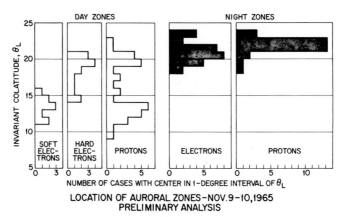

FIGURE 5. Location of auroral zones as defined by precipitation of electrons and protons during both day and night (JOHNSON et al., 1966).

keV) were observed around magnetic latitudes 75° N, while higher energies were found around 69° N (JOHNSON et al., 1966; see also FRITZ and GURNETT, 1965). This finding strengthens the conclusion of O'BRIEN (1964b) that the high-latitude boundary of trapping and the auroral zone are at much the same location. O'BRIEN's (1964b) data were based on his simultaneous observations of auroral luminosity and particle fluxes and were confined to local night. However, in 1961, O'BRIEN (1963) found that the high-latitude boundary of trapping was at invariant latitude $\Lambda \approx 69°$ at night and at $\Lambda \approx 75°$ in the day during magnetically quiet conditions. The data of JOHNSON et al. (1966), therefore, extend this interrelation of auroral zone and boundary of trapping to the day side also. Unfortunately, its theoretical implication is still not exactly understood, although a magnetospheric model such as that of DESSLER and JUDAY (1965) would lead to such an interrelation.

The Lockheed findings of a "hard" and "soft" daylight zone also serve to resolve a controversy about the applicability of O'BRIEN's (1964b) finding to the day side. It was pointed out (e.g. by N. Brice at the NATO Advanced Study Institute on Radiation Trapped in the Earth's Magnetic Field, Bergen, Norway, August 1965) that peak daytime auroral disturbance (e.g. as measured by riometers) is at $\Lambda \approx 65°$ rather than at the daytime boundary of trapping of $\Lambda \approx 75°$. Since riometers respond most efficiently to harder electrons such as those in the lower-latitude zone by JOHNSON et al. (1966), this discrepancy is removed.

Extensive studies of precipitation of low-energy protons have been made most recently again by the Lockheed group (SHARP et al., 1966; SHARP et al., 1964; and JOHNSON et al., 1966) and earlier by MIHALOV and MOZER (1963).

During a $2\frac{1}{2}$ day period of magnetic quiet, SHARP et al. (1966) found proton fluxes over northern and southern auroral zones with a peak of about 0.3 ergs cm^{-2} sec^{-1}. The spectra appeared crudely consistent with exponential forms with e-folding energies of some 10–20 keV, and the angular distributions appeared "consistent with isotropy over the loss cone to a factor of about two." With relatively few statistical samples two distinct daytime zones were found with maximum intensities at invariant latitudes $\approx 70°$ and $77°$, to be contrasted with the single nighttime maximum at about $68°$. Such zones of proton precipitation may be compared with electron precipitation discussed above (see Figure 5).

Such bimodal daytime zones are worthy of considerable theoretical attention. First-order approaches that invoke differences in longitudinal drifting of particles mirroring at low and high altitudes are being adopted by numerous workers, and other complex trajectory studies are being made (e.g. see TAYLOR and HONES, 1965), and it seems possible that in such studies lie answers to the fundamental questions:

(a) where were these "auroral particles" ten seconds ago, or a day ago?
(b) how did they acquire their energy?
(c) how were they precipitated and what happened to them on the way?

One associated problem that is receiving attention from the Rice University group is a photometric and rocket-borne experiment to seek alpha particles in primary auroral fluxes, thus using the p/α ratio as a "tracer" to determine the source of these ions.

The Lockheed group (EVANS et al., 1966) has made the very important simultaneous observations of the low-energy protons and electrons over the auroral zone. They found (Figure 6) that precipitated protons bring into the atmosphere an appreciable proportion (some 10–20%) of the total input from electrons and protons.

One of the most important measurements of auroral electrons is a determination of whether the differential energy spectrum has a pronounced maximum at a finite energy (about 1 keV). Such a condition could lead to growth of plasma instabilities (I am indebted to Dr. C. McIlwain and Mr. R. LaQuey for stimulating speculations on this problem). Unfortunately, it is not yet clear (from any experimental measurements known to me) that such a condition occasionally prevails. Threshold-type detectors which measure integral fluxes are inadequate to resolve this important matter, and differential instruments flown to date have had experimental uncertainties sufficiently large to obscure resolution of this matter. I regard this as one of the most urgent experimental problems to be resolved conclusively, and hopefully, at various pitch angles above an aurora.

Generalizations about characteristic energy spectra and time variations are difficult to make because each parameter is itself greatly variable with time and

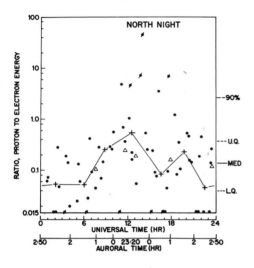

FIGURE 6. Comparison of total energy deposited in the atmosphere by precipitated electrons and protons (EVANS *et al.*, 1966).

space. In any event, as yet only balloon-borne and some rocket-based studies have definitely demonstrated the existence of significant temporal variations (see ANDERSON and MILTON, 1964) and their significance is not yet understood. Similarly, the significance of the widely variable energy spectra is not yet understood.

There is indeed a singular lack of coherence in any discussion of the above parameters. Such coherence may ultimately come from one of two sources:

(a) an exhaustive and very comprehensive experimental study of several auroral events, or
(b) from theoretical analysis of the causes, transportation, and effects of such particle fluxes.

Both these approaches are likely to take a considerable amount of time before there is a significant "break-through" in our comprehension of the particle dynamics involved in auroral phenomena. Indeed, one of the major problems in studies of particle precipitation is not so much the implementation of an experiment, but rather the very formulation of what is a truly definitive and conclusive experiment.

Acknowledgments   This research was supported in part by the National Aeronautics and Space Administration under Contract NAS6-1061 and by the Department of the Navy, Office of Naval Research Contract Nonr-4964(1). Valuable discussions with members of the Space Science Department of Rice University are acknowledged with thanks.

References

ANDERSON, K. A. and MILTON, D. W., 1964, *J. Geophys. Res.* **69**, 4457–4480.

BAME, S. J., ASBRIDGE, J. R., FELTHAUSER, H. E., OLSON, R. A., and STRONG, I. B., 1966, *Phys. Rev. Letters* **16**, 138.

CHAMBERLAIN, J. W., 1961, *Physics of the Aurora and Airglow*, Academic Press, New York.

CUMMINGS, D., LAQUEY, R. D., O'BRIEN, B. J., and WALT, M., 1966, *J. Geophys. Res.* **71**, 1399–1407.

DAVIDSON, G. T., 1965, *J. Geophys. Res.* **70**, 1061–1068.

DESSLER, A. J. and JUDAY, R. D., 1965, *Planetary Space Sci.* **13**, 63–72.

EVANS, J. E., JOKI, E. G., JOHNSON, R. G., and SHARP, R. D., 1966, *Space Research VI*, North-Holland Publishing Co.

FREEMAN, J. W., VAN ALLEN, J. A., and CAHILL, L. J., 1963, *J. Geophys. Res.* **68**, 2121–2130.

FRITZ, T. A. and GURNETT, D. A., 1965, *J. Geophys. Res.* **70**, 2485–2502.

GRINGAUZ, K. I., KURT, V. G., MOROZ, V. I., and SHKLOVSKY, I. S., 1962, Isk. Sput. Zemli, Ac. Sci. USSR, No. 6, 108, 1961; trans: *Planetary Space Sci.* **9**, 21.

HULTQVIST, B., 1964, Goddard Space Flight Center Publication X-611-64-97.

JOHNSON, R. G., REAGAN, J. B., SHARP, R. D., SHEA, M. F., and SHOOK, G. B., 1966, *J. Geophys. Res.* (to be published).

KONRADI, A., 1966, *J. Geophys. Res.* **71**, 2317–2325.

KRASSOVSKY, V. I., SHKLOVSKY, I. S., GALPERIN, Yu I., SVETLITSKY, E. M., KUSHNIR, Yu M., and BORDOVSKY, G. A., 1962, Isk. Sput. Zemli, Ac. Sci. USSR, No. 6, 113, 1961; trans: *Planetary Space Sci.* **9**, 27.

McDIARMID, I. B. and BURROWS, J. R., 1965, *J. Geophys. Res.* **70**, 3031–3044.

McILWAIN, C. E., 1960, *J. Geophys. Res.* **65**, 2727–2747.

MANN, L. G., BLOOM, S. D., and WEST, H. I., JR., 1963, *Space Research III*, North-Holland Publishing Co., 447–462.

MIHALOV, J. D. and MOZER, F. S., 1963, *Trans. Am. Geophys. Union*, **44**, 881–882.

MOZER, F. S. and BRUSTON, P. J., 1966, Technical Report on NsG 243–62, Series 7, No. 21, Space Sciences Laboratory, University of California, Berkeley.

NESS, N. F., SCEARCE, C. S., and SEEK, J. B., 1964, *J. Geophys. Res.* **69**, 3531–3569.

O'BRIEN, B. J., 1962, *J. Geophys. Res.* **67**, 3687–3706.

O'BRIEN, B. J., 1963, *J. Geophys. Res.* **68**, 989–996.

O'BRIEN, B. J., 1964 a, *Space Research IV*, North-Holland Publishing Co., 8–35.

O'BRIEN, B. J., 1964 b, *J. Geophys. Res.* **69**, 13–44.

O'BRIEN, B. J., ALLUM, F. R., and GOLDWIRE, H. C., 1965, *J. Geophys. Res.* **70**, 161–176.

O'BRIEN, B. J. and LAUGHLIN, C. D., 1962, *J. Geophys. Res.* **67**, 2667–2672.

O'BRIEN, B. J. and TAYLOR, H., 1964, *J. Geophys. Res.* **69**, 45–63.

O'BRIEN, B. J., VAN ALLEN, J. A., LAUGHLIN, C. D., and FRANK, L. A., 1962, *J. Geophys. Res.* **67**, 397.

OMHOLT, A., 1963, *Planetary Space Sci.* **10**, 247–262.

SHARP, R. D., EVANS, J. E., IMHOF, W. L., JOHNSON, R. G., REAGAN, J. B., and SMITH, R. V., 1964, *J. Geophys. Res.* **69**, 2721.

SHARP, R. D., JOHNSON, R. G., SHEA, M. F., and SHOOK, G. B., 1966, *J. Geophys. Res.* (to be published).

TAYLOR, H. E. and HONES, E. W., JR., 1965, *J. Geophys. Res.* **70**, 3605–3628.

VAN ALLEN, J. A., 1957, *Proc. Natl. Acad. Sci. U.S.* **43**, 57–92.

VAN ALLEN, J. A., 1963, *Space Science* (Ed. by D. P. LeGalley), John Wiley and Sons, New York, 226–274.

VAN ALLEN, J. A., LUDWIG, G. H., RAY, E. C., and McILWAIN, C. E., 1958, IGY Satellite Report, Series No. 3, National Academy of Sciences, National Research Council, Washington, D. C., 73–92.

Part II. Summary of Satellite Observations of Emissions

I. Introduction

Satellite or spacecraft observations of airglow and aurora emissions are relatively few in number if one excludes the manned spacecraft studies. Relevant measurements from unmanned spacecraft are listed in Table I. Several visual

Table I. Unmanned Spacecraft Used in Airglow/Aurora Studies

Spacecraft	Operational Life	Instruments	Airglow/Aurora		Reference
Injun 1	June 29, 1961– January, 1963	5577Å photometer	Obscured		O'BRIEN (1964)
USAF	November 6, 1962 (two orbits)	5577Å photometer	√	X	ELLIOTT et al., (1963, private
		6300Å photometer	√	X	communication)
Injun 3	December, 1962– September, 1963 (complete lifetime)	5577Å photometer	√	√	O'BRIEN and TAYLOR (1964)
		3914Å photometer	X	√	
		5577Å photometer	√	√	
OSO-B	February, 1965– 1966 (complete lifetime)	2 prs. photometers (4300 ± 500) Å (5200 ±500) Å	√	X	NEY (private communications)
OGO-II	October 14, 1965– October 24, 1965 (≈40 hrs operational with ≈2 hrs in eclipse).	6300Å photometer	√	√	REED and BLAMONT (1966)
		Multiple emission photometer	√	√	
		uv ion chambers (1230–1350Å, Lyα)	√	X	MANGE (private communication)
		uv spectrometer (1100–3400Å)	√	X	BARTH and WALLACE (private communication)
USAF	November, 1965 (125 auroral-zone crossings)	2-3914Å photometers	X	√	EVANS et al., (1966)
		2-UV photometers (≈1300–1800)Å	√	√	

√ = indicates this phenomenon *could be* detected in the experiment.
X = indicates phenomenon *could not be* detected in the experiment.

and instrumental studies of airglow have been made by U.S. astronauts (cf. GILLETT et al., 1964) with principal findings relating to the height of the 5577Å airglow emissions. There have been press reports of auroral observations by the USSR Cosmonauts in their higher-inclination orbits, but I know of no published scientific papers.

It is useful to summarize the reasons why one should trouble to make air-glow or auroral observations from a satellite as distinct from the ground. (I regard short-duration rocket-borne measurements here principally useful as exploratory probes rather than for systematic morphological studies.)

Satellite-borne measurements have the following advantages:

(a) They are made with no obscuring clouds and little absorbing or scattering atmosphere between the emission layer and the detector. Thus, one can study visible emissions with cloud-cover only a second-order problem (because of varied albedo). One can study, for example, ultraviolet emissions at $\lambda \lesssim 3800$Å which are absorbed at lower altitudes by ozone, etc. so that a ground-based instrument cannot measure them.

(b) As a consequence of advantage (a), one can easily study daytime auroras by measuring uv emissions where an aurora is bright but albedo and rayleigh scattering are weak, i.e., where the sunlit earth appears black. Suitable spectral ranges are ≈ 1400–1800Å. (This suggestion was first mentioned to the writer by Dr. F. Roach in 1961.)

(c) A satellite can rapidly make spatial surveys, particularly useful over un-inhabited regions.

(d) Particle detectors and other devices on a magnetically oriented satellite can be combined with photometers to measure both auroral cause and effects (see Figure 1, O'BRIEN and TAYLOR, 1964) or "input-output" effects (JOHNSON and MEYEROTT, this volume). The logistic problems for the alternative approach using just particle detectors on a satellite and photometers on the ground were found to be relatively severe (O'BRIEN et al., 1960).

(e) The satellite orbit, being essentially fixed in inertial space and, hence, temporarily fixed in local time, can be utilized, e.g., to test hypotheses such as the one that auroral structures are more or less fixed in local time.

Satellite observations of emissions do have unique potential sources of contamination, as summarized by O'BRIEN and TAYLOR (1964):

1. By sunlight scattering off the atmosphere on parts of the satellite.
2. By similar moonlight effects.
3. By reflection from the earth (variable, depending on surface).
4. By lightning.
5. By man-made lights.
6. By x-ray bombardment of the photometers producing enhanced "dark" current.
7. By heating of the photometers producing enhanced dark current.

Experimental techniques to minimize these effects were presented by O'BRIEN and TAYLOR (1964). An additional problem is the quantitative correction necessary because of variable albedo of the emission itself. We estimate that this sets an upper limit of $\pm 20\%$ to the absolute accuracy of satellite observations. Historically, a far more serious problem seems to have been that the gods frown on photometric studies from satellites. For example, the 5577Å photometer on Injun 1 operated perfectly for about eighteen months, but its field of view was blocked by a highly polished aluminum satellite, Greb, because a separation system failed (O'BRIEN and TAYLOR, 1964). Injun 2, with 5577Å and 6300Å photometers, was plunged into the ocean in January, 1962 due to a rocket failure. Elliott and his colleagues of Aerospace Corporation have attempted photometric studies with four satellites that — one after the other — sank into the ocean. (ELLIOTT, private communication). The observatory POGO or OGO-II was orbited satisfactorily, but its sophisticated orientation schemes failed and only about two hours of useful eclipsed data were acquired (REED and BLAMONT, 1966). Consequently, a summary such as this note illustrates the major disadvantage of satellite studies of aurora and airglow emissions, viz, only four successful launches out of twelve attempts are known to us.

II. Airglow and Dayglow

Manned spacecraft data indicate an airglow layer some (24 ± 3) km thick with an altitude varying between 77 km and 110 km (GILLETT et al., 1964). The principal result of importance was that the altitude of peak emission appeared to show a real variation in space. This is a problem of very great interest insofar as it bears on the chemical causes of airglow but is a problem unresolved by ground-based studies because of the inherent problems in the Van Rhijn technique, and unresolved by rocket flights (e.g. PACKARD, 1961; TAVASOVA and SLEPOVA, 1964; NAGATA et al., 1965; and O'BRIEN et al., 1965) because of cost and related factors that limit the number of flights.

Manned spacecraft (GILLETT et al., 1964) and OSO-B data (NEY, private communication) also appear to show that there is no dust layer of appreciable opacity at the airglow layers. The photographs made from manned spacecraft (GILLETT et al., 1964) also clearly indicate lightning strokes that can appreciably contaminate satellite studies. ELLIOTT (private communication) mentions that for part of his data the "satellite track followed a weather front and the spurious signals correlated with the weather station reports of lightning activity."

There are no *published* airglow data from unmanned spacecraft that as yet add materially to information collected from the ground. There is general support of the well-known general characteristics such as:

(a) 5577Å airglow displayed an absolute minimum at the equator (ELLIOTT, private communication).

(b) Airglow in the green and blue displays a patchiness, with an intensity variation of less than some 250% (NEY, private communication).

(c) 6300Å emission rate varied in the nightglow $\approx 25 - \lesssim 1$ photon cm^{-3} sec^{-1}, while in twilight it was typically 20–50 photons cm^{-3} sec^{-1} (REED and BLAMONT, 1966).

(d) The airglow 5577Å intensity is roughly the same at latitudes just above and below the auroral zone (e.g. see Figure 7 of O'BRIEN and TAYLOR, 1964).

To date, five years of these satellite measurements known to me have yielded relatively little. However, it may be expected that further satellite studies will contribute new and original data to the study of airglow. For example, the uv spectrometer and an ion chamber are measuring mainly the interesting dayglow emissions at 1216Å and 1304Å, (BARTH, private communication and MANGE, private communication).

III. Auroral Data

Satellites have been much more fruitful in studies of auroral phenomena. Their particular utility is in cause-and-effect or input-output studies (e.g., see Figure 1) where they have the advantage over ground-based measurements that detect only "effects" or the "output," e.g. of auroral light.

The simultaneous observation of an aurora and its cause as determined from

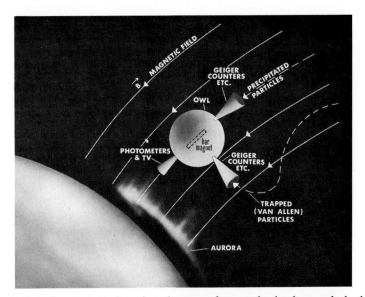

FIGURE 1. Use of a magnetically oriented spacecraft to study simultaneously both auroral "cause" (i.e. precipitated particles) and "effect" (i.e. emitted light). Note that the geomagnetic field constrains and guides the charged particles as they spiral in to hit the atmosphere. Gravitationally oriented satellites lack this advantage, although they have other advantages, e.g. they can view near horizon for brighter emissions and for altitude data.

the magnetically oriented satellite Injun 3 are plotted in Figure 2 (O'BRIEN and TAYLOR, 1964). Numerous other detectors and a VLF experiment gave correlated data not shown in this figure. Many such observations validated the

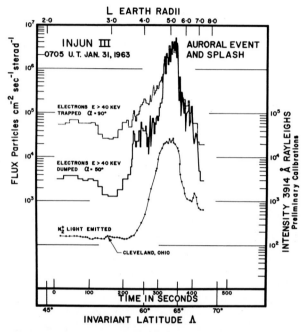

FIGURE 2. Simultaneous observation of an aurora and some of the precipitated particles that caused it. Note the approach to isotropy of trapped and precipitated particles, as well as the rapid decrease in intensity of both at higher latitudes, i.e. above the "boundary of trapping" (O'BRIEN, 1964).

concept of the "splash-catcher" model, wherein it was stated that, *if* Van Allen and auroral particles are related at all, it is only in the sense that both may have a common cause, rather than in the sense that the first category is the origin of the second (e.g., see O'BRIEN, 1964). Furthermore, this measurement established directly for the first time on an event-by-event basis, the very important association between the boundary of trapping and the auroral zone (see Part I, O'BRIEN, 1967, this volume).

From some fifty nighttime passes of Injun 3 (see Figure 3), profiles of intensity of 5577Å and 3914Å were derived (O'BRIEN and TAYLOR, 1964). Comparisons were made, for example, between the latitude profile of the mean 5577Å intensity and the classical VESTINE and SIBLEY (1959) "auroral zone" of *probability* of visible auroras (Figure 4). Rather a more useful graph (Figure 5) shows the very important fact that in the first few months of 1963 there was a continuous emission of N_2^+ 3914Å in the auroral zone. Since the energy of excitation of this emission is some 19 eV, it is generally agreed that its emission

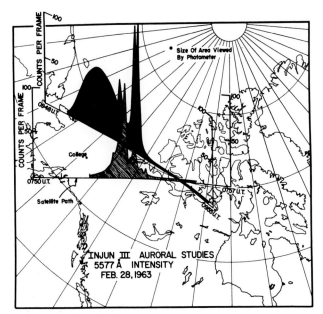

FIGURE 3. Samples of auroras detected by Injun 3. Note the decrease of intensity to the airglow plateau (O'BRIEN and TAYLOR, 1964).

at night requires a source of energetic radiation, e.g., auroral particles, cosmic rays, x rays, etc. (see O'BRIEN et al., 1965). From this it was concluded that auroras are continuously present in the auroral zone, albeit occasionally with less than the threshold of visibility (O'BRIEN and TAYLOR, 1964). Accordingly,

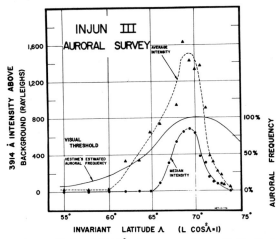

FIGURE 4. Comparison of Injun 3 3914Å photometer data with Vestine's auroral isochasms. The satellite data came from some fifty northern hemisphere nighttime new-moon passes early in 1963 (O'BRIEN and TAYLOR, 1964).

the source of auroral particles must be continuously active. This was verified by the same satellite (O'BRIEN, 1964). The Injun 3 data on 3914Å emissions were also used to derive the average total energy deposited by auroral particles in the earth's atmosphere and comparisons were again made with direct measure-

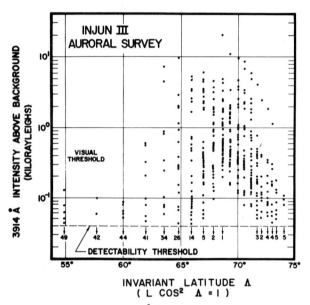

FIGURE 5. Individual measurements of 3914Å intensity as a function of latitude during some fifty passes of Injun 3. The accuracy of each datum point is much better than the scatter of points at a given latitude. Note that there is always finite emission in the auroral zone (O'BRIEN and TAYLOR, 1964).

ments of the particles with the same satellite (see Part I, O'BRIEN, 1967, this volume).

EVANS *et al.*, (1966) have obtained information on both 3914Å emission and middle uv (≈ 1600Å) auroral emissions. Several cases were found in which the intensity in each band was comparable, but in other cases the uv intensity was considerably greater than that of the 3914Å. The Lockheed group is currently studying particle-flux interrelations and characteristics that might lead to such real changes (EVANS, private communication).

In an earlier experiment, the Lockheed group made a satellite measurement of particle fluxes and compared this with ground-based measurement of the auroral light (SHARP *et al.*, 1964). The combined study indicated that, in at least one rather unusual auroral form and in the regions of low-level luminosity outside of discrete forms, electrons of energy less than a few keV carried an appreciable fraction of the precipitated energy.

REED and BLAMONT (1966) obtained photometric data from a few passes over the northern polar cap, during relatively quiet geomagnetic conditions (0321 and 1347 UT, October 23, 1965). Using as a first approximation the relatively crude assumption that the auroral emission was in uniform horizontal layers, they were able to deduce the altitude distribution of the emission of 6300Å. In particular, they found that the evening (1700 hr local time) sunlit aurora had peak emission at 250 km, while the morning aurora (0400 hr) had peak emission at some 200 km. Further examples and information on the actual horizontal distributions will be needed to validate this interesting finding.

In general, it may be concluded then, that satellite studies of auroral emissions have already provided uniquely valuable data. However, I suggest here again that the potential value of such studies has not yet been realized, in large part because of the ill fortune mentioned above.

IV. Future Studies

It seems appropriate to mention briefly some of the research problems that currently await satellite-borne measurements of auroral and airglow emissions.

Television photography of auroras is essentially within the state of an art, and it is planned to fly sensitive vidicons on the magnetically oriented Rice University/NASA satellites code-named OWLS early in 1968. The particular applications of this project are:

(a) to study conjugacy of auroral forms;
(b) to study auroral morphology (e.g. to examine their local time dependence, the occurrence of multiple arcs, etc.);
(c) to relate the TV snapshots to data from numerous photometers and particle detectors on the same satellites.

It may be useful to note here that if the Owls and their TV operate successfully, then once per week each will be able to provide interested auroral researchers with details and photographs of auroras in the area magnetically conjugate to each auroral observatory.

On this same point of collaboration, it is planned to orbit in the second quarter of 1967 a Rice University/ONR satellite code-named "Aurora 1." This magnetically oriented satellite will carry a particle detector to make differential and integral spectral measurements of precipitated electrons and protons with energy of some 50 eV to 150 keV in the northern hemisphere. Photometers will measure four auroral and airglow emissions. The satellite will transmit continuously in a simple FM/FSK mode suitable for easy reduction of data by interested auroral observers.

Distant television photography of terrestrial auroras is another technique of potentially great value and currently within the state of an art form. One can easily envisage a TV base from the moon or, more simply, from a geostationary satellite so as to photograph both Aurora Borealis and Aurora Australis. Alternatively, with a high-inclination, high-altitude satellite one could utilize an elliptical orbit to produce essentially a "zoom-lens" effect with varying spatial resolution.

It may reasonably be expected then, that principal future progress in space-borne investigations of auroral emissions will be in:

(a) TV studies;
(b) studies of uv and other "obscured" emissions;
(c) morphological or synoptic studies, and
(d) coordinated studies in which related experiments are performed on the single satellite.

Acknowledgments This research was supported in part by the National Aeronautics and Space Administration under Contract NAS6-1061 and by the Department of the Navy, Office of Naval Research Contract Nonr-4964(1).

References

EVANS, J. E., JOKI, E. G., and STARR, W. L., 1966, *Trans. Am. Geophys. Union* 47, 64.

GILLETT, F. C., HUCH, W. F., NEY, E. P., and COOPER, G., 1964, *J. Geophys. Res.* 69, 2827–2834.

JOHNSON, R. G. and MEYEROTT, R., 1967, this volume.

O'BRIEN, B. J., 1964, *J. Geophys. Res.* 69, 13–44.

O'BRIEN, B. J., ALLUM, F. R., and GOLDWIRE, H. C., 1965, *J. Geophys. Res.* 70, 161–176.

O'BRIEN, B. J. and TAYLOR, H., 1964, *J. Geophys. Res.* 69, 45–65.

O'BRIEN, B. J., VAN ALLEN, J. A., ROACH, F. E., and GARTLEIN, C., 1960, *J. Geophys. Res.*, 65, 2759–2766.

NAGATA, T., TOHMATSU, T., and OGAWA, T., 1965, *Planetary Space Sci.* 13, 1273–1282.

PACKER, D. M., 1961, *Ann. Geophys.* 17, 67–75.

REED, E. I. and BLAMONT, J. E., 1966, Goddard Space Flight Center Publication X-613-66-190 (revised).

SHARP, R. D., EVANS, J. E., IMHOF, W. L., JOHNSON, R. G., REAGAN, J. B., and SMITH, R. V., 1964, *J. Geophys. Res.* 69, 2721–2730.

TARASOVA, T. M. and SLEPOVA, V. A., 1964, *Geomagnetizm i Aeronomya* 4, 321–327.

VESTINE, E. H. and SIBLEY, W. L., 1959, *J. Geophsy. Res.* 64, 1338–1339.

PRELIMINARY OBSERVATION OF 6300Å
PREDAWN ENHANCEMENT AT ARECIBO

H. C. Carlson, Jr.

Arecibo Ionospheric Observatory
Cornell University
Ithaca, New York

Incoherent backscatter measurements of ionospheric electron temperatures made at the Arecibo Ionospheric Observatory are reported below. Their interpretation in terms of a streaming of photoelectrons from a sunlit magnetic conjugate ionosphere leads one to expect a predawn enhancement of 6300Å airglow (HANSON, 1963; COLE, 1965; CARLSON, 1966). Preliminary observational confirmation of this enhancement is presented.

The Arecibo Ionospheric Observatory (A.I.O.) (GORDON and LA LONDE, 1961; GORDON, 1964) is located at geographic latitude 18.4° N, longitude 66.9° W. However, as indicated in Figure 1, which is drawn to scale, its magnetic

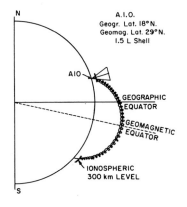

FIGURE 1. Scale figure of geomagnetic geometry relevant to A.I.O.

latitude is 29° N (300 km level is about the 1.5 L shell) so that its magnetic conjugate point is at about 46° S, and at roughly the same longitude. Thus there is a large difference between the sunrise times at A.I.O. and its magnetic conjugate point.

By means of the incoherent backscatter technique, ionic compositions and charged particle temperatures and density can be measured (e.g., see EVANS and LOEWENTHAL, 1964). Electron temperature, T_e, behavior for a day representative of the equinox and summer period is shown in Figure 2. Each data point

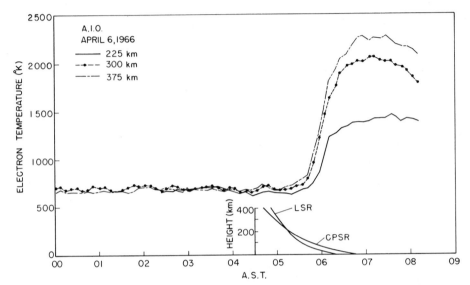

FIGURE 2. Variation of electron temperature with time characteristic of the equinox or summer. Local and conjugate point geometrical sunrise times are also shown vs. altitude.

represents an average of about 10 min in time (reducing the uncertainty to about ±5%) and an averaging in altitude over no more than 75 km centered on the altitude indicated. Data are taken at all altitudes simultaneously; however, for simplicity, only the 300 km data points are shown. Also shown are times of local and conjugate point geometrical sunrise vs. altitudes. Note the constant isothermal temperature through the F region until near local sunrise, at which time the temperature almost simultaneously starts to rise sharply at all altitudes.

By contrast, note the T_e behavior during the winter period, as on the day shown in Figure 3. The electron temperatures at and above 300 km start to rise well before the local sunrise increase occurs. At 225 km, T_e does not increase noticeably before near local sunrise. While the net change in T_e during this pre-sunrise heating period varies from day to day, the times at which T_e starts to increase during the pre-sunrise and local sunrise period change with season in a systematic way. These times are plotted against season in Figure 4. Also shown in this figure are curves of the seasonal variation of the times of ground sunrise and the times of a solar zenith angle of 98° and 99° for A.I.O. and its magnetic conjugate point. Thus the pre-sunrise increase in T_e is clearly associated with sunrise in the magnetic conjugate region.

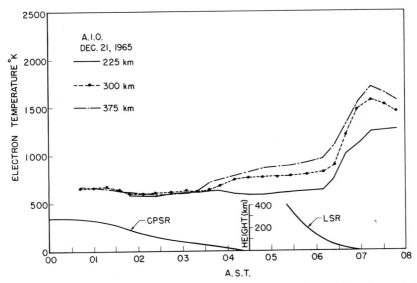

FIGURE 3. Variation of electron temperature with time characteristic of the winter solstice. Local and conjugate point geometrical sunrise times are also shown vs. altitude.

This pre-local sunrise electron heating is interpreted in terms of a streaming of photoelectrons from the sunlit magnetic conjugate ionosphere in view of this and a number of other consistencies with the data (CARLSON, 1966). The

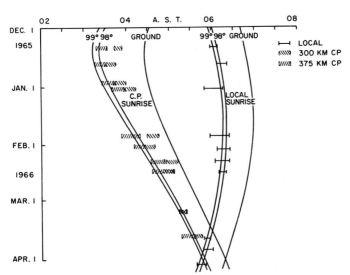

FIGURE 4. Seasonal variation of observed times of onset of electron temperature increases for the local and pre-local sunrise heating periods. Also shown are times of ground sunrise and 98° and 99° solar zenith angles for A.I.O. and its magnetic conjugate point.

following model for this mechanism emerges from current theory. An appreciable fraction of photoelectrons produced near and above an altitude of about 300 km (HANSON, 1963) in the 10–30 eV energy range (MARIANI, 1964) can escape upward without collisions and spiral along magnetic field lines to the conjugate ionosphere. This escaping flux near sunrise should not be much less than the order of HANSON's (1963) daytime estimate of 10^9 photoelectrons cm^{-2} sec^{-1}. The photoelectron travel time between conjugate ionospheres is a fraction of a minute; electrical neutrality is thought to be maintained by an ambient electron current; and the potential difference set up between hemispheres produces no significant retardation.

Upon entering the conjugate ionosphere from the topside, the photoelectron flux, essentially independent of altitude, first has its principal energy loss directly to the ambient electrons, thus raising T_e (HANSON and JOHNSON, 1961; HANSON, 1963; DALGARNO et al., 1963; GEISLER and BOWHILL, 1965). Then, descending to rapidly increasing neutral-particle densities, the photoelectrons are rapidly thermalized somewhat below 300 km, losing the great bulk of their energy through inelastic collisions with atomic oxygen, in which excitation of the 1D state is important.

This raises the question of a consequent 6300Å airglow enhancement by these photoelectrons. Indeed enhancement due to conjugate point photoelectrons has already been suggested by COLE (1965), although he suggested indirect enhancement by thermal electrons heated by the photoelectrons. To check such an enhancement at A.I.O., a turret photometer (PURDY et al., 1961) was installed in mid-February observing 6300, 5577, 5893, and the continuum 5300Å wavelengths once each 5 min cycle. In Figure 5, the relative intensities

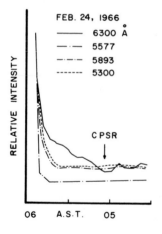

FIGURE 5. Relative intensity of the night sky observed through 6300, 5577, 5893, and 5300Å filters vs. time near sunrise. The arrow indicates expected time of onset of 6300Å enhancement.

seen on these wavelengths are plotted through the relevant sunrise period. The arrow, indicating the relevant conjugate point sunrise time for which photoelectrons start streaming in over the observatory, agrees quite well with the time at which the 6300Å starts to become enhanced for the day shown in this figure and on other days when observations could be made. This time is before the normal twilight increase of 6300Å airglow.

Data such as these, once reduced to absolute rayleighs and used in conjunction with the incoherent backscatter measurements of T_e (and electron density) should define the relative roles of indirect (COLE, 1965) and direct (CARLSON, 1966) enhancement of 6300Å airglow by the conjugate point photoelectrons during this predawn enhancement period.

There will be a lower and upper latitude limit to this predawn enhancement. The former is simply due to the eventual absence of a meaningful conjugate ionosphere. Qualitatively, the latter could be imposed by the magnetic field lines being swept out in the magnetospheric tail, by the potential difference built up between hemispheres by the stream, or by energy loss due to collisions in traversing the field line. It would, therefore, be fruitful to determine from past or future data, this upper latitude cutoff at a given time and also as a function of the solar cycle.

Acknowledgments The author is grateful to Dr. Franklin Roach for helpful discussions on photometry and for expediting the transfer of a photometer to A.I.O. and for making possible the photometric observations of last winter. He is grateful to Richard Alexander for installation and initial instruction in the use of the instrument, and to Sam Harris for automating many facets of the instrument.

The Arecibo Ionospheric Observatory is operated by Cornell University with the support of the Advanced Research Projects Agency under a research contract with the Air Force Office of Scientific Research.

References

CARLSON, H. C., 1966, *J. Geophys. Res.* 71 (1), 195.
COLE, K. D., 1965, *Ann. Geophys.* 21, 156.
DALGARNO, M. B., MCELROY, and MOFFETT, R. J., 1963, *Planetary Space Sci.* 11, 463.
EVANS, J. V. and LOEWENTHAL, M., 1964, *Planetary Space Sci.* 12, 915.
GEISLER, J. E. and BOWHILL, S. A., 1965 a, *J. Atmospheric Terrest. Phys.* 27, 457.
GORDON, W. E., 1964, *IEEE Trans.* AP-12, 872.
GORDON, W. E. and LALONDE, L. M., 1961, *IRE Trans.* AP-9, 17.
HANSON, W. B., 1963, *Space Res.* 3, 282.
HANSON, W. B. and JOHNSON, F. S., 1961, *Mem. Soc. Roy. Sci. Liége* 4, 390.
MARIANI, F., 1964, *J. Geophys. Res.* 69 (3), 556.
PURDY, C. M., MEGILL, L. R., and ROACH, F. E., 1961, *J. Res. Natl. Bur. Std.* 65C, 213–216.

Session

8

CONFERENCE SUMMARY

Edited by

Dr. Martin Walt

Lockheed Palo Alto Laboratory

CONFERENCE SUMMARY

Edited by Martin Walt

Lockheed Palo Alto Laboratory

In the final session, a panel consisting of Drs. S. Chapman, S.-I. Akasofu, B. J. O'Brien, A. Vallance Jones, A. Omholt, F. E. Roach, and L. Thomas presented its views on the status of auroral and airglow research. The purpose of the panel report was to give a concise review of the preceding papers, to emphasize the most important results, and to point out crucial areas where further effort is needed.

As will be brought out by the remarks of various panel members, progress in observing and understanding aurora and airglow has been widespread in the last few years. The enormous quantity of new data presented at this conference, the development of new concepts, and the rejection of ideas which have not withstood the test of further work all attest to the advances which are taking place. Unfortunately, the subjects of aurora and airglow involve so many scientific disciplines that it is difficult for an individual to be aware of the achievements in specialties which are far removed from his own. The present conference, in which investigators representing all aspects of aurora and airglow research convened for a two week period in an undistracting environment, was especially valuable in exposing specialists to the varied manifestations of these remarkable natural phenomena.

The reader is cautioned that the opinions of the summary *rapporteurs* are not always in agreement with those of the conference speakers, and indeed, the previous speakers have disagreed among themselves in many areas. Also, evaluating the importance of various achievements and assessing the need for further work are subjective matters, and another panel might arrive at different conclusions. These differing opinions are merely one consequence of the fact that the mechanisms of aurora and airglow are not understood at present, and there are many possible interpretations of the observational information.

The summary is divided into sections, each dealing with a somewhat self-contained aspect of auroral and airglow phenomena. This division was arbitrary and was dictated largely by the composition of the panel. However, an attempt was made to organize the material into a logical pattern beginning with solar-terrestrial relationships and the magnetospheric configuration, progressing to the energetic particle features and auroral classifications, and concluding with the detailed role of atmospheric processes in aurora and airglow production.

The Solar Wind and the Magnetosphere*

In 1930, Chapman and Ferraro inferred that a stream of solar plasma impinging on the geomagnetic field would compress and confine it in a cavity. Electric currents (DCF) flowing over the surface would annul the geomagnetic field in the plasma and distort it in the cavity. In 1940, further work showed in detail how the stream particles could be deflected from a magnetic field, with almost all the change of motion occurring in the thin DCF current layer.

Many years later, Martyn hypothesized the cavity formation as due to a balance between the normal component of gas pressure and the internal magnetic pressure at the boundary. This concept has been used by several authors to infer the form of the cavity. The calculations were made without the consideration of an interplanetary magnetic field or an atmosphere within the cavity. In 1962 Axford and Kellogg independently concluded that the magnetic field carried by the stream would give the gas a scale length (the Larmor radius) far smaller and, therefore, more significant than the mean-free-path between collisions. On this basis they inferred that a shock front would be outside the cavity boundary and a transition region of disordered magnetic field between the shock and the cavity. These inferences have been confirmed by satellite measurements.

When the plasma stream is enhanced, the geomagnetic field becomes intensified. This feature appears at the earth's surface as an increase in the horizontal magnetic force H, and is the first phase of a typical magnetic storm. The initial increase is usually followed by a much larger decrease known as the main phase. There is then a recovery period, proceeding rapidly at first, then at a slower rate. The main phase is ascribed to the growth and decay of a ring current (not necessarily symmetrical) within the cavity. This current and its field are called DR.

The great sweep of the main phase is made irregular by a current system that flows mainly in the ionosphere and most strongly along two narrow belts coinciding with the auroral oval. This current system is called DP. It may grow and decay spasmodically several times during a great storm. Each such episode is called a polar magnetic substorm, and it coincides with an auroral substorm. There is an association between the DR and DP (ring and polar) currents. The initial H increase caused by an enhanced plasma stream may or may not be followed by the development of the ring current field DR giving a main phase. If a ring current develops, there are also DP substorms, but not otherwise.

Akasofu and Chapman concluded that a solar stream must have some additional feature that will determine whether or not the initial increase is followed by DR and DP, and suggested this feature might be the magnetic field transported from the sun. Dungey ascribes great importance to this field through the neutral points produced by its combination with the geomagnetic field.

*Presented by Dr. S. Chapman

Recently Akasofu and McIlwain offered the alternative suggestion that the solar plasma might not be fully ionized and that the uncharged portion, mainly hydrogen atoms, might determine whether there would be significant growth of the DR current accompanied by the polar substorms. Such uncharged atoms would enter the cavity without hindrance and by ionizing collisions would become members of the Van Allen belts. This idea has been criticized, and it is very desirable that satellites should determine whether the solar stream does contain a significant amount of un-ionized atoms.

Ness has recently made the important discovery of the extension of the geomagnetic field into a long tail region. Axford gave a fascinating account of this region, which he characterized as a great store of magnetic field energy, whose intermittent partial conversion into particle kinetic energy he regarded as a vital feature in the development of DR and DP. Axford suggested that the development of DP is primary and that the ring current is secondary to it. Akasofu and Chapman would reverse this order. Axford ascribed the following tentative rates of energy dissipation to the two currents

$$DP \simeq 10^{18} \text{ ergs sec}^{-1}$$

$$DR \simeq 10^{18}\text{--}3 \times 10^{18} \text{ ergs sec}^{-1},$$

thus implying that in regard to energy rate, $DP \gtrsim DR$. On the other hand, Cole concludes that $DP \approx 10 \; DR$. In spite of this rough estimate, which indicates that DP is the more energetic of the two currents, Chapman considers DR as the primary and DP as the secondary consequence of instabilities occurring in the tail region.

In regard to the means by which solar stream energy may enter the magnetospheric cavity, suggested methods include the diffusion of charged particles across the boundary, the transfer of energy by hydromagnetic waves produced by instabilities at the boundary, and the passage of uncharged solar stream atoms through the boundary. Axford and Hines have suggested a fourth method: drag exerted on the gas in the cavity by irregularities at the boundary.

Theories of the development of the cavity naturally vary with the manner of introduction of the energy, and as yet the ideas remain speculative and uncertain. Progress will continue with further satellite exploration within the solar stream and inside the cavity. Auroral phenomena will also be an important guide in the search for the true theory.

The Auroral Oval and Magnetic Substorms*

At this meeting several polar diagrams of various types of polar geophysical phenomena (visual auroras, mantle auroras, hydrogen emissions, radar auroras, geomagnetic activity) were presented. In spite of the tremendous

*Presented by Dr. S.-I. Akasofu

progress made in recent years, all of these plots are far from satisfactory, primarily because of the lack of accurate observations beyond the auroral zone. We now realize that this is a very serious problem, since many of the polar geophysical phenomena mentioned in the above occur along the auroral *oval*, but not along the auroral *zone*. The auroral zone is simply the locus of the midnight part of the oval where most active auroras most frequently appear. This new concept of the oval, developed by Feldstein and others, can integrate a number of polar geophysical phenomena, which have been considered to be very puzzling (such as the spiral patterns).

One of the most important questions being asked today is, "Why do visual auroras and related phenomena tend to occur on such a peculiar oval band?" There is no doubt that the auroral oval is closely related to the internal structure of the magnetosphere. Also, it is known that the distribution of visual auroras changes from time to time and that these distributions are related to the changing internal structure of the magnetosphere. However, the relation between the magnetospheric structure and visual auroras is not understood at present.

Some people now tend to accept the view that the magnetospheric tail is a source region of auroral particles. However, at present it is not at all certain whether or not dayside auroras can also be explained by the particles from the magnetospheric tail. The so-called polar cap auroras are also an unsolved mystery.

The second major topic in this summary is that of auroral substorms. It is known that the polar auroral phenomena tend to have intermittent variations with lifetimes on the order of one to three hours. As I have indicated during the last few years, it seems clear that the auroral and polar magnetic substorms can be considered to be an *internal relaxation process* in the magnetosphere and are not directly generated by the solar wind. In essence, one has a solar wind and an energy storage place inside the magnetosphere. When this storage place has enough energy and becomes unstable, it tends to release the energy abruptly and produce the substorms. Axford agrees to this view and proposed that the energy stored in the tail drives the substorm, and furthermore, a small part of the substorm energy goes to form the ring current. However, as Chapman pointed out, the energy consumption of these processes is not very certain. It is fair to say at this stage that the energy deposited into the polar atmosphere by the substorm and the energy spent to build up the ring current are about the same (about 10^{18}–10^{19} ergs $\times$ lifetime of the storm in seconds). Therefore, one cannot be sure which process is the primary source, although there is no doubt that the formation of the ring current and the growth of substorms are very closely related, as pointed out by Chapman and myself. In fact, the ring currents could be a storage place and could release energy intermittently.

The auroral substorm picture presented here is only a very rough approximation and should be improved by new observations. However, it should serve as a frame of reference in dealing with much of the complex phenomena in the polar region. That is, when one is dealing with temporal polar phenomena, it is very important to know where one is in respect to the continuously changing pattern of the aurora over the entire polar cap. It would be of interest if people who observe radio absorption, x rays, and various auroral light emissions would present such phenomena in a pattern similar to that of auroral substorms.

One of the most important processes of the auroral substorm is the poleward motion of the auroral band. Also, there is a definite eastward motion of auroral structures. During this meeting, results of the barium cloud experiments were presented by Haser. These experiments showed that in the morning a southward electric field was associated with the eastward auroral motion. This portion of the experiment indicates that the polar electrojet is essentially a Hall current. One can think of a shell of plasma embedded in the upper atmosphere which shifts eastward with respect to the earth. Such a shift will be associated with a southward electric field in the north polar region or with an electric field directed toward the earth if the field is near the equatorial plane. However, this plasma shell motion is resisted by the neutral atmosphere, the resistance occurring in this rather thin transition region, namely the E region of the ionosphere. In the E region, ions cannot participate in the eastward plasma motion because of their high collision frequency with the neutral atmospheric particles. However, electrons can participate without difficulty since their gyro-frequency is much higher than their collision frequency with neutral atoms. The result is an eastward motion of the electrons which is in essence the westward current. Boström indicated that the Hall current should be associated with an intense Pedersen current. Magnetometers carried by a low-altitude satellite would be useful in such a study.

Energetic Particles*

There are three experimental devices — balloons, rockets, and satellites — which have been used extensively for direct studies of energetic charged particles. Each of these devices has its own particular advantages and disadvantages. As has been pointed out, balloons are very satisfactory for the long term observation of processes that vary with time (the purely temporal phenomena). With rockets and especially with satellites, it is very difficult to discriminate between a spatial and a temporal effect. Balloons, therefore, are the devices that have given the most definitive information to date on the temporal variations. The long term periodicities in electron precipitation with periods of the order of a hundred seconds or several hundreds of seconds were discovered with balloon-carried instrumentation. Also, the shorter-time pulsations, with periods of seconds, and the microbursts of Anderson were first

*Presented by Dr. B. J. O'Brien

detected with balloons. It is a challenge, with the aid of rockets and satellites, to study more definitively and directly what the balloons have found in the periodicities of order one, ten, and a hundred seconds and to analyze the causes of these fluctuations. It is attractive to think of these three decades of periodicities as separate entities rather than just a convenient cataloging technique. By virtue of the dynamics of the situation, it would appear that these fluctuations have different causes. However, one must remember that merely putting different labels on various features does not make them fundamentally different. Balloon measurements also gave the first strong evidence against the concept that the Van Allen radiation belts could possibly sustain the auroral phenomena. Subsequent satellite data have confirmed and extended this result.

The role of the rockets is more for exploratory purposes, since with rockets it is possible to see if a given phenomenon is present without waiting a couple of years, as is required for a satellite experiment. Also, rockets have a particular advantage in that one can choose the firing time and direct the vehicle into a specific type of aurora. With rockets one may investigate energy spectra, pitch angle distributions, and in particular, the details of the interaction of the energetic particles with the atmosphere. Rockets can accomplish these measurements as a function of altitude and extend the measurements to lower altitudes than are possible with satellites.

With satellites one can make rapid explorations and surveys in space. If one wishes to make coordinated measurements with satellites, one must either mount a fairly large expedition, the way Lockheed has done with the input-output series, or one must try to put all the instruments on the satellite itself, as was done with Injun III. As mentioned earlier, it is extremely difficult to separate the space and time variations in data taken with satellites. However, Anderson has reported some periodicities on the order of about six minutes in the electron flux deep in the magnetospheric tail. Observations with low-altitude satellites could not detect such effects.

There are three physically interesting phenomena associated with the energetic particles in aurora. The feature which is most puzzling, of course, is the source of the particles. The second topic concerns their principal effects, and the third is what may, for convenience, be called the anomalous effects. In regard to the causes or sources of the energetic auroral particles, if one asks the most elementary questions — "Where do the energetic particles come from? . . . Were they in the solar wind or were they once magnetospheric particles?" — the answers are simply unknown at present. Axford and Speiser described various means of accelerating the particles in the tail of the magnetosphere, but as mentioned in the summary by Chapman, these theories as yet remain speculative and uncertain.

The primary effects produced by the energetic auroral particles are ionization and auroral light. These phenomena were the most pertinent to the conference, and in this area there are some problems which are still unsolved. For example, if a number of energetic charged particles are injected into the top of the atmosphere, what is the complete energy budget of their effects? How much energy goes into heat, light, uv, magnetic disturbances, etc.? This energy balance question has not been properly approached thus far and there are order-of-magnitude uncertainties in the estimates of the energy distribution.

In the third area of physical interest, here labeled anomalies, one would put Mozer's observations of upward moving protons. Also, the anomalous backscattering of electrons measured by McDiarmid and Budzinski and some of the Rice group's results with the Sammy V rocket are in the same category. These anomalies may be thought of as the way the atmosphere feeds back on the energetic particles. The atmosphere is not static but fights back. For example, it is heated, thereby causing changes in the density gradients. This heating has a relatively minor effect; however, there may be electric fields that actually change the precipitation pattern. There certainly are magnetic fields caused, for example, by the auroral electrojet. These fields will produce a local magnetic anomaly which will tend to change the mirror points of the charged particles. On one side of this electrojet there is a forbidden cone of precipitation. On the other side, the magnetic anomaly will tend to increase the particle precipitation, and one can at least conceptually visualize the entire pattern moving toward the south or the north as the atmosphere feeds back against the precipitation effects.

In all three of the physical phenomena just mentioned, the greatest experimental deficiency lies in the electrical field measurements. Electric fields play a crucial role in the theories related to acceleration and may be the overriding factor in producing the anomalous effects. Until there are some good electric field measurements, one has difficulty in trying to evaluate the magnitude of this interaction.

Spectroscopic Measurements and Interpretation*

For the three kinds of emissions of greatest interest at this conference, namely those from the aurora, from the night airglow, and from the day airglow, the papers presented by Omholt, Roach, Noxon, Gadsden, and others showed that the spectrum of these atmospheric emissions is fairly well explored, especially in the visible region. In the infrared and ultraviolet regions the investigations have not been so complete, particularly for the dayglow.

It is perhaps interesting to note briefly the relative capabilities of some of the spectroscopic instruments which are available for this work. If one defines the luminosity, L, as the photon flux arriving at the detector per unit source brightness and R is the resolving power, $\lambda/\Delta\lambda$, then the product LR is in

*Presented by Dr. A. Vallance Jones

most spectral regions a constant. If for a grating spectrometer the relative value of this product is taken as unity, then for the Fabry-Perot interferometer the relative value is about 100. The third class of instrument, the interferometers such as the Michelson interferometer and the "mock" interferometer, have an LR value of about $100\sqrt{M}$, where M is the number of spectral elements in the spectrum which one wishes to observe. The full $\sqrt{M}$ gain is only realized in the infrared where detector noise is independent of signal. This comparison shows the enormous potential advantages in ascending this heirarchy of instruments. If one wishes to look at only one wavelength, the Fabry-Perot is just as good as the Michelson. However, if one wishes to look at a wide wavelength range in the infrared, particularly with high resolution, the Michelson has an enormous advantage. Many of the papers presented here show increasing exploitation of these techniques. For example, the dayglow studies reviewed by Noxon employed the high resolution of the Fabry-Perot instrument and also an ingenious polarization technique to study dayglow emissions from the ground. An account was given by Stair of the uses of the Michelson interferometer in the nuclear explosion airglow, artificial aurora, and the laboratory. Although it was not discussed here, there is also the very high resolution airglow spectrum which Gush has obtained with a balloon-borne Michelson interferometer.

Another promising advance is the application of the image orthicon to auroral spectroscopy as reported by Davis. This instrument is obviously going to be a powerful tool since it increases the time resolution with which auroral spectra and photographs may be compared.

Balloon measurements are becoming increasingly important in certain optical studies, particularly in the infrared, while rocket experiments have contributed greatly to our knowledge of the spectra in the ultraviolet and in the dayglow, where the scattered light from the lower atmosphere is usually too bright to permit measurement from the ground. The rocket also has the unique capability of making height measurements by observing the emission intensity as a function of altitude. Finally, spectroscopic devices are being used increasingly with satellites, and it is to be expected that important results will be obtained by this method in the future.

Among the many results presented at this conference are several notable developments which should be emphasized. One such result is the verification that, compared to twilight, there is excess sodium in the atmosphere during the daytime. The scale height of the sodium seems to be from 2–3 km, which is less than that of the atmosphere of the region in which it is found. The measurement of the variations in the OH band emissions during the course of the twilight and the measurement of the variation of the molecular oxygen 1.27μ emission in the twilight are also very important. The exploration of the chemistry of the processes giving rise to these emissions will be rather intensively followed in the next year or so. The spectra obtained from the nuclear explosions were impressive; particularly notable was the experimental demonstration of the long lifetime of the ^1D oxygen state. This state was shown to have a lifetime between 110–120 sec, which is very close to that predicted by theory.

The measurement of temperature variations in auroral fluctuations seems to be very significant because this constitutes a spectroscopically observable quantity which can probably be directly connected with variations in the particle energy spectrum. Also, the variability of the ratio between the ionized nitrogen lines and the green lines in different kinds of aurora is likely to indicate variations in the softness or hardness of the exciting particle spectrum, as well as possible variations in the types of the exciting particles. The remarkable progress made in finding a relationship between the red line emission in the nightglow and electron densities in the F region is a notable achievement. Finally, the possibility of making measurements of the dayglow emissions, the oxygen lines, the N_2^+ lines, and the sodium lines has led to a considerable advance in the theory of the upper atmosphere at 100–400 km during the daytime. Whereas several years ago the first reliable measurements had just been made, there is now a fairly complete set of observations and a substantial theoretical understanding of them.

It is important to outline some of the problems which will have to be solved in the next few years. Perhaps the most difficult is that of sodium in the dayglow, the twilight, and the nightglow. There are features of this emission which are very hard to explain, particularly, the small scale height. As Hunten and Gadsden have suggested, this may indicate a connection between atmospheric sodium and dust; perhaps there will be a complete theory soon. Another interesting problem is that of the nightglow continuum which Roach indicated made up 80% of the emission seen by the astronauts. The nuclear explosion data presented by Stair and Kofsky also showed a very important continuum contribution, both in the visible region and in the infrared. Another important problem in auroral physics was brought up by the artificial aurora pictures. At 85 km they showed a similar change from red to green as is observed at a similar but not accurately determined height in natural Type B aurora. The results suggest that the change has something to do with the atmospheric properties at 85 km, and in particular, with the transition between the atomic and molecular oxygen regions of the atmosphere; at present the relation between the role played by the deactivation of the ^1S state and the role played by the relative abundance of atomic oxygen is not clear. The question of the variations in the 3914Å/5577Å ratios and the ratios of the hydrogen lines to the other features is not yet fully explored. With increasing information from satellites on the energy and directional characteristics of the exciting particles, much progress should be possible in the understanding of these variations. It is hoped that there will be more laboratory measurements of excitation cross sections to provide a sound basis for the theory.

Finally, it is worth pointing out that the new solar maximum will be here soon, and there will be displays of aurora which will show strong heating effects in the upper atmosphere. One should, therefore, be concerned with developing suitable photometers and spectrometers to correlate the rises in temperature, the heights of the aurora, and the actual changes in the spectrum which occur under these conditions.

Auroral Observations and Dynamics*

This summary will emphasize some properties of the aurora as observed from the ground and balloons, and will relate these properties to the primary particles and to magnetospheric and ionospheric phenomena. Table I gives a

Table I

Observed Auroral Characteristics	Particle Type, Energy, Geometric Pattern
High 6300Å/5577Å ratio (Type A)	e, $E < 1$ keV, diffuse
Low 6300Å/5577Å ratio (ordinary)	e, 1–10 keV, any geometry
Red lower border (Type B)	e, 10–30 keV, striations, vivid motion
X ray emission	e, 10–100 keV, diffuse
Hα, Hβ	H$^+$, 1–100 keV, diffuse
Polar glow	H$^+$, MeV, entire polar cap

classification of the auroral emissions and identifies the emission characteristics with the particle type and energy. The first entry is the type of aurora characterized by a high red to green ratio, sometimes called the Type A aurora. It occurs high in the atmosphere and is probably caused by electrons with energies of about 1 keV or less. This aurora is often, but not always, very diffuse. The second entry has a low red to green ratio and contains mainly the ordinary, discrete aurora, but also diffuse and pulsating forms. It may occur with almost any geometry and is caused primarily by electrons in the range 1–10 keV. The next entry is distinguished by the red lower border and is called Type B. The particles responsible are probably electrons in the energy range of 10–30 keV, and the forms are characterized by striations and very vivid motions. The balloon results indicate a separate classification which may be called an x-ray emission aurora. In the previous papers it was pointed out that x rays may be observed without aurora being visible. The electron flux producing the x-ray aurora has a significant, but perhaps not dominating, contribution of electrons in the energy range 10-100 keV. The geometry of x-ray aurora seems to be very diffuse. Another class of aurora, one which is characterized by the Hα and Hβ emission, is caused by protons in the energy range from 1–100 keV. The final entry is the polar glow aurora which is caused by protons in the MeV range.

One should be aware of these various classes when one does statistical studies of auroral properties. Sometimes one observes several of these forms together, and there is as large a variety in the superposition of these forms as there is in the energy spectra observed in the energetic particle experiments.

*Presented by Dr. A. Omholt.

Most of the morphological studies which have been made so far are for aurora belonging to the second group. The morphology of the Hα and Hβ aurora is still somewhat ambiguous, and more observations are needed to study the precipitation zones for protons by means of ground-based equipment.

Table II summarizes some of the dynamic properties of aurora and the

Table II. Dynamic Properties

Observed Effects	Mechanism
Motion of aurora, large scale, structural, waves	Movements of particle source or variations in magneto-spheric configuration
Electric currents	Differential motion of electrons and ions
Ionospheric drifts and radar echo velocities	Drift of electron/ion density patterns
Radar Doppler velocity	Electron drift
Drift of artificial tracers, ions	Ion drift
Drift of neutral tracers	Winds, turbulence

various motions and currents observed in the aurora. Understanding the dynamic effects requires a separation of the causes and a knowledge of the relationship of the causes and observed motions. First, there is the general motion of the aurora which, on a large scale, may be a gross movement of the entire form or may be structured with rays moving within the auroral form. There also may be wave motions similar to the flaming aurora described by Cresswell. These processes are related to movements of the source of the electrons or to variations in the magnetosphere outside the ionosphere. The aurora is only a trace of the paths of the particles as they enter the atmosphere, and these motions are not at all related to atmospheric motions or to atmospheric electric fields as such.

Some of the papers at this conference dealt with electric currents that are due to the difference between the movements of electrons and ions. There were also reports on ionospheric drifts and on radar echo velocities which result from a drift of the electron/ion pattern in the atmosphere. These echo velocities may be a movement of the particles themselves, or they may be a kind of wave in the pattern of ionization. The radar Doppler velocities are linked to the drift of the electrons. On the other hand, the artificial tracers described by Haser give the ion drift. Finally, the artificial tracers of neutral particles discussed by Blamont are related to the winds and turbulence in the atmosphere, and these experiments have yielded quite significant information on these features. The motion of ionized tracers is related to the electric field in the atmosphere, although as shown in the detailed treatment, there are a number of other effects to be considered such as the interaction between the neutral gas and the ions and electrons.

Thus, auroral motions give information on the properties of the magnetosphere and perhaps on the occurrence of electric fields in the magnetosphere. The other measurements listed give information on the electric fields in the ionosphere, but none of these measurements directly measure the fields. Much work remains to be done especially with artificial tracers, but it is agreed that this approach to the measurement of the electric fields in the ionosphere is extremely important.

Excitation of Aurora and Airglow*

It is helpful to think of the various features of airglow and aurora in a two-dimensional diagram using height and magnetic latitude as coordinates. Most of the phenomena discussed at this conference can be sorted out within a magnetic latitude range from equator to pole and in the altitude region below about 600 km (see Figure 1, page 29). For example, the polar glow aurora envelops the polar region above latitude about 60°. The ordinary polar auroras are at 65–70° geomagnetic latitude, the green aurora being at about 100 km and the Type A red extending from perhaps 250–several hundred km. The 5577Å airglow has a reasonably well established maximum in a secondary auroral zone at about 45°. Associated with the 5577Å airglow is a continuum emission as well as the OH and the sodium emissions. Near 45° magnetic latitude there is the M arc, or mid-latitude red arc, and in the equatorial regions, there is the phenomenon whose spectral characteristic is about five parts 6300Å to about one part 5577Å. This description is not a complete picture of all the pertinent phenomena reviewed during this conference, but it is a helpful schematic.

A problem which is important in future considerations is the possible relationship between the Type A and normal auroras and the M arcs. For example, do the auroral observers know whether the Type A emission is fairly pure 6300Å in the upper region and is the 6300Å to 5577Å ratio for a Type A aurora the result of integrating along the line of sight? This question is pertinent because in the case of the M arcs, which are energetically very significant at the times of aurora, the spectral situation is rather clear, the emission being predominantly, if not almost exclusively, due to 6300Å. If there is a relationship between the Type A red and the M arcs, that is, if the two phenomena are excited by the same mechanism, one must consider whether heating is responsible in both cases. Certainly one of the prominent theories about the M arc origin is that it is a "heating" phenomenon, in which case one would perhaps associate the upper part of the Type A aurora with a similar kind of excitation. On the other hand, if the Type A aurora is caused by energetic particles coming down the field lines, one must explain how the energetic particles can pass through the upper atmosphere and not excite the N_2^+ or 5577Å emission. If 6300Å radiation is emitted, atomic oxygen must be present, and therefore, 5577Å should also be excited by energetic particles. Vallance

*Presented by Dr. F. E. Roach

Jones has urged the observers to be prepared to measure temperatures during the next sunspot maximum. Certainly the temperature of the upper region where 6300Å is emitted is a very important physical parameter on which to concentrate in the future.

In contrast to the uncertainties in the production of M arcs and of Type A aurora, the 6300Å and 5577Å radiation at approximately 250 km near the equator is one of the best understood of the upper atmospheric emissions. These F region equatorial emissions very definitely seem to be excited by the reaction $O_2^+ + e \rightarrow O + O^*$ and are, therefore, intimately associated with the ionosphere by means of the electron which participates in the reaction. The feature which requires further explanation is the surprising temporal and spatial detail of the intensity patterns. These corrugations, which are implied by the photometric observations discussed by Peterson and Steiger, are so complex that one wonders how the ionosphere can originate and maintain such irregularities.

Returning to the conventional 5577Å green line, there is fairly convincing evidence of a second auroral zone at about 45° geomagnetic latitude. This zone exhibits a seasonal variation, and this extremely interesting fact should be studied in more detail. An important consideration is that the seasonal change is actually a semiannual variation, the maxima (northern extreme) being near the solstices and minima (southern extreme) near the equinoxes. A systematic study of this variation is needed in both hemispheres to explore the possibility that there may be an interchange of energy between conjugate points in the two hemispheres.

Relevance of Auroral and Airglow Studies to the Ionosphere*

In this summary an attempt will be made to draw attention to the information having a direct bearing on our understanding of the ionosphere and to indicate the need for particular observations. It will be convenient to distinguish between the results relating to high, middle, and equatorial latitudes.

At high latitudes the general associations in time between the aurora and lower ionospheric phenomena are well known. The marked change in auroral forms near magnetic midnight and the tendency for anomalous ionization to occur above 100 km during evening hours (sporadic E and night E) and below 100 km during morning hours (auroral absorption), would imply a hardening of the high energy particle spectrum during the middle of the night. It would be valuable to compare the high energy particle spectra measured during evening and the following morning hours.

In attempting to correlate the intensities of auroral emissions with measurements of auroral absorption, it is important to realize that the two phenomena refer to different altitudes in the atmosphere and are, therefore, produced by

*Presented by Dr. L. Thomas

different parts of the particle energy spectrum. Furthermore, the actual areas of the atmosphere viewed by the riometer and the photometer could be different. However, Little mentioned that correlation coefficients of 0.6–0.7 had been found in comparisons of the 0-0 band of the First Negative system of N_2^+ at 3914Å and auroral absorption. In addition, studies of auroral absorption at a number of sites have shown that the absorption regions are circular in shape with dimensions of hundreds of kilometers and have lifetimes of about ten minutes. However, from the films shown by Davis and from other information, it seems that the auroral forms can have much shorter lifetimes.

The association of auroras with ionization at E region heights was discussed by King and Eather. Quantitative comparisons of the intensities of the First Negative system of N_2^+ and E region electron densities, as carried out previously by Omholt, provide estimates of the effective recombination coefficient. The previous work of Omholt and the study based on total electron content described by Johnson and Meyerott yielded values of about 10^{-6} cm^{-3} sec^{-1} for the effective recombination coefficient. This value is much larger than would be expected on the basis of studies at middle latitudes or from currently available laboratory measurements. A simultaneous rocket measurement of the height distribution of the emission in the First Negative system of N_2^+ and of the electron density would provide a more reliable estimate of this loss coefficient.

It seems certain that the 6300Å emission of atomic oxygen in Type A aurora results from the excitation of $O(^1D)$ by dissociative recombination of O_2^+, and perhaps of NO^+, from the excitation by thermal electrons and other processes. The preliminary estimates of electric fields in the auroral zone reported by Haser indicated meridional fields of tens of mV/m. If these represent typical magnitudes, as was suggested by Boström, it may be surprising that the Type A aurora is so infrequent, as Megill and Carleton have shown that electron heating by an electric field of about 100 mV/m would result in a very marked emission in 6300Å.

Little mention was made at this conference of the emissions and ionospheric effects associated with solar proton events for the polar cap region. For F region heights, Sandford showed that for conditions of low K_p during 1959, the 6300Å emission increased with latitude to an intensity of approximately 600 R near the pole. The energy source responsible for this emission is of interest in connection with the persistence of the F region at polar latitudes during winter. The corresponding intenstities of emission in the First Negative system of N_2^+ could have provided an estimate of the height integrated electron production due to particle fluxes, but unfortunately only an upper limit of about 50 R could be given for the 3914Å emission (i.e., 5×10^{-2}–10^{-1} ergs cm^{-2} sec^{-1}). A measurement of the absolute intensity of the First Negative band system of N_2^+ in the polar cap regions during winter could indicate the importance of particle fluxes in maintaining the F region ionization.

In middle latitudes no evidence was presented to confirm or reject the recent estimate by Barth of the concentration of the important minor constituent, NO, in the D region. However, the relatively large concentrations of $O_2(^1\Delta g)$ at D region heights indicated by Evans' observations of the 1.27μ twilight emission could support the previous suggestions by Megill and Schiff and Megill and Hasted that this electronically excited molecule could also be an important minor constituent in the D region.

At E region heights, Roach's reference to the work of Glaume concerning the latitude variation of 5577Å was of particular interest. Her conclusion that the position of the maximum intensity in different months seems to be governed by magnetic latitude rather than geographic latitude poses an interesting problem as to the mode of exciting the $O(^1S)$ state.

Theoretical studies of the sporadic E layer at middle latitudes have suggested that metallic ions could be important when concentrated by the action of a wind shear operating in the presence of the earth's magnetic field. The observations of the emissions of ionized calcium at twilight reported by Gadsden might provide some support for this suggestion, because the erratic behavior and maximum occurrence of the emissions in summer are characteristics also shown by the sporadic E layer.

Dissociative recombination of molecular ions certainly contributes to the 6300Å emission, but excitation of the $O(^1D)$ state by photoelectrons and by thermal electrons attracted greater attention. The heating effect of photoelectrons arriving from the sunlit conjugate point before local sunrise was demonstrated in the ionospheric observations at Arecibo presented by Carlson. The high electron temperatures necessary to cause thermal excitation of $O(^1D)$ would be expected to have interesting implications for the F region. In particular, one would expect an increased vibrational excitation of the N_2 gas present and, from the laboratory measurements of Ferguson, a resulting increase in the electron loss rate.

The meridional electric fields of about 2 mV/m reported by Haser for middle latitudes would be expected to give rise to zonal movements of ionization in the F region which need to be included in theoretical studies. At equatorial latitudes very little attention was paid to airglow emissions at D or E region heights. Weill did mention, however, that the intensities of OH bands observed at Tamanrassett in North Africa were not correlated with the corresponding observations at Haute Provence, France. While this result could arise from a difference in the chemistry involved in producing vibrationally excited OH at the two latitudes, it could alternatively represent a difference in the influence of dynamical processes which are believed to affect airglow intensities. It would seem that comparisons of measurements made at middle and low latitudes of the OH, 5577Å, and other emissions originating near or below 100 km altitude could provide information on horizontal and vertical air movements which also seem to be involved in the behavior of the lower ionosphere.

The papers presented by Peterson, Steiger, and Weill demonstrated the close relationship between the 6300Å emission and the variations in height and electron density of the F region at low latitudes. It is evident from their studies and from previous work that the $O(^1D)$ atoms are generated in the dissociative recombination of molecular ions. However, as Peterson pointed out, only a small proportion of such recombinations (10% at 300 km) are effective. In addition to the 6300Å emission which could be attributed to dissociative recombinations, the observations showed a background component which remained constant on a given night, but varied from night to night. There was some controversy as to whether this background actually represented a 6300Å emission or arose from contamination by OH bands.

AURORA AND AIRGLOW
CONCLUSIONS

W. O. Davies and B. M. McCormac
IIT Research Institute

After over forty lectures and numerous discussions on the various aspects of aurora and airglow, some effort should be made to present a conclusion. The purpose of the Institute was not to attempt to reach agreements or to determine popular opinion, but rather to see that the experimental and theoretical results were presented and adequately discussed. Each individual must make his own evaluation as to the importance and credibility of the information. Our personal conclusions about the Institute are presented below from the point of view of future research requirements. The Institute did much to identify important areas of agreement and disagreement and focused attention on multidisciplinary research and the key problems of the future. The participants concluded that another two-week Aurora and Airglow Institute should be held in 1968.

General

The study of aurora and airglow requires a multidisciplinary approach in that it involves the ionosphere, atmospheric physics, and solar wind-magnetosphere interactions, as well as particle and electromagnetic wave observations. It is difficult for an individual to be aware of the results of investigations in disciplines other than his own, let alone to utilize these results.

It would be convenient to have a generally accepted definition of aurora and of airglow. It was suggested that the excitation source could provide such a definition: if the excitation is generated by bombardment of the atmosphere by nonthermal charged particles, the emission is called aurora; otherwise it is airglow. Definitions based on location of the emission were also suggested. Significant exceptions exist to all possible definitions and it is concluded that there is no suitable definition. It is unlikely that either aurora or airglow will be eliminated from the technical vocabulary or that a precise substitute will be found. One must then keep in mind that the words aurora and airglow are ill-defined and insure that for each use the meaning will be understood. Fortunately, many of the morphological terms which were selected on the basis of insufficient data are being discarded. As more data are accumulated, the early names are recognized as inappropriate. An example of unsuitable terminology is the tropical red arc: this is a geomagnetically controlled phenomenon which does not lie entirely in the tropics, is not an arc, and is not completely red.

Coordinate System

The greatest single obstacle to a better understanding of aurora and airglow is the lack of a suitable coordinate system. Although a coordinate system is urgently needed, none has been suggested that will satisfy the requirements. McIlwain's B, L coordinate system is useful where the magnetic field is well behaved (out to about $L = 4$–5 earth radii). However, the B, L coordinate system is not useful at the trapping boundaries or beyond. Much airglow and all auroral phenomena are associated with changing magnetic field phenomena or high L shells.

The desired coordinate system would allow the presentation of the observations in a manner that relates the observed phenomenon to its environment rather than to arbitrarily chosen parameters. Geographic coordinates should be used with care and are probably only appropriate for a few D-region phenomena. All geomagnetic coordinates should be based on the invariant field. The auroral zone and other phenomena need a coordinate system which is tied to the boundary between open and closed field lines. Such a system rotates with time and depends on solar activity, etc.

Altitude does not appear to be a useful coordinate. Most phenomena associated wtth aurora and airglow depend on the column mass along the magnetic field line. Above about 125 km altitude there are variations with solar cycle, time of day, etc. At altitudes above 200 km, these differences are very large. Column mass along the field line is suggested as a more appropriate parameter.

Data Base

The quantity of optical data as a function of time, latitude, and longitude is completely inadequate for both aurora and airglow. More lines and bands need to be recorded. Synoptic data are needed. Magnetically conjugate observations are practically nonexistent. Coverage of magnetic latitude and longitude for airglow is also practically non-existent. The variation of equipment from site to site makes analyses difficult. Similar arguments can be provided for other kinds of data.

Interaction of the Solar Wind and the Magnetosphere

The sun seems to be the source of energy for all aurora and airglow phenomena. The solar wind has about 100 times the energy required to power all the observed phenomena. Understanding aurora and airglow requires a knowledge of energy storage and distribution. However, this knowledge would not be sufficient to understand the excitation mechanisms, since the solar wind particles do not possess the energy to excite the observed energy levels and the solar wind does not possess the 10^6 factor in variability that is observed in particle precipitation. A more complete description of the mechanism must account for the observed auroral behavior and requires a knowledge of the energy storage, energy release, and particle acceleration mechanisms.

The solar wind-magnetosphere interaction forms a collisionless shock wave producing suprathermal particles and a turbulent random wave field (Axford, Speiser). A geomagnetic tail is formed downstream. It was suggested that the solar wind plasma is injected via the tail into the magnetosphere, producing the aurora and radiation belts. In the quiet magnetosphere the field lines are closed for magnetic latitudes less than 72–75°. The open lines join the planetary field in the tail. The trapping boundary is not the boundary between open and closed lines, but is at a lower latitude. There is always a continuous precipitation of particles. Initially the instabilities develop slowly and are then triggered, resulting in aurora and polar substorms. The boundary moves to higher latitudes on the night side. Islands of electrons are bound by the reconnected field lines. New reconnected lines tend to contract violently, propagating a hydromagnetic impulse toward earth. About 100 earth radii of tail has enough energy for a magnetic storm. It is believed that the tail is between 200 earth radii and 0.1–0.2 A.U. Multiple reconnection points result in multiple aurora arcs which are much more common than single arcs. Electrons and protons incident on the neutral sheet are trapped, accelerated, turned toward the earth, and ejected from the neutral sheet with small pitch angles. Thin beams of electrons and protons are produced with the protons appearing at 0.5° lower latitude than the electrons.

No suitable measurements which would resolve temporal and spatial variations have been made. Two or more satellites that are separated by a short distance are needed. Instabilities and turbulence have not been investigated. An investigation should be made to see if the solar wind has a neutral component.

Anderson has studied the electron islands in the tail. Around the antisolar portion of the stable trapping region is the cusp which extends out to about 16 earth radii. Particles in the cusp can mirror but not drift. A key problem is the location of the aurora in relation to the cusp. Experimentation is needed to determine whether the field lines in the vicinity of the islands are open or closed. An experiment is needed to correlate particles in the solar wind with particles in the tail and to correlate tail particles with precipitation in the atmosphere. An unsuccessful attempt has been made to correlate the electron islands with magnetic bays; such a correlation may not be appropriate. It may be impossible to make electron island motion measurements with one satellite.

Particle Precipitation

Satellite-, rocket-, and balloon-borne instrumentation has been used to measure the precipitation of charged particles. O'Brien and Johnson summarized the satellite particle measurements. Auroral zone particle precipitation is continuous, varying by 10^6, and is about 4×10^{17} ergs sec^{-1}. At the equator the loss cone is about 2° and is seldom measured by Van Allen belt satellites. Nothing observed in the equatorial plane has approached the intensity of the low altitude spikes which are often observed at a high latitude. The latitude of the trapping boundary varies inversely with particle energy and appears to be quite variable. The trapping boundary for electrons >40 keV may decrease to an L of 3.5–4 during a storm. It is clear that Van Allen particles are not a source of auroral particles. Craven stated that the auroral electrojet is always poleward of the 40 keV trapping boundary. Protons have about 10–20% of the energy of electrons and are $\frac{1}{2}$–1° latitude equatorward of the electron boundary. The proton trapping boundary was 68° magnetic latitude at night and 70–80° in the daytime. At times the backscatter of precipitated particles is greater than can be explained by Coulomb scattering. Satellite and rocket measurements seem to agree with optical emissions. Rocket measurements are significantly different from flight to flight. There is an indication that electrons <10 keV have different dynamic processes than for electrons >40 keV.

Electron deposition has been observed from balloons by means of x-ray bremsstrahlung and provides some information on the electron precipitation region and spectrum (Kremser and Anderson). The x rays are produced by much harder electrons than those which produce the visual aurora. Before local midnight there are impulsive short duration bursts associated with magnetic storms or substorms. For high K_p they may occur as low as $L = 2.5$. Hydromagnetic waves may precipitate electrons just after midnight, producing periodic deposition over several cycles with a period of 1–30 min. They are confined in latitude to the auroral zone but are very broad in longitude. Fast pulsations, called microbursts, may occur in the early morning. They are observed for periods as long as several hours during the daytime following geomagnetic activity and have an unexplained dominant 1.2 sec period.

Much more spectral data are needed on precipitating electrons and protons. In some unknown manner, trapping boundaries depend on energy. Different energy electrons may participate in entirely different dynamical processes. Perhaps particles can be injected and followed. Proton-alpha ratios may be useful as a tracer. The source, energy, and precipitation mechanism of auroral particles are needed, as is the relation between the auroral and trapping boundaries. More effort is required to correlate all the various particle measurements to optical observations. The pitch angle distribution of precipitated and backscattered electrons is needed.

Aurora

Akasofu pointed out that auroral phenomena lie in a narrow oval region, which is eccentric with respect to the dipole and is displaced about 3° toward the dark side. The auroral maximum occurs near geomagnetic latitude of 67° on the nightside and 78° on the dayside. The classical auroral zone is the locus of the midnight part of the auroras. The zone inside the oval should be defined as the polar cap. The zone equatorward of the oval is the trapping region. Stations at a low enough magnetic latitude are continuously in the trapping region. Stations at a high enough magnetic latitude are always in the polar cap. Intermediate stations will be crossed by the oval twice a day; thus, they are outside the auroral activity, inside, and then back outside, experiencing two maxima a day. A station on the auroral zone has one maximum a day and is never inside the polar cap. Of course, the auroral oval location varies with season and magnetic activity. According to the old definition (station's location with respect to the auroral zone), a station at a magnetic latitude of 70° is permanently in the polar cap; however, according to this new definition it is outside the polar cap in the daytime and inside at midnight. This may explain why the observations at a station may correlate at certain K_p levels and not at others.

Since at least two major polar geophysical phenomena, the aurora and polar electrojets, occur along the oval, Akasofu suggested that this oval might be a natural frame of reference for geophysical phenomena. This oval would not be a fixed coordinate, as the dimensions vary with solar activity and the time of day. However, it was suggested that the use of these flexible coordinates simplify the interpretation of geophysical phenomena that appear quite complex when described in other coordinates. The shift of the oval toward the equator suggests a similar movement of the outer boundary of the trapping region, and both may result from changes in the structure of the magnetosphere caused by storm-induced electric currents.

There is also a regular expansion and contraction of the oval that is correlated with the expansion and recovery phase of substorms. Akasofu concluded that the auroral substorms are probably generated by a plasma instability of either a shearing mode of a neutral sheet instability or an interchange instability in the ring current boundary.

Development of advanced techniques (Davis) to record auroral forms and spectra are leading to a much better understanding of the visual phenomena. It was found that even stable aurora possess an internal structure that is never static on time scales of the order of .05 sec. The homogeneous auroral arc is composed of thin, parallel arclike structures, streaming parallel to the arc, in addition to transient irregularities with lifetimes of the order of 1 sec. Widths of auroral arcs are much thinner than originally thought, as 400 m is the maximum and most are found to be less than 100 m, which is the limit of current measurement techniques. Auroral motion is only a change in the charged particle deposition point. Very rarely does an aurora appear to consist of only one arc.

Auroral motions seem to be up to 3 km per sec; however, it is very difficult to follow the life of a particular arc. A strong longitudinal dependence is suggested by the occurrence rate of auroral forms in the zone. Riometer absorption is said to be twice as great in Alaska as in Norway or Canada. However, the data may not be properly referred to the auroral oval. Precipitation may have a longitude dependence, but Little finds no mirror point dependence in his conjugate regions measurements at $L = 4, 7,$ and 15. The hf absorption in conjugate regions is produced by much higher energy electrons than produce the visual aurora. The maximum hf absorption occurs in a belt slightly equatorward of the nighttime aurora and 10° equatorward of the daytime aurora. Variations in absorption seem to be due to temporal variations in precipitating particles rather than systematic motion of enhanced ionization past the station.

Auroral spectra are dominated by the nitrogen and oxygen atomic and molecular bands from both neutrals and ions. Visual aurora are produced primarily by electrons of a few keV. Sometimes the Hα and Hβ lines are observed. Fairly constant ratios between intensities of First Negative N_2^+ 3914Å, which requires 19 eV for excitation, and OI 5577Å, which requires 4 eV, indicate that variation in the secondary electron spectrum is minor. Aurora spectrum changes are more likely caused by variations in atmospheric density and composition.

The OI 6300Å line is often observed at high altitudes. It has a half-life of about 110 sec and is de-excited at low altitudes by collisions. It is important to know if the OI emitting species are produced where they are observed or if they rise as a result of lower altitude heating. It is also important to know if the sunlit aurora is produced where it is observed, or if the excited species rise from lower altitude heating.

In general, the temperatures of the OI emitting source are found to vary between 1200 and 2000° K; however, much more work on auroral temperatures is in order. The temperature is experimentally observed to vary inversely with brightness. Brighter aurora are produced by more energetic precipitating particles at a lower altitude. Because of the increase in ambient temperature with altitude in the F region, the higher the altitude of the aurora, the higher the temperature.

Egeland reported the results of some recent height analyses on more than 12,000 auroral photographs collected by Størmer from 1911–43. The lower edges of the auroras show a pronounced maximum at 90–120 km altitude. Over 50% of the auroras occur between 24 and 28° geomagnetic latitude. To be of most value, auroral altitudes should be given in terms of gm/cm² along the magnetic field line above the lower edge of the aurora. These data could readily be programmed out of the CIRA 1965 model atmosphere for diurnal and solar cycle variations. The altitude of aurora may vary by as much as 50 km just from a difference in the integrated mass of ambient air along the field line. In addition, geomagnetic latitude does not seem to be a suitable coordinate for presenting the height data. More work is required to integrate properly these height analyses with other work.

VLF, radar, and ionosonde measurements have been recorded for a number of years; however, to obtain the best comparison with other types of observation or theories, the data have not been adequately displayed. Lack of a suitable coordinate system makes correlation difficult. VLF amplitudes depend on the source strength and the absorption along the propagation path which need to be separated. Radar frequencies above 100 mHz should be used to avoid absorption and diffraction. Theoretical models for the interpretation of radar backscatter have limited application. The radar scattering centers are located in the E region at a height of 110 km.

A correlation between polar cap phenomena and magnetic and auroral observations seems quite difficult at this time. Part of this difficulty results from the lack of a suitable coordinate system. The weak polar glow aurora is excited by solar protons and alpha particles of about 1–100 MeV. The N_2^+ 3914Å and OI 5577Å and 6300Å emissions are observed, although observation of the 6300Å line is often difficult because of the auroral background. This red line may be excited by thermal heating from high temperature electrons. The proton-alpha ratio in these auroras should be measured.

A system needs to be developed which would relate all auroral phenomena to the auroral oval. More stations are needed both at magnetic latitudes above 70° and at latitudes equatorward of the auroral zone, especially for the forthcoming solar maximum. The conjugacy of many phenomena must be investigated in detail. Measurements are needed to determine whether the field lines on which aurora are observed are open or closed. Multiple-type measurements of different phenomena from satellite and surface stations are needed, as well as selected balloon and aircraft observations.

Airglow

For the purposes of this discussion, airglow includes the visual phenomena observed equatorward of the classical auroral zone.

A. Nightglow

Most of the nightglow investigations made to date are on the 5577Å and 6300Å OI lines from the F region, the 5577Å line from the 97 km altitude region, and the sodium and hydroxyl emissions from 85–95 km altitude. Weill discussed the equatorial region airglow which has the same spectral features as that of other latitudes but a different morphological and dynamical behavior. The general morphology and synoptic behavior of airglow in this region is difficult to determine because of poor meteorological conditions in most of the earth's equatorial region and the limited number of observing stations. The neutral atmosphere is controlled by the geographic equator, whereas airglow seems to be controlled by the geomagnetic equator.

The altitude grouping of the airglow into the 85–95 km sodium and hydroxyl emission, the 100 km 5577Å atomic oxygen layer, and the higher altitude 6300Å atomic oxygen emission is the same as at other latitudes. Very little is known about Na or OH; however, they seem to be at a minimum at the equator. The Na emission shows a weak minimum at midnight, and at these low latitudes the Na and OH emissions do not appear to be correlated as they are at higher latitides. Sodium shows no significant diurnal or solar cycle variation, in contrast to the oxygen emissions. The seasonal behavior of sodium exhibits a strong spring and weak fall enhancement in intensity which is similar to that of the 5577Å line from the same low altitude regime.

The green line observations from 97 km were discussed by Roach. The 5577Å, equatorward from the aurora, is 0.1 the aurora 5577Å intensity and shows a maximum at about 44° magnetic north ($L = 2$) and a minimum at the equator. The glow comes from 97 km (± 5 km for thickness) and is geomagnetically controlled. There is a semiannual period. There is essentially no N_2^+ radiation; therefore, the glow is not from energetic precipitating electrons. It would require electrons of >5 keV to penetrate to the altitude of 97 km, while the excitation levels of N_2^+ and 5577Å are 19 eV and 4 eV, respectively. The trapped radiation slot is also at $L = 2$. All data should be converted to invariant magnetic latitude. The location of the maximum in the southern conjugate region and its variation with time are needed. Perhaps the trapped radiation slot and the 5577Å maximum result from a common source. Hernandez has measured the average temperature of the 5577Å to be 208° K; however, there are occasional fluctuations which may reflect height changes and contributions for the F region. The 5577Å shows a patchiness with intensity variations up to 25% as seen from satellites.

The 6300Å OI line is emitted from the F region at an altitude of approximately 240 km. There is an accompanying emission of 5577Å from the same altitude which has an intensity of about 25% of the 6300Å intensity. The F region emission at 5577Å is usually hidden by the much stronger 5577Å emission from 97 km. These F region airglows show much variation in intensity, structure, and location. The emission is localized into broad maxima which lie roughly at about geomagnetic latitudes of $\pm 15°$ but show large diurnal amplitude and latitude variations. These red maxima move closer to the equator as night progresses, and are closely correlated with the ionospheric F region, electron density, and height of the maximum electron density. Severe geomagnetic storms disrupt the red maxima and lower the average intensity while creating enhanced localized disturbances. Steiger has shown that the spatial structure of the red line emission varies greatly with position and geomagnetic activity. Projection of the data on isophoto maps shows that the red maxima are highly structured and that their relationship to the ionospheric parameters is adequately described by the Barbier formula. Thus, the ionosphere has electron density gradients so high in the horizontal direction that the ionosphere is effectively tilted by 45° over a very short distance. The gross features of the red line emission are followed by the green line intensity in the F region. There are bright elongated features of about 100 km by 1000 km which are separated by valleys. These features tend to indicate a wave structure drift with time.

The M arc is usually subvisual and has a life span of approximately one day. Almost all emission is 6300Å at 300–700 km in altitude. The arc has a north-south dimension of about 600 km, occurring between 41 and 60° magnetic latitude, and is geomagnetically controlled. It is doubtful if the M arc is related to the F region 6300Å enhancement. No 5577Å is observed, which indicates that electrons above 4 eV are not involved; however, energetic electrons are not required for production of either 5577Å or 6300Å.

Much more data are needed to determine the seasonal, spatial and temporal variations of the M arcs. An attempt should be made to separate the wave and drift motions of the 6300Å F region data. More care should be taken in separating the 5577Å produced at 97 km and in the F region. Since all airglow appears to be geomagnetically controlled, these data should be presented in invariant magnetic coordinates. Conjugate correlations need to be investigated.

B. Twilight

Twilight measurements are difficult to interpret because of the physical changes occurring during the observations. Also, winds can significantly modify the effective solar terminator velocity.

The OI (6300Å) red line is enhanced at twilight, possibly because of O_2 Schumann-Runge dissociation, and the 5577Å line is also observed. The 6300Å observations indicate a conjugate effect due to photoelectrons.

Natural lithium may be difficult to investigate because of the rocket and nuclear bomb releases. However, it would be interesting to compare the quantity of these artificial additions to the total inventory of lithium. There are indications that gravity acoustic waves may affect the ratio of neutral to ionized lithium. The abundance of alkali metals shows large diurnal and seasonal fluctuations. In mid-latitudes the Na peaks at 85–95 km, while the Li layer is 10 km lower. The lack of thermochemical data on the oxides of sodium precludes a quantitative discussion of sodium kinetics. It was suggested that aerosol might provide a solid surface for attachment of electrons, thereby increasing the recombination rate. Satellite optical measurements have not confirmed the existence of a dust layer. Meteoritic dust might be a source of atomic sodium. Conjugate effects should be investigated.

Orthohelium twilight measurements at 10830Å may be used to monitor the extreme ultraviolet if the total abundance of He remains constant. By measuring the scale height of He, the temperature can be inferred if it does not change during the observation.

Much more data are needed to determine temporal and spatial variations of twilight. Care should be given to the conjugate implications. The details of all photochemical processes are not well known and should be investigated.

C. Day Airglow

The major dayglow excitation processes are chemical reaction, fluorescent and resonant scattering, electron impact, and photon absorption, all of which may be produced by the solar energy incident on the atmosphere. Noxon pointed out the difficulties involved in assessing the importance of chemical reactions because of the uncertainty in applying laboratory reaction rates and the assumption of local thermodynamic equilibrium. On the other hand, the efficiency of resonant or fluorescent scattering can often be calculated accurately.

Dayglow observations have been made on several ultraviolet and infrared bands; however, there are difficulties in accounting for the observed abundance and altitude distribution. Observations in the visible spectrum on Na have the same difficulties. The resonant scattering of solar radiation at the 3914Å band shows a sharp rise in emission at 150–200 km altitude. However, little data at other altitudes exists for comparison.

Most existing measurements are for the two forbidden OI lines. The 5577Å has two maxima, one at 100 km, as for nightglow, and one above 200 km altitude. This line may be produced by both electron excitation and chemical reactions. If chemical reactions are important, both maxima should also be seen at night. The 6300Å line appears from about 200 km altitude and results from a combination of O_2 photodissociation, dissociative recombination, and electron excitation. However, at low altitudes, the 6300Å line is quenched by collisional deactivation. It is difficult to explain the large variations observed — 30 kR on some days and 3 kR on others.

Much more data on dayglow are needed to establish seasonal, latitudinal, and longitudinal variations. It appears that the structure of the Fraunhofer spectrum may vary and that the lines are shallower in the daytime sky than in the direct sunlight. Resonant scattering may involve excitation of higher states. Transport processes for metastable states make interpretation difficult. Electron temperatures may differ from ion temperatures.

Electric Fields

Electric fields were suggested to explain many observations. For each suggestion there was usually a serious objection. The implications of electric fields are hampered by the lack of experimental measurements of field strengths because there are far too many possibilities.

Boström suggested that a theory of aurora must include a description of electric fields for a number of phenomena. Such electric fields may be produced by plasma motion driven by the solar wind, charge separation induced by magnetic field gradients, winds in the ionosphere, and rotation of the ionosphere. It has been suggested that electric fields must exist along the magnetic field lines to preserve electrical neutrality if pitch angle distributions of electrons and ions are different, that currents must flow along the field lines to drive auroral electrojets, and that currents along the field lines may generate ion-acoustic waves. Boström estimated that the total voltage drop along the lines should be about 10 kV. Such parallel electric fields may produce the observed "anomalous" charged particle reflections.

The motion of visual and radio auroras are probably drifts of the source region. Differences are attributed to the ionization lifetime and influence of the electric field on the charged particles, both of which contribute to more extensive motion of radio auroras. With the current state-of-the-art, it seems impossible to derive the electric field from auroral observations. The order of magnitude of the auroral electric field is 50 mV/m in the E region, or a few millivolts per meter in the outer magnetosphere. Ionospheric winds are probably too weak to induce significant electric fields.

The use of barium clouds injected into the atmosphere at altitudes of 130–2000 km was described by Haser. The velocity of the barium ions perpendicular to the magnetic field was measured by observing the resonant lines at twilight. This motion is attributed to an electric field normal to the magnetic field. The results indicate that the field points south in the evening and north in the morning. At the latitudes of Sardinia and the Sahara, this electric field has a strength of 4 mV/m. At Fort Churchill, preliminary results indicate that the field has the opposite vector but is about 10 times greater in strength.

Several experimenters have reported a backscattering of electrons which is too large to be accounted for by Coulomb scattering of the precipitating flux. This is often explained by postulating the existence of an electric field between the rocket and the outer atmosphere, although other possible explanations are: 1) a pitch angle distribution of the downward flux peaked at a value not viewed by the detectors, and 2) a modification of the mirror condition by local ionospheric currents. Walt summarized the available experimental data on electron precipitation, and considered the possibility that plasma instabilities, local electric fields, or phenomena other than electron bombardment could contribute to the auroral luminosity. The results suggest that a few cases exist in which the observed electron reflection is higher than accounted for by the theory, although the meagerness of data precludes an exhaustive study.

Direct experimental measurements of the electric fields are urgently needed. Simultaneous measurements of protons and electrons should be helpful. Blamont pointed out that there is anticorrelation of electron and proton auroral fluctuations as seen by his optical measurements of 3914Å, 5577Å, and Hβ. The barium ion clouds show instabilities and help map magnetic field lines and electric fields normal to the magnetic field. These techniques should be applied to the study of auroral phenomena. Perhaps certain F region investigations which can indirectly aid in estimating the electric fields are possible.

Artificial Airglow and Aurora

One unusual and thought-provoking feature of the Institute was the artificial aurora and airglow session, which included presentations of the optical emission measurements made during nuclear weapons testing and from laboratory studies intended to simulate this emission. This was the first time that much of these data were placed in the open literature. The temporal input of energy is known for a nuclear weapon, in contrast to the natural case, where the input is not known.

The prominent features of airglow produced by nuclear detonations are the same as observed in natural airglow and aurora. A persistent chemiluminescent continuum following ionization of the D and E regions, fluorescence, and the red and green atomic oxygen lines were observed by Kofsky. In addition to the continuum observed near the bursts, a similar glow was observed in the magnetic conjugate region. The chemiluminescent spectrum peaked at approximately 5500Å and had a decay characteristic of a 1500 sec half-life. This emission may be attributable to NO^+ and oxygen reacting to produce the NO_2^+ yellow-green glow. The nuclear case shows a peak at 1.6 microns, which has not been observed in laboratory experiments. There are different excited states in the nuclear case which indicate that the atmospheric mechanisms are not understood.

The air fluorescence is excited primarily by beta and gamma radiation below the D region, and the characteristic blue glow is from the nitrogen molecular bands, e.g. 3914Å and 4278Å. At 32 km altitude the fluorescent efficiency for 3914Å is 0.8×10^{-3}; at 65 km, it is 4×10^{-3}.

Nuclear radiation which produces E region ionization produces 5577Å atomic oxygen emission. The lifetime was measured to be 0.75 sec. The excitation of the 6300Å line in the F region was observed to have a lifetime of 118 sec.

Stair presented laboratory measurements of the rotational temperature variation of the 3914Å bands produced by electron impact in nitrogen. These data indicated that the observed temperature variation was caused by secondary electron energy variation with pressure in the system and was not strongly dependent upon primary electron energy. Electron excitation of 3914Å for electron $> 100\,\mathrm{eV}$ gives a constant fluorescent efficiency of 2.8×10^{-3} where collisional deactivation is unimportant. Infrared measurements were used to obtain fireball temperatures. IR observations hold promise for the determination of the relative concentrations of species and the degree of internal excitation.

Boquist discussed the characteristics of intense beta auroras produced at an altitude of 44 km up to about 100 km. There is a significant color boundary change in the beta aurora at 84–87 km altitude. The natural Type B red aurora exhibits a similar color change, but it has not been measured to this altitude accuracy.

These nuclear investigations indicate that laboratory studies of reactions between various species do not lead to a satisfactory understanding of atmospheric processes where different excited states are involved.

Summary of Current Research Problems

The more important problems which have been identified are summarized below and are listed in order of importance.

Coordinate systems which properly order the observations and predictions are urgently needed. All airglow phenomena discussed in detail are geomagnetically controlled. Phenomena occurring within an L of 4 should be based on the invariant magnetic field system. Airglow above an L of 4 may use the invariant magnetic field if the field is well behaved. Otherwise, for airglow, auroral, and polar cap phenomena, there is no suitable coordinate system and all current presentation techniques are inadequate. Auroral phenomena should be related to the trapping boundary or to the closed field line boundary in the magnetosphere. Perhaps a coordinate system can be established around the rotating auroral oval.

The altitude above the earth's surface is a poor parameter for phenomena occurring above about 100 km altitude because of the large diurnal and solar cycle density variations. It is suggested that the integrated mass along the field line is a better parameter.

No area of investigation has sufficient sites for the study of temporal and spatial variations. Magnetically conjugate stations are urgently needed, even near the magnetic equator.

There should be a trend toward carefully designed, integrated experiments. Satellite and ground measurements should be combined, as well as the use of balloons, aircraft, and rockets. A large variation in types of simultaneous observations is needed.

Auroral morphology requires investigation in a large number of areas, such as motion, temperature, intensities, and altitude.

In general, the whole airglow morphology requires much more data and study, and needs to be related to other geophysical phenomena. Some current questions are: Why is there a broad maximum in 6300Å airglow from the F region at about 15° magnetic latitude? Why is there a maximum in the 5577Å airglow at approximately 44° magnetic latitude? Is this maximum related to the slot in the trapped radiation belt, or is there a common source? Are the higher latitude airglow emissions and aurora related?

Electric field measurements are needed for the solar wind-magnetospheric interactions, particle precipitation, aurora, polar cap events, and airglow. So many electric fields have been hypothesized that measurements are essential.

Optical measurements should be extended to cover the ultraviolet and infrared. The ultraviolet background as seen by satellites appears to be conveniently low.

The details of all important atmospheric reactions are needed. Laboratory experiments do not appear too promising, as the excited states produced are different than in the atmosphere.

INDEX

INDEX

Absorption, radio, 11, 63, 575–588
Aerosol, 112–113, 130–131, 307–309
Airglow, 9–12, 667–680
  artificial, 341–363, 678–679
    atomic oxygen lines, 343
    electromagnetic radiation source, 341
    ion source, 341, 361
    nuclear radiation source, 341–355
    strong shock source, 341, 358–359
  artificial continuum, 342–349
    half life, 344
    irradiance, 344–345
    nitric oxide emission, 345–349
    spectrum, 344–345
  artificial emissions, 391–403
    barium, 391–403
  artificial fluorescence, 342, 349–362
    5577 Å, 354–357, 360–362
    6300 Å, 357, 360–362
    beta source, 349–353
    efficiency, 349, 352–354
    gamma source, 351, 353
    half life, 355, 358
    irradiance, 349, 356–360
    nitrogen molecular ion emission, 350–354
  dayglow, 12, 123–130, 313–321, 676
    atmospheric band emission, 129–130
    atomic oxygen emission, 124, 126, 128–129, 318–320
    chemical reactions, 315–316
    continuum, 123–125, 130–131
    electron impact, 315–316
    fluorescent scattering, 315–316
    height, 126–127
    hydroxyl emission, 130–131, 318
    infrared emission, 129
    Lyman α emission, 318
    molecular nitrogen ion emission, 319
    molecular oxygen emission, 317
    nitric oxide, 317
    nitrogen second positive emission, 319
    photodissociation, 315–316
    polarization, 124
    resonant scattering, 315–316
    sodium, 112
    sodium emissions, 124, 126, 128–129, 316–317
    ultraviolet emission, 125–126
  equatorial, 407–417
    atomic oxygen emissions, 409–417
    hydroxyl emission, 410
    magnetic storm effects, 417
    predawn enhancement, 416
    seasonal variation, 414–415

Airglow, equatorial (cont.)
    sodium, 410
    solar cycle variation, 415
    spectrum, 409–414
  history, 24–25
  infrared emission, 375–379, 385–389
  ionosphere relations, 93–106
  low latitude stations, 408–409
  nightglow, 29–39, 673–675
    atomic oxygen emission, 380–381, 420–433, 511–518
    atomic oxygen temperature, 435–440
    background, 95
    continuum, 379–381
    D region, 30–35
    diurnal variation, 420–421
    emission altitudes, 35–36
    F region, 35–36, 94
    geomagnetic control of 5577 Å, 31–33
    geomagnetic control of 6300 Å, 37
    high latitude observations, 451
    hydroxyl, 382–385
    latitude effect, 35–36
    low latitude observations, 419–433
    low latitude variations, 441–442
    midlatitude emission, 37–39
    midlatitude red arcs, 11, 96–97
    seasonal variation, 421–429
    semiannual variations of 5577 Å, 33–34
    sodium emission, 420–429
    spatial variations, 424–429
    tropical arcs, 95
  nightglow observations, 419–433, 511–518
  nitric oxide, 375–379, 386
  red arcs, 662–663
  twilight, 11, 109–122, 305–314, 407–417, 675–676
    atmospheric scattering, 111
    atomic oxygen, 117–118, 122
    atomic oxygen emission, 643–647
    atomic oxygen emission source, 118–119
    calcium, 115–116, 122, 309–310, 665
    continuum, 119
    dust, 307–308
    emission height, 112–113, 115–116
    helium emission, 102, 119, 305–306
    hydroxyl, 120, 658
    lithium, 114, 116, 309–310
    magnesium, 116, 309–310
    molecular nitrogen ion emission, 118–119
    molecular oxygen emission, 119, 658
    ozone, 111
    photoelectron excitation, 645–647
    potassium, 114–116, 309–310

Airglow, twilight (cont.)
  radiance, 113
  resonant scattering, 111, 114–119
  satellite observations, 634–642
  seasonal variation, 115–116
  sodium emission, 101, 111–116, 308–313, 658–659
  tropical F region, 29–30
Albedo
  neutron, 4, 9
  solar radiation, 111
Alkali metals, 114–115
Alkaline-earth metals, 114–115
Alpha particles, 10
Artificial airglow. *See* Airglow
Atmospheric dust, 112–114, 307–308, 659
Atmospheric dynamics, E region, 159–168
Atmospheric reactions, 10
Atmospheric scattering, 6, 9, 110, 214, 289
  aerosol, 130–131
  trapped particles, 4
Aurora, 9–10, 667–680
  annual variation, 460
  artificial, 325–339, 678–679
    beta particle source, 327–333
    color changes with altitude, 328, 339
    debris source, 327–333
    radiance time history, 335–338
    spectral emissions, 337
    thermal X-ray source, 341, 354
  atomic oxygen emission, 172, 177, 372–375, 638–640
    5577 Å, 136–137, 141, 232–233, 246–247
    6300 Å, 136–137, 445–446, 448–449, 451
  correlation with ionosonde measurements, 589–598
  correlation with particle precipitation, 9
  discrete visual, 444–446, 448–449
  electric fields, 293–303
  electrojet, 5, 76, 79–81, 301–302, 657
  electron density, 172
  electron microbursts
    characteristic times, 253
    correlation with magnetic activity, 254–256
    diurnal variation, 254, 255
    energy spectrum, 258–261
    frequency of occurrence, 253–256
    precipitation, 250–263
  electron spikes, 262
  electrons, 191–209, 211–223, 227–237
    angular distribution, 181–182, 194, 214–215, 243–247
    density, 211–213, 228–231, 232–237
    energy spectrum, 183, 193, 200–209, 215–223, 227–228, 243–247
    flux fluctuations, 195
    motion, 296

Aurora (cont.)
  emissions, 660
  correlation with particle precipitation, 637–641
  form
    arcs with ray structure (RA), 145, 148, 150, 153, 156
    bands with ray structure (RB), 145, 148, 153, 156–157
    cloudlike auroras (DS), 145–148, 150–151
    draperies (D), 145, 148, 150
    homogeneous arc (HA), 145, 147–150, 153, 156–157
    homogeneous band (HB), 145, 153
    pulsating arcs (PA), 145, 148, 153
    pulsating surfaces (PS), 145, 148, 151–153
    rays (R), 145, 148, 153, 156
  frequency, 461
  frequency with magnetic activity, 270–271
  height, 22, 63–67, 70–71, 143–158
    geomagnetic latitude, 145–153
    local time variation, 153–154
    seasonal variation, 155
    sunspot cycle variation, 155–158
  high latitude emissions, 444–452
  history, 15–25
  homogeneous arc, 138–140
  hydrogen emission, 172, 445, 465–468
  individual arc width, 281
  ion density, 228–231
  ionosphere relations, 93–106
  latitudinal distribution, 42–45, 51–53
  longitudinal variations, 55–58
  M spiral, 268–269
  mantle, 446–449, 653
  molecular ion emissions, first negative band, 172, 175–189
  morphology, 41–58, 138–141
  motion, 55, 655, 661
  N spiral, 268–269
  nitrogen molecular ion, 465–476
    first negative band, 134, 137, 235, 246–247, 372–375, 448–450
  optical emissions, 9
  outstanding, 23–24
  particles, 623–633, 660
    electrons, 171, 174–189, 477
    magnetosphere tail source, 491–498
    protons, 171, 174–189, 449–450, 466–467
    source, 262–263, 281–282, 656
  polar, 64
  polar cap, 58, 453–464, 654
    annual variation, 456–457
    diurnal variation, 454
    frequency, 455
    magnetic storm effect, 462–464
    solar cycle variation, 457–458

Aurora (cont.)
  polar glow, 450
  protons
    drift, 296–297
    energy spectrum, 179, 184
  pulsating, 138
    correlation with microbursts, 256
  radio, 519–562
    aspect with magnetic field, 520–521
    backscatter theory, 563–571
    bistatic backscatter, 524–527
    communications, 550–556
    correlation with field disturbance, 531–535, 537–538
    latitude effect, 539–542
    reflection mechanism, 522–525
  radio backscatter
    centers, 542–550, 556–559
    correlation with visual aurora, 546–550
    diurnal variation, 528–535, 537–538
  radio wave absorption, 575–588
    correlation with field activity, 585–586
    correlation with luminosity, 584–585
    layer height, 582–584
    layer temperature, 586–587
    production by bremsstrahlung, 584
    spatial variations, 579–582
    temporal variation, 578–579, 581–582
  rotation temperatures, 468–474
  solar cycle dependence, 46–47
  spatial variations, 51–53
  spectra, 134–137
  spectrum, 21–22, 59–74
    infrared, 60–61
    ultraviolet, 60–61
    variations, 64–67, 71–72
  substorm, 49–51, 54–56, 274–278, 501–505
  sunlit, 67, 97, 155–158, 472, 476
  sunspot cycle relation, 21
  temperature, 69–71, 468–476, 659, 662–663
  temporal variation, 43–58
  total energy dissipation, 191
  type A, 64, 470–472, 660, 662–664
  type B, 65, 67, 71, 214, 659–660
  ultraviolet emissions, 175–176, 179–189, 640
  variations, 133–141, 239–241
  visual, 653–654
  VLF emissions
    anticorrelation with absorption, 609–615
    correlation with visual aurora, 600–602
    low latitude, 619–622
    morphology, 603–605
    physical characteristics, 615–619
    polar, 609–619
    temporal variation, 610–615
    waves, 141
    X ray, 477–488

Aurora arc
  east-west dimension, 281
  multiple structure, 281–285
Aurora observations, 191–241, 325–339, 465–476
  aircraft, 169–190
  rockets, 191–241
  satellite, 169–190, 634–642
Aurora oval, 52, 79, 267–279, 281, 653–654
  equatorial shift, 271–273
  relation to trapping boundary, 271–273
Aurora precipitation, plasma instability, 275–277
Aurora zone, 43–45, 654
  microbursts, 249–263

Balloon measurements, 655–656, 658
Barium, 391–403
Barium clouds, 391–403
  spectra, 393–397
Barium injection, 655
Beta, 4
Bow shock, 1, 3, 11, 652
  thickness, 3
Bremsstrahlung, X-ray spectrum, 195, 216–220, 224

Calcium, 115, 119, 122, 309–310
Charged particles
  artificial sources, 10
  backscatter, 58, 181–182, 215–216, 656
  backscattering, 9
  drift, 7–8
  electromagnetic wave interaction, 10
  energy loss, 9
  injection into magnetosphere, 653
  loss, 6
  loss cone, 58
  magnetic moment, 5
  mirror points, 6–7
  mirroring, 57–58
  precipitation, 8–9, 57–58, 169–190, 625, 657, 670
  variation, 9
Chorus, 600
Collision frequency, 655
Collisionless shock, 2
Conjugate measurements, 77, 86–87, 92, 325–339
  Arecibo, 643–647
  photoelectrons, 665
  radio wave absorption, 580–581
Conjugate regions, 118, 122
Coordinate system
  aurora oval, 267–271
  auroral behavior, 41
  B, L, 7, 668
  column mass along field line, 668

Coordinates
  geographic, 4–5
  magnetic, 5
  system for outer magnetosphere, 5
Coulomb backscatter, 182
Coulomb scattering, 9, 289

Dayglow. *See* Airglow
Deionization, 10
Diffusion coefficient, atmospheric, 159–160
Dissociative recombination, 95, 118, 212–213, 299, 666
Drift, 7–8
Dust, 112–114, 307–308, 659

Electric currents, 283, 297–298, 661
  DCF, 652
  DP, 652–653
  DR, 652–653
  ring, 654
Electric fields, 9, 39, 69, 96–97, 206–207, 281–282, 293–303, 391–403, 492, 495, 503, 655, 657, 662, 664, 676–678
  parallel to magnetic field, 294–295
  production, 294
  transition region, 2
Electrojet, 5, 11, 76, 79–81, 268, 271, 277–278, 301–302, 657
Electron islands, 261–263, 502–503
Electrons
  artificial source, 10
  aurora, 61–63, 171, 174–189, 191–209, 211–223, 227–237, 660–661
    angular distribution, 181–182, 194, 214–215, 243–247
    density, 211–213, 228–237
    energy spectrum 183, 193, 200–209, 215–223, 227–228, 243–247
    flux fluctuations, 195
    spikes, 262
  aurora microbursts
    characteristic times, 253
    correlation in the magnetic activity, 254–256
    diurnal variation, 254, 255
    energy spectrum, 258–261
    frequency of occurence, 253–256
    precipitation, 250–263
  backscatter, 290–292
  collision with neutrals, 655
  drift, 296–297, 661
  drift in magnetic field, 8
  energy deposition, 287–292
  energy spectrum
    magnetosphere, 3
    transition region, 2–3
  F region density, 11

Electrons (cont.)
  flux
    magnetosphere, 3
    transition region, 2–3
  nuclear source, 10
  precipitation, 287–292, 477–487, 627–632, 655
    dependence on K, 629
    latitude variation, 628
    source, 631
    spectra for tail electrons, 629
  secondary ionization, 62, 63
  solar wind energy, 2
  solar wind flux, 2
  temperature, transition region, 2–3
  trapped, 3–4
  trapped radiation
    cycles, 8
    energy spectrum, 8
    flux, 8
    spikes, 8
Equatorial electrojet, 5, 11
Equatorial sheet current, 284–285

Fabry-Perot interferometer, 124–125, 658
Fraunhofer spectrum, 119, 123–125, 130–131
  Doppler shift, 111

Grating spectrometer, 658
Gravity waves, 166
Gyrofrequency, 655

Hall currents, 300–301, 655
Helium, 61, 119
Helium emission, 305–306
High latitude currents, 77–79, 86–87, 92
  conjugate relations, 77, 86–87, 92
Hiss, 600
Hydrogen emission, 61, 68–69, 172, 445, 465–468, 653, 660
Hydromagnetic waves, 250–251, 653
Hydroxyl emission, 100, 120, 130–131, 318, 382–385, 410, 658, 665–666

Image orthicon, 133–134, 137–139, 658
Infrared emission, 10, 129, 375–379, 385–389
Instabilities, 11
Ion
  auroral density, 228–231
  collision with neutrals, 655
  correlated with aurora, 183–184
  drift, 661
Ionization, 10
Ionosonde measurements, 11
  absorption, 577–578
  correlation with aurora, 589–598
Ionosphere, 663–666
  absorption, 58, 202, 228–229, 256, 484, 575–588

Inosphere (cont.)
 absorption in auroral region, 141, 663–664
 airglow and aurora relations, 93–106
 D region, 10, 665
  absorption, 99–101
  currents, 300–301
  drift, 661
  ionization, 99
  polar cap event, 99
 E region, 655, 664
  electron density, 98–99, 211–213
  enhanced E layer, 591–598
 F region, 94–97, 103–104, 664–665
  airglow, 413–414, 429–431, 511–518
  conjugate effects, 96
  correlation with 6300 Å, 94–95
  correlation with airglow, 35–36
  electron temperature, 96
  motion, 95
  nightglow, 441–442
  temperature, 96–97, 643–647
 inhomogeneities, 11
 sporadic E, 98, 663, 665

Laminar flow, atmosphere, 160–163, 165, 167
Langmuir probe, 211
Larmor radius, 652
Lithium, 114, 116, 309–310
Loss cone, 6

M arcs, 29, 37, 39, 64–65, 662–663
M spiral, 268–269, 368
Magnesium, 116, 309–310
Magnetic bay, 76, 79–80, 92, 138, 202, 230
Magnetic field
 aurora region, 9
 high latitude disturbances, 75–92
 horizontal component, 44
 Jenson and Cain model, 5
 shell parameter L, 6–9
 source, 5
 South Atlantic anomaly, 5, 8
Magnetic field pressure, 3
Magnetic moment, 5
Magnetic storm, 652
 correlation with X rays, 484–486
Magnetic substorm, 250, 652–654
Magnetograms, 82–83, 85
Magnetohydrodynamic wave, 10
Magnetopause. See Magnetosphere
Magnetosphere
 charged particle acceleration, 656
 cusp, 262
 electron islands, 502–503
 electrons, 3
 energy content, 4
 hydromagnetic waves, 3
 injection of solar particles, 500–501

Magnetosphere (cont.)
 interaction with solar wind, 499–509
 internal structure, 267–279
 magnetic field line merging, 505–508
 magnetopause, 1, 3, 11
 neutral sheet, 275–277
 particle acceleration, 500–505
 particle acceleration model, 491–498
 protons, 3
 solar wind interaction, 1–4, 652, 668
 source of auroral particles, 281–285, 491–498
 tail, 4, 250, 653
 trapped electrons, 3–4
 trapped protons, 3–4
Michelson interferometer, 658
Microbursts, 249–263, 655–656
 characteristic times, 253
 correlation with magnetic activity, 254–256
 diurnal variation, 254–255
 energy spectrum, 258–261
 frequency of occurrence, 253–256
Mirror points, 6

Neutron decay, 4
Nightglow. See Airglow
Nitric oxide, 317, 375–379, 386, 665
 airglow emission, 345–349
Nitrogen
 atomic, 61
 first negative system, 664
 ionized molecule
  first negative, 61–63, 66–72, 96–100, 102, 103
  Meinel bands, 61, 63, 66
 molecular
  first positive, 61, 65
  second positive, 61, 319
  Vegard-Kaplan, 61, 65
 molecular ion
  in aurora, 446–450, 465–476
  in aurora first negative bands, 134, 137, 172, 175–189, 235, 246–247
  cross section, 366–372
  electron excitation, 365–372
  emission spectrum, 366–371
  first negative band, 30, 118, 126–127, 319, 350–354, 365–375
  fluorescent efficiency, 369–371
  Meinel band, 365–371
  rotational temperature, 371–372
Noctilucent clouds, 112–113, 307
Nuclear detonations, 10, 114, 116, 310
Nuclear tests, 325–339, 341–363
 Blue Gill, 325–327, 329, 331, 333–337
 Check Mate, 325, 327, 329, 331, 337, 338
 infrared spectra, 385–389
 King Fish, 325–326, 329, 330, 338

Nuclear tests (cont.)
  Orange, 326–327, 338
  Teak, 326–327, 359
  Tight Rope, 325–326
  Star Fish, 325, 327, 329, 333, 335–339, 357–358

Oxygen
  atomic emission, 372–375, 380–381, 420–433, 441–442, 659–660
    5577 Å, 29–37, 59, 61–62, 64–69, 71, 94, 98, 100, 124, 126, 128, 354–357, 360–362, 662–663, 665
    6300 Å, 29–30, 35–38, 61, 63–65, 71–72, 94–96, 102, 357–362, 643–647, 660, 662–666
    7774 Å, 61, 66–67
    8446 Å, 61, 66–67
    emission heights, 35–36
    emission latitudes, 35
    energy levels, 30, 35–37, 64
    equatorial region, 409–417
    half life, 355, 358
    lifetimes, 59, 64–65
    production by dissociative recombination, 118
  atomic emission in aurora, 445–446, 449, 451, 638–640
    5577 Å, 136–137, 141, 172, 177, 232–233, 246–247
    6300 Å, 136–137, 172
  atomic emission in dayglow, 318–320
  atomic emission in nightglow, 511–518
    5577 Å, temperature, 435–440
    energy levels, 511–512
    source, 512–518
  atomic emission in twilight
    5577 Å, 117–118
    6300 Å, 117–118, 122
  molecular emission, 658
    atmospheric bands, 61, 66, 119, 129–130
    dayglow, 317
    first negative, 61
Ozone, 111, 113, 116, 118–119, 383

Pedersen current, 655
Photoelectrons, 95–96
  conjugate region, 118
Pitch angle, 6
Plasma oscillations, 11
Polar cap aurora, 453–464
Polar cap event, 99
Polar cap morphology, 10
Polar cap region, 269–270
Polar chorus, 600
Polar electrojet, 268, 271, 277–278
Polar glow, 660, 662
Polar substorm, 501–505

Positrons, 10
Potassium, 114–116, 309–310
Proton
  artificial source, 10
  auroral, 68–69, 171, 174–179, 184, 189, 449–450, 466–467, 660–661
  backscatter, 657
  drift in magnetic field, 8
  energy spectrum
    magnetosphere, 3
    solar wind, 1–2
    transition region, 2–3
  flux
    magnetosphere, 3
    solar wind, 1–2
    transition region, 2–3
  precipitation, 627–632
  temperature
    solar wind, 1–2
    transition region, 2–3
  trapped, 3–4
    energy, 8
    flux, 8
  velocity in solar wind, 2

Radar doppler, 661
Radio aurora, 299–300
  aspect with magnetic field, 522–523
  backscatter
    centers, 542–550, 556–559
    correlation with visual aurora, 546–550
    diurnal variation, 528–535, 537–538
    theory, 563–571
  bistatic backscatter, 524–527
  communications, 550–556
  correlation with field disturbance, 530–535, 537–538
  latitude effect, 539–542
  reflection mechanism, 522–524
Radio emission, 11, 653
  correlation with airglow, 11
  correlation with aurora, 653
Radio observations, 95
  aurora, 519–562
radio propagation through aurora, 172–173, 176, 178–179
Radio wave absorption, 11, 63, 575–588
  correlation with field activity, 585–586
  correlation with luminosity, 584–585
  layer height, 582–584
  layer temperature, 586–587
  production by bremsstrahlung, 584
  spatial variations, 579–582
  temporal variation, 578–579, 581–582
Radio wave scintillation, 38–39
Rayleigh scattering, 110
Recombination coefficient, E region, 664–665
Refraction, 109

Resonant scattering, 111
Ring current, 272–275
Riometer measurements, 578–588
Rocket measurements, 655–656, 658
  dayglow, 125–129
  Sammy V, 656
  spatial measurements, 2
  temporal measurements, 2

Satellite measurements, 655–656, 658
  airglow measurements, 10
  auroral measurements, 10
  INJUN 1, 634
  INJUN 3, 634, 638–639
  OGO-II, 634
  OSO-B, 634, 636
  POGO, 5
  spatial measurements, 2
  spatial variations, 8, 10, 263, 655, 669
  temporal measurements, 2
  temporal variations, 8, 10, 263, 655, 669
Sodium, 61, 67, 111–116, 124, 126, 128–129,
    159–165, 308–317, 658–659, 662
  equatorial airglow, 410
  nightglow, 420–429
Solar
  flares, 9
  magnetic storms, 9
  proton events, 9
Solar plasma, 652
Solar radiance, 113
Solar radiation, 118
Solar wind
  auroral relation, 9
  electrons, 2–3
  energy content, 1–4, 191
  magnetosphere interaction, 1–4, 499–509,
    652, 668
  neutral component, 653
  proton temperature, 2–3
  proton velocity, 2–3
  protons, 1–3
  turbulence 2–3
South Atlantic anomaly, 8
Star Fish, 10
Sunspot cycle, 21
Synchrotron radiation, 11

Three body recombination, 98
Transition region, 1–3
  electron temperature, 2–3
  electrons, 2–3
  magnetic field, 2
  proton temperature, 2–3
  protons, 2–3
  turbulence, 2–3

Trapped radiation, 3–4
  artificial sources, 10
  backscatter, 626
  boundary, 281
  drift periods, 8
  efficiencies, 10
  electrons, 8
    boundary for > 40 keV, 268, 279
  lifetimes, 10
  loss, 9
  loss cone, 626
  pitch angle, 626
  precipitation, 8, 251
  protons, 8
  slot, 8
Trapping boundary, 8, 267–268, 500–501
Turbopause, 160, 166
Turbulence, 661
  bow shock, 3
  solar wind, 2
  transition region, 2
Turbulent, atmosphere, 159–163, 165, 167
Twilight. *See* Airglow

Ultraviolet, 10, 125–126, 640
  aurora emissions, 175–176, 179–189

VLF emissions, 599–621
  correlation with absorption, 609–615
  correlation with aurora, 600–602
  low latitude, 619–622
  morphology, 603–605
  physical characteristics, 615–619
  polar, 609–619
  temporal variation, 610–615

Winds, 661
  atmospheric, 159–160
  zonal, 112

X ray
  aurora energy spectrum, 258–260
  balloon observations, 477–488
  correlation with aurora, 483
  correlation with magnetic storm, 484–486
  correlation with microbursts, 256–260
  detectors, 478
  energy spectrum, 478, 480–483
  flux, 478–480
  intensity, 254
X-ray bremsstrahlung, 216–224
X-ray emission, 660